# BIRDS of CANADA

BY

P. A. TAVERNER

ILLUSTRATED IN COLOUR BY

ALLAN BROOKS AND F. C. HENNESSEY

173 COLOUR PLATES AND 488 BLACK
AND WHITE ILLUSTRATIONS

TORONTO
THE MUSSON BOOK COMPANY LTD.
1 9 3 8

Published by special permission of
THE NATIONAL MUSEUM OF CANADA

MUSSON
MADE IN CANADA

# CONTENTS



## Illustrations

# Birds of Canada

## INTRODUCTION

### OBJECT OF THE BOOK

Of late years there has been a great awakening of interest in the subject of natural history. More and more people are beginning to realize how much pleasure and profit can be derived from observation of common natural objects. In this growing field of nature study, few subjects have attracted as much popular attention as birds, and few forms of life appeal so strongly to the æsthetic sense. They are beautiful; they arouse curiosity; their elusiveness piques the imagination; and by constantly presenting new aspects they escape becoming commonplace.

Ornithology is one of the problems of nature that may be successfully attacked from so many points of view and in so many ways that there is interesting and valuable work for all to accomplish according to individual taste or opportunity. Those who incline towards systematic work may split their definitions as fine as human powers of observation permit. The animal psychologist can develop his problems as far as ingenuity can devise methods for experimentation. The ordinary nature lover can observe and note as painstakingly as opportunity permits; he may record information of scientific as well as popular interest, take pleasure in observing passing beauties, train his powers of observation, and acquire a knowledge that greatly increases his capacity for appreciating nature. Even the unsentimental, practical man, who has little outward sympathy with abstract beauty, has his attention attracted by the evident economic value of birds.

*Birds of Canada* has been written to awaken and stimulate an interest, both æsthetic and practical, in the study of Canadian birds; to suggest the sentimental, scientific, and economic value of that study; to assist in the identification of native species; to furnish the economist with a ready means of determining bird friend from bird foe so that he may act intelligently towards them and in the best interests of himself and the country at large; to present in a readily accessible form reliable data upon which measures of protective legislation may be based; to point out some of the pitfalls that have caught the inexperienced in the past, and to suggest methods for their future avoidance.

### SCOPE

This book deals with all kinds of birds known to occur in Canada. A few species of doubtful, or not too well authenticated, occurrence have been included to call attention to species about which more data are desirable.

### PLAN OF THE BOOK

The systematic arrangement (*See* Classification, page 4, and Nomenclature, page 6) used is that of the American Ornithologists' Union Check-list of North American Birds, 4th edition, 1931. This is a radical change from the previous works, *Birds of Eastern Canada* and *Birds of Western Canada*, and many familiar with them may at first find the new arrangement difficult and confusing. However, once the readjustment is made the new system will seem as natural as the old. The change is inevitable if American ornithology is to keep in step with that of the rest of the world. The old system was antiquated and misleading and the change is already long delayed. The new system will probably be used for the next fifty years, the old one having been accepted for an equal period, so the sooner we learn it the better.

Although the scientific nomenclature and taxonomy of the check-list have been followed closely, certain variations have been made from the vernacular adopted therein. These, however, are not serious and need cause no confusion. They consist mostly in the application of English names to the *species*. That this has, in some cases, necessitated the transference of the check-list name of the type or first described subspecies to the more inclusive unit is regrettable, but it seems inevitable if we are to express true and logical relationship in the vernacular nomenclature. The fact is that certain scientific concepts have outgrown the traditional means of their popular expression. According to the original concept a species and its dependent subspecies were separate entities. The modern one is that a species is composed of co-ordinate subspecies. Under the earlier idea the form first described and named was regarded as the species; later discovered forms were viewed as subordinate variant subspecies. Thus we had the Song Sparrow, meaning thereby only the eastern race of Song Sparrows and regarding it as the species. The other races, the Dakota Song Sparrow, the Rusty Song Sparrows, *et al*, were inferior subspecies. This, too, in spite of the self-evident facts that all these are equally Song Sparrows of co-ordinate rank; that a first description confers no particular taxonomic patent of superiority; and that the form accidentally discovered first is in reality no more than one of the races of Song Sparrows which for historical and other convenience only we designate the "type race." It is, in fact, only the eastern race of a widespread species of Song Sparrow. Under the more modern concept, all subspecies combine to form the species, which thus may be a group of subspecies the name of which should not be limited to any one of its component parts. The past editions of the check-list have well presented this in the scientific nomenclature, but have failed to adapt to it the vernacular system, which remains under the older and discarded concept.

In *Birds of Canada*[1] it has been the aim to express, in the English or vernacular names, as accurate a relationship between species and subspecies as is in vogue in the scientific nomenclature, and to reduce to their relative taxonomic importance those minor subspecific differences that an earlier treatment has unduly emphasized. It will be too much to expect that the result attained will satisfy everyone: the writer hopes, however, that it will be accepted until the American Ornithologists' Union committee take the matter up and make authoritative decisions.

In the following pages the number and vernacular name, which have been taken from the American Ornithologists' Union Check-list and modified as little as possible, appear first as a specific heading in heavy type.

[1] The old "A.O.U. numbers" of the species have been retained in the new sequence, though the rearrangement has necessarily thrown them out of their natural order. They will assist the reader to co-ordinate the new system of classification with the old and may be specially useful to the amateur in connecting species whose names have been changed with their equivalents in the "Birds of Eastern Canada" and "Birds of Western Canada" books previously published by this department.

Following, in smaller type, are the more common local names by which the species is, or has been, known in various localities; the French name is also given in this type.

The Latin specific name follows in italics and is always binomial.

In the treatment of subspecies, species have been treated as aggregations of subspecies, each of equal rank and importance, and not, as is customary, as species with subordinate subspecies dependent upon them. The species is first given as a whole, including its subspecific races, and, under a subhead, mention is made of the special subspecies that occur within the geographical scope of the work.

Preceded by the initial "L" the average length of individuals of the species is next given in inches and decimals of an inch. The length of a bird is determined by measuring it, in the flesh, in a straight line from the tip of the bill to the end of the longest tail feather, the bird being stretched only enough to straighten the neck curves. The measurements given are those of the average adult male. They are generalized indications of comparative size and are not always to be relied upon for exact specific identification, as in most species there is more or less individual and sexual variation.

Only an outline description of species is given, and where there are illustrations the description is omitted and the reader referred to the illustration.

Under "Distinctions" an attempt is made to bring out the salient points by which the species, when in hand, may be distinguished from other similar forms. In this attempt the work of other authorities has been freely drawn upon to supplement the writer's observations. Many of the distinctive points, naturally, are only superficial, but all, so far as possible, are reliable.

Under the head "Field Marks" the features by which the species may be recognized in life are mentioned. In these the writer has been guided largely by his own experience and has stated the points that seem to him most characteristic. For species with which he has had little experience in life he has relied upon other authorities.

"Nesting" is merely a brief description of the nest and its situation. Much of this is drawn from other authors.

Under "Economic Status" is given a summary of present knowledge of the species in its relation to man. Most of this is drawn from the admirable work done by the United States Biological Survey. Of necessity only a brief outline of the data upon which conclusions are founded can be given, and the reader is referred to the section on Ornithological Literature for the titles of books and articles that afford further details.

Under "Distribution" it has been deemed best to give the distribution in such general and well-understood terms that all may get at least a general conception of the ranges of the species. The result may be a little vague owing to the lack of sharply defined boundaries of the ranges, but the centres of distribution are made clear. For definite ranges the reader is referred to the "Catalogue of Canadian Birds" by John and James M. Macoun, issued by this department in 1909.

In the paragraphs in larger type as many facts of general interest relating to the species have been included as the importance of the species warrants. The descriptions of the various species include discussions of numerous matters and statements of general laws governing zoological life. Many of these apply to a number of species and some might well be included under each specific heading were it not for the constant repetition that it would necessitate. An attempt has been made to encourage a wholesome protective attitude from æsthetic, humane, and economic points of view without over-emphasizing any of them.

Throughout it has been the endeavour to avoid the use of technical terms, substituting familiar words wherever possible. Some technical terms, however, have no general vernacular equivalent and a glossary of these is given.

#### ACKNOWLEDGMENTS

The writer reiterates his acknowledgment of indebtedness for all the valuable assistance individually acknowledged in the Birds of Eastern Canada and the Birds of Western Canada and thanks numerous correspondents and advisors who have since assisted in bringing information up to date. A number of new coloured plates are included in the present volume and numerous additional text figures. The coloured plates are from the brush of the Museum's bird-artist, Allan Brooks, the text figures, with the exception of those in the "Key" by Claude Johnson, are from the pen of the writer.

#### CLASSIFICATION

The present system of generic grouping of species was first advanced by Linnæus in his epoch-making "Systema-Naturæ" and has since been followed consistently by zoologists. By this system species are grouped together in *genera* according to fundamental structural relationships and not accidental resemblances. The fact that upon the discovery of the laws of evolution these relationships were found to agree with lines of descent proved the logic of the system and gave it an added meaning. Thus the various specific members of a genus may be conceived as having descended from a common specific ancestor; the genera of a family from a common generic ancestor, etc.

Existing North American birds may be divided into a number of *Orders*, the largest groups with which the Canadian ornithologist has direct concern. Orders are divided into *Families*, Families into *Genera*, and Genera into *Species*. These divisions may be again subdivided into *Suborders*, *Subfamilies*, *Subgenera*, and *Subspecies*, whose positions in the scheme are evident from their titles.

Though the limitations of book construction necessitate linear arrangement of the classification scheme as a succession of forms following one another in single file, it should be borne in mind that the system is not linear in conception. The component species, instead of following a single line of relationship and sequence from the lowest to the highest, present many parallel or divergent lines of equal or subordinate rank. The class *Aves* or Birds may be represented by a tree, the height of the tree representing time in geological ages from the earliest at the bottom to the present near the top. The trunk should be double at the base; one stem a short, dead stump to represent the fossil, toothed birds which became extinct before present geological time; the other, large and thrifty, to represent the modern, untoothed forms. The latter should divide a short way from the base into two main branches to represent the two subclasses, the raft-breasted and the keel-breasted birds. The former would be represented by much the smaller branch, whereas the latter would divide and subdivide into branches representing orders, next families, then genera, and finally species.

The value of these divisions—that is, the amount of differentiation sufficient to raise a group of genera to a family, or a collection of families to an order—is a matter for experienced individual decision, as there is no authoritative ruling upon the subject. However, there has gradually grown up an approximate agreement on this subject, though the constant tendency among specialists has been to make finer and finer distinctions and to multiply the number of the various groups.

The smallest division generally accepted is the *Species.* Though everyone has some conception of what a species is, whether it be called by that name or another, no satisfactory definition has ever been constructed for it. It is what is commonly known as a "kind of an animal." Thus the horse is a different "kind" or species from a donkey, a bluebird from a robin. They are sharply marked off from each other, regularly breeding only within the species and producing offspring of like species. Distinct species do not commonly interbreed; when they do they form crosses or hybrids that are usually sterile. Up to comparatively recent years no smaller division was recognized, but from intensive study of material it has become evident to advanced students that within the species there is considerable individual and geographical variation.

*Individual variation* is the normal difference that may occur at any time between members of common parentage such as full brothers and sisters. Though like begets like, within certain limits like begets unlike, for no two creatures are ever exact duplicates. This individual variation, usually small, occasionally larger and more distinct, the "mutations" of some authors, irregular in appearance and direction, but in some cases persisting progressively generation after generation in one direction, forms the successive steps by which present-day evolutionists explain the origin of new species.[1] Individual variation, however, is disregarded in classification unless it has proceeded far enough to produce marked and constant differentiation over a definable natural group of a species.

### GEOGRAPHICAL RACES OR SUBSPECIES

*Geographical variation* may be regarded as a common variation of the individuals of a community trending towards a common goal, and is held to be directed by local climatic and other conditions. In many widespread species all individuals inhabiting certain localities have characteristics that separate them from those of surrounding areas. Individuals in a dry desert country are apt to be smaller and lighter in coloration than those in a warm, moist country. These differences are in some cases marked and obvious; in others they are so slight as to be noticeable only by comparing large numbers of specimens and can be detected only by averages. Thus there is every degree of differentiation, due to geographical habitat, from pronounced departures from type, of almost specific value, to the finest shades of difference that the skilled specialist can distinguish and which are inappreciable to the ordinary eye. The outstanding fact, however, that prevents the most marked geographical variation from being given full specific standing, is that in intermediate localities every shade of difference between the extremes can be found. Between species this gradual merging of character is not supposed to occur, and however fine the distinctions may be, the divisions should be sharply defined. We

[1] It is this difference of opinion as to the relative importance of small and gradual or great and mutational steps of evolutionary progress that divides modern biologists into two schools of thought.

therefore recognize these intergrading variations due to or based upon geographical distribution as Geographical Races, Varieties, or Subspecies, the last term being now the most usual. We regard them as species in the making before the connecting stages binding them to the original stock have, owing to the increasing sterility between the variants, disappeared. Except in such rare cases of physical isolation as where an oceanic island habitat precludes continuous distribution, we take, in practice, the existence of intergrades as the evidence of subspecific status.

Subspecific varieties or geographic races are, therefore, divisions of the species, and except in special lines of work, or where special exactitude is necessary, are of minor importance. As these subspecies are also in many cases based upon points of difference perceptible to only the most experienced observers, they are mainly outside the sphere of interest of the average amateur observer.

Besides these divisions of taxonomic value there are a few other variants that, owing to their erratic occurrence, cannot be recognized in our classification. These are "Albinos," "Melanos," and "Dichromatic Forms."

Albinos and Melanos are individuals suffering from an abnormal deficiency or superabundance of colouring matter in the skin and its appendages. White mice and black foxes are examples, respectively. Dichromatism (and its extreme, polychromatism) is the occurrence of two (or more) colour types normal in a species. Domestic cats in their various colours can be regarded as polychromatic.

### NOMENCLATURE

Every North American bird has a common or vernacular English name authorized by usage and recognized by the leading ornithologists, and there is seldom ordinary necessity for the scientific name. However, it is well for all who are interested in birds to familiarize themselves with as many of the scientific names as possible, as they are essential in more advanced work and of practical use in grasping the general relationships between various species. They are a necessity for international scientific intercourse and familiarity makes them much less forbidding than they seem at first. The ease with which such scientific names as geranium and hippopotamus, to say nothing of Junco and Vireo, have glided into popular usage shows that they are not as difficult and awkward as they appear on paper.

The French vernacular names have been the subject of much consideration. There is at present no generally recognized system of French common names as there is of English ones for the birds of Canada. Such French names as have appeared in Canadian ornithological literature have applied only to a limited number of species or have left much to be desired from a practical standpoint. Further, they have seldom been used in the particular specific or subspecific sense called for by the plan of this work. The names used in this book represent an attempt to combine current usage and convenience with approximate scientific accuracy in harmony with universal practice. They are employed as a temporary expedient to serve until a system can be evolved by French-Canadian ornithologists.

The present binomial system of nomenclature was introduced by Linnæus, the great Swedish botanist, and embodied in his "Systema-Naturæ," the tenth edition, 1758, which is the authority accepted by American ornithologists. In this system each species is given a double name, the first term being that of the genus to which it belongs, the second that of the species. Generic names are not duplicated within the sphere of zoology, nor are specific names within the genus. Thus, the American Robin is *Turdus migratorius*, that is, that species of the genus *Turdus* that is named *migratorius*. Other species of *Turdus* have other specific names.

The three objects of scientific nomenclature are exactitude, universality, and permanence. To this end the naming of zoological material is subject to strict laws whose principles are universally accepted and applied according to strict codes. Under these laws the scientific name of a species is not a matter of personal preference, but is fixed so that few or none can dispute it, and only such changes can be made in scientific nomenclature as are necessary to correct current mistakes in the application of the laws of the code. With increased knowledge it has become necessary to depart slightly in letter, though not in spirit, from the strict binomial system of Linnæus, and by adding a third term as name of the subspecies to make it a trinomial one. Wherever a three-term name is used, it is that of a subspecies. The first specimen described, or the first specimen to which a name has been attached, is regarded as the so-called "Type" form. In dividing a species into subspecies the form which was first named as a species is automatically given precedence and its subspecific name is a repetition of its specific name. Thus the American Robin that was first described and specifically named by Linnæus in 1766 as *migratorius*, when mentioned subspecifically in distinction from the Southern Robin or the Western one becomes *Turdus migratorius migratorius*. The Western Robin, first separated by Ridgway in 1877, was named by him *Turdus migratorius propinquus*, and the Southern Robin was named *Turdus migratorius achrusterus* by Batchelder in 1900. In practice, where the generic or specific names are evident from the context, it is customary to indicate them by initial, as *T. migratorius*, or *T.m. migratorius*.

### GEOGRAPHICAL DISTRIBUTION

The broader facts of the geographical distribution of life are patent to the most casual observer. The primary divisions of distribution, the Tropics, Temperate, and Arctic zones, are obvious, but closer study shows within these broad divisions, minor and less obvious ones. In America, north of the Gulf of Mexico, there are three life regions, roughly coinciding with the above, called the Tropic, the Austral, and the Boreal. These are subdivided into life-zones each characterized by its own peculiar assemblages of plants and animals.

The Tropic region is sufficiently characterized by name and need be only mentioned.

The Austral region corresponds roughly to the popular geographical conception of the Temperate zone. It is divided into three life zones, the Lower Austral, the Upper Austral, and the Transition. The Lower Austral might be designated as subtropic; it includes the Gulf of Mexico and the south Atlantic states, but does not reach Canada. The Upper Austral is the first zone in which we in Canada are directly interested. In the east, it merely crosses the border on the Lake Erie shore and includes the famous Niagara fruit belt. In the west it touches our southern boundaries in Saskatchewan and perhaps adjacent parts of Manitoba and Alberta and penetrates into British Columbia along the southern fruit-growing valleys. The northernmost Austral or Temperate life-zone is the Transition, which includes the greater part of the highly cultivated areas of Canada. In the central provinces it is practically co-extensive with the prairies, ceasing against the spruce forest of the north and the slopes of the mountains to the west. In British Columbia it follows up the warm interior valleys to the vicinity of the Canadian Pacific Railway and along the coast in a narrow belt to a point opposite the head of Vancouver Island, including also most of the east coast of that island.

The Boreal region is divided into Canadian, Hudsonian, and Arctic zones. The Canadian zone includes the coniferous forested region north of the Transition to the limit of practical cultivation. It sends intrusive fingers far north along Mackenzie Valley and Peace River and up the west coast, including most of the immediate coast and islands of the Alaska Panhandle almost to Skagway. The Hudsonian zone is the more northern country of small shrubs and stunted tree growth and is generally unsuitable for agriculture. The Arctic zone includes the Barren Grounds north to the pole.

These life zones are based fundamentally on temperature and if physiographic conditions were uniform would be determined by latitude. However, they are deflected from their natural east and west sweep by the shielding effects of mountain ranges, the vicinity of large bodies of water and warm or cold ocean currents, temperature of prevailing wind, and elevation. Hence the very irregular boundaries of these zones across our continent.

Elevation is an important factor in the distribution of life. Even in the tropics, the top of a mountain high enough will be of extreme arctic character with perpetual snow, and down its sides at their proper elevation will be found belts of the above zones. This is well exemplified in the mountainous region of British Columbia. The mountain tops may be of Hudsonian character, their peaks even Arctic, and the valleys between may descend to Canadian, Transition, or even Upper Austral. Consequently, the zones that on the level prairies are separated by hundreds of miles may, in this more rugged country, be within a few hours climb of each other. Also, elevations here and there in level country may produce islands of more northern life associations in southern zones. Thus, along the southern boundary in the Prairie Provinces, we find Turtle Mountain and Cypress Hills as Boreal islands surrounded by Austral lowlands; and a long, narrow tongue of Hudsonian zone follows the backbone of the Rocky Mountains from northern British Columbia south across the boundary line.

Ocean currents have an important effect on the climatic conditions of the shores adjoining them. The fact that Land's End in England, washed by the last energies of the warm Gulf stream, is in the same latitude as bleak Labrador, bathed by a cold Arctic current, well illustrates this. On the Pacific, the great Japan current sweeps against our coast and prolongs Canadian zone conditions as far north as the latitude of southern Greenland, and moderates the climate of southern Alaska and the far-flung Aleutian islands to a surprising mildness.

Besides these purely thermal controls of climate, there are other influences. Important among these is rainfall. The west coast, bathed in winds moisture-laden from the warm sea, receives a copious rainfall and the vegetation is almost tropical in its profusion. These rain-laden winds, robbed of most of their moisture by the cold peaks of the coastal range, pass on over to the interior valleys of British Columbia and the prairie regions beyond, which are consequently dry, and in some cases almost arid.

Other conditions affect the distribution of bird life. The treeless prairies, with their dry uplands interspersed with myriads of shallow lakes and sloughs, fed largely by the melting of the winter's snow and in many cases strongly alkaline, attract an entirely different class of birds than do the heavily forested woodland to the north or east, or the mountainous country farther west. Another cause of differentiation in bird life is the barrier formed by the great western mountain ranges, which permits free range up and down the continent, but limits it east and west. Many species cross these mountains without difficulty, but others find them an almost complete barrier. Their effect has been to populate the regions west of the Rocky Mountains with many species that have never found their way east. These mountains have also broken up the country into numerous more or less isolated communities, with their own peculiar physical characteristics that have developed a large number of geographical or subspecific races. In consequence many species that show homogeneous characters from the Atlantic to the mountains break up into a number of special forms from the mountains westward.

Taking the eastern forms as typical in the ordinary acceptance of the word, comparable birds of the prairie are slightly smaller and considerably paler in coloration, whereas on the humid Pacific coast they are larger and much darker. Through these influences we find in the west many subspecies of eastern forms. Comparatively few species range unmodified across the continent; many are represented east and west by two or more subspecies showing greater or less differentiation, and in other cases are locally replaced by closely allied species or are absent altogether. So far as birds are concerned these faunal divisions have to be based entirely upon breeding individuals. Birds travel so widely and along so many devious routes in their migration, that they may pass through several faunal areas in spring and autumn, though breeding in only one. Therefore, in determining the faunal zone to which any given area should be referred, transients must be disregarded.

The following birds are representative of each life-zone. All of any one group may not be entirely confined to their zone, but in it they reach the centre of their breeding abundance and, associated together, they give the dominant characteristics of the bird life. Nor may all these species occur throughout the faunal zone to which they belong; for instance, some Transition species of the prairies do not extend across the mountains into the Transition of British Columbia, and vice versa. The lists are merely suggestive and might be greatly extended.

*Upper Austral—*

- Sage Grouse
- Dickcissel
- Grasshopper Sparrow
- Chat
- Sage Thrasher
- Canyon Wren
- White-throated Swift
- Cardinal
- Orchard Oriole
- Blue-grey Gnatcatcher

*Transition*[1]*—*

- Bobolink
- Baltimore or Bullock's Orioles
- Eastern or Spotted Towhees
- Catbird
- Brown Thrasher
- Eastern and Western Bluebirds
- Ferruginous Rough-legged Hawk
- Sprague's Pipit
- Chestnut-collared Longspur
- Wood Thrush
- Cuckoo
- Field Sparrow

[1] Most of the species of this zone also occur in the Upper Austral, but reach their northern limit here. The occurrence of these, with the absence of the species mentioned as peculiar to the bordering zones, are the most marked characteristics of the Transition zone.

| *Canadian*— | *Hudsonian*— | *Arctic*— |
|---|---|---|
| Brown-headed Chickadee | Fox Sparrow | Ptarmigan |
| Olive-backed Thrush | Northern Shrike | Snowy Owl |
| Hermit Thrush | White-crowned Sparrow | Snow Bunting |
| Three-toed Woodpeckers | Bohemian Waxwing | Gyrfalcon |
| Canada Jay | Evening Grosbeak | Lapland Longspur |
| White-throated Sparrow | Pine Grosbeak | Leucosticte |
| Junco | | Eider Ducks |

## MIGRATION

The migration of birds, their periodical and seasonal appearance and disappearance, is one of the most obvious phenomena of nature. The fact that many birds disappear in winter is common knowledge and has attracted attention for ages. Though once regarded as a mystery, and still far from being thoroughly understood in many of its details, we are beginning to wonder less but admire more as accurate knowledge replaces vague speculation. Today we know where most of our northern species spend the winter and many of the routes by which they come and go have been mapped. We know that on the whole they are governed by ordinary and well known, though perhaps highly developed, senses and common every-day influences and not by the mysterious powers and instincts once ascribed to them.

The fundamental cause of migration is obviously the waxing and the waning of the food supply. Birds leave the northern land of their birth because there is no other way by which to avoid starvation. Many species can withstand extreme cold, but none can go long without food, and though some bird food remains in Canada throughout the winter, its amount is sufficient for only a limited population and even that supply rapidly decreases, or, to the north, is buried under deep snow. The cause of the southward migration in the autumn then is obvious, but why should a bird leave the soft climate and plentiful food supply in the south to brave dangerous travel to a land where retiring winter still lingers and the danger of starvation is imminent? Many ingenious explanations have been advanced to account for this: homesickness, hereditary memories of an ancient home that have endured through geological ages; the seeking of special food for nestlings; and insufficiency of nesting sites in the southern areas, have all been given as possible reasons. However, it is unnecessary to advance an extraordinary explanation, when a simple one exists. If we remember that in the nesting season the bird population is increased many times by the birth of young; that though in winter there may be room for a considerable number of birds in the southern stations, the natural spring increase in population outgrows the supporting power of even that fruitful land; and that just at this critical time the whole northern temperate region is by the coming of summer thrown open to occupation with an abundance of food, the subject is less mysterious. In fact, only by migration is it possible to use the supporting power of the temperate regions unless the birds fast or hibernate through the winters, to neither of which customs the avian nature takes kindly. Though food supply was the fundamental or originating reason for migration we must look for other and more immediate impulses for an explanation of its methods today. Originally forced to and fro by hunger, the annual movements now have become instinctive and take place before the actual hunger pinch is felt, or the physical system is weakened by want. It is much as with ourselves. We eat to prevent starvation, but habit calls most of us to the table at stated times before the pinch of hunger is acutely felt. Superficially we eat by the clock; fundamentally to keep alive. The great question in bird migration is, what is the clock that strikes this migrational hour? Professor Rowan of the University of Alberta has conducted some ingenious experiments with captive birds and has advanced the theory that the seasonal lengthening and shortening of the days induces physiological changes in the birds that awaken or actuate this migrational impulse, and urge them to be gone. This hypothesis is being well considered by ornithologists.

The extent of the migrations of different species varies. A very few species do not, in the true sense of the word, migrate at all. In other species only the more northern individuals recede from their stations, the southern remaining almost stationary, though in the majority of Canadian species the whole body moves south. Though the general rule is that migrant birds move south in winter, some do it by rather indirect routes; others, although they make considerable geographic or climatic changes in their situations, lose little or none of their northing in the process and winter at nearly as high a latitude as they summer. A few achieve milder climate simply by descending a mountain-side to the valleys. A number of the birds of the interior cross the mountain ranges at various points to the adjacent Pacific seacoast; others nesting nearby traverse in migration all the central provinces in a nearly easterly line and winter on the Atlantic coast. The whole country is thus criss-crossed with aerial lines and each species is more or less a law unto itself as to the route and objective of its journey. The bird performing the greatest migratory journey is doubtless the Arctic Tern, which nests from the Gulf of St. Lawrence to the polar regions and winters as far south as the Antarctic continent.

The methods of migration are nearly as varied as their direction or extent. Some species drift along throughout the day from treetop to treetop, from wood patch to wood patch, gradually working their way in the desired direction. Others take long flights, some high in the air, some lower. Some travel altogether by day; others travel at night and we are aware of their passage only through accidental opportunities, their faint voices coming down to us from overhead in the darkness, or their sudden appearance about us in the morning. They travel in flocks of single or mixed species, scattered groups, or as individuals.

Many species, if not all, follow more or less definite routes to and from their breeding grounds, and some go and return by altogether different paths. Comparatively small bodies of water deflect some species from their course; other species unhesitatingly cross vast reaches of sea, indifferent to nearby and convenient land passages that are used by closely allied species. In some species the older birds precede; in some the males precede the females.

How birds find their way is still only vaguely understood. Individuals far out of their natural range and course show clear evidence of being as hopelessly lost as any other animal would be on unfamiliar ground. Certainly experience has much to do with it and undoubtedly young birds are largely guided by the movements of their elders, who, presumably through previous experience, already know and can lead the way. We can understand how birds can follow great landmarks—large river systems, mountain ranges, or seacoasts—in their journey, but no sense with which we are familiar explains how some species return unerringly to lonely oceanic islands over wastes of monotonous sea. It may be that they have a special sense which aids them in orienting themselves.

## PROTECTION

In food habits birds are eminently adaptable: seeds, plants, fruit, insects, flesh, or fish are all acceptable to various species and, consequently, nearly all regions have their quota of appropriate birds. A bird lives fast. Its heart beats more rapidly than that of other animals, the blood temperature is higher, and it consumes an enormous amount of energy in flight. This feverish heat and strenuous exertion require a correspondingly large amount of food; consequently the bird as an economic factor is to be regarded seriously. It has been estimated by some who question the economic value of birds that they can have no more than a 5 per cent influence upon the insect world; yet even with this minimum effect it is evident that the absence of a 5 per cent deterrent, compounded over the years, would probably have a most profound and disastrous effect against man in his battle with the insect hordes. The destruction of tons of weed seeds and millions of insects must necessarily have a great influence upon human welfare, and neglect of this fact must seriously react upon any community that fails to give proper protection to its birds. As one of the factors in the delicate balance of nature, birds should be respected.

However, the problem of the status of individual species of birds is not the simple thing that it superficially appears to be. More than a cursory examination is necessary, and many things must be considered in order to arrive at the truth. Sometimes birds work in harmony with human welfare and sometimes against it. They may be directly beneficial at one season and harmful at another, or their indirect influence may alter the sum of their direct effects in a most surprising manner.

General impressions, then, as to whether a bird is beneficial or harmful require careful checking. Mere casual observation in life is never sufficient to determine even its food supply. Modern practice bases such conclusions almost entirely upon the examination of the stomach contents of wild birds taken throughout the year, which is the only evidence that is not subject to question. The United States Biological Survey and others have examined and passed upon thousands of bird stomachs and the results of their researches are available to those who care to study and use them.

There are certain birds which from their size, habits, and general food value are regarded as legitimate game. The pursuit of these is invigorating sport, tends to the healthful welfare of the sportsman, and teaches woodcraft, hardihood, out-of-door adaptability, and marksmanship. The true sportsman has a code of ethics of his own founded upon economic as well as humanitarian principles. He shoots nothing without giving it a fair chance and little that cannot be used as food. He is also careful not to deplete the game upon which his future sport depends. True sportsmanship, however, has not been universal, and its too common absence has resulted in a gradual but steady depletion of our game. Restrictive measures have been enacted, but have usually followed rather than preceded the need for them. The regulations that are enacted today should have been adopted yesterday and the consequence is that, over much of the country, game is a thing of the past.

This has been especially true in the east; the west is younger and its wild-life resources have not yet been so depleted, conservation sentiment has developed, and it rests with the people whether they will follow in the footsteps of an older and more wasteful generation or see that their patrimony is handed to posterity undiminished. Probably no greater single act of conservation of wild life was ever inaugurated than the Migratory Birds Convention Act with the United States, ratified in 1916, and the various provincial acts in harmony with it. Under this it is recognized that the protection of migratory birds is an international question, not a local one, as it is only by international agreement under federal auspices that we can be assured that protection equivalent to that extended in one country will be given migrant birds by other jurisdictions. Under this agreement migrant insectivorous birds, certain sea birds, herons, cranes, and all the shore birds or waders except a definitely named few, are absolutely protected throughout the year in all parts of Canada and the United States. The shooting season for migratory game birds is definitely limited to not more than three and one-half months in any given locality and all spring shooting is prohibited. A secondary effect, but probably of primary importance to the species concerned, has been the stopping of the sale of migrant game birds throughout the United States and most of Canada. Under the enforcement of the terms of this treaty there has been a very decided increase in the number of birds of the species affected and it seems as if its continuation will provide for their permanent welfare.

The above was written during the early days of the Migratory Bird Convention when its beneficial effect was most apparent and the future of migratory game looked promising. Today we are not so optimistic. The convention has accomplished what could be expected of it and has staved off an evil day, but new factors have developed or have increased in importance. With a momentary increase of game more guns have been produced to kill and the killing has been better organized: more marshes have been drained and meadows trodden by cattle. Strange diseases have swept in epidemic through the feathered ranks and dry seasons have destroyed thousands. Lately comes news of the disappearance (perhaps permanently) of the eel grass of the Atlantic coast, the main food reliance of many wintering geese. The prospects are not promising and, unless means are found to reduce the annual kill or to materially increase production, the future of North American migratory game will afford deep concern to sincere conservationist and thoughtful sportsman alike.

It is not desired to be pessimists or alarmists, but with all these adverse factors appearing and no favourable ones adequate to the situation developing, the future of our waterfowl is far from hopeful. The only factor that seems possible of direct or immediate control is the legal kill, but this, the generality of sportsmen seem most reluctant to apply to the practical needs of the case.

Some compensation for the general situation has been made by both federal and provincial action in the establishment of wild-land reservations in addition to the National and Provincial parks already established. Not only will these areas give sanctuary, protection, and suitable living conditions in the midst of cultivation and settlement, but they will act as reserves from which surplus native stock can overflow into adjoining country where agricultural and other development prevents its permanent occupation. Today, when cultivation is being rapidly extended this seems the only method by which we can retain much of the life that was originally distinctive of the country.

### MEANS OF ATTRACTING BIRDS

To anyone interested in birds, the pleasure of having them about the house and garden, where they can be observed at leisure, is very great. A small garden patch can be made attractive to many species by proper methods. The effects of strict protection are well illustrated in some of the larger parks where the shyest waterfowl, finding there is nothing to fear from man, become almost as confiding as barnyard poultry. This is the case also with the smaller garden species. Next to freedom from disturbance by human inhabitants, protection from the domestic cat is necessary.

The supplying of food in winter is also important. Shrubs carrying fruit, suet hung in trees, and grain, broken nuts, and small fragments of dried meat sheltered from the snow, rarely fail to attract birds in the winter.

In summer, when natural supplies are plentiful, food seldom has to be supplied, though a row of fruiting sunflowers or the seed heads of many garden flowers well repay the trouble they may cost. A shallow pool of clean water is a never failing source of pleasure to nearly all the common garden birds. They both bathe in it and drink it, and on a hot day it is no uncommon sight to see several birds awaiting their turn to enjoy the grateful coolness. The simplest form of bird bath is a shallow pan, set well out in the open and away from cover as a protection from cats. In cities where the trees are well cared for and dead wood is promptly removed, and on the treeless prairies, certain species of birds are always hard pressed to find suitable nesting sites. There are at least half a dozen species, naturally nesting in hollow limbs, that readily come to bird boxes of various kinds, and a number of other birds can be occasionally induced to do so. Suitable boxes are described in some of the books listed on page 22. In many schools where manual training is taught the boys are encouraged to build bird houses. Scope is thus given to their natural inventive genius, and at the same time they become interested in the birds that occupy the houses.

On the prairies nothing is more attractive to birds of many species than a tree plantation, which not only serves to shelter the crops but brings birds to assist in combating insect plagues and please us with their song and beauty.

### BIRD STUDY

The study of birds can be approached from several angles. Far from the occasionally advanced idea that ornithology is a worked-out study, that we have learned all that is necessary to know about birds, there is still plenty of work to be done and in no branch of it have we even approached finality. The æsthetic bird lover, of course, can never exhaust his personal interest in the subject and is continually finding new beauties and personal appeals. To him, the first observation of even a trite and well-known fact comes with all the pleasure and force of a new discovery and there is little fear of the subject ever growing commonplace. To those who are ambitious of advancing the world's knowledge, ornithology offers many opportunities. Rarely will the complete life-history of even a single species fail to repay intensive work.

Our knowledge of bird distribution in Canada is still far from complete and there are vast areas in which it is based on assumption. Even some large and important political divisions, such as provinces, are without recent authoritative lists of their birds. In many cases nothing but scantiest data for their compilation are available. It is only by the study of many local areas that such broader lists can be satisfactorily written, and in such local studies as these much good work can be done by the amateur. It must not be assumed that such local faunal work is easy; when conscientiously done it becomes one of the most difficult fields of ornithology. Ten years spent on such work assisted by all available literature and the advice of experts is little enough to form a satisfactory basis for work. Literature must be searched, weight of authorities estimated, evidence verified, specimens accurately identified, and all must be subject to the observer's experience and the probabilities. Knowledge of adjoining localities and general and local literature is indispensable for this. To satisfy modern standards of accuracy the making of a faunal list is one of the severest tests of ornithological ability.

The economic effect of bird life is an important study, and one in which the greatest caution is necessary. General impressions are so often misleading that conclusions should be founded only on irrefutable evidence. Stomach examination of what has actually been taken into the alimentary canal is practically the only positive evidence of food habits and in some cases leads to surprising results. No species should be condemned until a thorough study by this method has been made by experienced investigators. Such a study is beyond the amateur, but he can assist greatly by preserving the stomachs of those specimens he collects in the course of his work and forwarding them to the Victoria Memorial Museum, where they may be either immediately examined or stored for reference later. Field observations of the economic status of species when accurately made and reported are often of great value, but must be used with the greatest caution.

Of late years "banding" has become an established and valuable method of bird study. Numbered aluminium bands with return address are locked about the legs of nestlings and trapped birds in such a manner as not to interfere with their normal activities, and the bearers are released. Full records are kept of species, date, locality, age, and circumstance in each case. Returns from these banded specimens are coming in now in considerable numbers and we are getting exact, demonstrable knowledge of them, where hitherto we had nothing but guesswork or analogy to go upon. The practice of systematically banding on a limited home area throughout the season, and year after year, has been particularly fruitful and has opened up an entirely new field of interesting research to the amateur observer of limited opportunity. Such work, of course, has to be regulated to prevent unqualified persons from participating and the confusion of duplicate records, bands, and systems. In Canada such work is under the control and supervision of the National Parks Branch of the Department of the Interior, who issue the necessary permits to anyone wishing to engage in this form of research in Canada.

Some very interesting results that could have been secured in no other way have been obtained from these banding studies; for instance, we are gradually learning how long birds may live in a state of nature and some interesting plumage age-sequences are being solved. We are finding out something of the constancy, or the contrary, of the mating of many of our familiar garden visitors, how the young scatter from their natal homes in successive seasons, and the extent and relative permanency of individual territorial domain. We are tracing individual birds through the course of their migration and are finding many remarkable deviations from previously assumed north and south movements. The irregular dribble of European Widgeon along our Atlantic coast is found to originate in Iceland and not in America as was beginning to be suspected. Common Tern raised on our east coast have been found in winter scattered on both sides of the south Atlantic from the River Niger in Africa to the Amazon in South America and the Arctic Tern is shown to cross to Europe on its way south to the Antarctic. These and many other difficult questions are gradually finding their answers by this new method of study.

A serious word should be said on the much discussed question of the collection of specimens as a method of bird study. Various persons take various interests in bird study. Some are satisfied just to see or hear birds about them, and take little interest in what they are, what they do, or what they are named. At the other extreme are those who are unsatisfied until they know all about the objects of their admiration and interest, and have pried into the innermost secrets of their relationships, habits, and economy. Between these extremes are every degree and combination of æsthetic and scientific interest. It is not necessary for all to become highly developed scientific ornithologists, but every art or science requires a certain leaven of experts to direct the amateur, assist him with short-cuts, and present conclusions that he may not be qualified or inclined to discover for himself. Equally necessary is it to healthful development of any such line of inquiry that there be these experts and specialists to set, by example, standards of excellence and method. This is as true in ornithology as it is in art, athletics, or stock raising. Considerable æsthetic pleasure and some information can be obtained by merely watching birds in life, more can be obtained by use of field glasses and systematic study, but it is no more possible for one to obtain accurate and comprehensive knowledge of birds than of plants or insects without collecting or at least handling specimens. It would be impossible for anyone to write such a book as this without constant access to complete or extensive series of specimens. Scientific ornithologists are necessary, but they cannot be developed without conceding them the right to collect and study at first hand the material through which they can develop. That such a right cannot be distributed too freely is obvious. In consequence, for collecting in Canada for scientific purposes, birds covered by the Migratory Birds Convention Act, a permit from the Canadian National Parks Branch of the Department of the Interior is necessary. These permits are granted to applicants who show that they are sincere and bona fide bird students, qualified to make proper use of them. The spirit in which these permits are issued and the guards against their abuse are well shown by the following "principles" that are attached to and form a part of them.

### PERMIT PRINCIPLES

Permits to take migratory birds, their nests and eggs, under the Migratory Birds Convention Act and Regulations, are granted for the sole purpose of scientific study and not for the collection of objects of curiosity or personal or household adornment. Therefore, only such persons as take a serious interest in ornithology, and are competent to exercise the privilege for the advancement of knowledge, are eligible to receive such permits.

It is expected that the holders of permits will use them with reasonable discretion, taking only such specimens as their scientific requirements demand and avoiding unnecessary waste of life. The habitual taking of numbers of individuals for the purpose of obtaining a few specially desirable ones is deprecated; and it is urged that the collector take no more specimens than he has reasonable prospects of caring for and that he conscientiously endeavour properly to prepare each and all when taken.

It is also recommended that the holders of permits will, so far as is consistent with their object, be considerate of the local feeling in the neighbourhood where they collect and will demonstrate both by actions and speech that the scientific collector is sympathetic towards the principles of wild-life conservation and is not the rival of legitimate sportsmen.

It is required as an evidence of good faith that holders of permits label their specimens with the customary scientific data and properly care for them, not only at the time of collection but thereafter, giving them all reasonable protection against insect pests and other agencies of destruction, and will not permit them to be destroyed through carelessness or indifference.

As permits are granted for the purpose of general scientific advancement and not for individual benefit, specimens taken under them are to be regarded as being in the nature of public trusts, and should be accessible to all duly qualified students under only such reasonable restrictions as are necessary for their protection or as are consistent with the owner's work.

Finally, it is urged that provision be made so that specimens taken will ultimately find their way into permanent or public collections where they will be available for study by future generations and not be wasted and lost through neglect.

Although all these conditions are not strictly mandatory, and their spirit will be liberally interpreted, they will be considered in the granting or renewal of each permit, and evidence of gross violation of them may be deemed sufficient ground for the refusal of an application or for the revocation of any permit already granted.

It is hoped and expected that the justice of these principles will be realized and that collectors will co-operate in advancing science to the utmost without unnecessary waste of valuable bird life.

In concluding this subject of bird study attention is called to the fact that the various departments of the Government stand ready to assist the earnest student in every possible way. Their greatest usefulness will usually be found in the identification of specimens. The National Museum of Canada, Ottawa, will gladly identify and return any specimens that may be submitted for that purpose. Sometimes a fragment, such as a wing or tail, sometimes even a feather or two, will suffice. Of course, complete, well-made skins of the whole specimen are best, but the reader is urged, when these are not available, to preserve as many as possible of the easily prepared parts of birds he may be in doubt about and submit them to the Museum for examination. The Canadian National Parks Branch of the Department of the Interior, Ottawa, being in charge of the administration of the Migratory Birds Convention Act, is particularly interested in all questions of protection and public education and the services of its officers in allied subjects are equally at the disposal of inquirers. Earnest students are also always welcomed by the more advanced ornithologists, who are ready to assist them and give advice most freely.

## ORNITHOLOGICAL LITERATURE

The ornithological literature of eastern North America is rich and varied; that of the western parts is slightly less so. However, there are extant a number of works concerning the birds of various provinces or localities, or those of adjoining areas, which may be consulted with advantage for details of various species other than those here given. The following manuals are recommended:

Bird Guides—Western Bird Guide, Birds of the Rockies and West to the Pacific. Water and Game Birds East of the Rockies (including Hawks and Owls). Land Birds East of the Rockies. By Chester A. Reed. Doubleday, Page, and Co., Garden City, N.Y. Price each $1 in cloth, $1.25 in leather.

These are small, almost vest-pocket editions in limp bindings, 3¼ by 5½ inches, very convenient for carrying in the pocket. They contain brief descriptions and small, coloured illustrations of all the birds of both sexes. Considering their size, convenience, and price, they are excellent.

Colour Key, North American Birds, by Frank M. Chapman and Chester K. Reed; 8vo., Doubleday, Page, and Co., Garden City, N.Y.

Similar in plan to above, but more detailed and instructive.

A Field Guide to the Birds, Including all Species Found in Eastern North America, by Roger Tory Peterson; Houghton, Mifflin, and Co., 1934. Exceptionally well illustrated. A book of field marks, very excellent for the amateur and of value to any field man.

The Handbook of the Birds of Eastern North America, by Frank M. Chapman: 12 mo., D. Appleton & Co., price $3.50.

This is an almost complete text book on the birds of eastern North America and is invaluable for the advanced as well as the beginning student. It contains detailed accurate descriptions of all plumages, measurements, and migration dates, and an immense amount of interesting and valuable detail with a most valuable introduction on birds and bird study. As soon as a student is familiar with the rudiments of ornithology, he should supply himself with this handbook.

Handbook of Birds of the Western United States, by Florence Merriam Bailey; 8vo. Revised edition, 1920, Houghton, Mifflin, & Co., Boston.

This does for the western United States nearly what the previous book does for the east, and is of especial value for use in British Columbia. However, its field being limited to the United States, there are a few Canadian species with which it does not deal. In spite of this it is invaluable to the far-western observer.

Key to the Birds of North America, by Elliot Coues; 5th edition, 1903, 2 vols., large 8vo., Dana Estes & Co.

This is perhaps the most generally accepted authority on American birds. It is primarily intended for the advanced student, but it contains a mass of information that can be found nowhere else and is a final court of appeal for the majority of ornithologists.

Birds of the Northwest, by Elliot Coues, Department of the Interior, United States Geological Survey of the Territories. Miscellaneous Publication No. 3, Washington. Government Printing Office, 1874.

This is a handbook of the ornithology of the region drained by Missouri River and its tributaries. It contains an immense amount of technical and popular information regarding a great number of birds of interest to the Canadian observer. It is notable as much for its literary style as for its scientific accuracy. Unfortunately it is out of print.[1]

Birds of the Colorado Valley, Part I, Passeres to Laniidæ (all that was ever published), by Elliot Coues, Department of the Interior, United States Geological Survey of the Territories. Miscellaneous Publication No. 11, 1878.

This is similar and supplementary to the above. In addition it contains an important Bibliography to American Ornithology. It, too, is out of print.

[1] Books that are out of print are usually difficult to obtain. Fortunately there are a number of dealers who specialize in various second-hand books. Many of these dealers issue periodical catalogues of volumes they have for sale, and any of them when given particulars of books desired will make every effort to fill the order.

A manual of North American Birds, by Robert Ridgway, J. B. Lippincott Co., Philadelphia, Pa., 1887.

Birds of North and Middle America, by Robt. Ridgway: Bulletin No. 50, 8vo., United States National Museum.

This is a monumental work planned in ten volumes, of which eight are in print, the remainder to follow as rapidly as the work can be prepared. It is the latest and the most detailed and scientific work on the subject, but it contains nothing on life histories or allied popular subjects. It is not for general sale, but may be procured from second-hand book dealers or through the Department of Public Documents at Washington.

Catalogue of Canadian Birds, by John and James M. Macoun; 8vo., published by the Department of Mines, Geological Survey Branch, Ottawa, 1909.

This is a complete list of all the species and subspecies of birds known to occur in Canada, Greenland, and Newfoundland, with their breeding and migratory ranges as thoroughly stated as the condition of knowledge at the time of publication permitted. It is based largely upon the explorations and experience of the authors, supplemented by knowledge from all available sources, and contains considerable information regarding breeding habits but little else of popular interest. It is now out of print.

## *Books Dealing with Special Groups of Birds*

The Warblers of North America, by Frank M. Chapman; D. Appleton & Company.

North American Land Birds, by Baird, Brewer, and Ridgway; Little, Brown & Co., 3 vols. Reprint of the original.

The Water-birds of the series was originally published in Memoirs of the Museum of Comparative Zoology, Harvard College, 1884, but is now out of print and very difficult to obtain.

The Game Birds of California, by Grinnel, Bryant, and Storer; University of California Press, Berkeley, California, 1918.

A work of great value to the sportsman and the conservationist. Almost as applicable to Canada as to California.

Life Histories of North American Birds, by A. C. Bent, United States National Museum, Washington. Diving Birds, Bulletin 107 (1919). Gulls and Terns, Bulletin 113 (1931). Petrels, Pelicans, and their Allies, Bulletin 121 (1922). Wild Fowl, Ducks, Part I to Ringneck, Bulletin 126. Wild Fowl, Ducks, Part II to Swans, Bulletin 130 (1925). Herons, Cranes, Rails, etc., Bulletin 135 (1926). Shore-birds, Part I, Bulletin 142 (1927). Shore-birds, Part II, Bulletin 146 (1929).

Others to follow as rapidly as possible. This is a monumental work in which, as far as possible, all sources of information have been exhausted in the treatment of life history and plumage sequences of North American birds. It is a continuation of—

Life Histories of North American Birds, by Major Chas. Bendire, United States National Museum. Vol. I, Gallinaceous Birds, the Pigeons and Birds of Prey, Special Bulletin No. 1 (1892). Vol. II, Parrots to the Grackles, Special Bulletin (unnumbered) (1895).

Unfortunately these are both out of print and very rare.

## *Books of Special Geographical Interest*

The Birds of Ontario, by Thomas McIlwraith, 2nd edition, 8 vols., 1894. Wm. Briggs, Toronto.

The Birds of Toronto, by J. H. Fleming: Auk, vol. XXIII, pp. 437-453; vol. XXIV, pp. 71-89.

The Natural History of the Toronto Region. Birds by J. H. Fleming: Published by Canadian Institute, Toronto, 1913, price, $2 or $2.50.

Les Oiseaux de la Province de Québec, par C. E. Dionne: Dussault & Proulx, 1906.

The Birds of Montreal, by E. D. Wintle: Drysdale & Co., Montreal, 1908.

Birds of Nova Scotia, by A. Downs, edited by Harry Piers: Proc. and Trans., Nova Scotia Inst. Sc., vol. VII, pp. 142-178.

A Catalogue of the Birds of New Brunswick, by M. A. Chamberlain: Bulletin Natural History Society, New Brunswick, No. 1, pp. 23-68.

The Birds of Manitoba, by Ernest Thompson-Seton. Proceedings United States National Museum, XIII, pp. 457-641 (1890).

A complete annotated list of the birds of Manitoba as known at that time, with much valuable information as to occurrence, distribution, and life-history notes.

Fauna of Manitoba, Birds, by Ernest Thompson-Seton. British Association Handbook, 1909.

This is a summarized reprint of the above brought up to date of publication.

The Birds of Churchill, Manitoba, by P. A. Taverner and Geo. Miksch Sutton. Carnegie Museum, Pittsburgh, 1934.

Catalogue of the Birds of Saskatchewan, by H. Hedley Mitchell. The Canadian Field Naturalist, vol. XXXVIII, Special Number, pp. 101-118 (1924). Separates also obtainable from the Department of Agriculture, Regina, Sask. This is a list with distributions of all birds known to occur in the province.

A Biological Investigation of the Hudson Bay Region, by Edward A. Preble. United States Department of Agriculture, Bureau of Biological Survey, North American Fauna No. 22, 1902. Of particular application to northern Manitoba.

A Biological Investigation of the Athabaska-Mackenzie Region, by Edward A. Preble. United States Department of Agriculture, Bureau of Biological Survey, North American Fauna No. 27, Washington, 1909.

The bird section of this work, pp. 251-500, is of particular value, summarizing as it does all the information available on the Northwest Territories and the western Arctic islands. It deals mostly with the distribution of species.

Guide to Natural History and Ethnological Exhibitions in the Provincial Museum of British Columbia, Victoria, B.C., 1909.

The list of birds, pp. 21-71, is in effect a catalogue of the birds of the province developed from the Check-list of British Columbia Birds by John Fannin, published by the Museum, 1898. It is merely distributional.

Report on a Collection of Birds and Mammals from Vancouver Island, by Harry S. Swarth. University of California, Publications in Zoölogy, vol. 10, No. 1 (1912). Birds, pp. 13-113.

This should form the basic list for future development of check-lists of the birds of Vancouver Island and contains critical studies of species and subspecies as well as their distribution.

Birds and Mammals of the Stikine River Region of Northern British Columbia and Southeastern Alaska, by Harry S. Swarth. University of California, Publication in Zoology, vol. 24, No. 2 (1922). Birds, pp. 194-308.

Birds and Mammals of the Skeena River Region of Northern British Columbia, by Harry S. Swarth. University of California, Publications in Zoology, vol. 24, No. 3 (1924). Birds, pp. 323-372.

Bird Study in British Columbia, by J. A. Munro. Published by The Department of Education, Victoria, British Columbia, 1932. Pp. 99. A popular brochure on ornithology particularly adapted to school use in British Columbia.

Natural History of the Queen Charlotte Islands, by Wilfred Osgood. United States Department of Agriculture, Bureau of Biological Survey, North American Fauna, No. 21 (1901). Birds, pp. 38-50.

Biological Investigations in Alaska and Yukon Territory, by Wilfred H. Osgood. United States Department of Agriculture, Bureau of Biological Survey, North American Fauna No. 30, 1909.

Results of a Biological Reconnaissance of the Yukon River Region, by Wilfred H. Osgood and Louis B. Bishop. United States Department of Agriculture, Bureau of Biological Survey, North American Fauna, No. 19, 1900.

Birds Collected or Observed on the Expedition of the Alpine Club of Canada to Jasper Park, Yellowhead Pass, and Mount Robson Region, by J. H. Riley. The Canadian Alpine Journal, pp. 47-75, 1912.

Addenda to Birds of Jasper Park, by P. A. Taverner. The Canadian Alpine Journal, 1918. pp. 62-69.

A Distribution List of the Birds of British Columbia, by Allan Brooks and Harry S. Swarth. Cooper Ornithological Club, Pacific Coast Avifauna No. 17, being Contribution No. 423 from the Museum of Vertebrate Zoology of the University of California, 1925. This is a list of all the species and subspecies of birds known to occur in British Columbia, with full detailed distributions.

Besides these works on particular Canadian areas there are several on adjoining localities of special interest to nearby Canadian observers. Among them are:

A Preliminary Survey of the Bird Life of North Dakota, by Norman A. Wood. University of Michigan, Museum of Zoology, Miscellaneous Publications No. 10, Ann Arbor, Michigan (1923).

A Distributional List of the Birds of Montana, by Aretas A. Saunders. Cooper Ornithological Club, Pacific Coast Avifauna No. 14, Berkeley, California, 1921.

The Birds of Washington, by Wm. Leon Dawson. British Columbia Edition with Supplementary matter by Allan Brooks. The Occidental Publishing Company, Seattle, Washington, 1909.

This contains a large number of coloured and uncoloured illustrations and much life-history, in a very entertaining form.

A Guide to the Birds of Eastern New York, by Ralph Hoffman: 8vo., Houghton, Mifflin & Co., price $1.50.

A most desirable book which, though dealing with an extralimital area, treats of most of the birds of eastern Canada. It contains keys for the birds of each season based upon colour, detailed descriptions, and also many illustrations in black and white showing specific details, and gives much information of various kinds.

The Birds of Minnesota, by Thomas S. Roberts, 2 vols. Museum of Natural History, University of Minnesota, 1932. A monumental work lavishly illustrated with full page illustrations in colour and many text figures. Of particular interest to ornithologists in the adjoining province of Manitoba.

Michigan Bird Life, by Walter B. Barrows. Michigan Agricultural College, 1912.

Birds of Massachusetts and other New England States, by E. H. Forbush. Three vols., Massachusetts Department of Agriculture, Boston (1925-1927). Probably one of the most elaborate and beautiful, popular sets of bird books ever published. Contains an extraordinary amount of detailed information on plumages, occurrence, and life history of the birds of the region indicated in the title.

Ornithology, like other branches of science, has its own periodicals. The chief of these in North America is the "Auk," a quarterly magazine, the official organ of the American Ornithologists' Union. In addition to purely scientific papers, it contains hundreds of articles of interest to Canadians, including local lists copiously annotated with life-history notes from all over the Dominion and popular descriptions of habits. Subscription $3 a year. Editor, beginning 1912, Witmer Stone, Academy of Science, Philadelphia, Pa.

The "Condor," a bi-monthly magazine of Western Ornithology, is the official organ of the Cooper Ornithological Club. Edited by Joseph Grinnell, Berkeley, California. Subscription in Canada $3.25 a year. Address W. Lee Chambers, Business Manager, Eagle Rock, California. This is a well edited and beautifully illustrated periodical devoted to the study of western birds and contains much of popular as well as scientific interest.

Bird-Banding. A quarterly journal of ornithological investigation published by the North-eastern, Eastern, and Inland Bird-banding Associations. Now (1933) in its fourth volume, a continuation of the Bulletin of the Northeastern Bird-Banding Association under which title it ran for five years. Subscription $1.50 a year. Address, Chas. B. Floyd, 95 South St., Boston, Massachusetts.

The Condor (*See* above) is the organ for western bird-banding activities.

The Murrelet. A quarterly journal devoted to Northwestern (including western Canada) ornithology and mammalogy. In fourteenth year (first eleven years in mimeograph form). Subscription $2 a year in Canada. Address, Geo. K. Couch, Room 101, Old Capital Building, Olympia, Washington.

"Bird-lore" is a popular, monthly magazine notable for its beautiful make-up and illustrations. It is the official organ of the National Audubon Societies, and is devoted to the popular study and protection of birds; it is edited by Frank Chapman. Subscription in Canada $1.75 a year. Address, Bird-lore, Crescent and Mulberry Streets, Harrisburg, Pa.

The "Canadian Field-Naturalist," the continuation of the "Ottawa Naturalist," is a monthly (nine numbers a year) published by the Ottawa Field Naturalists' Club. Subscription $2 a year. Address, Wilmot Lloyd, Mariposa Avenue, Rockcliffe Park, Ottawa, Canada. This publication represents numerous Natural History Societies of the Dominion. It contains a great deal of interesting zoological material and numerous ornithological notes and articles, and is the only Natural History magazine published in Canada.

On the subject of protection and attraction of birds about the home, among the great mass of literature available, the following can be specially recommended:

How to Attract and Protect Wild Birds, by Martin Hiesmann. Witherby & Co., London, 1s. 6d.

This is an extended account of the methods pursued by Baron von Berlepsch in Germany, and gives numerous methods by which the end can be obtained on both large and small estates.

Wild Bird Guests, by Harold Baynes. E. P. Dutton & Co., New York, 1915, $2.

This gives a most interesting and readable account of the method pursued by the writer and his friends whereby they made Meriden, New Hampshire, a veritable model bird village, where the birds became as familiar and friendly as household pets, coming when called and alighting freely upon the person. It is beautifully illustrated with numerous photographs showing both methods and results.

The Domestic Cat, by Edward H. Forbush. State Ornithologist, Mass. State Board of Agriculture, Bulletin No. 2 (1916).

This is an exhaustive treatment of the house cat in its relation to wild-bird life.

Bird Houses and How to Build Them, by Ned Dearborn. United States Department of Agriculture, Farmer's Bulletin No. 609. Address, Department of Public Documents, Washington, D.C. Cost about 10 cents.

Bird Houses and Their Occupants, by P. A. Taverner. Reprinted from The Canadian Field-Naturalist, vol. XXXII, pp. 118-126 (1919), by the Canadian National Parks Branch, Department of the Interior, Ottawa, from whom copies may be obtained.

Attracting Birds with Food and Water, by R. Owen Merriman. Canadian National Parks Branch, Department of the Interior, Ottawa.

The Conservation of Wild Life of Canada, by C. Gordon Hewitt. Chas. Scribner's Sons, New York, 1921.

Jack Miner and the Birds, by Jack Miner. Ryerson Press, Toronto, 1923.

Many publications, pamphlets, and reports on these and other subjects are published by various federal, provincial, and state governments and may be obtained either free of cost or at a nominal price. The National Museum of Canada, Ottawa, and the Canadian National Parks Branch, Department of the Interior, Ottawa, issue numerous such brochures which can be obtained on application. The United States Department of Agriculture has published a great number of scientific, economic, and popular reports which can be obtained at a nominal price. Many of them apply directly to Canadian conditions. A catalogue and price list of them can be obtained from the Department of Public Documents, Washington, D.C.

On the subject of the English Sparrow as a pest the following can be recommended:

The English Sparrow in North America, by Walter B. Burrows. Bulletin No. 1, United States Dept. of Agriculture, pp. 405 (1889).

How to Destroy the English Sparrow, by Ned Dearborn. Farmer's Bulletin No. 383, United States Dept. of Agriculture (1910).

The English Sparrow as a Pest, by Ned Dearborn. Farmer's Bulletin No. 493, United States Dept. of Agriculture (1912).

These reports give the English Sparrow a fair trial and an honest conviction, and suggest various means of keeping its number under control.

## KEY TO THE BIRDS OF CANADA

The method of its use is as follows. Given a bird of unknown species, in the hand, to determine its name it is first compared with the first heading in **boldface** numbered in Roman numerals—**I, Feet Fully Webbed.** If this description does not fit the bird, the next Roman numeral heading is referred to—**II, Feet Partly Webbed,** or **III, Feet Without Pronounced Web.** Assuming that the last correctly describes the bird under discussion, we refer to the headings of the next lower rank, which are numbered alphabetically with capital letters, where we find the alternatives —"F, Legs long," and "G, Legs short." Sometimes it may be difficult to decide whether a leg should be regarded as long or short, and the various pictured details following may then assist determination. In this case the legs, we decide, are not remarkably long, no longer in proportion to size of the bird than are the legs of a chicken or sparrow; we, therefore, under G, refer to a number of subordinate alternatives, distinguished by small initial letters—"l, feet chicken-like, strong, and compact for scratching"; "m, feet strongly clawed for holding prey"; "n, feet small and weak"; "o, feet small or medium-sized, solidly made, and legs covered with horny scales or plates." Glances at various feet shown under each heading will assist in determination. Assuming a decision in favour of the last, we compare our specimen with the next alternatives, numbered with ordinary Arabic numerals—"20, two toes in front"; "21, three toes in front." There can be little confusion here and we assume that our specimen having three front toes is one of the great body of perching birds. We, therefore, compare it with the following line detail drawings to see with which it agrees most closely. The bill is not wide and flat, it is, therefore, not a flycatcher; there are no ear-tufts or long hind toe and the nostril is not covered with feather tufts, therefore it cannot be either a Horned Lark, a crow, or a jay. The next picture, the bobolink's bill, catches our eye and the sparrow bill in the next lot. A glance through the remainder shows that our bird must be a bobolink or one of the sparrows. The picture (Plate LXXI A) and description of the former are nothing like it; therefore, we turn to the sparrows, read the general sparrow description, and remarks on page 379, and then work through the pictures. After looking at all the illustrations we find that our specimen agrees with that of the Song Sparrow, and on reading over the distinctive characters we have our opinion confirmed. It has the sharply striped breast aggregated in the centre, and is without either the yellow stripe over the eye of the Savannah Sparrow or the white outer feathers of the tail, as in the vesper. We are, therefore, confident that, starting with no other ornithological knowledge than that the specimen was a Canadian bird, we have been able to refer it to its proper species.

## *Key*

Figure 1

Plumage areas of a typical bird.

**I. Feet Fully Webbed**—Two or three complete webs to each foot.

A, Toes, four.

a, Tarsus flattened.

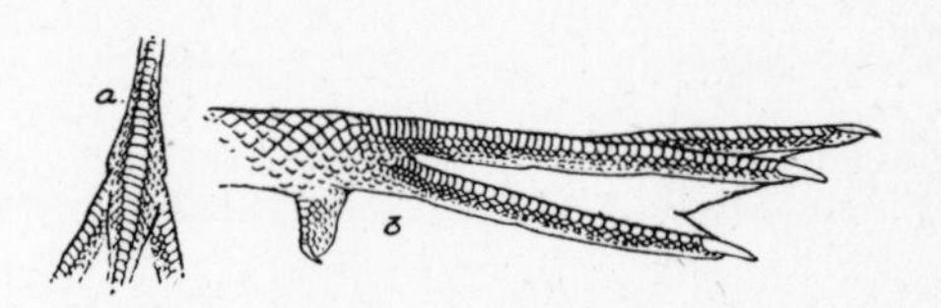

Figure 2

*Loons*.......................................... p. 37

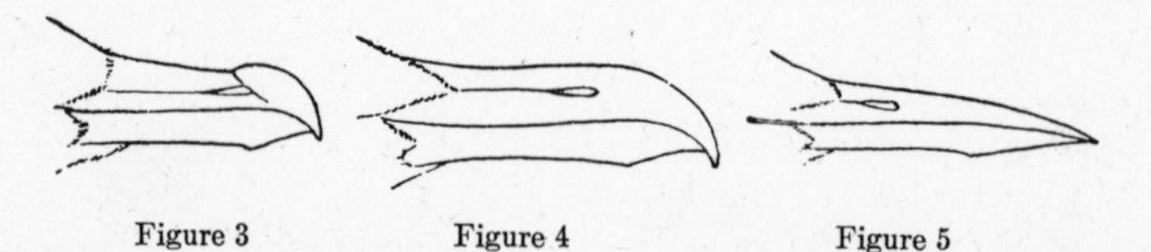

Figure 3 Figure 4 Figure 5

b, Closed wing longer than tail, except in some jaegers (Figure 3) and terns (Figure 5), in which the rule only holds if the greatly elongated central tail feathers of the former or the outer ones of the latter are disregarded. Bills as below.

*Long-winged Swimmers*—gulls, terns, jaegers.................. p. 214

Lower mandible much longer than
upper.

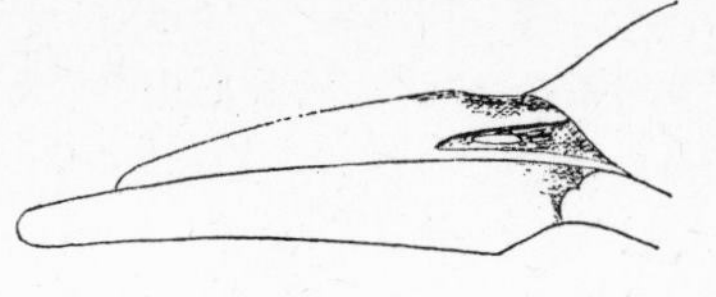

Figure 6

*Skimmers*.................................................. p. 240

c, Webs between all toes (3 webs).

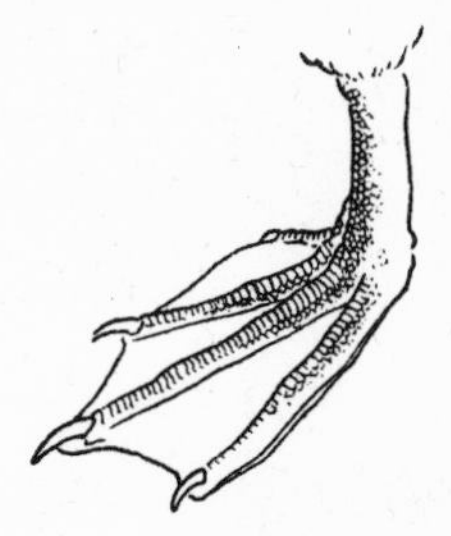

Figure 7

*Full-Webbed Swimmers*—gannets, cormorants, etc............... p. 51

d, Bill toothed or flattened (duck-like).

*Sieve-billed Swimmers*—mergansers, ducks, geese, and swans...... p. 68

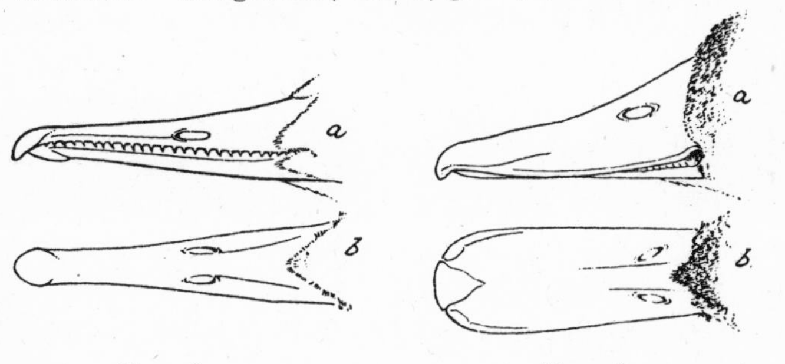


Figure 8 Figure 9

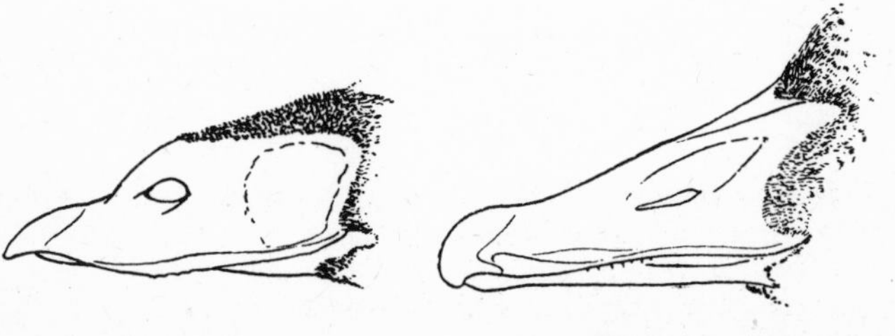

Figure 10 Figure 11

e, Nostrils in tubes on top of bill.

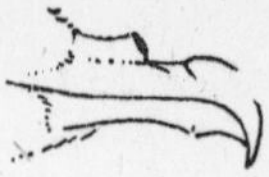

Figure 12

*Tube-nosed Swimmers*—petrels, etc. . . . . . . . . . . . . . . . . . . . . . . . . . p. 44

B, Toes three (without hind toe), except Kittiwake (p. 232).

Figure 13

*Auks*, *Murres*, etc. . . . . . . . . . . . . . . . . . . . . . . . . . . . . . . . . . p. 240

**II. Feet Partly Webbed**—Webs reduced to scallops, bordering flaps or small webs at base of toes. Toes four, except as otherwise noted.

C, Tarsus much flattened; webs as shown.

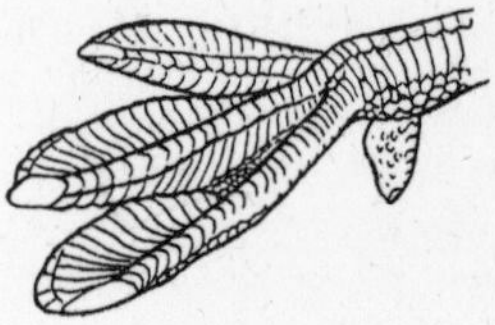

Figure 14

*Grebes* . . . . . . . . . . . . . . . . . . . . . . . . . . . . . . . . . . . . . . . . . . . . . p. 40

D, Bill extending on to forehead and forming frontal plate.

Figure 15

*Coot* . . . . . . . . . . . . . . . . . . . . . . . . . . . . . . . . . . . . . . . . . . . . . . p. 175

E, Small birds; bill long and slender, in some cases decurved or recurved; toes three or four.

f, Bill without hard terminal enlargement; toes four, except sanderling (p. 210).

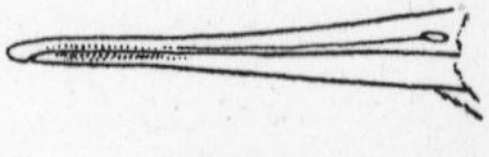

Figure 16

*Shore Birds*—phalaropes, snipe, sandpipers, plover. . . . . . . . . . . . . . p. 176

g, Bill with hard terminal enlargement; toes three, except Black-bellied Plover (p. 184).

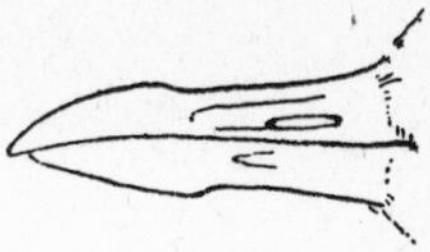

Figure 17

*Plover* .................................................. p. 179

h, Bill long and straight, much flattened to a strikingly chisel-shaped tip, and bright red in colour.

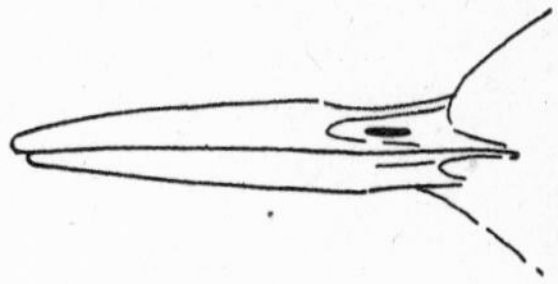

Figure 18

*Oyster-catcher* .................................................. p. 177

## III. Feet Without Pronounced Web.

F, Legs long, for wading in water or mud; toes long, slender, and flexible at joints.

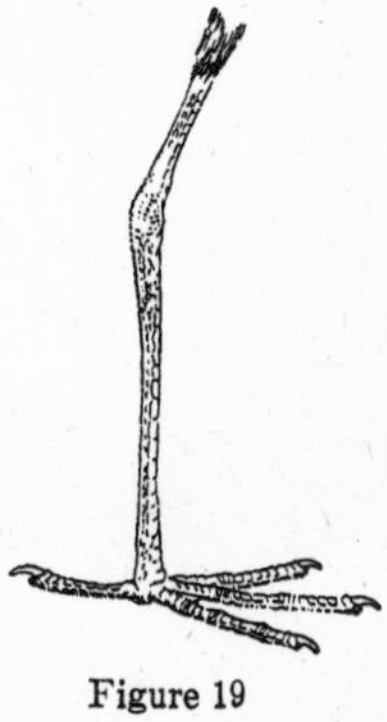

Figure 19

i, Bill stout and horny; bare space about eyes.

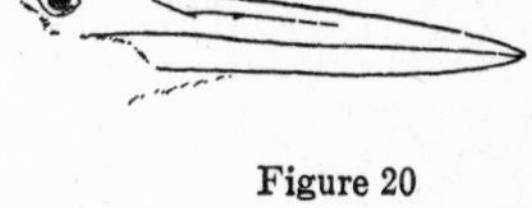

Figure 20

1, Middle toe with comb.

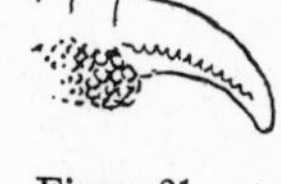

Figure 21

*Herons* .................................................. p. 59

2, Forehead bare, bill straight.

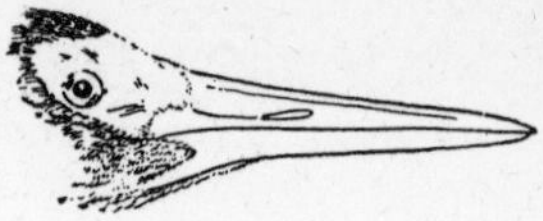

Figure 22

*Cranes* .................................................... p. 167

j, Bills long, flexible, and evenly tapered.

Figures 23 and 24

3, Bill rather slender, not markedly deeper at base than tip, in some cases markedly decurved or recurved. Toes four, except sanderling (p. 210).

*Phalaropes, Snipe, Sandpipers* .................................. p. 186

4, Bill rather decidedly heavier at base than at tip.

Figure 25

*Rails* (Virginia Rail) ........................................ p. 172

k, Bills short.

5, Bill soft at base ending in hard terminal enlargement. Toes three, except Black-bellied Plover (p. 184).

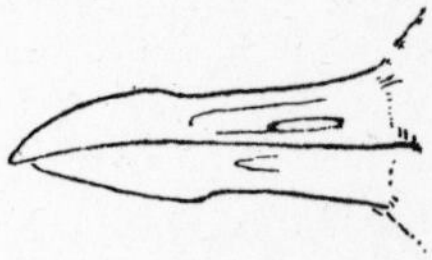

Figure 26

*Plover* .................................................... p. 179

6, Bill quite stout.

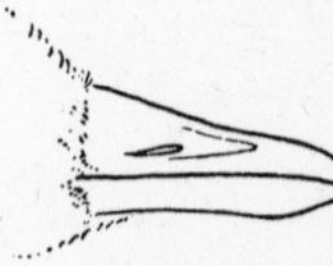

Figure 27

*Rails* (Sora and Yellow Rails) ................................ p. 173

7, Bill horny to base, wedge-shaped in profile, and appearing to be slightly turned up.

Figure 28

*Turnstone* . . . . . . . . . . . . . . . . . . . . . . . . . . . . . . . . . . . . . . . . . . p. 185

G, Legs short for perching, walking, climbing, and living in trees or on land.

1, Feet chicken-like, strong and compact; toes less flexible; claws strong and blunt for scratching. Tarsus feathered or bare. With or without comb-like appendages on toes.

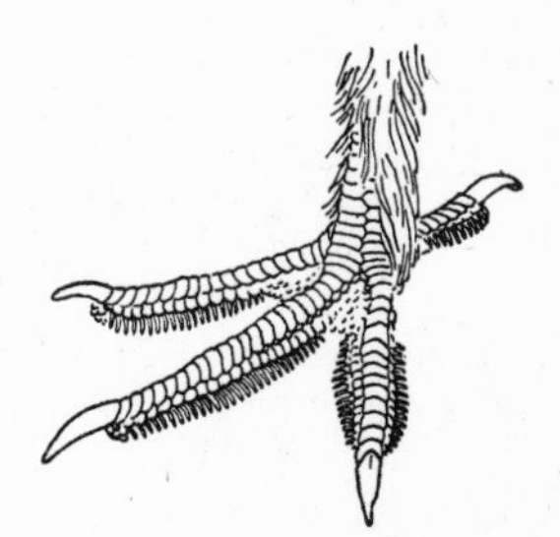

Figure 29

8, Bill rather conical; feathered to or about nostril.

Figure 30

*Grouse and Quail* . . . . . . . . . . . . . . . . . . . . . . . . . . . . . . . . . . . . . . p. 149

9, Bill hooked; neck and head bare.

Figure 31

*Vultures* . . . . . . . . . . . . . . . . . . . . . . . . . . . . . . . . . . . . . . . . . . p. 114

m, Feet powerful for holding prey; claws long, strong, sharp, and curved.

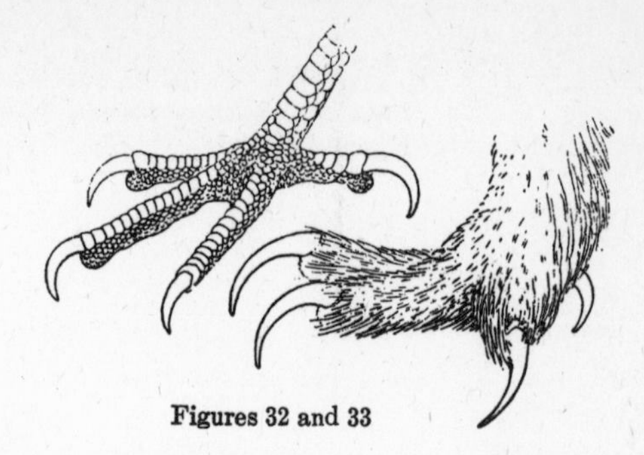

Figures 32 and 33

10, Naked cere at base of bill. Tarsus always (except on Rough-legged Hawk, and Golden Eagle) bare. Toes always bare (Figure 32).

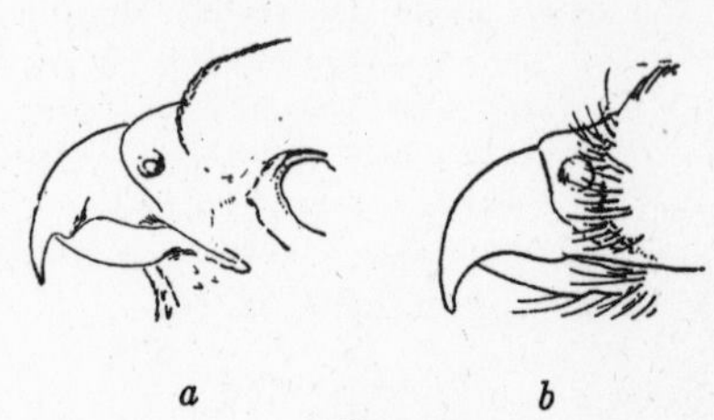


Figure 34

*Hawks and Eagles* . . . . . . . . . . . . . . . . . . . . . . . . . . . . . . . . . . . . . . . . . p. 116

11, Cere hidden in feathers; eye in centre of more or less circular feather disks. Tarsus and toes feathered (Figure 33).

Figure 35

*Owls* . . . . . . . . . . . . . . . . . . . . . . . . . . . . . . . . . . . . . . . . . . . . . . . . . . p. 255

n, Feet small and weak.

12, Nostrils opening in a soft and somewhat swollen base.

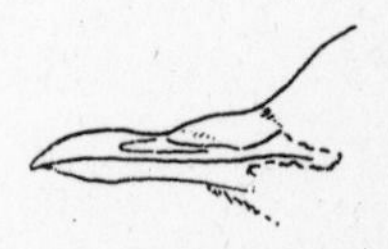

Figure 36

*Pigeons* . . . . . . . . . . . . . . . . . . . . . . . . . . . . . . . . . . . . . . . . . . . . . . . . p. 249

13, Two outer toes joined together for half their length.

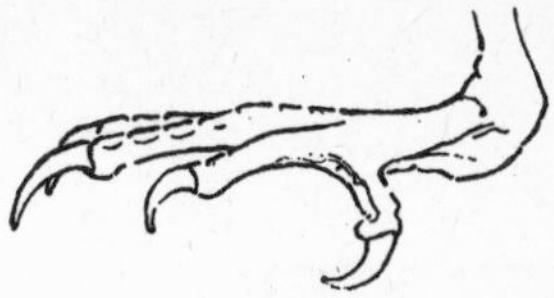

Figure 37

*Kingfishers* . . . . . . . . . . . . . . . . . . . . . . . . . . . . . . . . . . . . . . . . . . . . . . p. 276

14, Two toes directed forward, two backward (*See also* woodpeckers).

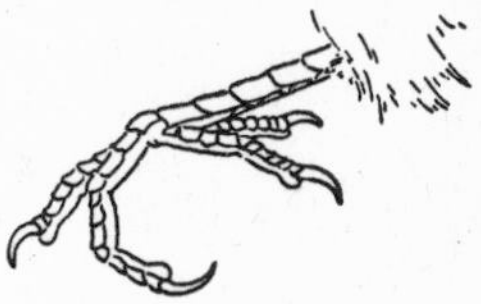

Figure 38

*Cuckoos* . . . . . . . . . . . . . . . . . . . . . . . . . . . . . . . . . . . . . . . . . . . . . . . . p. 253

15, Bill very small; mouth enormous, opening to below eyes.

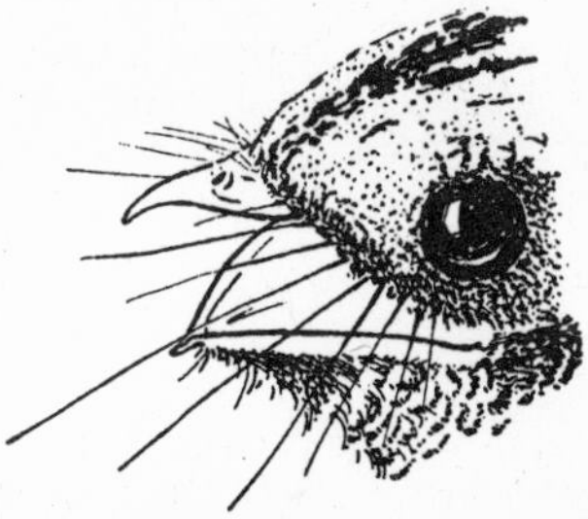

Figure 39

*Goatsuckers* . . . . . . . . . . . . . . . . . . . . . . . . . . . . . . . . . . . . . . . . . . . . . p. 266

16, Uniformly sooty coloration, tail feathers not ending in spines.

*Black Swift* . . . . . . . . . . . . . . . . . . . . . . . . . . . . . . . . . . . . . . . . . . . . . . p. 270

17, Feet and toes partly feathered.

*White-throated Swift* . . . . . . . . . . . . . . . . . . . . . . . . . . . . . . . . . . . . . . . p. 272

18, Tail feathers ending in sharp spines.

Figure 40

*Chimney Swift or Vaux's Swift* . . . . . . . . . . . . . . . . . . . . . . . . . . . . . . . . . p. 271

19, Bill very slender, and awl-shaped. Exceedingly minute birds.

Figure 41

*Hummingbirds* .................................... p. 273

o, Feet, medium-sized or small, but not noticeably weak, flabby, or loose jointed. Legs covered with scales or plates.

20, Two toes in front, either one or two directed backwards. Bill chisel-shaped at tip.

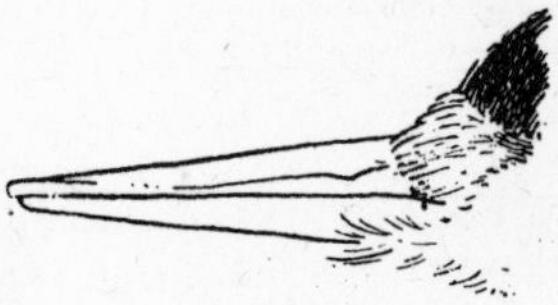

Figure 42

*Woodpeckers* .................................... p. 277

21, Three toes in front; hind toe as well developed and as long as middle toe; claw on hind toe usually as long as, or longer than, that on middle toe.

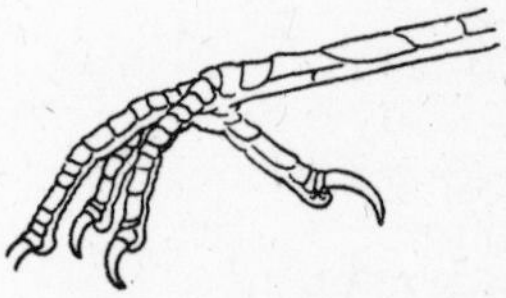

Figure 43

*Perchers* .................................... p. 287

*Recognition Details of the Perchers*

Bill wider than high at base; tip slightly hooked.

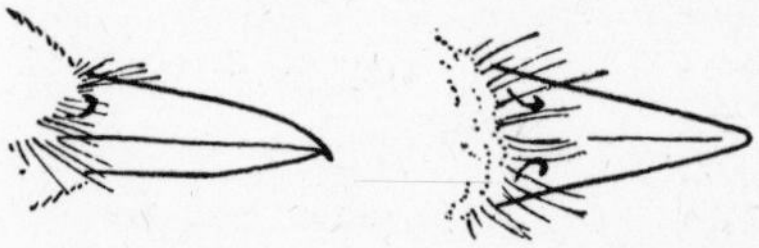

*a* Figure 44 *b*

*Flycatchers* .................................... p. 287

Ear tufts and long hind toenail. Longspur and pipit (Figure 61) only other species having latter feature.

*a* Figure 45 *b*

*Horned Lark* .................................... p. 297

Bill stout, nostrils covered by bristly tufts.

Figure 46

*Crows, Jays, etc*. . . . . . . . . . . . . . . . . . . . . . . . . . . . . . . . . . . . . . . . p. 303

Keel of bill usually extending more or less up on forehead.

Figures 47 and 48

Cowbird and bobolink (Figure 47) have bills resembling those of the sparrows. *See* species.

Figures 49 and 50

*Starlings*. . . . . . . . . . . . . . . . . . . . . . . . . . . . . . . . . . . . . . . . . . . . p. 368

Figures 51, 52, and 53

Bill conical, stout for seed cracking. (Bills of bobolink (Figure 47) and cowbird superficially similar, *See* descriptions.)

*Sparrows*. . . . . . . . . . . . . . . . . . . . . . . . . . . . . . . . . . . . . . . . . . . . p. 379

Slight or marked tooth on cutting side of upper mandible.

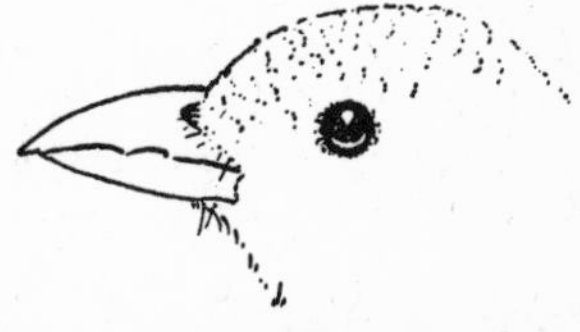

Figure 54

*Tanagers*. . . . . . . . . . . . . . . . . . . . . . . . . . . . . . . . . . . . . . . . . . . . p. 377

Bill very small, wide, and flattened at base.

(a) (b)
Figure 55

*Swallows*.......................................................... p. 298

Crest and black eye-band most conspicuous.

Figure 56

*Waxwings*.......................................................... p. 337

Tooth near tip of upper mandible.

Figure 57

*Vireos and Shrikes*.......................................... pp. 339, 343

Small, brightly coloured birds. Olive-greens, yellows, and black are perhaps the commonest colours, but blues, reds, and other colours are often present.

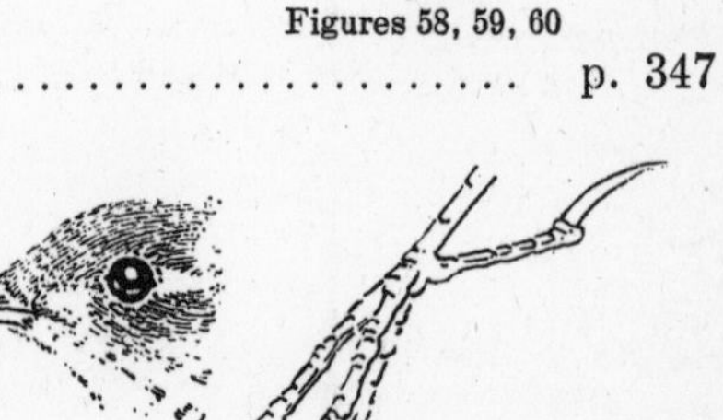

Figures 58, 59, 60

*Wood Warblers*.................................................... p. 347

Fine, sharp bill and long claw on hind toe (Compare with Figure 45).

(a) (b)
Figure 61

*Pipit*.................................................................. p. 335

Figures 62, 63, 64

Large and medium-sized birds. Bills as shown. Thrasher, large red-brown and white bird; Catbird, even slate grey with black cap; Dipper, uniformly grey with short tail.

*Thrasher, Catbird, or Dipper* .......................... pp. 317, 324

Small birds coloured in shades of wood-brown.

Figure 65

*Wrens* .............................................. p. 318

Small birds in wood-brown colours. Tail long and stiff, feathers pointed at end.

Figure 66

*Creepers* ........................................... p. 316

Bill pointing slightly upwards.

Figure 67

*Nuthatches* ......................................... p. 314

Very small birds; dark cap and throat and pronounced white face area.

Figure 68

*Titmice* ........................................................ p. 311

Very small birds, olive-coloured. Males with small, brightly coloured crown patch.

Figure 69

*Kinglets* ........................................................ p. 334

A medium-sized bird; uniform soft grey with white eye-ring, a long tail, and no black cap.

Figure 70

*Townsend's Solitaire* ........................................ p. 332

Medium-sized birds, coloured usually, except robin and bluebirds, in soft browns with more or less spotted breast.

Figure 71

*Thrushes* ........................................................ p. 321

# DESCRIPTIVE ORNITHOLOGY

## CLASS—AVES. BIRDS

Birds, as a class, may be divided into toothed and toothless birds, although the former are now extinct and are known only by their fragmentary remains preserved as fossils. All modern birds are toothless. Some species, for example the Mergansers, are furnished with serrations in the horny bill that have a superficial resemblance to teeth (Figure 8, page 25), but examination shows that they are not true teeth.

All Canadian birds have deep keels to their sterna for the purpose of anchoring the powerful flight muscles. They so differ from the *struthious* or ostrich-like birds which have flat breast bones. They, therefore, fall into the

## SUPERORDER—NEOGNATHAE, NON-STRUTHIOUS BIRDS

Of these keel-breasted birds we have several orders, of which the first is:

## Order—Gaviiformes. Loons

### FAMILY—GAVIIDAE. LOONS

*General Description.* The loons are large divers, with straight, sharply pointed bills and with the feet fully webbed (Figure 2, page 24). In the adult state they are coloured in strikingly contrasting patterns, mostly black and white.

*Distinctions.* Larger than ducks and with shorter necks than geese. These features and the sharp, pointed bill are diagnostic. Tails more evident than in the grebes.

*Field Marks.* Size, length of neck, and bill. In flight, the feet are trailed behind the tail.

*Nesting.* On low shores, in the immediate vicinity of water where they can dive almost directly from the nest.

The loons are probably even better divers than the grebes, but they rise less easily from the water, and unless there is a good breeze that they can face, require a long, splashing start over the surface before becoming wing-borne.

*Economic Status.* Their food is composed almost entirely of fish, but owing to the small number of loons usual in any one locality their direct economic importance is small.

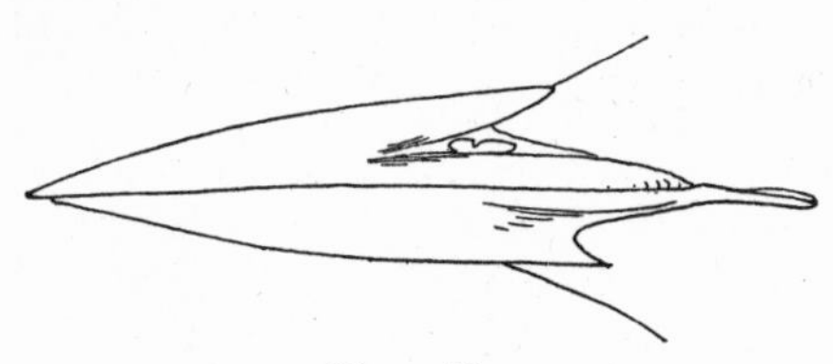

Figure 72

Bill outline of Common Loon; scale, ½.

7. **Common Loon.** LOON. GREAT NORTHERN DIVER. LE HUART COMMUN (Le Grand Plongeon). *Gavia immer.* L, 32. Plate I A.

*Distinctions.* The summer adult Common Loon is easily distinguished from any of the other loons, except the Yellow-billed, by its marked coloration, but young birds may be more difficult to differentiate. From the Yellow-billed, which is but slightly larger, adults may be distinguished by the black instead of yellow bill and green instead of purple reflections on the throat. Juveniles and summer adults have rather pale bills and the shape, slightly arched instead of straight culmen (Compare Figure 72 with Figure 73), is probably the best distinction. As the latter occurs regularly only in the far north there is little opportunity for confusing these two.

From the immature of the Red-throated Loon young birds may be told by size and their lack of small, sharply defined white spots on the back. From the juvenile Black-throated or Arctic Loon, size appears to be the only reliable criterion in immaturity or winter.

*Field Marks.* All black head, throat, and bill. In juvenility or in winter plumage, size, and unspotted back. Most of the loons seen on our inland waters are this species.

*Nesting.* On boggy or rocky shores close to fresh water where, when alarmed, it can slide directly into the water. The rather bulky nest is built of decaying vegetable matter.

*Distribution.* Over the whole of continental Canada, rare on the northwest arctic coast, breeding wherever conditions are suitable and the birds are not disturbed. In many cases they remain in winter as long as the water is open.

*SUBSPECIES.* Two subspecies are recognized in America, the Greater Loon (le Grand Huart commun) *Gavia immer immer* on the Atlantic coast and in eastern North America, and the Lesser Loon (le Petit Huart commun) *Gavia immer elasson* of the interior, probably from Manitoba westward. They differ slightly in size as indicated by their common names.

Most frequenters of our waterways and lakes are familiar with the long, loud laugh of the loon. The loon has many other strange, wild notes; among them one beginning low, rising high, and then dropping suddenly. It is often noisy at night or just before a storm and birds frequently call to and answer one another across the water.

Owing to the constant encroachments of settlement, and the consequent disturbance of its nesting places, the loon has been growing scarcer of late years, and in many of its old haunts it is now seldom seen except during migration. However, there are still many lonely lakes in the great uninhabited north where it can live and breed undisturbed, and the immediate loss of this picturesque species need not be anticipated. Proper local protection, enforced by an awakened public opinion, would undoubtedly restock our lakes and ponds in summer as well as augment the number that make passing visits. Loons are strictly protected at all times by the terms of the Migratory Birds Convention Act. They may be legally killed nowhere in either the United States or Canada. Under the terms of this treaty, only where their depredations are proved to be serious may permits be issued for their destruction.

The damage to game fish charged against loons by anglers may locally have some foundation in fact, but is often exaggerated. The failure of fish supplies is commonly attributed to every possible cause except the most important one, viz., human over-fishing. Too often any fish-eating bird or beast is looked upon by self-centred anglers as an intolerable rival to be suppressed at any cost, irrespective of the relative importance of its depredations. Loons are probably no respecters of any species of fish, but they do not frequent swiftly running streams such as trout inhabit nor are they often seen in the marshy shallows where game fish usually lurk. By preference they keep to open, fairly deep water and their prey is mostly small fish of the coarser and less gamy varieties. Where loons do occur on limited or special waters, such as preserves or hatchery ponds, or even elsewhere, in abnormal numbers, they may interfere more or less seriously with special interests. Each such case, however, should be settled on its own merits and with consideration for the general good. Many people get more enjoyment from the presence of loons than from fishing, and there are many out-door recreation centres to which loons give a desirable touch of native wildness. The requirements of those people for the enjoyment of such places are as worthy of recognition as those of fishing enthusiasts and should be carefully considered.

General destruction of loons, as has been, and is being, constantly advocated, is like stopping a small crack in the barrel while the bung-hole remains open. Fish were once plentiful in spite of the loons and if today proper fishing regulations were enforced and the purity of the waters preserved the number of small fry taken normally by loons would rarely be missed. In specific and special cases some control may be advisable.

On some of the small lakes loons have an effect on other bird life. They are impatient of too-close neighbours and are quite likely to drive away nesting ducks, coots, and similar water-birds. They make their attack from under water and harry the objects of their jealousy until they vacate the premises and leave the loon in sole possession. However, as most waters that loons choose for a home are not particularly attractive to other water-birds, this trait can generally be looked upon with curious interest rather than animosity by the bird lover or sportsman.

*Economic Status.* Although the loon is a large bird its small gullet limits the size of the fish it takes. This, together with the small number of birds on the small lakes and the large number of fish in the large lakes, makes its depredation economically unimportant. The species, therefore, should not be destroyed.

8. **Yellow-billed Loon.** LE HUART À BEC BLANC. *Gavia adamsi.* L, 36. In general this is a big Common Loon with bill ivory-yellow instead of black.

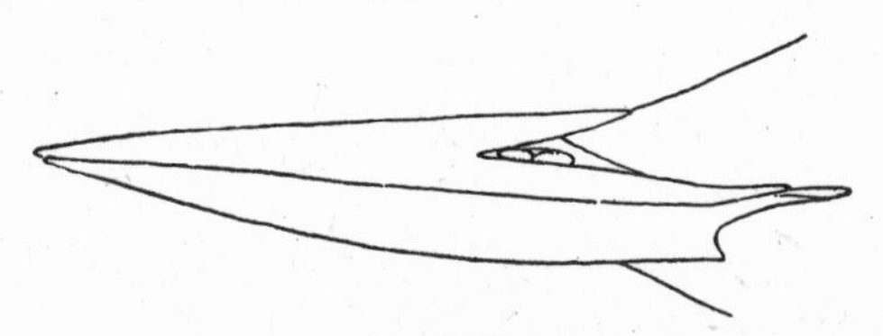

Figure 73
Bill outline of Yellow-billed Loon;
scale, ½.

*Distinctions.* In full plumage easily known from the Common Loon by its size and yellow bill. The reflections on the throat are purple instead of green. In submaturity, when size is not a reliable specific guide, the bill shape offers the best distinction. In the Yellow-billed the culmen line is almost straight, whereas in the Common Loon it is slightly arched (Figure 73, compare with Figure 72). This will probably distinguish all specimens except those distinctly immature.

From the Arctic or the Red-throated Loons size is sufficient distinction.

*Field Marks.* Large size and conspicuous yellowish white bill are said to make excellent field marks for the adult.

*Nesting.* Practically unknown, but probably similar to that of other Loons.

*Distribution.* The northwest Arctic coast and the great lakes of Mackenzie, probably nesting on the ponds of the tundras where no one goes in summer.

The migrations and breeding range of the Yellow-billed Loon are among our unsolved ornithological problems. It evidently winters in some numbers, at least occasionally, on the south Alaskan coast, but we have no British Columbia records. It should be looked for there with care, and identified with caution.

9. **Arctic Loon.** LE HUART ARCTIQUE. *Gavia arctica.* L, about 24. Similar to, but smaller than, the Common Loon, from which it differs in colour principally on the crown and hindneck (Figure 74), dark grey on the forehead but gradually becoming a light smoky ash down the hindneck.

*Distinctions.* General colour as above, in adults. Juveniles are distinguished from the Common Loon by their distinctly smaller size and from the Red-throated Loon, with which they agree closely in that particular, by the general coloration; in juvenility and winter plumages, by the lack of fine, V-shaped white specks on the back.

*Field Marks.* The grey hindneck, and black throat and foreneck should make excellent field marks. In juvenile plumage, size separates it from the two big loons, and, when determinable, the unspeckled back distinguishes it from the Red-throated.

Figure 74
Arctic Loon; scale, about ⅟.

*Nesting.* Similar to the other loons.

*Distribution.* In summer an inhabitant of the far north from Lake Athabaska northward. In migration rarely down through the prairies, but wintering in numbers on the British Columbia coast. Of only occasional occurrence in southeastern Canada.

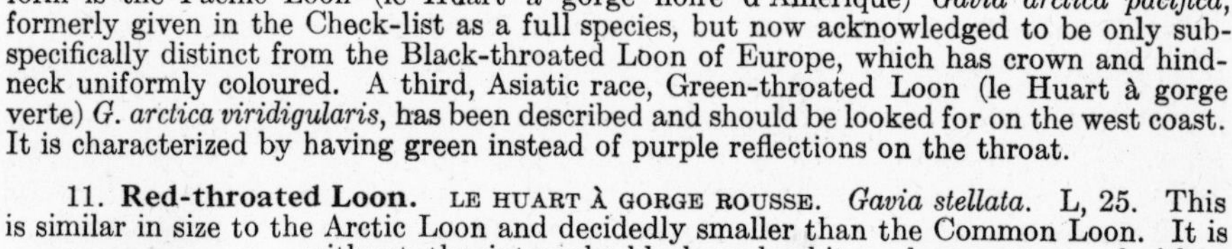

*SUBSPECIES.* The Arctic Loon is a circumpolar species. The common American form is the Pacific Loon (le Huart à gorge noire d'Amérique) *Gavia arctica pacifica,* formerly given in the Check-list as a full species, but now acknowledged to be only subspecifically distinct from the Black-throated Loon of Europe, which has crown and hindneck uniformly coloured. A third, Asiatic race, Green-throated Loon (le Huart à gorge verte) *G. arctica viridigularis,* has been described and should be looked for on the west coast. It is characterized by having green instead of purple reflections on the throat.

11. **Red-throated Loon.** LE HUART À GORGE ROUSSE. *Gavia stellata.* L, 25. This is similar in size to the Arctic Loon and decidedly smaller than the Common Loon. It is without the intensely black and white colour pattern of either. The head and neck of the adult are of soft, even, slate-grey with a maroon-red throat patch (Figure 75). The back is an even, greyish brown, the rest of the body white.

*Distinctions.* The colour pattern is absolutely distinctive in the adult. Juveniles and winter birds are without the grey neck and red throat, these colours being replaced by white which continues unbroken from the underparts, producing a coloration very similar to the Arctic except that the back is sprinkled with small, white specks instead of grey feather edgings. The species is so much smaller than the two large loons that there can be little confusion with them.

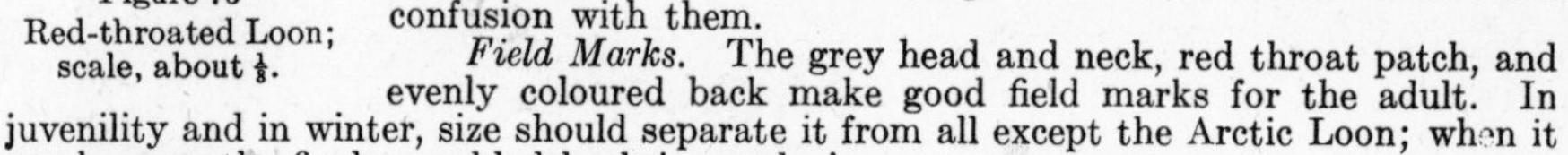

Figure 75
Red-throated Loon; scale, about ⅛.

*Field Marks.* The grey head and neck, red throat patch, and evenly coloured back make good field marks for the adult. In juvenility and in winter, size should separate it from all except the Arctic Loon; when it can be seen the finely speckled back is conclusive.

*Nesting.* Similar to the preceding species.

*Distribution.* Ranges over the whole of Canada, scarce in the interior, more common on either coast. Breeds north of regular settlement through the Arctics.

## Order—Colymbiformes. Grebes

*General Description.* Grebes are divers with feet lobed and not fully webbed, and without perceptible tails. Instead of full webs extending from toe to toe, as in most swimming birds, the digits are provided with a scalloped edging of flat, lobe-like flaps or processes hinged to the toe (Figure 14, page 26). These make excellent paddles during the stroke and, folding away, offer the minimum of resistance to the water on the return. Their wonderful diving ability has given these birds the common sobriquets of Hell-diver, Water-witch, etc., but they are almost helpless on land. All our grebes have the secondaries more or less tipped with white, making a white border to the spread wing, absent in the loons.

*Distinctions.* Scalloped toe webs, short tail, straight, pointed bill, and the peculiar silvery sheen of the feheatrs of the underparts.

*Field Marks.* Duck-like in outline and bearing. Pointed bill and inconspicuous tail. Feet carried straight out behind when flying.

*Nesting.* In reeds or rushes bordering sloughs or ponds, on floating or stationary heaps of vegetable matter.

*Distribution.* Grebes are distributed over the whole of Canada, well into the Arctic zone. In the breeding season they are generally more common on fresh than on salt water.

Grebes are, typically, inhabitants of fresh ponds and lakes, though at times they frequent the sea in numbers. The adults are coloured in rather broad masses; the young usually show sharp stripes, especially about the head, indicating that the family has descended from a common striped ancestor. The grebe breasts, formerly much used for trimming and millinery purposes, are procured from birds of this family. The former sacrifice of large numbers for this purpose and the continued drainage of many of their natural breeding grounds have greatly reduced their number.

Fortunately the Migratory Birds Convention Act with the United States protects these birds at all seasons of the year over most of the continent and their slaughter for millinery purposes is now a thing of the past.

*Economic Status.* Feeding almost entirely upon water-inhabiting creatures they are of little direct economic importance. Considerable masses of feathers are found in many grebe stomachs, but the reason for their presence is not perfectly understood. They are commonly feathers from the bird's own body and it has been suggested by Wetmore, "Condor," 1920, pages 18-20, that they serve as a plug to prevent fish bones from being carried from the stomach into the intestine before they are properly softened by digestion. Why such mechanical assistance is necessary in this particular division of birds is an enigma.

2. **Red-necked Grebe.** LE GRÈBE JOUGRIS. *Colymbus grisegena.* L, 19. This is one of our two larger grebes (*See* Western Grebe). Summer adults have a jet black cap continuing down the back of the neck, white cheeks and throat faintly tinted with grey, and a rich chestnut-red neck (Figure 76).

Figure 76
Holboell's Grebes; scale, $\frac{1}{3}$.
Winter Summer

*Distinctions.* Size will distinguish this grebe from all but the Western, and colour from the Western. Juveniles generally have a suggestion of rufous mixed with the dull grey neck, but are otherwise similar to the young Western, though colours are much less contrasted and more blended.

*Field Marks.* The pearly grey or silvery white cheek patch against the darker crown and neck makes the adult recognizable at long range. The shorter, greyer, and less graceful neck will separate the juvenile from the Western Grebe, and the white wing patches, shown in flight, will distinguish it from any of the loons. In flight the Red-necked Grebe shows two white areas on each wing; that on the forward edge of the limb from wrist to body is very striking and characteristic.

*Nesting.* On floating or stationary vegetable compost or marshy islets near the shores of freshwater lakes.

*Distribution.* Europe, western Asia, and across the American continent, breeding along our southern border from Manitoba westward and northward.

This grebe in the breeding season is commonly seen on all the prairie sloughs. Those who live close to such localities have probably heard its loud, raucous notes and perhaps have wondered whence they came.

*SUBSPECIES.* The American form of this species is Holboell's Grebe (le Grèbe à cou rouge) *Colymbus grisegena holboelli.*

3. **Horned Grebe.** LE GRÈBE CORNU. *Colymbus auritus.* L, 13·50. The Horned Grebe is about the same size as the Pied-billed and Eared Grebes mentioned next. The Horned and Eared Grebes have a general similarity of appearance, and both have sharp, slender bills instead of high, stumpy ones like the Pied-bill. The Horned Grebe has a rich chestnut neck and flanks, and full, black, outstanding ruff from throat to hindhead (Figure 77), where it joins with and supports light ochre ear tufts or "horns." In autumn and winter it is a black (or grey) and white bird very similar to the juvenile of the Eared (*See* Plate I B), but quite different from the browner, more rusty-necked Pied-bill.

Figure 77
Horned Grebe; scale, ½.
Winter Summer

*Distinctions.* Its sharp, slender bill will distinguish it in any plumage from the Pied-bill. From the Eared, which more closely resembles it in summer plumage, it is distinguished by its red instead of black neck, its full ruff, and light ochre ear tufts instead of golden cheek plumes (Figure 77, compare with 80). In winter and juvenile plumages its black and white coloration separates it from the dingier Pied-bill, and the bill when fully developed is a safe distinction from the Eared (Figure 78, compare with 79). The bill is somewhat shorter, and is a little higher than wide, instead of wider than high, at the base. Immature birds, however, may be difficult of separation.

*Field Marks.* In adult: the large ruff, giving a "buffle-head" appearance, red neck, and light ochre ear tufts. In juvenility: the narrow pointed bill, and shiny white foreneck and breast, distinguish it from the Pied-bill, but not from the Eared.

*Nesting.* Similar to the preceding.

*Distribution.* Across the continent, breeding sparingly in the east but throughout the Canadian prairies and British Columbia north to the Arctic coast.

Figure 78
Bill details of Horned Grebe; scale, ½.

On migration the Horned Grebe prefers the larger bodies of water, but in the breeding season it may be found in almost any little slough or water-hole on the prairies or in British Columbia. The Eared and Pied-billed Grebes require considerable reed or tule marsh for nesting, but the Horned Grebes in many cases nest in pools with bare shores and with little or no cover.

4. **Eared Grebe.** BLACK-NECKED GREBE. LE GRÈBE À COU NOIR. *Colymbus nigricollis.* L, 13·20. Plate I B. This, the smallest of our grebes, is very similar to the Horned in size, general coloration, and the possession of a slender, sharp bill instead of a short, stumpy one like the Pied-bill.

*Distinctions.* Like the Horned it has red flanks, but the neck is black and instead of the full ruff and ochre ear tufts it has a spray of golden plumes on the cheek and a helmet-like crest on the crown (Figure 80, compare with 77).

The juvenile and autumn plumage is quite different from the dingier and rustier Pied-bill, and similar to the young Horned, from which it is separated only with some difficulty by the bill characteristics. The bill of the Eared Grebe is longer and narrower and somewhat depressed at the base so as to be wider than high (Figure 79), instead of the converse (Figure 78).

*Field Marks.* General appearance of head and neck, the helmet-like crest coming to a point over the middle of the crown instead of over the hindhead as in the Horned Grebe, the absence of ruff and consequent lack of "buffle-head" appearance, and the presence of the spray of golden feathers on the cheeks instead of the ochre tufts over the ears. Silhouetted against the bright water the bill seems to have a slight *retroussé* effect not noticeable in other grebes. In autumn it may not always be separable in life from the Horned.

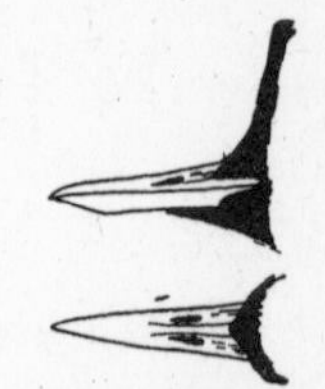

Figure 79
Bill details of Eared Grebe; scale, ½.

*Nesting.* Breeding habits similar to other grebes, but often in communities so dense that a canoe can hardly pass between nests. It seems to require larger bodies of marsh and water in which to nest than the Horned Grebe, and often associates with nesting communities of Western Grebes.

*Distribution.* Temperate parts of the Northern hemisphere. In Canada, on the prairies and in southern British Columbia, breeding almost wherever found. Strangely enough it has not been noticed east of Manitoba even as a straggler.

*SUBSPECIES.* The Eared Grebe inhabits the Old as well as the New World. The American Eared Grebe (le Grèbe à cou noir d'Amérique) is subspecifically separated from the European form under the name *Colymbus nigricollis californicus.*

Figure 80
Eared Grebe (summer); scale, $\frac{1}{2}$.

1. **Western Grebe.** SWAN GREBE. LE GRÈBE DE L'OUEST. *Aechmophorus occidentalis.* L, 27·25. This and Holboell's Grebe are the largest of our native grebes; the Western measures the longer because of its great length of slender neck. This grebe is in all plumages a pure black and white bird (Figure 81) without variation of colour. It has slightly developed crests over each ear.

*Distinctions.* Size, long, slender neck, and pure black and white coloration distinguish this from all other of our grebes. The bill is exceptionally long and pointed, and occurs in two types without apparent connexion with sex, age, or geographical distribution (Figure 82). One large and straight (a), and the other small and recurved (b).

Figure 81
Western Grebe, swimming; scale, about $\frac{1}{10}$.

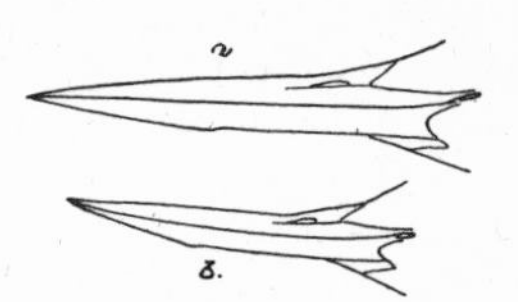

Figure 82
Types of bill of Western Grebe; scale, $\frac{1}{3}$.

*Field Marks.* Size, sharply contrasted black and white coloration, and long, graceful neck that suggests its popular name of Swan Grebe. The black cap, descending in a sharp line down the back of the neck, and slight ear tufts, make this bird very distinctive in life. The white patch in the open wing will distinguish it from any of the smaller loons in flight. The presence of only one wing patch will distinguish it from the Holboell's Grebe which has two white areas on each wing.

*Nesting.* On floating or stationary masses of dead reeds or tules in wet marshes about freshwater lakes, in some cases in communities so dense that one can almost step from nest to nest.

*Distribution.* Westward from the beginning of the prairies in Manitoba to the Pacific coast, north not far beyond the southern edge of timber. Though rather common on the lakes and seacoast of southern British Columbia all summer it has to date only once been found nesting in that province.

One of the most graceful, beautiful, and characteristic birds of the prairie sloughs. While the females are performing the duties of incubation in the marshes, the males, non-breeding birds, or those on relief, are to be seen floating about the open water, curling their sinuous necks with graceful ease and occasionally uttering a fine, high "*Krik-a-all*" that can be heard a considerable distance and is quite different from the raucous cries of some of their near relatives.

6. **Pied-billed Grebe.** DAB-CHICK. HELL-DIVER. WATER-WITCH. LE GRÈBE À BEC BIGARRÉ. *Podilymbus podiceps.* L, 13·50. Plate II A.

*Distinctions.* The Pied-bill can be separated from all other Canadian grebes by its relatively heavier and stouter bill with its spot and more strongly arched culmen; from the juvenile Horned or Eared Grebes in any plumage, also by its darker and dingier coloured foreneck, breast, and underparts.

*Field Marks.* Size, high stubby bill, spot on bill, and in the spring adult, black throat patch. This grebe is more often seen in flight than the others.

*Nesting.* Along the marshy edges of ponds and lakes on stationary or floating platforms.

*Distribution.* Across the continent, breeding from our southern borders northwards; probably any grebe found nesting south of a line drawn between Ottawa and Sault Ste. Marie will be of this species. In western Canada north to Great Slave Lake, breeding wherever found.

This grebe frequents clear, open water less than do its relatives, and usually confines itself to open leads and lagoons in tule and cat-tail marshes. In its chosen habitat it is a wonderful hider, evading observation with almost mysterious elusiveness. The names Hell-diver and Water-witch are descriptive of its powers in this direction. No sooner does its quick eye discern an intruder than it gradually sinks low in the water until in some cases only the bill projects, in which position it may quietly await the withdrawal of danger or it may paddle without a ripple to some marshy cover where the eye cannot detect it. Diving at the flash of the gun, it is often safe under water by the time the shot reaches the spot recently occupied, but the use of smokeless powder has put it at some disadvantage. Though seldom seen, and showing remarkable powers of vanishing amidst seemingly insufficient cover, its loud, far-reaching voice is often heard and to many the origin of the sound is one of the mysteries that make the marsh so interesting. Its note may be rendered "*Kuck-kuck-kuck-Gulup-gulup-gulup,*" with a rising inflection in the series of "kucks," which are repeated quickly, then a slight pause, and the "*gulups*" uttered with even tempo and with strong accent on the liquid letters. It can be heard under favourable conditions for a mile or more.

## Order—Procellariiformes. Tube-nosed Swimmers

*General Description.* Tireless fliers of the deep sea, of various sizes from the large albatross to the small petrel. Usually dull and evenly coloured birds, but some strikingly black and white.

*Distinctions.* Nostrils are encased in tubes on top or on sides of the bill proper (Figures 83-88).

*Field Marks.* General flight habits and coloration.

Familiarity with the various species is necessary to recognize members of the order.

*Nesting.* On the ground or in burrows in out-of-the-way localities, often on rocky islets far out at sea to which they find their way in some mysterious manner that we cannot explain.

*Distribution.* As a family, they are birds of the southern hemisphere, for it is there that they reach their fullest development in numbers of individuals and species. However, some inhabit the north far into the Arctics.

The Tube-nosed Swimmers are essentially marine, using the land only for breeding purposes. The ocean is their home and its lonely waste is sufficient for all their needs except that of rearing their young. They, therefore, as a class, rarely come into shallow water and are most commonly seen by the deep-water sailor, the offshore fisherman, or the ocean voyager. There are three families of the order: the albatrosses, *Diomedeidae;* the fulmars, shearwaters, and petrels, *Procellariidae*, that are here called for convenience the Greater and Lesser Tube-nosed Swimmers owing to their comparative sizes; and *Hydrobatiidae*, the Storm Petrels.

*Economic Status.* Owing to their pelagic habitat they are of little if any known economic interest.

### FAMILY—DIOMEDEIDAE. THE GREATER TUBE-NOSED SWIMMERS. ALBATROSSES

*General Description.* Tube-nosed Swimmers (*See* previous description) 30 to 36 inches long with an extent of 10 feet or more. Nostrils in independent tubes, one on each side of the culmen and not united or rising above it as in next family (Figures 83, 84, compare with 85-88).

*Distinctions.* Decidedly larger than any of the Lesser Tube-noses. Bill built up of large plates with well-defined divisions. Nostrils as above.

*Field Marks.* Great size and immensely long wings.

*Nesting.* On the ground, usually in large communities on lonely oceanic islands.

*Distribution.* The family is most characteristic of the southern hemisphere but wanders all over the deep seas.

The albatrosses are true pelagics and seldom come to land except to nest. Even along our outer seashores they are rarely seen, as they prefer the wide expanse of the trackless deep to coastal waters. The deep-sea fisherman sees them far out from land and the transoceanic traveller glimpses them in mid-ocean. Very rarely is this bird captured along the shores and there are few birds about which we know less. The untiring flight of the albatross is proverbial. Sailing for hours in the wind, seemingly without apparent motion of wing or expenditure of exertion, they are the wonder and admiration of aviators. The manner in which the albatrosses find their way in nesting season, without guide or landmark across trackless water, to particular small specks of ocean islands, is truly marvellous and suggests the possession of special powers of orientation. The mystery and interest that surround these birds are well expressed in Coleridge's poem "The Ancient Mariner" and the bird is still looked upon with a certain awe and superstition by old-time sailors.

Albatrosses come too seldom in contact with man or his works to have any economic importance except as victims of one of the most iniquitous practices of the millinery trade. It was long the custom for plume-hunting ships to fill their holds with the commercial fragments of their skins at the islands where they nested in countless thousands. The trade was often accompanied by the most horrible, unnecessary cruelty. On one occasion, hundreds were confined on Laysan island until they starved to death that their skins might be the freer of oil and grease. The immense number of the birds in nesting localities and the degree of destruction that the trade entailed are well shown by the fact that poachers, disturbed in their work, left behind them on the same island a large shed piled to the roof with wing tips alone.

Fortunately, however, certain countries such as Canada, Great Britain, and the United States have forbidden, with certain exceptions, the importation of millinery feathers and so have destroyed the best markets for the trade and have done much to discourage it.

These tireless fliers are great wanderers and although only three species have actually been recognized on our coasts, almost any may occasionally be seen. Specimens should be carefully examined, as any one of them may represent species new to the Canadian or even the North American list.

81. **Black-footed Albatross.** GONY. L'ALBATROS À PATTES NOIRES. *Diomedea nigripes*. L, 32. An almost black albatross, slightly lighter about face, with black legs and feet and dark bill.

*Distinctions*. The bill plate covering the culmen widening back of nostrils and meeting the plates on sides of the mandible (Figure 83, compare with 84). This feature separates our two most common albatrosses, the Black-footed and Short-tailed, from the rarer Yellow-nosed. Plumage, feet, legs, and bill are always dusky or black. The feet and bill of the similarly plumaged Short-tailed are light.

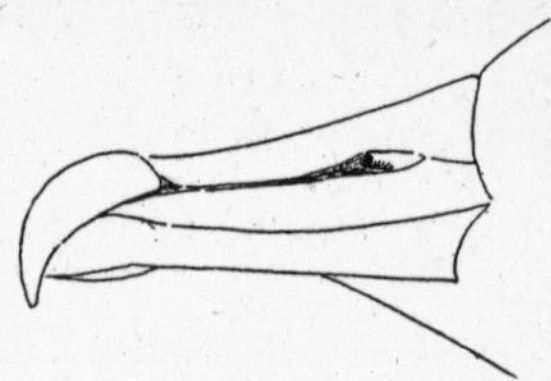

Figure 83
Bill of Black-footed Albatross; scale, ⅓.

*Field Marks*. A dark albatross with dark bill, legs, and feet.

*Distribution*. North Pacific. Breeding on the Hawaiian and Marshall Islands.

This is probably the albatross of most common occurrence off the British Columbia coast. There are a number of records from the south end of Vancouver Island and up along the Alaskan coast.

82. **Short-tailed Albatross.** L'ALBATROS À QUEUE COURTE. *Diomedea albatrus*. L, 33-37. Adult: a white albatross with wings and tail largely dusky. Bill, legs, and feet light. Juvenile: sooty brown like the Black-footed, but with light-coloured bill, legs, and feet.

*Distinctions*. Plate on culmen widening back to nostrils (similar to Figure 83) distinguishes this and the preceding species from the Yellow-nosed. Adult: mostly white with tail largely dusky, and without the decided dark mantle and wings of the Yellow-nosed. Juvenile: dark like the Black-footed Albatross, but bill, legs, and feet pale.

*Field Marks*. A white albatross with dusky wings and tail, but without a decided black mantle, or, in juvenility, a dark one with light-coloured legs, feet, and bill.

*Distribution*. North Pacific Ocean, breeding on Wake, Laysan, and Bonin Islands.

This species has been taken near Victoria, and on the Alaskan coast of Bering Sea.

83. **Yellow-nosed Albatross.** L'ALBATROS À NEZ JAUNE. *Thalassogeron chlororhynchus*. L, 36. A white albatross with dark mantle and wings, pale legs and feet, and a yellow culmen.

*Distinctions*. Plate on culmen narrow, not widening behind nostrils to meet the plates of the sides of the mandible (Figure 84, compare with 83) distinguishes this from the previously mentioned and more common albatrosses. Head and neck greyish shading into a decidedly dark, cinnamon brown mantle and wings.

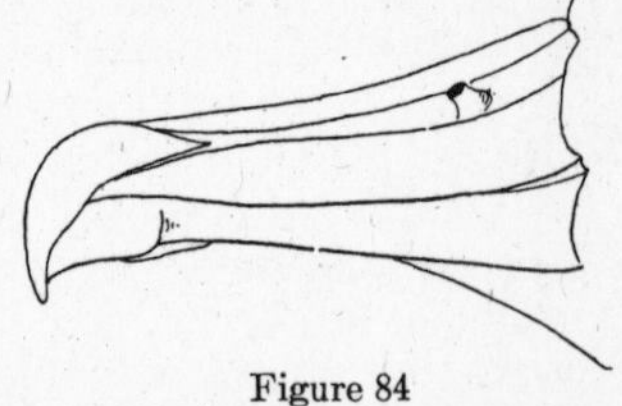

Figure 84
Bill of Yellow-nosed Albatross; scale, ⅓.

*Field Marks*. A white albatross with greyish head and neck and a cinnamon brown mantle and wings.

*Distribution*. The southern Atlantic, Pacific, and Indian Oceans. Of accidental occurrence on Gulf of St. Lawrence and off southern New Brunswick. These specimens were for years referred to another species *T. culminatus* and were so recorded. An old occurrence recorded on the west coast is now disregarded.

FAMILY—PROCELLARIIDAE. LESSER TUBE-NOSED SWIMMERS.

FULMARS AND SHEARWATERS

*General Description*. See previous description of order.

*Distinctions*. Lesser Tube-nosed Swimmers are smaller than the albatrosses. Nostril tubes on top of bill, fused together or separate (Figures 85-88).

*Field Marks*. General coloration and flight habits. Wings stiffly held straight out from the body and long, steady glides on motionless wings.

A. Common Loon; scale, $\frac{1}{9}$

Summer adult — Juvenile

B. Eared Grebe; scale, $\frac{1}{6}$

In winter — Summer adult

A. Pied billed Grebe; scale, $\frac{1}{6}$

Summer adult Juvenile

B. Double-crested Cormorant; scale, $\frac{1}{9}$

Spring adult Juvenile

*Distribution.* The family is distributed over the oceans of the world north and south. Though many species are regularly confined to the southern hemisphere they are great wanderers and the list of stragglers on our northern coast is comparatively large. Of many species very little is known, and our knowledge of several of them is confined to single, or a few specimens, that have found their way into collectors' hands. Other species than those here listed may be eventually found on our coasts, but their identification should be made with the greatest caution.

*Economic Status.* Though feeding almost entirely on fish and offal, their deep sea habitat renders these birds of little economic importance.

### *Shearwaters*

*General Description.* Large birds, 11 to 20 inches long. Solid dark brown coloration, or dark above and white below.

*Distinctions.* Bill stout. Nostril tubes not closely fused, but laid on either side of culmen, with space between as wide as, or wider than, nostril (Figure 85).

*Field Marks.* Large size, solid dark coloration, or dark above and white below. The square or rounded tail and flight habits will distinguish the shearwaters from the hawk-like jaegers with long, graduated tail, which may be similar in size or colour. Colour should separate them from the Fulmar which has similar size and flight. The long, narrow wings, held stiffly at right angles to the body, the rapid wing-strokes alternating with long glides often of half a mile or more, are characteristics of these birds and the Fulmar.

*Nesting.* Little is known of the nesting of the shearwaters. Mostly in holes in the ground, or crevices among rocks on isolated islets in the south seas. Migrate north in our summer.

96. **Slender-billed Shearwater.** LE PUFFIN À BEC MINCE. *Puffinus tenuirostris.* L, 14. Of the west coast. May be regarded as a smaller form of the Sooty Shearwater. *See* next species.

*Distinctions.* Smaller and rather greyer than the Sooty Shearwater and with grey rather than white underwing-coverts. The name Slender-billed is rather misleading. The bill is if anything shorter and relatively stouter than the preceding species (Figure 85).

*Field Marks.* A dark shearwater, light grey along the forward edge of the underwing. Smaller than the Sooty Shearwater.

*Distribution.* Southern hemisphere, north in summer to Bering Sea.

Our records for this species cover southern Vancouver Island and the north end of Queen Charlotte Islands. May be commoner than our records indicate as on sight it may be confused with the Sooty.

95. **Sooty Shearwater.** LE PUFFIN FULIGINEUX. *Puffinus griseus.* L, 16–18. Of the west coast. All dark brownish grey. Lining of wings nearly white.

*Distinctions.* Rather browner and less greyish, underwing-coverts whiter, and bird larger than the Slender-billed Shearwater, the only shearwater it is likely to be confused with.

*Field Marks.* A dark shearwater with considerable white along the forward edge of underwing. Larger than the Slender-billed.

*Distribution.* Oceans of southern hemisphere. Breeds among the islands of Tierra del Fuego. In summer, north to Canadian waters on both coasts, in the west to the base of the Alaska panhandle.

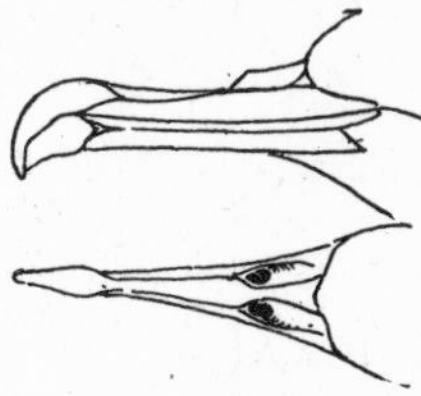

Figure 85
Bill of Sooty Shearwater; scale, ½.

This is the commonest shearwater to be seen on our coasts.

90. **Manx Shearwater.** LE PUFFIN MANX. *Puffinus puffinus.* L, 14. A medium-sized shearwater of the east coast, strikingly black and white.

*Distinctions.* In its contrasting black and white coloration plainly distinguishable from any other shearwater of the east coast except the Allied Shearwater, of which it is a larger edition, with wing about 9 inches instead of only 7 inches.

*Field Marks.* An easily recognized, sharply contrasted black and white shearwater of fairly large size.

*Distribution.* North Atlantic, chiefly the east side where it breeds. Was taken on or near New Brunswick waters many years ago.

93. **Black-vented Shearwater.** LE PUFFIN DE COUES. *Puffinus opisthomelas.* L, 12. Of the west coast. Practically a smaller form of the Pink-footed Shearwater. Upper parts sooty grey to nearly black, lighter on head and neck, white below.

*Distinctions.* To be confused only with Pink-footed Shearwater, but is a smaller bird and with greater contrast between upper and lower surfaces.

*Field Marks.* Extensive white below. Smaller than the Pink-footed.

*Distribution.* Pacific Ocean, breeding off coast of Lower California and Mexico.

Has been taken off the south end of Vancouver Island, but is apparently only a straggler so far north.

92. 1. **Allied Shearwater.** LE PUFFIN OBSCUR. *Puffinus assimilis.* L, 11. A diminutive shearwater of the east coast, strikingly black and white.

*Distinctions.* In contrasting black and white coloration plainly distinguishable from any shearwater of the east coast except the Manx Shearwater of which it is a small edition, with a wing about 7 inches instead of 9 inches.

*Field Marks.* An easily recognized, sharply contrasted black and white shearwater of small size.

*Distribution.* North Atlantic Ocean, mainly east side along the coast of Europe. Has been known to occur on Sable Island, Nova Scotia.

91. **Pink-footed Shearwater.** LE PUFFIN À PATTES ROSES. *Puffinus creatopus.* L, 19. Of the west coast. Dark brownish grey to nearly black above, white below from vent to throat.

*Distinctions.* Colour readily separates it from the dark-coloured shearwaters of the west coast.

*Field Marks.* Extensive white colour below, larger than the Black-vented Shearwater.

*Distribution.* The eastern Pacific, south to Chile, breeding on Juan Fernandez Island.

This shearwater has been taken at Forrester Island, just north of the British Columbia boundary on the coast, and at sea off the southern end of Vancouver Island. It is probably of only casual occurrence in Canadian waters. It should be identified with considerable caution.

89. **Greater Shearwater.** LE GRAND PUFFIN (le Puffin majeur). *Puffinus gravis.* L, 20. The larger of our two commoner eastern shearwaters, lighter below with undertail-coverts ashy grey.

*Distinctions.* Its light colour below should separate this from the Sooty Shearwater; and its general brownness of back instead of greyness and its variegated colour differentiate it from the fulmar.

*Field Marks.* Flight habits as described previously, together with brown coloration and white underparts, should separate this in life from either the fulmar or the next species.

*Nesting.* There is little if anything known of the nesting habits of this species. Probably breeds in the southern hemisphere on lonely islets that have not been ornithologically investigated.

*Distribution.* Ranges over the whole Atlantic Ocean from the southern arctics to Cape Horn. Visits the east coast of Canada irregularly in summer.

*Economic Status.* Of no economic importance.

88. **Mediterranean Shearwater.** LE PUFFIN CENDRÉ. *Puffinus diomedea.* L, 20·5. A large, dark brown and white shearwater of the east coast, like the Greater.

*Distinctions.* Of the east coast. Large, and light coloured, only likely to be mistaken for the Greater, but the back contains more or less grey, and the colours, especially about the face and throat, are blended instead of being clearly defined. The undertail-coverts are white instead of dusky and the under surface is pure white without distinct traces of dark mottling.

*Field Marks.* A large, light-coloured shearwater of the east coast. Said to be separable in life from the Greater by showing a grey head gradually blending into a white throat without sharp contrast and no trace of light half collar.

*Distribution.* Mediterranean Sea and eastern Atlantic Ocean. Occasional in autumn to the west side of the Atlantic. Has been taken off Nova Scotia and Newfoundland.

*SUBSPECIES.* The form occurring in America is Cory's Shearwater (le Puffin cendré d'Amérique) *Puffinus diomedea borealis*, characterized by having less white on the underwing surface.

98. **Black-capped Petrel.** LE PÉTREL HASITE (Diablotin). *Pterodroma hasitata.* L, 16. Like a black and white shearwater with a short bill, and white uppertail-coverts.

*Distinctions.* Much like a short-billed, black and white shearwater with the cap separated from the mantle by a white collar and with much white in uppertail-coverts. Bill short and stout like that of a fulmar, but with short, nasal tubes with septum between as wide as the nostrils themselves and the tip of the lower mandible distinctly decurved.

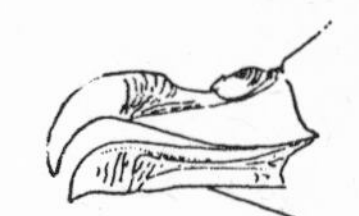

Figure 86
Black-capped Petrel; scale, $\frac{1}{3}$.

*Distribution.* The warmer parts of north Atlantic, but individuals are given to strange wanderings. The only Canadian records are for near Toronto on Lake Ontario.

## *Fulmars*

*General Description.* Among the larger of the lesser tube-nosed swimmers. Smoky grey, or white with pale grey mantle, like a gull.

*Distinctions.* Bill comparatively short and stout, heavily built. Nostrils in tubes closely fused together and, in the single species so far noted on the Canadian coasts, extending almost to the base of the terminal hook (Figure 87, compare with 85, 86, and 88).

*Field Marks.* *See* species, following.

86. **Northern Fulmar.** LE PÉTREL FULMAR. *Fulmarus glacialis.* L, 19. A large bird of gull-like coloration (light phase), or evenly dark, slaty grey (dark phase), and tube-encased nostrils (Figure 87).

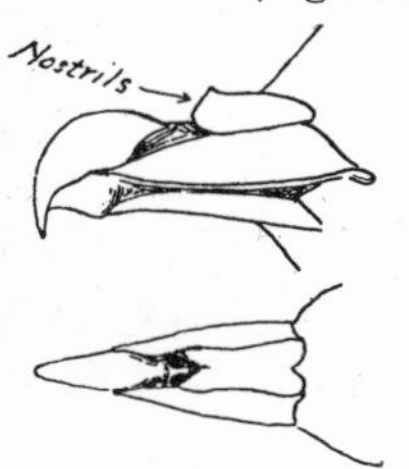


Figure 87
Bill of Fulmar; scale, $\frac{1}{2}$.

*Distinctions.* One of the larger of the lesser tube-noses, even grey, or white and grey, gull-like coloration.

*Field Marks.* Flight habits, stiffly held outstretched wings, and long glides, together with light or grey coloration instead of dark brown as in the shearwaters, which approach the fulmars in size, should usually render this species recognizable in life.

*Nesting.* In large communities on ledges of rocky cliffs.

*Distribution.* North Atlantic and north Pacific Oceans, breeding in high latitudes. Of regular occurrence off both coasts in migration, but usually keeping well off shore.

*SUBSPECIES.* Two races are recognized: *Fulmarus glacialis glacialis*, Atlantic Fulmar (le Pétrel fulmar de l'Antlantique); *Fulmarus glacialis rodgersi*, Pacific Fulmar (le Pétrel fulmar du Pacifique). Slightly smaller than the above and averaging a little darker.

### FAMILY—HYDROBATIDAE. STORM PETRELS

## *Petrels*

*General Description.* In our waters represented by small birds about 8 inches long. Evenly sooty brown with white rump; or ash-grey in colour.

*Distinctions.* Small size. Nostril tubes closely fused so that the division between is reduced to a narrow septum (Figure 88). Tail slightly to decidedly forked.

*Field Marks.* Small, evenly coloured birds flitting close to the surface of the water at sea, pattering up and down the waves as if walking on them.

*Nesting.* In burrows in the ground or under rocks.

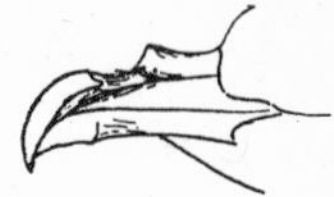

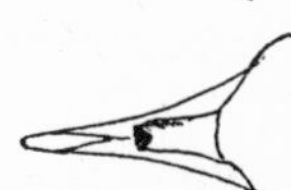

Figure 88
Bill of Leach's Petrel; natural size.

The birds are well known to sailors and travellers under the name of "Mother Carey's Chickens" and their appearance is said to presage a storm. In spite of their diminutive size they are met with far out at sea and are seldom seen by the longshoreman except in the vicinity of their breeding grounds. Even where they nest in numbers, they may remain unnoticed by the ordinary observer, owing to their nocturnal habits when breeding.

*Economic Status.* The petrels though feeding on fish are too small and live too far from civilization to be of calculable economic importance.

105. **Fork-tailed Petrel.** LE PÉTREL À QUEUE FOURCHUE. *Oceanodroma furcata.* L, 8-9. An ashy grey petrel, lighter below and on throat. Tail decidedly forked, outer feathers nearly an inch longer than the centre ones.

*Distinctions.* Ashy grey coloration instead of smoky brown. A Pacific species.

*Field Marks.* The ashy colour and lack of white rump patch.

*Distribution.* North Pacific and adjacent Arctic Oceans. Breeds along the Pacific coast south to Oregon. Our only substantiated breeding records are from Queen Charlotte Islands, but it is recorded as nesting both to the north and the south of our shores.

106. **Boreal Petrel.** LE PÉTREL BORÉAL. *Oceanodroma leucorhoa.* L, 8. A small, sooty brown petrel, very slightly paler below, with a white rump. Tail slightly forked, outer feathers three-quarters of an inch longer than centre ones.

*Distinctions.* An Atlantic and Pacific species. Sooty brown coloration instead of ashy grey as the Fork-tailed Petrel. The only brown petrel of the west coast. On the east coast distinguished from Storm Petrel by forked tail and dark underwing surface; from Wilson's by black instead of yellow web feet and feet extending beyond tail.

*Field Marks.* Sooty brown coloration and white rump, forked tail, and clock feet.

*Distribution.* North Pacific and north Atlantic Oceans. In the former breeding south to Lower California. Our only ascertained breeding locality for this species in British Columbia is on Queen Charlotte Islands, and one is reported from Cape Flattery in Washington. On the Atlantic side of the continent it nests from Maine to southern Labrador and in southern Greenland.

*SUBSPECIES.* The new American Ornithological Union Check-List recognizes two subspecies on Canadian waters, *Oceanodroma leucorhoa leucorhoa*, Leach's Petrel (le Pétrel de Leach), of the Atlantic, and *Oceanodroma leucorhoa beali*, Beal's Petrel (le Pétrel de Beal), on the Pacific side. A third form, *Oceanodroma leucorhoa kaedingi*, Kaeding's Petrel, once attributed to Canada, is now restricted to Lower California and adjoining water.

106. 2. **Madeira Petrel.** LE PÉTREL DE MADÈIRE. *Oceanodroma castro.* L, 7·75. Evenly sooty brown with white rump like Leach's Petrel, but tail only slightly or not evidently forked.

*Distinctions.* Averaging slightly smaller than Leach's Petrel which it resembles closely except for tail which when closed is only slightly or not evidently forked, and the longer white rump feathers which are strongly and sharply tipped with black instead of being just clouded with brownish. Easily distinguished from the Storm Petrel by larger size and lack of whitish on underwing surface and from Wilson's Petrel by much shorter legs, the tarsus being not longer than middle toe and claw.

*Field Marks.* Too undistinctive and too rare in American waters to be reliably identified in life.

*Distribution.* Breeds on Madeira, the Azores, and Cape Verde Islands, to St. Helena. Usually confined to the eastern side of the Atlantic. Only a very few American records. One bird was picked up in exhausted condition in the Rideau River near Ottawa, August 28, 1933.

104. **Storm Petrel.** MOTHER CAREY'S CHICKEN. LE PÉTREL DE TEMPÊTE. *Hydrobates pelagicus.* L, 5·75. The smallest of our petrels. Blackish brown with white rump.

*Distinctions.* An Atlantic species. Like Leach's or Wilson's Petrels, but smaller. Separable from Leach's by round or unforked tail and from Wilson's by black webs to feet.

*Field Marks.* A small, dark petrel with some white on under wing.

*Distribution.* Eastern parts of north Atlantic Ocean. There is a single record for Canada—from northern Ungava.

109. **Wilson's Petrel.** MOTHER CAREY'S CHICKEN. LE PÉTREL DE WILSON. *Oceanites oceanicus.* L, 7. A slightly smaller bird than Leach's Petrel, of same general colour but averaging slightly darker, less forked tail, and with toe webs mostly yellow instead of all black.

*Distinctions.* An Atlantic species. Smaller size, slightly darker coloration, square instead of forked tail, and the yellow foot webs will separate this petrel from Leach's, and the yellow webs from the Stormy.

*Field Marks.* Square instead of slightly forked tail is probably the most reliable guide to the specific identity of this petrel in life, but accurate observation is necessary to make the distinction.

*Nesting.* In ground burrows or rock crevices.

*Distribution.* From the Antarctic to Labrador and to the British Isles across the Atlantic.

Wilson's Petrel is notable as being one of the very few North American species that nest at the southern end of their migratory range. Hence, individuals seen here in the summer are migrants and do not breed.

## Order—Pelicaniformes. Fully webbed Swimmers

*General Description.* Birds with webs between all four toes, making three webs instead of the usual two as in other orders (Figure 7, page 25).

*Distinctions.* The feet characters are always distinctive.

This order is represented in Canada by three suborders: *Phaëthontes,* Tropic-birds; *Pelecani,* Pelicans, Gannets, and Cormorants; and *Fregatae* the Frigate-birds of only casual occurrence on our east coast.

*Economic Status.* This order, being composed of large birds, all fish-eaters, and many of them frequenting inshore or inland waters in considerable numbers, is open to a certain amount of suspicion as to its economic effect. However, no step should be taken against any species until careful investigation has proved its necessity.

### SUBORDER—PHAËTHONTES. TROPIC-BIRDS

Medium-sized birds, largely white in colour, with greatly elongated whip-like central tail feathers (Figure 89).

113. **Red-billed Tropic-bird.** L'OISEAU DES TROPIQUES À BEC ROUGE. *Phaëthon aethereus.* L, 33, of which 22 inches may be tail. In contrasting black and white like next species, but back finely barred with black and white and bill bright red.

*Distinctions.* With gently tapered, sharp-pointed bill and long whip-lash centre tail feathers, to be mistaken only for the Yellow-billed Tropic-bird, for which see above characters.

*Distribution.* Tropical seas on both sides of the continent. There is a single record for the Newfoundland Banks.

Figure 89

Yellow-billed Tropic-bird; head scale, ½. Tail much reduced. (Compare with Figure 93.)

112. **Yellow-billed Tropic-bird.** L'OISEAU DES TROPIQUES À BEC JAUNE. *Phaëthon lepturus.* L, 30, of which 20 inches may be tail. Contrasted black and white, back not barred. Bill yellow.

*Distinctions.* With gently tapered, sharp-pointed bill and long, whip-lash tail feathers, to be mistaken only for the red-billed Tropic-bird for which see above characters.

*Distribution.* Tropic seas of both hemispheres. Of accidental occurrence in Nova Scotia.

## SUBORDER—PELECANI. PELICANS, GANNETS, CORMORANTS, ETC.

### FAMILY—PELECANOIDEA. PELICANS

Among the very largest of American birds, with very long, flattened bill, and enormous throat patch.

In Canada, only two species need be considered, both strongly characterized. One is very common on the prairies; the other is met with only on the two coasts and there but rarely.

125. **White Pelican.** LE PÉLICAN BLANC. *Pelecanus erythrorhynchos.* L, about 64. Pure white, with black wings, long flattened bill (12 inches or over), and an enormous yellow gular pouch capable of holding several quarts (Figure 90). On the top and midway the length of the bill there is in some cases an extraordinary, horny plate irregular in outline, but erect like a rifle sight and up to an inch and a half in height. This ornament is said to be deciduous and shed annually. It is common to both sexes, and not the peculiar property of the male as is generally stated. Juveniles have more or less clouding of brown on nape and hind head.

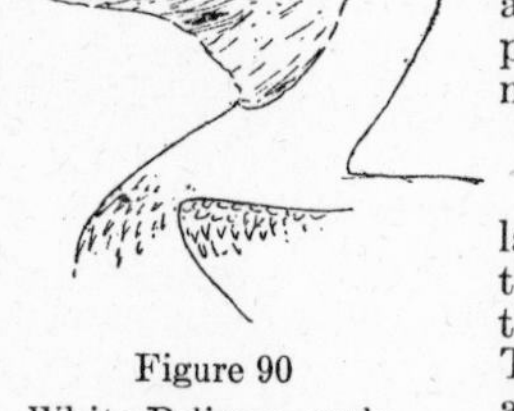

Figure 90
White Pelican; scale about $\frac{1}{18}$.

*Distinctions.* The above are absolutely distinctive.

*Field Marks.* A great white bird with black wings and large, yellow throat pouch that can be seen almost as far as the bird itself. The only other white birds that approximate the pelican in size are the swans and the Whooping Crane. The swans have all white wings, and the crane very long legs, and in flight carry legs and neck outstretched, instead of hunching the head up on the shoulders as do the Pelicans (Figure 91, compare with 112 and 239).

*Nesting.* On the ground, usually on bare or stony islands in the larger lakes.

*Distribution.* Most of temperate North America breeding in Canada, across the prairies and north to near Great Slave Lake. Rare east of the Prairie Provinces, also rare through most of British Columbia, but is found there on some of the large lakes.

The ponderously serious flight of these great white birds with their slow beat, beat, beat, and then a long dignified sail, is a common sight near the larger prairie waters, as they wing back and forth between the lakes and feeding grounds. They fly in long, evenly spaced lines, abreast, in tandem, or in V's. Pelicans are communists, individualism is unknown among them. The way one faces, they all face; as one poses, they all pose. Standing on a bare sandbar, they line up in military formation and digest their dinners together. Flying, they assume their appointed positions, and, taking the beat from their leader, keep time with him, flapping and sailing together. No more beautiful sight may be seen on the prairies than a long line of these great white birds, black pinioned, with golden pouches tucked under their chins, all sparkling in the sunlight in brilliant contrast with the deep blue water or azure sky. The realization of how well these seemingly awkward and ponderous hulks of birds can fly comes with some little shock of surprise. We expect them to drag their great bulk about clumsily

Figure 91
White Pelican, appearance in flight.

just over the water, instead of which—after a somewhat splashy start that can be excused in such large, heavy birds—once they get in the air their rise is so easy and rapid that before one is aware they are circling up and up until, at times, they vanish in the blue sky.

In feeding, pelicans paddle about the shallow water, head high, bill turned down against the breast, intently regarding the water below. When food is sighted, the bill is opened and plunged down and forward, the long slender sides of the lower mandible bow out, and the luckless victim is fairly scooped up. At the end of the scoop when the pressure of water in the pouch is relieved the sides spring together, the upper mandible closes down to a narrow opening, and, as the water is strained out, the contents are retained either to be swallowed immediately or to be carried safely in the capacious pouch to the gangling fledglings at home. Pelicans often fish far from their nests and they may be seen for many miles about a colony passing back and forth engaged in the toil of keeping themselves and their families supplied with food.

Pelicans are one of the spectacular features of prairie wild life and are a great æsthetic asset where objects of striking interest are particularly desirable. They are well worth the small price of such coarse fish as they feed upon. All large birds suffer from thoughtless persecution by careless men. It would seem as though size alone were regarded as crime sufficient to turn every gun against its unhappy possessor. This has been true of the pelican, as it has been of other large birds of greater sporting or food value. Pelicans are never eaten and their carcasses serve no other purpose than to befoul the air, yet gunners are all too few who can withhold their shot when such striking targets come within range. The fact that they eat a few fish is the expressed excuse, but if this class of fish protectionists were as concerned about the acts of poaching humans as they are about those of birds there would probably be more fish, and those taken by the pelicans would not be missed.

Pelicans generally nest in large communities on islands or other isolated spots in the larger lakes, where they are fairly secure from their natural enemies. They are in many cases associated with cormorants, herons, and gulls. Although such a community is by its insularity normally secure from foxes, coyotes, and other vermin, it is not safe from man. Cases have been known where adjoining residents have placed pigs on such islands to fatten on the eggs and young. It is to be hoped that such things are of the past. With the settling of the country, the draining of the lakes, reclamation and other improvement schemes, inaccessible and retired spots where these and similar birds can nest undisturbed are constantly growing scarcer. These almost unavoidable changes, added to promiscuous shooting, are constantly reducing the numbers of these birds, and if nothing were done to check the destruction, they, together with the Trumpeter Swan and the Whooping Crane—which resemble them in size and nesting range—would shortly be extinct. Fortunately, a number of bird reserves have been established about many of the prairie lakes by Provincial and Federal legislation. It is hoped and expected that some or all of these species may survive indefinitely, and continue to add their attractions to the prairie landscape.

*Economic Status.* Probably almost entirely fish-eaters. All stomachs examined by the writer have contained the coarser and more sluggish, easily caught fish of the weedy shallows, usually those of smaller size.

Undoubtedly, too many pelicans on shallow lakes would injure the fishing, but the greater danger today is to the pelicans rather than to the fish. They are conspicuous birds, their numbers are likely to be over, rather than under, estimated, inducing an uneasiness as to their effect that a more careful comparison with the area covered would quiet.

126. **Brown Pelican.** LE PÉLICAN BRUN. *Pelecanus occidentalis.* L, 53 or more. Sooty brown below; grey, narrowly streaked with brown above. Face, and narrow line along gular pouch, white, in striking contrast with very dark brown hindneck. Gular pouch dark in colour.

*Distinctions.* Above description obvious.

*Field Marks.* Any dark-coloured pelican in Canada would be this species.

*Nesting.* On the ground, in large communities, on islands, sometimes on steeply sloping shores.

*Distribution.* Southern coasts of United States on both oceans southward. There are only casual occurrences in Canada, Nova Scotia and southern British Columbia coasts.

*SUBSPECIES.* Two subspecies are recognized: *Pelecanus occidentalis occidentalis* Eastern Brown Pelican (le Pélican brun de l'Est), and *Pelecanus occidentalis californicus* California Brown Pelican (le Pélican brun de Californie), differing from the former in having the gular pouch dull reddish in place of dull dusky.

Figure 92
Brown Pelican;
scale, about $\frac{1}{18}$.

FAMILY—SULIDAE. GANNETS

*General Description.* Large birds, mostly white when adult, bill sharp and straight without hook or pronounced throat or gular pouch.

*Distinctions.* The bill characters of this family serve to distinguish it from all excepting Tropic-birds, one species of which has been taken off Newfoundland (*S*ee Figure 89). As the Tropic-birds, however, have enormously elongated middle tail feathers there is little chance of confusion, even if they were not too rare in our waters to merit detailed consideration here.

The gannets are strictly marine birds, never seen away from the sea except as stragglers. The family on the whole is tropical and only one species occurs in Canada.

117. **Gannet.** SOLAN GOOSE. LE MARGOT (le Fou de Bassan). *Sula bassana.* L, 35. A completely webbed swimmer with straight bill without pronounced hook or conspicuous throat or gular pouch.

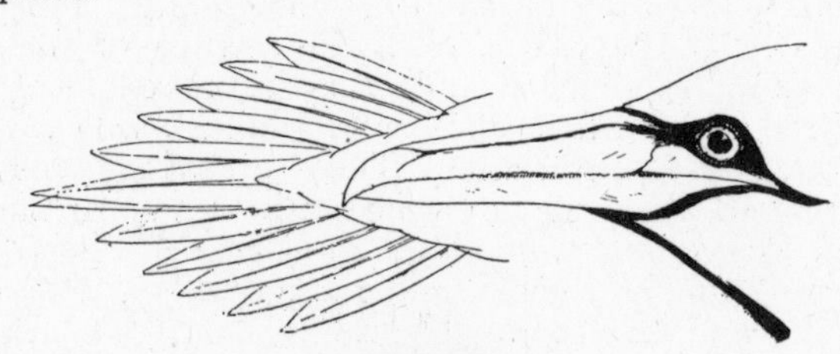

Figure 93
Details of Gannet,
scale, head, $\frac{1}{4}$.
Tail much reduced.

*Distinctions.* The bill characters are distinctive. The adult is pure white except for the black primaries and a rich creamy suffusion over the crown and hindneck. The young bird of the year is greyish brown, lighter below, and each feather has a small white V at the tip that gives an even mottling over all. Several intermediate spotted stages occur between these plumages.

A. Great Blue Heron; scale, $\frac{1}{10}$

Juvenile Summer adult

B. Black-crowned Night Heron; scale, $\frac{1}{6}$

Juvenile Adult

PLATE IV

A. American Bittern; scale, $\frac{1}{6}$

B. Canada Goose; scale, $\frac{1}{8}$

*Field Marks.* Dazzling white body and black wing tips of the adult are distinctive. The habit of diving from the wing, entering the water head first like an arrow, and remaining under an appreciable length of time is also characteristic. Terns dive from the wing, but they rise again almost immediately and seldom completely disappear from sight like the gannet. Even were it otherwise the great difference in size would be diagnostic.

*Nesting.* In large communities on the rocky shelves of sea cliffs; nests made of seaweed.

*Distribution.* Both sides of the north Atlantic, breeding in Canada only on Bird Rock off Magdalen Islands, Bonaventure Island, Gaspe County, Quebec, Anticosti Island, and Cape St. Mary, Newfoundland.

The gannet had at one time a much wider and commoner distribution than now, nesting as it did on many of the rocky islets on both sides of the north Atlantic. Of very small value either for food or other uses, except in the most primitive communities, it has been driven from one breeding station after another until in the New World only four remain and, if prompt measures had not been taken, these would probably have gone the way of the others.

*Economic Status.* Though the gannets have been accused of doing considerable damage to fishing interests their harmful effects have been much overestimated. The greater part of the life of the gannets is spent on or near the deep sea. When they come inshore for breeding purposes they can make very little impression on the mighty shoals of herring and other fish they pursue.

### FAMILY—PHALACROCORACIDAE. CORMORANTS

*General Description.* Large birds 25 to 36 inches, black or very dark brown in colour. Bill, long and slender, abruptly and strongly hooked at tip. No external nostrils. Skin around eyes bare, and usually a small, unfeathered gular or throat pouch (Figures 94-97). Highest mating plumages have variously shaped crests and filamentous plumes, but these ornaments are retained for only a short time (sometimes suppressed [?]) and are often absent.

*Distinctions.* The general form and outline of the bill are superficially similar to those of the jaegers or the shearwaters, but are fundamentally quite different. The lack of external nostrils, the bare space about eyes, and bare gular pouch easily distinguish the cormorants from them. These bare spots are usually highly coloured. In some specimens of the Pelagic Cormorant the bare gular pouch is small and may be largely overgrown with feathers.

*Field Marks.* Flying, the long, outstretched head and neck, long tail, rapidly beating wings, and direct flight of this family are easily recognized. On the water cormorants look somewhat like loons, but the motions of the head and neck are more graceful and serpentine and the long tail when shown is distinctive.

*Distribution.* Cosmopolitan, but naturally confined to the vicinity of large bodies of water. We have one species in the interior of the continent, two on the east coast, and three on the west coast.

Cormorants are fish-eaters and capture their prey by straight pursuit under water. With extraordinary ease they secure their agile prey in its own element. As seen in clear water or a tank, their subaquatic movements seem unhurried, yet such is the economy of effort that they take speedy fish with absurd ease. They never dive from the wing, but first alight and then disappear below with a serpentine gliding motion without splash. They seldom remain under more than forty seconds, though it seems longer to the observer. They bring their prey to the surface for swallowing, often with it crosswise in the bill, then deftly toss it in the air and unerringly catch it so that it goes down easily head first without danger from fins and spines.

Though cormorants are thoroughly aquatic, their plumage seems to be less adapted for such habits than that of other water birds and it appears necessary for them to come ashore at intervals to dry their feathers. Then they love to sit in the warm sun on crags, rocks, or isolated perches such as buoys, which in the neighbourhood of their operations are always liberally whitened with their guano. There, with wings hanging flaccidly, and a general air of dejection, they drape themselves with all the grace of a wet rag.

*Economic Status.* The danger of jumping at conclusions based upon superficial observation or common report is well illustrated by the result of a study of the food of these birds in the neighbourhood of the Gaspe salmon rivers.[1] Though commonly accused of damaging the salmon fisheries by devouring small fish and fry, careful examination of about thirty specimens showed that the birds were eating fish of no economic value and no salmonoid remains were found in them. Probably the eels, sculpins, and other fish taken by the cormorant make the species beneficial rather than harmful to the salmon, and may more than compensate for the few valuable fish that it occasionally takes. The evidence of Dr. Lewis (*See* footnote) strongly suggests that salmon and trout are not only distasteful to cormorants but may even be positively harmful to them. This provides a good example of the caution that is necessary in condemning any species of birds.

119. **Black Cormorant.** COMMON CORMORANT. LE CORMORAN NOIR. *Phalacrocorax carbo.* L, 36. *See* family description previously given.

*Distinctions.* With the family description above, easily recognized as a cormorant. In America restricted to the east coast where it needs distinction only from the Double-crested. Somewhat larger than that species with heart-shaped gular pouch bordered with white or whitish and with fourteen instead of twelve tail feathers. When adult, with conspicuous, small, white flank patches ("watch-pockets"). In highest nuptial plumage with no crest, but nape and neck frosted with many, fine, white filaments. The absence of crest, however, even when adult, is not a safe guide for specific recognition (*See* next species). Juveniles have considerably lighter or whiter breasts and abdomens than have similar plumages of the Double-crest.

Figure 94
European Cormorant; scale, ½.

*Field Marks.* Unless size or the white on throat and flanks is obvious it is rarely possible to separate the two cormorants in life.

*Nesting.* Similar to that of the next species.

*Distribution.* The three continents of the northern hemisphere. In America, only the east coast where in Canada a few remnants of formerly populous and more numerous nesting colonies remain. Rarely seen inland from salt water.

*SUBSPECIES.* The American form is the same as that found in the British Isles—the European Cormorant (le Grand Cormoran) *Phalacrocorax carbo carbo.*

[1] "The Double-crested Cormorant, Phalacrocorax Auritus, and its Relation to Salmon Industries on the Gulf St. Lawrence"; Geol. Surv., Canada, Mus. Bull. No. 13, Biological Series No. 5 (1915). Much additional evidence to the same general effect is also given by Harrison F. Lewis in his monograph "The Natural History of the Double-crested Cormorant," privately printed under the auspices of the Province of Quebec Society for the Protection of Birds, 1929.

Though hitherto called "Common" Cormorant this is the rarest of our eastern Canadian cormorants. The species occurs on the European coast and was given the name "Common" because of its abundance about the British Isles.

*Economic Status.* Owing to its rarity it is of little economic importance in Canada.

120. **Double-crested Cormorant.** CROW DUCK. LE CORMORAN À AIGRETTES. *Phalacrocorax auritus.* L, 36. Plate II B. A large Cormorant. Adult: solid black, with greenish reflections. Feathers on back dull bronze with black edges, giving suggestion of overlapping scales. Bare face and square-cut gular pouch, orange. Crest when present, double, one over each ear, of filamentous plumes. Juvenile: dark sooty brown, lightening below, the scaly appearance of back evident.

Figure 95
Double-crested Cormorant; scale, $\frac{1}{3}$.

*Distinctions.* This species in the east is likely to be confused with the preceding one only. In adult plumage the absence of any white at the base of the gular sac and on the flanks is diagnostic. In other plumages, size, the presence of twelve instead of fourteen feathers in the tail, and the whitening of the feathers adjacent to the gular pouch must be relied upon. Early in the spring the filamentous crests on the sides of the head instead of a ragged ruff as in the previous species are characteristic; but these features are lost early in the season, before nesting begins, and hence are usually of little help in determination.

Through the interior of the continent it is the only cormorant likely to be met with, but on the west coast it may need distinction from several species. Size similar to Brandt's Cormorant, much larger than Pelagic. Black edgings to dull bronze black feathers evident in all plumages. Lower line of gular pouch cut square across throat not indented to heart-shape (Figure 95, compare with 96 and 97). No distinct lightening of plumage around gular pouch.

*Field Marks.* Size, and yellow face and sides of bill should distinguish from Pelagic. Black or evenly coloured featheration about base of gular pouch, when seen, will separate it from Brandt's.

*Nesting.* In bulky nests, among rocks on islands, cliffs, or other almost inaccessible localities. Occasionally in trees.

*Distribution.* Across the continent. Breeding in Canada at various points on the Atlantic coast, the Gulf of St. Lawrence, Lake Superior, and throughout the Prairie Provinces north to Great Slave Lake. Common on the Pacific coast, but almost absent from the interior of British Columbia. Nests at Cape Flattery, and Forrester Island, just across the border to the north, but known to breed within British Columbia only on Bare Island, off the south end of Vancouver Island.

*SUBSPECIES.* The bird of the west coast is separable from that of the prairie interior and the east, the Eastern Double-crest (le Cormoran à aigrettes de l'Est) *Phalacrocorax auritus auritus*, by somewhat larger size and the presence of considerable white in the crest, hence the name, White-crested Cormorant (le Cormoran à aigrettes blanches) *Phalacrocorax auritus cincinatus.*

This is the common cormorant, or Crow Duck, of the east coast and of the prairies and large central lakes. It nests on bare islands or rocky cliffs, occasionally in trees, on or by large bodies of water, sometimes in immense communities, or in company with pelicans, gulls, or herons. In British Columbia it is confined to the coast, where it seems more or less of a migrant, or a winter visitor. Although it has been found nesting directly north and south of the Canadian coast we have only the single breeding record for British Columbia. Colonies should be looked for on the outer shore of Vancouver Island.

These cormorants often fish in companies. They spread themselves across the mouth of a shallow bay, and, facing inward, make a drive in towards a common centre. As they advance, the enclosed area becomes smaller and more closely guarded, the finny population more congested and easily caught. The divings grow shorter and more rapid and more fish are tossed and swallowed in hurried haste for another catch. As the shore is approached, the surviving fish make a despairing rush outward through their enemies, and there is much commotion and excitement; then quietness, and the birds form line again along another section of the water to repeat the operation.

*Economic Status.* See the heading under family. Much said under the pelican applies here with even greater force, owing to the smaller size of the birds and consequent less capacity for harm.

122. **Brandt's Cormorant.** LE CORMORAN DE BRANDT. *Phalacrocorax penicillatus.* L, 35. About the same size as the Double-crested, and considerably larger than the Pelagic. Adult: black, iridescent with green and blue. A fawn-coloured patch about the blue gular pouch, blending into the surrounding black. No crests, but in highest plumage with sparse, long, yellowish filaments on sides of neck and throat.

Figure 96
Brandt's Cormorant;
scale, ⅓.

*Distinctions.* Size, similar to Double-crested, and much larger than Pelagic. No dark edgings to feathers of back. Lower edge of bare gular pouch intruded by throat feathering, making its outline heart-shaped (Figure 96). A light fawn patch about the base of gular pouch, conspicuous in adult, evident as a soft yet distinct lightening in the juveniles.

*Field Marks.* Size, and absence of yellow on bill or gular pouch. The light fore-throat should be quite conspicuous in birds approaching maturity.

*Nesting.* On rounded shoulders or ledges, or flat tops of rock islands, or similar localities.

*Distribution.* Pacific coast, from south end of the Alaska Panhandle to Lower California. Breeding from the west coast of Vancouver Island (Solander Island) southward.

123. **Pelagic Cormorant.** LE CORMORAN PÉLAGIQUE. *Phalacrocorax pelagicus.* L, about 25. The smallest of our cormorants. Adult: black, with beautiful purple and green reflections. Bare face and gular pouch dull carmine red. Bare gular pouch very small for the family, heart-shaped by the intrusion of a point of throat feathering, in some cases completely obliterated. In highest plumage, with two crests, one over forehead, the other on rear crown (Figure 97). Iridescent purple neck thickly sprinkled with loose, white filaments. A conspicuous white patch on lower flank. These crests, filaments, and body patches may be entirely absent in otherwise high plumaged specimens. Juvenile: even, sooty brown, with very little lightening anywhere.

Figure 97
Pelagic Cormorant;
scale, ⅓.

*Distinctions.* Small size, even coloration, with large amount of iridescence that is suggested on the back in even juvenile plumages.

*Field Marks.* Small size, colour unrelieved by light face patch or yellow bill or gular pouch. The two crests and white flank spots when present.

*Nesting.* On cliffs, sea-wall ledges, and similar situations.

*Distribution.* Coasts of north Pacific, breeding south to California. Breeding colonies have been noted at the south end of Vancouver Island and on Queen Charlotte Islands.

*SUBSPECIES.* Two subspecies are recognized in the 1931 edition of the Check-list. *Phalacrocorax pelagicus pelagicus* Violet-Green Cormorant (le Cormoran vert violet) has a comparatively heavy bill. It is restricted to Kamchatka and Alaska, including the Panhandle. *Phalacrocorax pelagicus resplendens* Baird's Cormorant (le Cormoran de Baird), with more slender bill, inhabits the coast of British Columbia and southward.

This is the most beautiful of the American cormorants, and in summer at least the commonest one on our western coast. Unfortunately, few of the cormorants keep their plumage ornaments for any length of time and their greatest beauty is seldom seen.

124. **Red-faced Cormorant.** LE CORMORAN À FACE ROUGE. *Phalacrocorax urile.* L, about 33. A large, solidly black plumaged cormorant like the Double-crested, but when adult as highly iridescent as the Pelagic and with a heart-shaped gular pouch. The bare part of face from orange to red and extended across the forehead. The juvenile is brown like the other cormorants, but the forehead may not be bare in the earlier stages.

*Distinctions.* A large cormorant without whitish or light border to heart-shaped gular pouch.

*Distribution.* The islands of Bering Sea and Kamchatka. One juvenile specimen from the inside coast of Vancouver Island has been referred to this species.

### SUBORDER—FREGATAE. MAN-O'-WAR-BIRDS

#### FAMILY—FREGATIDAE. MAN-O'-WAR-BIRDS

We have a single well-characterized species.

128. **Man-O'-War-Bird.** FRIGATE-BIRD. LA FRÉGATE MARINE. *Fregata magnificens.* L, 40. Large, black birds with bill hooked like that of a cormorant and long, deeply forked tail.

*Distinctions.* With general blackness and long, hooked bill likely to be compared only with the cormorant, but note long, narrow gular sac, tip of lower mandible at hook distinctly turned down, and deeply forked tail.

*Distribution.* Tropical and subtropical shores of both hemispheres. Of casual occurrence only on our east coast.

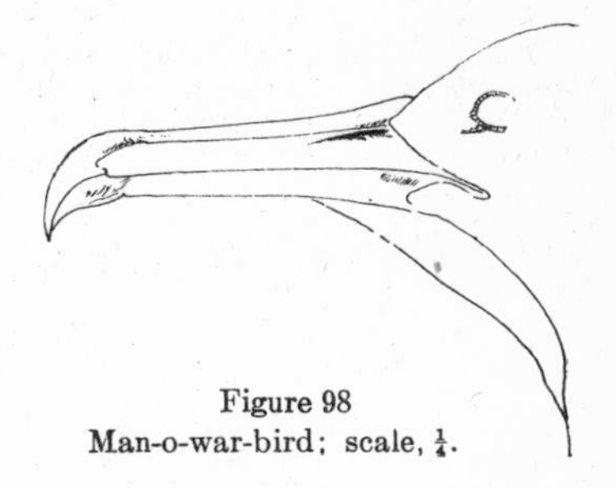

Figure 98
Man-o-war-bird; scale, $\frac{1}{4}$.

## Order—Ciconiiformes. Deep-water Waders. Herons, Storks, and Ibises

*General Description.* Usually large birds with long legs, neck, and bill, fitted for wading and obtaining food below the surface in rather deeper water than do the majority of Waders. Bills may be either straight and sharp (Figure 20, page 27), or gently curved and blunt as in the ibises (Figures 108 and 109, page 67). Legs are bare for a considerable distance above the heel joint and all four toes are perfect, well shaped, and adapted for perching as well as walking on soft ground, and with only small, rudimentary webs or none (Figure 99).

*Distinctions.* Birds of this order may be mistaken for either the cranes or the curlews. From the cranes they may be distinguished by their feathered foreheads, hind toe not elevated above the others, and the septum between the nostrils being solid and unperforated; from the curlews by the bare space in front of the eyes.

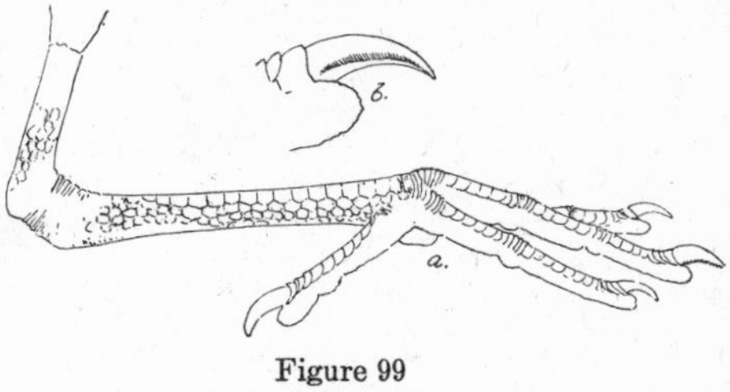

Figure 99
Leg of Herodione:
*a*, Leg of Great Blue Heron, scale, $\frac{1}{5}$.
*b*, Pectinate middle claw.

Two suborders are recognized in Canada: *Ardeae*, the Herons and bitterns; and *Ciconinae*, including the storks and ibises.

## SUBORDER—ARDEAE. HERONS AND BITTERNS

As this suborder is represented in Canada by only one family, *Ardeidae*, the description under that heading is sufficient.

### FAMILY—ARDEIDAE. HERONS AND BITTERNS

*General Description.* Heron-like birds with straight and very sharply pointed bills. Forehead feathered, but space in front of eyes bare. A peculiar feature with this suborder is the occurrence of "powder-down tracts"—aggregations of peculiarly modified feathers giving off a dry powder of unknown use. These feathers are found on various parts of the body hidden under the visible plumage. Claw of the middle toe is pectinate, that is, furnished with a series of well-defined, comb-like teeth (Figure 99), not merely roughnesses as in the ibises.

*Distinctions.* This suborder might be mistaken for cranes, but the feathered forehead is distinctive (Like Figure 20, compare with Figure 22, pages 27, 28). Back of neck bare, the feathers of sides reaching around and behind and hiding the bareness from casual observation. Hind toe very long, set level with the other toes, and not slightly raised as in other waders.

*Field Marks.* Obvious heron-like outline, with long, graceful neck, long, sharp bill (Figure 20, page 27), and lengthened legs (Figure 99). Neck folded in flight, bringing head close to shoulders, the legs trailing behind. The cranes, with which they may be confused in life, carry their necks outstretched when flying (Compare Figure 100 with 239, page 167).

Figure 100
Appearance of Heron in flight.

Perhaps no birds are so well known to the general public by common repute and observation as these, yet we seldom hear them correctly named. The terms herons, storks, and cranes, are applied and misapplied indiscriminately. There are no true storks in Canada. The cranes are of quite distinct character from herons. The birds most commonly called "cranes" in the east are usually true herons. True cranes are quite rare or absent east of Manitoba.

The family is divided into two subfamilies: *Ardeinae*, the herons and egrets; and *Botaurinae*, the bitterns.

#### Subfamily—Ardeinae. True Herons and Egrets

*General Description.* More slender and graceful birds than the bitterns and, on the average, larger. The smallest are slightly smaller than the American Bittern. Colour makes the best character for popular recognition from the bitterns.

*Distinctions.* Herons are usually slate-blue or dull green, but sometimes white. The juvenile Night Heron is dull, pale brown, the bitterns have pronounced yellow coloration. All Canadian herons in full breeding condition have long, fine plumes on crown, lower throat, or back, which are lost in the autumn.

*Field Marks.* The characteristic outline in flight, with straight, sharp-pointed bill, head drawn in to the shoulders, and legs trailing behind, is common to both bitterns and herons, which are better recognized apart by species than as subfamilies. However, any such bird that is obviously not a bittern is probably a heron.

*Nesting.* Herons commonly build in communities, usually in tree tops in wet forests, but sometimes, especially on the prairies, on the ground in marshes or on islets in the lakes.

The herons are as a rule fishers in open shallows, haunting grassy bogs less than do bitterns. Instead of stalking their prey they are quite likely to remain motionless in the shallows until it comes within reach, or only move after it slowly and by imperceptible movements.

194. **Great Blue Heron.** (Incorrectly BLUE CRANE). BLUE HERON. LE GRAND HÉRON BLEU. *Ardea herodias.* L, 42. Plate III A.

*Distinctions.* The largest heron found in Canada; the Sandhill or Little Brown Crane is the only bird for which it may be mistaken. The fully feathered forehead is diagnostic (Compare Figure 20, page 27, with 242, page 169).

*Field Marks.* Heron-like outline, large size, and general coloration make the best field marks. Unlike the cranes that fly with neck outstretched, the Great Blue, like other herons, travels with neck folded and head drawn in to shoulders (Figure 100, compare with 239, page 167).

*Nesting.* Usually in large communities in wet woods, such as tamarack, ash, or elm swamps. Nest a large, bulky structure of sticks in tree tops. On the treeless prairies it nests on the ground on islets well out in the lakes and removed from prowling coyotes and other enemies.

*Distribution.* Across the continent north to the Maritime Provinces, the lower St. Lawrence, the Great Lakes region, the central prairie sections, and on the west coast to southern Alaska.

*SUBSPECIES.* The bird of the greater part of Canada is the type form Eastern Great Blue Heron (le Grand Héron bleu de l'Est) *Ardea herodias herodias.* On the west coast occurs the Northwest Coast Heron (le Grand Héron bleu du Nord-Ouest), *Ardea herodias fannini*, an appreciably darker bird, especially on neck and back, and with tarsus averaging shorter. From present information, this race is confined to the coast from Washington northward. The heron of the interior of British Columbia has not been definitely determined, but is probably typical *herodias.*

This bird throughout most of its range is mistakenly called "Blue Crane" or "Fish Crane." It is not a crane, however, and especially in the west where cranes occur commonly such confusion should be avoided.

The Great Blue Heron haunts open, shallow water. It rarely frequents dense reed-beds, though it is often found on their outskirts or on the edges of pools within them. It prefers wide, shallow reaches of rivers, or open flats of marsh or tidal shores. It is a still-hunter, cautiously wading with almost imperceptible movements, or standing statuesquely regarding the water until its prey comes within reach when, with a lightning stroke of the sharp bill, it is secured. Herons, nesting in large rookeries in wet woods, have been peculiarly liable to the senseless persecution that seems to follow all our larger birds. Wary and suspicious ordinarily, in the vicinity of their nests they lose much of their usual caution and in the rookeries the birds can be shot in numbers. Heronries are usually known to all the surrounding country and are in the breeding season often visited by the rural sportsman who kills the parent birds and leaves the young to die of hunger, although a landowner has occasionally sufficient public spirit to protect heronries on his property. The result is that this picturesque bird is becoming scarce. Heronries once destroyed in this manner are seldom if ever repopulated and new ones are rarely established. Birds breeding in communities are seldom driven away to new locations. They remain until the individuals composing them are exterminated. The Blue Heron is a harmless bird and should receive every protection possible.

*Economic Status.* The food of the Great Blue Heron is almost entirely animal in its nature, consisting mainly of frogs, snakes, and small fish usually of no economic importance. Cranes frequent the fields for food, but the herons never do so. Occasionally herons may visit trout streams where they meander through open meadows, but such cases are rare and insufficient for the condemnation of the species. Herons often frequent the pound nets of the fishermen, but the limited size of their gullets precludes their taking anything of economic importance and the suspicion of the net owners against them is unfounded.

76916—5

### WHITE HERONS OR EGRETS

Though not forming a recognized systematic division of the herons, there are several species showing pure white plumages that are distinct enough to warrant discussion.

In some of these species, particularly the egrets, white is the adult plumage; in others, it is dichromatism, that is, the species occurs in two colour phases, either of which is normal, and cannot be referred to either albinism or melanism, or to sex, age, or season. In still other species the white is a plumage of juvenility. These white plumages were a source of considerable confusion in identifying species until they were fully worked out. All the white herons are of southern distribution and are rare in Canada.

196. **Great White Egret.** LA GRANDE AIGRETTE. *Casmerodius albus.* L, 41. Almost as large as the Great Blue Heron, but always pure white. In breeding season a cascade of some fifty, fine, straight plumes originates in middle back region and festoons over lower back and tail. No plumes on head or neck.

*Distinctions.* Large size, colour, and obviously heron-like outline. Straight plumes from back (Compare Figure 101 with Figures 102 and 103).

*Field Marks.* As above.

*Nesting.* In communities, in nests of sticks in trees or bushes over water.

*Distribution.* The southern and Gulf states, appearing in Canada only as an accidental straggler. Most frequent in the east, but there is one record for Manitoba.

*SUBSPECIES.* Of almost world wide tropical and subtropical distribution. The form in North America is the Great American Egret (la Grande aigrette d'Amérique) *Casmerodius albus egretta.*

The Great Egret, with the Little Egret and some other species of like character, constitute the source of the well-known "aigrette" or "osprey" plumes of the millinery trade. As these plumes are grown only in the breeding season and as the immediate neighbourhood of the breeding rookeries is the place where these wary birds can be most easily approached it is evident that the harvesting of the beautiful crop is accompanied by great cruelty. The defence is often made that the plumes are picked up after being shed by the parent bird. If any one searches domestic poultry yards for good shed feathers he will quickly realize that recovered "aigrette" plumes will probably be few in number and of poor quality. The explanation is more absurd as the rookeries are situated in dense, subtropical swamps where all below is mud and water and the undergrowth prevents close, systematic search even were the spoils worth retrieving. The plume hunter usually hides in the rookery and with a small calibre rifle shoots the birds one by one until the

Figure 101
American Egret; scale, ⅛.

PLATE V

A. Brant; scale, 1/10

Black Brant White-breasted Brant

B. Snow Goose; scale, 1/14 White-fronted Goose; scale, 1/14

Adult Juvenile Adult

A. Mallard; scale, $\frac{1}{6}$

Male Female

B. Black Duck; scale, $\frac{1}{8}$

flock is exterminated. After the plumes are removed the bodies are left to rot on the ground while the young starve in the nests above. Local laws were passed against killing the birds, but without avail. Originally the waters of Florida and the Gulf Straits were made beautiful with the forms of these immaculate birds; a few years ago this great attraction was almost lost, as the birds were approaching extinction. As it was found impossible to distinguish between foreign and native plumes or prevent the traffic in the one while permitting it in the other, a federal law was finally passed in the United States prohibiting the importation of feathers for millinery purposes. Similar laws have since been passed in Great Britain, her colonies, and Dominions, including Canada. Today, owing to these measures and the practical suppression of the plume trade, the birds seem to be increasing again.

Figure 102
Snowy Egret;
scale, ⅛.

197. **Little White Egret.** LA PETITE AIGRETTE. *Egretta thula.* L, 24. A small, pure white heron. A cascade of fine, filamentous plumes falling over the back and recurved at the ends. Similar straight plumes from back of head and from neck over breast. Bill black, yellow about eyes. Legs black, feet yellow. Juveniles and autumn adults without plumes.

*Distinctions.* Much like several other small, white herons, but characterized by size, black legs, yellow feet, and absence of any colour on tips of flight feathers. Wing, 9·50 to 11. Bill, 2·8 to 4. Tarsus, 3·7 to 4·15. Middle toe and claw, 2·6 to 2·8 (Compare Figure 102 with 101 and 103).

*Field Marks.* A small white heron. Not always separable in life from some other species that may occur, though under favourable circumstances the yellow feet on black legs are quite conspicuous.

*Nesting.* Nest of sticks in trees or bushes over water.

*Distribution.* South and North America, formerly north to New Jersey, Illinois, Indiana, and Oregon. Of only accidental appearance in Canada. There have been occasional occurrences in the southern parts of eastern Canada and the bird has been taken as far west as southern Alberta. Many of the older records of these small white herons are of uncertain identity. The eastern records can be referred to the Snowy Egrette (l'Aigrette neigeuse) *Egretta thula thula*, the western one may be Brewster's Egret (l'Aigrette de Brewster) *Egretta thula brewsteri.*

Figure 103
Little Blue Heron
(juvenile, white plumage);
scale, ⅛.

200. **Little Blue Heron.** LE PETIT HÉRON BLEU. *Florida caerulea.* L, 22. A small, dark-coloured heron, mostly even bluish slate, not lightening below, in adult. Pure, immaculate white when juvenile.

*Distinctions.* The small size and even, over-all dark blue-greyness makes the adult quite distinct from any other heron in Canada. The absence of green anywhere, and of any trace of white on throat, foreneck, and underparts will readily separate from the Little Green Heron of somewhat similar appearance. The juvenile is pure white like an egret, but has no plumes anywhere and the primaries are almost always more or less clouded with greyish.

*Field Marks.* A small, evenly dark-coloured heron of longer, more graceful, outline than the Green Heron. In white plumage the legs, dull greenish instead of black or black with yellow feet, will distinguish it from the egrets (Compare Figure 103 with Figures 101 and 102).

*Distribution.* North and South America, formerly bred as far north as New Jersey and Illinois. Only accidental in Canada. There are a few records for Nova Scotia and the Lower Great Lakes.

201. **Green Heron.** FLY-UP-THE-CREEK. LE HÉRON VERT. *Butorides virescens.* L, 17. Smallest of the common herons. Back lustrous grey-green with short, plume-like feathers draping over the wings. Face, sides of neck, and throat, as well as the underparts, rich chestnut. Head has a black cap lengthened into a small crest.

*Distinctions.* The above description may seem to resemble the last species, but the evident green sheen of back, absence of neck plumes, smaller size, and heavier build, prevent serious confusion. This is, moreover, a common species within its range and the one most likely to be met with in the Great Lakes region. Any comparable species is very rare.

*Field Marks.* Size and general coloration.

*Nesting.* Solitary and not in communities, in flimsy and open nest of sticks in bushes or trees, usually over water.

*Distribution.* Moderately common in southern Ontario, but rare or absent to the east or west. Breeds wherever found in Canada.

Figure 104
Little Green Heron;
scale, $\frac{1}{4}$.

*SUBSPECIES.* The Green Heron is subspecifically divided, but the type form, Eastern Green Heron (le Héron vert de l'Est), is the only one that occurs in Canada.

The Green Herons are not as prone to frequent open water as is the Great Blue Heron, nor grassy marshes like the bittern. Alder thickets in drowned land, the bushy edges of quiet bayous, back waters of slack streams, and beaver meadows are their preferred habitat. They are more solitary than the other herons at nesting time and though several pairs may occupy a peculiarly favoured locality it is community of interest that draws them together and not sociability.

*Economic Status.* The food of the Green Heron consists of crawfish, insects, frogs, and small fish. An accusation has been brought against it that it is harmful to certain fish, but as the bird is small and comparatively scarce and as its usual still water habitat does not bring it in contact with many valuable species, it cannot be regarded as a serious menace.

202. **Black-crowned Night Heron.** QUA-BIRD. SQUAWK. LE HÉRON DE NUIT À COURONNE NOIRE (le Héron Bihoreau). *Nycticorax nycticorax.* L, 24. Plate III B. Adult: body in soft white and pale grey; cap and back black with greenish reflections. Two, long (often coherent), white, pencil-like plumes falling back from head. Juvenile: light brownish, heavily striped with light cream above, below, and on neck and head. Yearling: light fawn colour on back, lightening, however, to nearly white below and on throat; without stripes except vague ones on head.

*Distinctions.* About the size of an American Bittern, the adult is too distinctly marked to be confused with anything else. The striped young bird, however, is somewhat similar to the Bittern, but never shows decided yellow colours, and the back and wing coverts are coarsely marked with white instead of being very finely vermiculated with minute specks of various colours. The intermediate plumage is in solid masses without any detail on the back.

*Field Marks.* About the size of an American Bittern. Black and pearl grey colour of adult and brownish appearance of juvenile lacking any yellow tendency. The wing quills are slightly if any darker than the back instead of being black as in the bittern. This species often alights in trees or bushes, which the bittern never does.

*Nesting.* Often in communities with Great Blue Herons, either in trees or on the ground in the marsh.

*Distribution.* The warmer parts of eastern and western hemispheres. In Canada irregularly common from the east coast throughout the southern prairies to Saskatchewan. There is only one record for British Columbia, Okanagan Lake, although the bird is not uncommon in central Washington.

*SUBSPECIES.* Occurs in both eastern and western hemispheres. The American Black-crowned Night Heron (le Kouac, le Héron Bihoreau d'Amérique) is subspecifically distinct from that of the Old World under the name *Nycticorax nycticorax hoactli.*

The Black-crowned Night Heron is a somewhat heavily built heron. Though not without beauty and grace it lacks the fine, slender lines of most of the herons and resembles the bittern in build as well as habit.

203. **Yellow-crowned Night Heron.** LE HÉRON DE NUIT À COURONNE D'OR. *Nyctanassa violacea.* L, 23. About the size of the previous species or the American Bittern

Adult generally slate-grey with conspicuously white patched head and face. Juvenile very similar to juvenile of preceding species.

*Distinctions.* The adult is quite distinctive. The juvenile is rather like an American Bittern, but shows no strong yellow and the back has no vermiculated pattern. It may take careful work to separate it from the juvenile Black-crowned Night Heron. The bill is shorter and heavier and the tarsus is decidedly longer than the middle toe and claw instead of being of same length or shorter.

*Distribution.* Warm, temperate, and tropical America. Has occurred, very rarely, in southern Nova Scotia and near Toronto, Ontario.

Figure 105
Yellow-crowned Night Heron (adult); scale, ¼.

**Subfamily—Botaurinae. Bitterns**

*General Description.* Marsh-inhabiting, heron-like birds of heavier and less graceful build and habit than the true herons.

*Distinctions.* Though forming a well-marked subfamily they are difficult to define in a non-technical explanation. We have but two species under consideration. The Least Bittern is so small, only 13 inches long, as to be unmistakable for any other Canadian heron-like wader. The American Bittern with its strongly ochraceous yellow coloration and size can be confused only with the juvenile Night Heron (*See* that species).

Bitterns are bog and marsh haunters. They do not frequent wide, open reaches of water, but drop down in the middle or on the edges of grass or reed-grown marshes, stalking their prey by silent approach through the close cover.

190. **American Bittern.** MARSH HEN. THUNDER-PUMP. STAKE-DRIVER. LE BUTOR D'AMÉRIQUE. *Botaurus lentiginosus.* L, 28. Plate IV A.

*Distinctions.* With its size, general yellowish coloration with fine vermiculation and pattern above, this bird can be mistaken for no other Canadian species. It is most like the juvenile Night Heron, but a comparison of Plates IV A and III B will show that the latter has no pattern on the back, or only a simple one, whereas this bittern shows a very fine and intricate vermiculated design. The black line from the sides of the face may be present or absent, regardless of sex, age, or season.

Figure 106
American Bittern
in breeding display.

*Field Marks.* As the bird rises from the reeds or grass its long neck, dangling legs, and general yellowish coloration are easily recognized. The juvenile Night Heron may seem similar but is never so decidedly yellow and the wing quills are not in such black contrast with the rest of the body. At a distance, in flight, its outline—head drawn in to the body and legs reaching out behind—is so similar to that of the herons that unless the light so falls as to show the colour, only apparent size differentiates them. Rapidity of wing beat is often a clue to difference in size when other bases of comparison are absent. A large bird can never beat its long wings as rapidly as a small one can. In spring, in mating display, the American Bittern shows a small bunch of pale yellow plumes springing from over the bend of the wing (Figure 106).

*Nesting.* On the ground, in grass, hayfields, or reed-grown marshes. Nest of grass or reeds.

*Distribution.* Across the continent: north to southern Labrador, southern Hudson Bay, Great Slave Lake, and southern Alaska, breeding wherever found.

References to the lonely booming of the bittern are frequent in English literature. We can hardly say that our American Bittern "booms," but its note is most peculiar and is unique amongst American bird notes. The common names, "Thunder-pump" and "Stake-driver," are applied in reference to the strange noises it makes. Near a marsh one may hear a sound as of some one driving a stake with a wooden maul into soft mud. There is the dull thud of the blow with a sucking liquid echo, followed closely by a squdgy drive. At other times sounds are heard like some one frantically working a dry suction-pump that draws the water part way and refuses to lift it farther. These are variants of the Bittern's love song and contain no recognizable vocal qualities.

*Economic Status.* The American Bittern is a bog haunter and eats frogs, crawfish, snakes, small fish, crustaceans, insects, and probably even young birds and mice. It eats little or no vegetable matter. Bitterns are quite harmless as a class and may be useful.

191. **Least Bittern.** LE PETIT BUTOR. *Ixobrychus exilis.* L, 13. Smallest heron-like wader found in Canada. Coloured in broad masses of creams, ochres, and Indian reds, with black or brown back and cap, depending on sex.

*Distinctions.* Owing to its small size and striking coloration can be mistaken for no other bird in Canada except perhaps its very close and rare relative, Cory's Least Bittern *Ixobrychus neozenus.* This latter bird has the creams and ochres replaced by seal or reddish brown and it is still undecided whether or not it is only a colour phase of the common form.

*Field Marks.* Small size and striking colours make the species unmistakable. Seldom seen except at close range when colour and size are evident.

*Nesting.* Generally over water, in nest on platform of dead rushes in a marsh or reed-patch.

*Distribution.* Eastern North America, regularly only just crossing our border in Ontario and Quebec. There are several records for Manitoba.

191. 1. **Cory's Least Bittern.** LE PETIT BUTOR DE CORY. *Ixobrychus neoxena.* L, 13. Like the previous species, but the whites and creams replaced by rich chestnut brown.

*Distinctions.* As above.

*Distribution.* Except for stray specimens, known only from southern Florida and Ashbridge Bay, Toronto. With the filling up of the latter locality the species may be extinct today. Individuals have been taken in various places in southern Ontario, Michigan, and a few other northern states of the middle west.

Figure 107
Least Bittern (male); scale, ½.

Cory's Least Bittern is not recognized in the Check-list as it is regarded as a colour phase of the previous species. As, however, practically every specimen that has been taken shows more or less intrusive white feathering and it is improbable that true melanism and albinism as distinct from dichromatism can exist coincidently in the same individual, it seems desirable to give the race full specific standing. The prevalence of albinism in the species suggests an impoverished race that is dying out through inherent weakness.

## SUBORDER—CICONIAE. STORKS, IBISES, ETC.

### SUPERFAMILY—CICONIOIDEA. STORKS AND WOOD IBISES

#### FAMILY—CICONIIDAE

188. **Wood Ibis.** LA CIGOGNE DES BOIS. *Mycteria americana.* L, 40. A large, heron-like bird, all white with black wings, with long, stout bill decurved near the tip, not grooved along upper mandible and very heavy at base (Figure 108). In adult, whole head and back of neck bare; in juvenile, those parts downy except in front of eyes and on forehead.

*Distinctions.* As above.

*Distribution.* Temperate and tropical America. We have record of only accidental occurrences in Canada—New Brunswick and southern Ontario.

Figure 108
Wood Ibis; scale, 1/6.

It is a mistake to call this species an "Ibis," it is much nearer the storks than the true ibises.

### SUPERFAMILY—THRESKIORNITHOIDEA. SPOON-BILLS AND IBISES

This group includes one family and two subfamilies: Spoonbills which do not occur in Canada, and *Threskiornithinae* only two of which occur in Canada, and those rarely.

#### Subfamily—Threskiornithinae. Ibises

Of this subfamily we have but two closely related species of only accidental occurrence in Canada.

*General Description.* Birds with long, decurved bill, quite blunt at the point and the upper mandible grooved throughout its length. Space in front of the eye bare (Figure 109).

*Distinctions.* Curved, blunt, and deeply grooved bill is characteristic. Claw of the middle toe may be broadened and roughened at the edge, but is not perfectly pectinate or furnished with well-formed, comb-like teeth as in the heron-like waders of the suborder *Herodii* (Compare with Figure 21, page 27).

### *Black Curlew*

186. **Common Glossy Ibis.** L'IBIS FALCINELLE COMMUNE. *Plegadis falcinellus.* L, 24. All dark brown or chestnut colour with many purple reflections and a long decurved bill, suggesting a dark-coloured curlew.

*Distinctions.* Generally eastern distribution. General resemblance to a curlew, but colour and bare space in front of eye quite distinctive. The resemblance to the White-faced Glossy Ibis is very close, it lacks the white bordering line to the bare forehead and facial patch and the legs and face are dull greenish instead of reddish. The two species are too far apart geographically to cause much confusion.

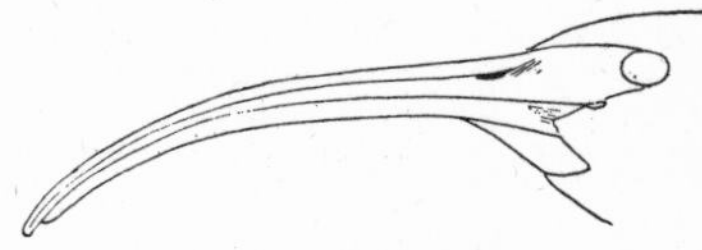

Figure 109
Bill of Glossy Ibis;
scale, 1/3.

*Distribution.* Tropical and subtropical regions, mainly eastern hemisphere. In North America, Florida and Louisiana. Of only accidental occurrence in Canada. We have individual records for Nova Scotia, Quebec, and southern Ontario.

187. **White-faced Glossy Ibis.** L'IBIS À FACE BLANCHE. *Plegadis guarauna.* L, 23. Adult: a dark chestnut bird with green and bronze reflections on back and wings. A long, decurved bill grooved along the upper mandible; a bare spot in front of eyes, coloured a dull red bordered with a band of white feathers. Legs reddish. Juvenile: dull greyish brown with green and steel blue reflections above; head and upper neck narrowly streaked with white.

*Distinctions.* Generally western distribution. A large, curlew-like bird with face bare in front of eyes with white border to bare facial area.

*Field Marks.* A large, curlew-like, or small heron-like, bird with decurved bill. Bright chestnut coloration with iridescence or appearing solid black; flight rapid and somewhat duck-like, but the neck carried outstretched.

*Nesting.* In reedy swamps or low bushes.

*Distribution.* Temperate and tropical America. On the west coast of South America to southern Oregon. Only two records in Canada, both from the southern coast of British Columbia.

## Order—Anseriformes. Lamellirostral Swimmers. Sieve-billed Swimmers

*General Description.* Swimming birds with four toes but only two webs, having bills with a hooked or flat nail at tip and furnished with tooth-like projections or thin laminæ on the sides (Figures 110, 111), through which they strain the water from their food.

Figure 110
Mergansers.

Figure 111
Surface feeding Ducks.

Bills of Sieve-billed Swimmers.

*Distinctions.* As above.

*Field Marks.* The outstretched neck, obvious tail, and rapid wing beats of the ducks, or the long, powerful wing strokes of the geese, are familiar to most of us. In the water some species bear superficial resemblance to the divers, but the straight, narrow bills of the divers, the obvious tails of the ducks, the general outline and carriage, and the readiness to fly instead of dive when disturbed, should make differentiation easy.

*Nesting.* Usually on the ground, sometimes in hollow trees, and only rarely in deserted nests of hawks or other large birds, but seldom far from water. The young are able to run about and take to water as soon as hatched, but how they are brought to the ground from a tree nest 20 or 30 or even 100 feet in the air is a subject upon which opinion is divided. Probably methods differ according to species and conditions.

*Distribution.* The *Anseriformes* are of world-wide distribution. In America the majority of the species breed north of our southern boundary. They may, therefore, be regarded as birds of northern distribution. In winter, the hardier species are likely to remain with us as long as open water continues and large numbers are to be found throughout the season on the waters of the west coast.

The order *Anseres* contains but one family—*Anatidae,* composed of the mergansers, ducks, geese, and swans. It comprises, therefore, the great bulk of the larger wild fowl pursued by sportsmen. One of the greatest sources of confusion in distinguishing the various species is the occurrence of what is called the "eclipse plumage." In midsummer the males of most species of ducks moult into a special body plumage, closely resembling that of the female, and known as the "eclipse plumage." It is retained for only a short time, giving way to the autumn plumage which is retained throughout the winter, and with wear and some renewal usually serves as the basis of the following spring or breeding regalia. While the eclipse plumage is carried the birds remain in the deepest recesses of the marshes or well out in the open water where no danger can approach unseen. So secretive are they at this time, that even in the best of duck grounds they are seldom seen, and specimens in this plumage are difficult to secure and rare in collections. Another peculiarity of the summer moulting of this order is that all the wing feathers are shed at once and the birds are flightless until the wings are grown again. Most other birds lose and replace the flight quills gradually, corresponding feathers being progressively dropped from each wing so that balance is not disturbed and the power of flight is never lost. However, it is a mistake to imagine that such wingless birds are helpless. Marsh-inhabiting ducks are expert hiders and can elude the eyes of most of their enemies, and those that betake themselves to open water at this time are such accomplished divers that they can evade most attacks that do not take them by surprise.

By the time the legitimate shooting season has opened most ducks are well pinioned again and almost in full winter plumage, but enough changing and unchanged birds remain to make a confusing number of obscure plumages that greatly complicate identification.[1]

In certain northern localities the more primitive Indians and Eskimos formerly took advantage of this flightless season to make regular organized drives, against which the bird's usual means of escape were useless, and numbers of "flappers" were taken and salted for winter use. Throughout the north the necessity for this is growing less, but there may still remain a few native communities where life is dependent upon such sources of food supply, of which they cannot be deprived without grim hardship unless some substitute is offered. However, although we must recognize this necessity at times in aboriginal inhabitants, it does not follow that strangers who enter such country for the purposes of personal gain or adventure should be allowed to rely on its scanty resources. Such adventurers should provide themselves beforehand against the known conditions of the country they are about to enter.

One of the most serious problems of the conservationist is the terrific mortality that occasionally overtakes large numbers of ducks on certain inland lakes. Much of the prairie water and some of the interior waters of British Columbia contain large amounts of various salts in solution. Such waters are colloquially called "alkaline," irrespective of the chemical nature of their impurities. Most of the sloughs and lakes are mere catch-basins without outlet and are in consequence dead water. Alkali is constantly being washed into them and the water-level is governed only by evaporation. The consequence is that the alkali content becomes concentrated. At the end of long, dry spells, many lakes of formerly large superficial area are represented by small pools of stingingly bitter water of complicated chemical content. Many of these waters become highly poisonous to certain species of ducks that flock to them from neighbouring drying sloughs and pools, and they perish by hundreds and are washed

[1] Another common source of confusion is the prevalence of a red rust coloration that often occurs on various parts of the head or body, and is common to many species of *Anseres*. It is due to an iron deposit from the water the birds inhabit and should be distinguished from normal plumage coloration.

up in windrows along the shores. The preliminary illness is not contagious and birds, if not too far gone, when given pure water make rapid recovery.[1] Another and similar disaster occasionally occurs. When, in a specially dry season, large slough areas dry up late in summer, we find them thronged with young ducks not yet able to fly, or with old ones in flightless moult. These, neither able to leave the locality nor to find food in it, also perish. No practical preventive has yet been proposed. Over a course of years many hundreds of thousands of birds have perished in this manner on the continent, for the condition is not peculiar to Canada.

There is an unexpected danger to large numbers of ducks lying latent in some of the most attractive ducking grounds. Marshes that have been shot over considerably contain large amounts of spent shot scattered over their beds. In sifting the mud ducks swallow the pellets with most serious effect. Shot can be swallowed by soft-stomached animals with impunity, but trituated in gravel-filled gizzards poisonous lead compounds are developed and absorbed. It has been demonstrated that four number four shot so ingested are fatal to a mallard, and to other species in proportion to their size. In the late winter of 1925 an important proportion of a specially protected flock of the rare and disappearing Trumpeter Swan in British Columbia perished from this cause. Of course the character of the bottom soil has much to do with this danger. In soft mud, shot rapidly sink below the reach of most ducks, but on hard, gravelly bottoms it may remain exposed for years and be a potential danger to any water-fowl that may feed upon the grounds.

Recently another serious situation threatened our eastern water birds. Many ducks and geese that frequent the Atlantic coast are almost entirely dependent on the great beds of eel grass for their winter food. Beginning in 1931 this eel grass has been progressively disappearing northward, due, apparently, to some bacterial infection there seems no way of combating. The effect, on the geese, and brant particularly, of the east coast and along their migrational highway, has been most disastrous and unless the eel grass becomes abundant very rapidly, or some unlooked for compensation is developed, these birds may shortly become extirpated over a large section of the east.

*Economic Status.* The *Anseriformes* form economically one of the most important orders of birds; not, as in the case with other birds, so much on account of their food habits—these being largely of negative influence in human affairs—as in other ways. In the early days of settlement of the country, ducks and geese furnished a most important food supply to the struggling inhabitants and even now the total number annually killed by sportsmen is an impressive addition to our food resources. Undoubtedly, the greatest usefulness of these birds is as a source of healthy, wholesome recreation, lending attraction to the outdoors and assisting in the upbuilding of a strong, virile race, familiar with field life and the use of firearms—qualities of no mean importance to any nation in time of need.

Of the great flocks of wild fowl that formerly frequented the marshes of the east, only a shadow remains. Those of the west, too, were fast becoming depleted, and to the older prairie residents the number of water-

---

[1] Recent investigation has shown that alkali poisoning is not the sole effect of these conditions. Accompanying them may be a form of bacterial infestation called bolulism that is deadly in its results and highly infectious in character. The disease, however, does not become epidemic as long as the water is pure and clean.

A. Baldpate; scale, $\frac{1}{6}$

Female Male

B. Pintail; scale, $\frac{1}{6}$

Male Female

A. Blue-winged Teal; scale, $\frac{1}{6}$ Green-winged Teal; scale, $\frac{1}{6}$

Female Male

Male Female

B. Shoveller; scale, $\frac{1}{6}$

Male Female

fowl today, though still the envy of the eastern sportsman, is sadly reduced. The causes of this are various, some unavoidable, though others may be controlled. Contrary to a very general impression, the great breeding stronghold of wild water-fowl is not a great, vague, far north, but on the lakes and sloughs of our prairies in the midst of what is now settled cultivation. We cannot expect that vast acreages can be brought under cultivation without some reduction of wild life, nor that the temptation of an easy food supply right at the door could always be resisted by the early settlers when meat was scarce, and game laws, if any, difficult of enforcement. The draining of sloughs and marshes has also progressively restricted the breeding and feeding area of many of these birds—a further word of caution in this direction is given under the heading of Franklin's Gull, page 229.

Even on grounds suitable only for grazing, the new conditions have seriously affected the breeding of various species. Cattle crop close around the margins of sloughs, and often the nests that escape the trampling of feeding herds are exposed to the eyes of natural enemies. Haying, when extended close to pools, although carried on too late in the season to disturb the current nestings, destroys the cover for early use next season. Leaving a belt of growth about the ponds is only a partial amélioration as it crowds the nesting life into narrow belts, conspicuous in the mown meadows and tilled fields, and makes an easy hunting ground for predacious crow, fox, coyote, cat, or dog. Among the natural enemies, undoubtedly the crow ranks high. Accounts indicate that these birds of ill repute have increased enormously since the first settlement of the country, and experience shows that under present conditions they work havoc with the eggs and young of all kinds of nesting birds. Of this, more will be said under crow, page 309.

But all these natural or indirectly human causes of the decrease of our ducks are probably unimportant in comparison with the direct effect of man in his spring shooting, wanton over-shooting, market-hunting, and general wasteful practices. Spring shooting is particularly pernicious as it takes the best of the breeding stock—the strongest and hardiest birds that have survived the dangers of a double migration, the severity of winter conditions, and are just ready to increase and multiply. To kill these birds is like drawing on the principal instead of the interest for current expenses. Previous to the conclusion of the Migratory Birds Convention Act with the United States each province and state had its own independent game laws. Some legal seasons were long, some were short, but on the average each was set to get the maximum toll from the passing flocks. In many cases the birds were never out of hearing of the guns that spread destruction among them from the time the season opened in the autumn on our prairies until the following breeding season. Our open seasons may have been but a scant two months, but many of the birds owing to their moving from one jurisdiction to another in their migratory flights suffered eight months or more of continuous lawful shooting. As long as each province or state through which the birds passed in their great annual journeys made its own game laws, with only the advantage of its own constituents in view, the general good was certain to suffer. The tendency of each community to shoot as long as there was anything to shoot and to make certain that each got as much as its neighbour, could be corrected only by a central control that had power to adjudicate between interests and apportion them according to the recuperative powers of the species affected. This was accomplished by the Migratory Birds Convention between the United States and Canada. By this treaty, for the first time, Canada has a voice in the formation of game laws in states outside her jurisdiction and is assured that protection to Canadian migrating game birds follows them south, and that we are not protecting birds solely for the benefit of foreigners.

The effect of the Act on wild fowl has been more beneficial than its most enthusiastic advocates had hoped. With the elimination of spring shooting and market-hunting, and with reasonable open seasons intelligently allotted to various localities over the whole continent, the rapid reduction of our wild fowl was momentarily stayed and the numbers even increased. If no additional factor had arisen we might feel confident that the problem of using our migratory game, without depletion, had been solved. The effect of the Migratory Bird Convention has been importantly beneficial; whether it is sufficient under the cumulative effect of the various adverse agencies acting today there is cause to doubt, unless greater self denial on the part of our shooters becomes more evident than it has been in the past.

One other important question remains to be solved, that of shooting grounds for the general public. It matters little to the ordinary man whether we have many or few game birds if the best shooting grounds are in the hands of private individuals and clubs. As Canadians we do not take kindly to private preserves and privileged classes. Already, large, suitable areas have been set aside from the government lands for reserves, where birds may breed undisturbed by cattle or by haymaking and other human activities. These reserves will tend to scatter their surplus life about the surrounding country and offer sport beyond their confines. Some of them may, under proper regulation, furnish suitable shooting grounds for the general public in localities where many such spots are already under private control and open to none but a privileged few. Just how far it is possible to proceed along these lines will depend altogether on the attitude of the interested public.

The grain-eating proclivities of some ducks is a factor that cannot be quite overlooked. It seems hardly believable to experienced eastern shooters that wild ducks can occur in such numbers as to be seriously detrimental to agriculture. In some parts of the Prairie Provinces, where large numbers of some species—mostly Mallards—concentrate in the early autumn, the cost of their support in some cases falls heavily upon the fields they frequent. Geese are occasionally as bad, cropping the newly sprouting grain to such an extent as to make replanting necessary and thus cause the loss of valuable growing time. Complaints of this kind are naturally often selfishly exaggerated, but there is enough truth in them to warrant serious consideration. When the duck season opens the remedy is obvious, but if closed there is occasionally a race between the harvesters and the ducks as to who will get the most grain from certain fields. It is not always the grain actually consumed that is in question, but the trampled condition of the straw may prevent proper harvesting. It is said that in spring when the grain is well rooted geese bite off only the tender tops without disturbing the roots, and thus encourage a stronger growth of the plants, which is an advantage rather than a detriment. When the ground is soaked and soft the roots may come up with the tops and cause real loss to the farmers. Though the Migratory Birds Convention Act provides for just such cases, it requires the nicest discrimination to recognize legitimate complaints and to furnish necessary relief in time to be effective. This is one of the problems of game protection that can be solved satisfactorily only with the honest and sincere co-operation of all concerned. Local sentiment among neighbours who personally know specific conditions can do more to secure quick action in such matters than any amount of official investigation that would otherwise be necessary.

A peculiar condition affecting ducks occurs on the northern Pacific coasts. The immense number of salmon that frequent the western streams differ in habit from the eastern fish in that they spawn but once in their lives. After working upstream they spawn and die, and are washed ashore in windrows to pollute the atmosphere or sink to the bottom where, in slack-water pools, they lie in decaying masses. Many of our otherwise most palatable and elsewhere eagerly prized ducks feed upon this disgusting offal—and on salmon eggs—to such an extent as to become unfit for human consumption and even offensive to handle. Local conditions and the food they have been subsisting upon are important factors in deciding the palatability of different ducks. In the east a wild duck is a wild duck and even mergansers and coarse, heavy scoters are sought for eagerly in some localities. Undoubtedly a shortage of numbers limits the choice and renders the consumer less critical. Wild-celery fed Canvas-back is the synonym for high-living in the east, whereas on the prairies grain-fed mallard takes first place in the estimation of epicures, and such birds as whistlers (Golden-eyes) and bluebills (Scaup Ducks) are often looked upon as next to worthless. In the interior of British Columbia, other standards of excellence exist, and on the coast the edibility of wild fowl is strictly limited both by species and season because of the fish-eating habits just described.

## FAMILY—ANATIDAE. SWANS, GEESE, AND DUCKS

### Subfamily—Cygninæ. Swans

*General Description.* Very large, white water-fowl. Excepting perhaps the Whooping Crane or the Wild Turkey, the largest of American birds.

*Distinctions.* Size combined with colour is sufficient to diagnose the two American swans. Lores (space between eye and bill) unfeathered. Bill begins high on the forehead, at base is almost rectangular in cross-section, and the tip is provided with a flat nail (Figure 113).

*Field Marks.* Size and colour; our only very large, *all* white bird.[1] Swans fly with neck outstretched like cranes but do not trail long legs behind. The only other large white bird comparable in flight is the White Pelican which has black wings and flies with its head drawn into its shoulders. (Compare Figure 112 with 91 and 239.)

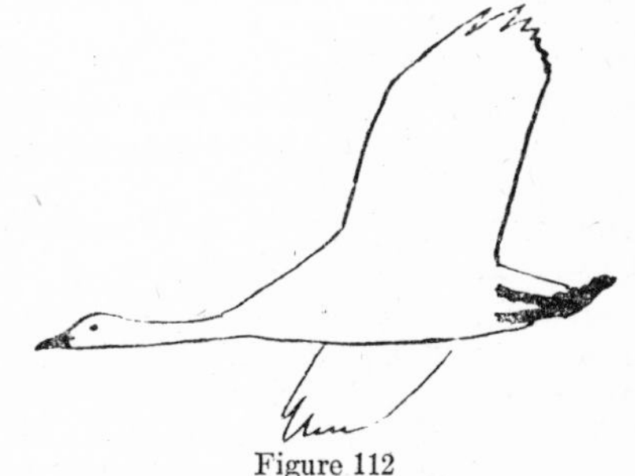

Figure 112
Appearance of Swan in flight.

*Nesting.* On the ground, nest of grasses lined with down plucked from parent bird.

*Distribution.* Most of the swans are found in the northern hemisphere, but are not entirely confined to it. In America, one species nests only in the far north, but what remains of the other and rarer one nests south near, and across, our southern border.

[1] Other large white birds occurring in Canada (except a possible Egret, Glaucous Gull in adult plumage, and some Snowy Owls) have more or less black on the flight feathers.

From time immemorial swans have figured largely in Old World folk-lore and the fairy tales of childhood are filled with references to them, but it comes with a little shock of surprise to many people to learn that even today wild swans are actually common in Canada. Geese are wild and wary, but a swan is even wilder and more wary. Its long neck allows it to feed in deeper water than other non-diving species and through the day it keeps well out from shore, where unobserved approach is impossible. It rarely comes into the shallow marshes that may hide the huntsman and, therefore, it is rarely taken.

The common names of the swans of the northern hemisphere are indicative of their vocal powers; thus in America we have the Whistling and the Trumpeter, and in Europe the Whooping and the Mute Swans. Peculiar and complicated modifications of the windpipe (Figures 114 and 115), in the form of various convolutions in special bony recesses of the breast bone or sternum, are evidently directly connected with the voice and their complexity increases directly with the quality of the voice as indicated by the above descriptive names; thus the Mute Swan is without any tracheal convolution and the highest complexity is reached in the Trumpeter and Whooping. All swans receive absolute protection under the Migratory Birds Convention Act and cannot be taken legally anywhere in the United States or Canada.

180. **Whistling Swan.** LE CYGNE SIFFLEUR. *Cygnus columbianus.* L, 52. A very large, white bird without any other colour in plumage, except in juvenility when there are fleckings and cloudings of light, ashy grey, especially about the head; or at any age red rust stains may be present on the crown and cheeks. Legs, feet, and bill black. Most adults have a small yellow or orange spot (pink-flesh coloured in juvenility) on the bare skin in front of the eye. (*See* shaded spot, Figure 113.)

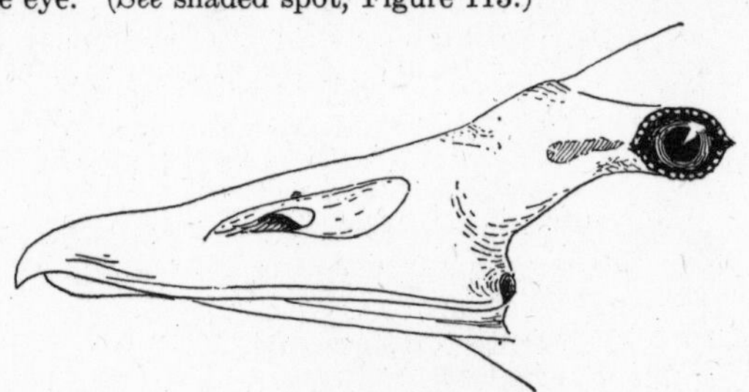

Figure 113
Bill of Whistling Swan; scale, ½.

*Distinctions.* Because of its large size and entire whiteness it may be mistaken only for the Trumpeter Swan, but the Whistling is much the smaller. Its weight goes up to 18 pounds and that of the Trumpeter is given as high as 36. Any swan under 55 inches long with wing under 23 inches and weight (unless emaciated) less than 20 pounds is probably a Whistling. The bill characters usually given as diagnostic are unreliable. The position of the nostril is not determinative. The presence of a yellow spot in front of the eye is characteristic of the Whistling, but its absence in that species is quite common. The only positive character for the separation of these species, except size and voice, is the sternum or breast bone. In both these swans the windpipe as it comes down from the neck enters the end of the keel bone, which is thickened into a deep, flat tube for the purpose, proceeds to the rear end of the sternum, and there, upon the bony floor, forms a broad, horizontal loop and returns and leaves the sternum on its way to the lungs through the same opening by which it entered. In this species this return is made directly without other decided flexure (Figure 114). In the Trumpeter Swan another loop is made, rising in a perpendicular hump just before the windpipe emerges from the sternum (Figure 115). The development of this convolution is progressive with age. In very young autumn birds a loop of the windpipe barely enters the sternum. A little later in life it penetrates farther and makes a sharp, angular return about half-way back to the sternum. At maturity the loop extends to the rear of the sternum and widens with age until it occupies the whole rear end of the sternum floor and even overhangs it, making a loop 3½ inches or more across.

*Field Marks.* As a swan, by size and complete whiteness. In flight, swans carry their long necks outstretched like cranes (Figure 112, compare with 239), but do not thrust out long legs behind. The presence of a yellow spot in front of the eye is indicative of this species, but its absence is of little import. The best means of separation from the Trumpeter in life is probably the voice, that of the Trumpeter being considerably deeper, more sonorous, and of a totally different quality. Recognition of this, however, requires familiarity with the voices of both species.

*Nesting.* On the ground, nest of grasses, moss, etc., lined with down.

*Distribution.* Breeds on the Arctic coast and islands west of Hudson Bay. During migration passes through the interior of the continent, rare on the coasts.

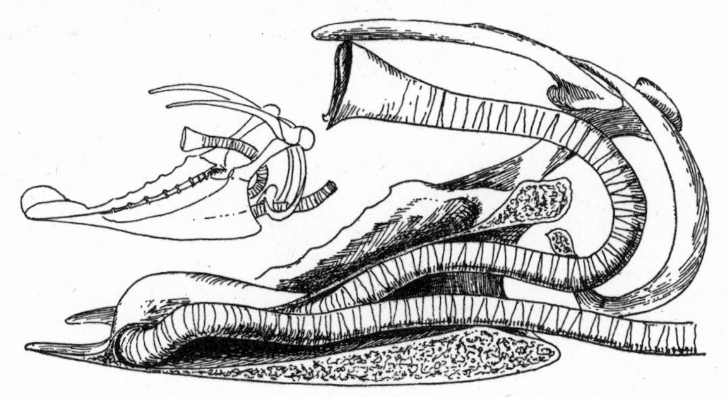

Figure 114
Longitudinal section through sternum of Whistling Swan; scale, ½.

Owing to its extreme wariness and its breeding far in the north the Whistling Swan has not been seriously reduced in numbers during the past generation. Its larger relative, the Trumpeter, whose breeding grounds, within the borders of settlement, were early disturbed, is now on the verge of extinction. Because of the great difficulty of telling the two swans apart, the Migratory Birds Convention Act has declared a close season in both of them, in an attempt to save the last few Trumpeter Swans from extermination.

Swans rarely come into shallow marshes where cover may hide the sportsman. They are seldom seen except in dense white masses, like ice floes, far out in the open water, or in flocks flying high overhead and beyond the reach of guns. Their regular migration is generally by night and usually silent, though sometimes extremely noisy. To such habits as these is probably due the fact that few, even of our most experienced sportsmen, know the swan in life, and fewer still can boast of having taken it. Though flocks of hundreds appeared annually on Lake St. Clair not more than two or three individuals were taken there each year before the continuous closed season was declared.

The species also occurs in large numbers on Niagara River where on misty or foggy nights in the spring they often drift down with the current into the swift, rough waters of the rapids and are carried helplessly over the falls. This catastrophe has occurred several times within the last decade and hundreds of swans have lost their lives in this manner; some have every bone in the body broken, whereas others are only slightly hurt. As the birds do not seem able without great difficulty in the close quarters to rise above the sides of the gorge, and show marked reluctance to pass beneath the bridges that span the lower pass, all are confined in the narrow waters below the falls where there is no escape. The flesh of the swan is not usually very suitable for eating and the birds are of little value to those who take them except as curiosities.

181. **Trumpeter Swan.** LE CYGNE TROMPETTE. *Cygnus buccinator.* L, 65. A very large, white bird, like the Whistling Swan but larger and never with a yellow or orange spot in front of the eye.

*Distinctions.* Because of its large size and entire whiteness, may be mistaken only for the Whistling Swan. This is considerably the larger of the two swans. Its weight is given as high as 36 pounds; the Whistling seldom goes over 18. Any swan over 55

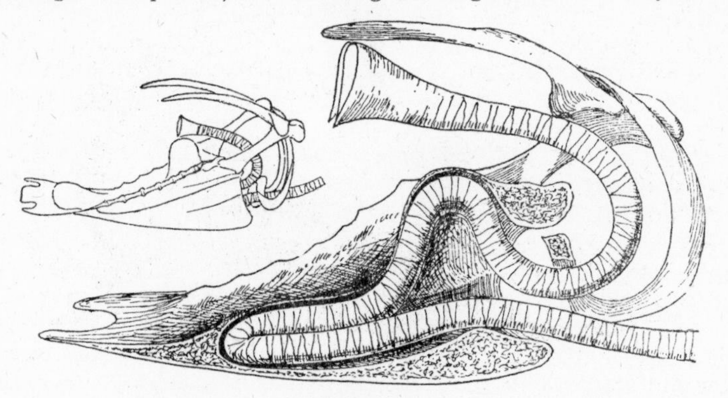

Figure 115
Longitudinal section through sternum of Trumpeter Swan; scale, ½.

inches long, with a wing over 23 and weight above 20 pounds, is probably a Trumpeter. The bill characters usually given as distinctive are unreliable. The position of the nostril is not determinative. The Trumpeter, unlike the Whistling, never has a yellow spot in front of the eye, but its absence is not necessarily diagnostic. The only positive character for the separation of these species, except size, is the sternum or breast bone. In both these swans the windpipe as it comes down from the neck enters the end of the keel bone, which is thickened into a deep, flat tube for the purpose, proceeds to the rear end of the sternum, and there, upon the bony floor, forms a broad horizontal loop, returns, and forms another loop, rising perpendicularly in a hump just before it passes out of the sternum on its way to the lungs, by way of the same opening through which it entered. In the Whistling Swan this final loop is missing (Compare Figures 115 and 114). The development of this labyrinth is progressive with age and undoubtedly follows much the same progress as in the Whistling Swan. A bird known to be 18 months old had a perpendicular loop raised 1·8 inches above the sternum floor, but the horizontal loop showed an angular return without broad loop, quite similar in development to a Whistling of the same age. It is doubtful, however, if the species ever gets quite as broad an horizontal loop as do very old birds of the Whistling. The fact that the perpendicular loop develops more rapidly than the horizontal one renders identification of young birds by these characters easy.

*Field Marks.* Size and complete whiteness. In flight, swans carry their long necks outstretched like cranes, but do not trail long legs behind (Figure 112, compare with 239). The best separation of the Trumpeter from the Whistling in life is probably the voice. That of this species is considerably deeper and more sonorous. This distinction, however, is recognizable only by those familiar with both species.

*Nesting.* On the ground, nest of grass, moss, etc., lined with down.

*Distribution.* A bird of the interior, breeding northward from the northern boundary of the United States, west of the Great Lakes. Apparently originally common as a migrant in southern Ontario, now never seen there and approaching extinction elsewhere.

The Trumpeter was at one time a fairly common migrant in the Great Lakes section and a regular nester throughout the prairies and British Columbia. Now, only a few small flocks and individual pairs are known in British Columbia, Alberta, and in the Yellowstone National Park, Wyoming. The causes of its nearly complete disappearance were various. It nested in what is now well-inhabited country and it is very difficult to retain such a spectacular bird in communities that are much shot over. Swans are not prolific and once their number is reduced it takes several generations of undisturbed peace to restore them. They are not nearly so wild nor so difficult to kill as the still common Whistling Swan. The latter migrates in great flocks that pitch out in the middle of the larger waters, rarely coming inshore except at night, or when it is perfectly certain that there is no danger. In spite of their great numbers, very few Whistling Swans are shot. The Trumpeter, on the other hand, travels in smaller companies, often family groups, coasts the shore more frequently, often passing the hunter's blind. This difference in habit may have been a determining factor in the disappearance of this bird over most of its range, where the Whistling Swan has survived. In the early days, the Hudson's Bay Company did a very large trade in swan's breast skins; the Trumpeter, being the larger and more valuable bird and more easily killed, was probably cleared from its more northern ranges at an early date.

At present strenuous efforts are being made to preserve the last remaining individuals of this beautiful species. Attempts have been made to make reserves of waters they frequent, but they refuse to stay in narrow but safe confines and their numbers are still diminishing. Unfortunately, only the stations at the winter end of the migratory range can be reserved, the other end is scattered and difficult to protect from occasional intruders. A single visit of an irresponsible white or Indian may occur at any time on the loneliest lakes of the northland and destroy a small community, and it has now come to the point where every pair counts. Naturally, under these conditions, exact information as to the localities these birds frequent has been kept confidential, but it is also necessary that no information of this kind should be lost. All who know of a new station for these birds are urged to communicate with the officials responsible for their protection, not only to assist them in the present but that the data may be preserved until such time as it is safe to publish it more widely.

### Subfamily—Anserinae. Geese

*General Description.* Geese resemble ducks, but are larger with a less flattened body and comparatively longer legs; bill (Figures 120, 121, 123) is higher and generally somewhat narrower at base, stouter and less flattened at tip, hardly to be termed spatulate but with the broad nail at tip characteristic of the order. The tarsi of geese are reticulate, that is, covered with small, roughly six-sided, mosaic-like plates (Figures 116b) instead of scutellate, with broad, overlapping scales (as in the ducks, *See* Figures 125, page 87, and 164, page 109).

*Field Marks.* The strong flight of the geese is familiar to most people. Size, coloration, and flight habits are the best field guides. All the dark-coloured geese in flying straight away from the observer show a conspicuous white V on the rump, the apex behind.

*Nesting.* Generally on the ground.

*Distribution.* Geese are of world-wide distribution. All American species but one breed well to the north, migrating through the interior as well as along the coasts.

Figure 116a
Comparative sizes and colorations of the various subspecies of Canada Goose.

The geese are more terrestrial and herbivorous than the ducks, but they are equally at home on the water. They do not normally dive, but secure food from the bottom by tipping and, by means of their long necks, reach considerable depths. The sexes are alike and there is little seasonal change of plumage. Geese are excellent table-birds and for this reason and on account of their superior size they are much sought after by sportsmen. Geese are exceedingly wary and although they take better care to avoid danger than many other large game birds, their former numbers have been greatly reduced.

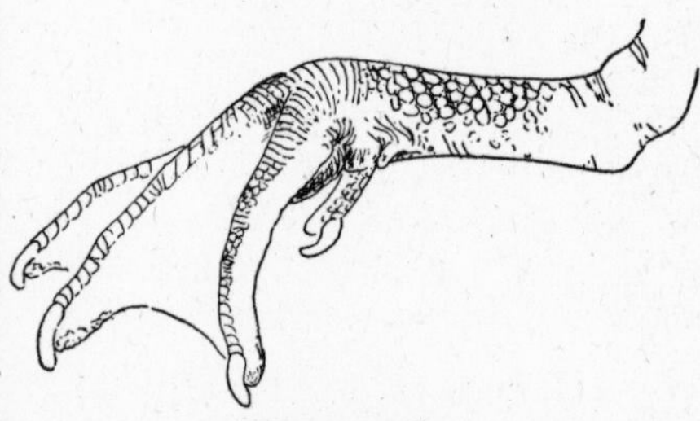

Figure 116b
Reticulate tarsus of goose.

172. **Canada Goose.** HONKER. GREY GOOSE. CALLING GOOSE. L'OUTARDE CANADIENNE. *Branta canadensis.* L, 23-39. Plate IV B. A grey-brown goose, usually lighter below, somewhat wave-marked with lighter feather edges. Head and neck black with white cheek patches. In size it is variable and may be as small as a large mallard weighing less than 4 pounds, whereas the record for size is 18 pounds. Underparts may be nearly white or as dark as the back. The cheek spots may or may not be joined together under the chin and there may be a narrow white collar at the base of the black neck or "stocking." There is very little difference in plumage with sex or age.

*Distinctions.* This highly variable species may always be recognized by its black head and neck, the so-called stocking, which stops abruptly at the shoulders, and the conspicuous white cheek patches. It can be confused with no other species at present recognized.

*Field Marks.* The black stocking, white cheek patches, and the sonorous and well-known honk are the best of field marks.

*Nesting.* On the ground in the grass, on hummocks and elevations like old hay-cocks, or occasionally in hawk's deserted nests in the tops of tall trees.

A. Wood Duck; scale, $\frac{1}{6}$

Female Male

B. Canvas-back; scale, $\frac{1}{6}$

Male Female

PLATE X

A. Lesser Scaup Duck; scale, $\frac{1}{6}$

Male Female

B. Common Golden-eye; scale, $\frac{1}{6}$ Barrow's Golden-eye; scale $\frac{1}{6}$

Female Male Male

*Distribution.* Across the continent, migrating commonly everywhere in the interior and on the coast. Breeding in the east from the north shore of the Gulf of St. Lawrence and in the west from south of our boundary, indefinitely northward.

*SUBSPECIES.* Although a very well known bird to the sportsman and the general public, few species have been so little understood by either ornithologist or layman. It has considerable individual as well as geographic variations, which have to be carefully distinguished if sound conclusions as to racial affinities are to be arrived at.

Various slight colour differences between individuals are evident. The cheek patches may or may not meet across the throat and there may be a more or less complete white collar around the neck at the bottom of the black stocking. These variations may occur in any form, but seem rather more common in birds of the west than of the east. The only colour distinction that seems to have connexion with distribution is the depth of colour of the underparts. Eastern and interior birds have light fawn or almost cream-coloured breasts and abdomen. Those of the west coast are likely to be deep mouse colour. This seems to be the most distinctive character of the White-cheeked or Western Goose and the Cackling Goose, the only ones that are appreciably differentiated by colour. This dark coloration seems to have been transferred to west coast Lesser Geese through interbreeding with the dark-breasted forms. Based on these characters and upon size, several subspecies have been generally recognized, but it was not until the rediscovery of a very small race from Hudson Bay that a hitherto unrecognized or rather a forgotten race was introduced into the series, which demonstrated that the old name *hutchinsi* (Hutchin's Goose) had been consistently misapplied for many years. The Canada Goose seems to stand about as follows:

### *Common Canada Goose.* GRAY GOOSE. HONKER. L'OUTARDE CANADIENNE COMMUNE

*Branta canadensis canadensis.* The largest of the American geese, weighing up to 12 to 14 pounds or even more. Wing, 15·70 to 20. Bill, 1·9 to 2·3 (Figure 117a). The black stocking is long and extends down to the base of the neck, in the Lesser it is shorter. The Honker is perhaps best recognized by its deep, sonorous voice. Its range extends

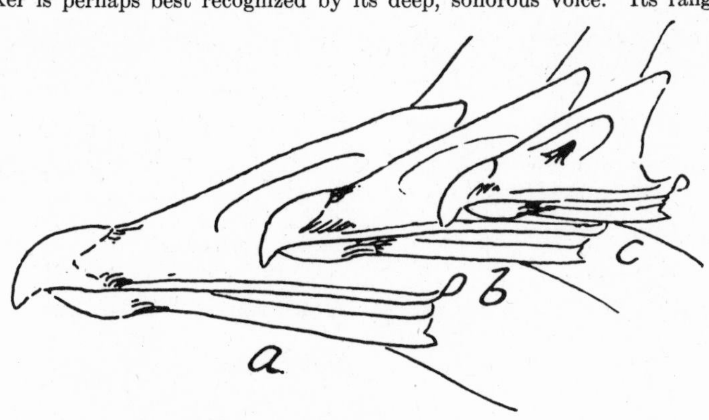


Figure 117

Typical bills of the various forms of Canada Goose:
*a*, Honker and Western Geese.
*b*, Lesser Canada Goose.
*c*, Cackling and Richardson's Geese.
Natural size.

across the continent, from coast to coast. East of the Great Lakes there is no present indication of regular breeding south of Newfoundland, north shore of the Gulf of St. Lawrence, and the vicinity of James Bay, but the Honker nests north to Baffin Island. West of the Great Lakes the breeding range is from well south of the International Boundary northward indefinitely to where it is replaced as a breeding bird by the Lesser Canada Goose (known hitherto as "Hutchin's Goose"). It is the bird of all British Columbia, except the north coastal area where it is replaced by the White-cheeked or Western Goose. It meets with the Lesser Canada Goose somewhere in the Yukon.

This is one of the most highly prized game birds of western Canada. It is the wisest and wariest of birds and the goose hunter has need of all his wiles in its pursuit.

### *Western Canada Goose.* WHITE-CHEEKED GOOSE. L'OUTARDE CANADIENNE DE L'OUEST

*Branta canadensis occidentalis.* As large as the Honker (bill, Figure 117a). Originally described from a more or less abnormal bird and was supposed to be distinguished by a white collar at base of stocking and the intrusion of the black throat between the cheek patches. These characteristics, however, are found to be of casual occurrence in the other forms, though more common in western than in eastern birds, the term white-cheeked is no more applicable to it than to any other race of the species, and the only distinguishing characteristic it seems to have is its large size together with very dark, mouse-coloured underparts. The damp west coast has a tendency to develop heavy, dark colours in its birds. This darkening in colour does not occur in so marked a degree in geese away from the coast. The Western Canada Goose breeds along the coast from Queen Charlotte Islands (perhaps from Vancouver Island) to Prince William Sound, Alaska. Along the British Columbia coast we find the greatest mixtures of plumage among the migrant geese. Four Canada goose races occur here in varying degrees of characterization and specimens occur that may be referred to two or more subspecies without decided leaning towards any one in particular.

### *Lesser Canada Goose.* CALLING GOOSE. SHORT-NECKED GOOSE. L'OUTARDE CANADIENNE MINEURE

There are numerous other names of local usage. This was formerly Hutchin's Goose, but lately it has been discovered that it has no title to that name.

*Branta canadensis leucopareia.* Wing, 13·15 to 17·25. Bill, 1·25 to 1·7 (Figure 117b). Next in size to the Honker, the same colour with the exception of perhaps a shorter black stocking. In life, it is best distinguished, probably, by its voice which is higher and sharper, and experienced shooters can recognize it at great distances. In the interior of British Columbia and on the prairies it is likely to be confused only with the Honker. It does not associate regularly with its big relative, neither will the latter decoy well to captive Lesser Canada Geese. This may be merely a demonstration of the clannish nature of the species, but it is suggestive of the idea that the apparently slight difference between them may be more fundamental than would be gathered from an examination of specimens. The Lesser Canada Goose breeds west of Hudson Bay on the barren grounds indefinitely northward, and migrates down the west coast and through the interior west of the Great Lakes. On the west coast it may intergrade with the Cackling Goose and the Western as well as the Honker, and many puzzling specimens may be taken there.

The Lesser Canada Goose is the common goose in the hunting season on the prairies, and takes second place only to the Honker, the larger size of which gives it the preference.

### *Richardson's Goose* (*Hutchin's Goose* of the 1931 Check-List). L'OUTARDE CANADIENNE DE RICHARDSON

*Branta canadensis hutchinsi.* A very small goose. In migration, in Canada, practically confined to Manitoba. It was discovered in 1831, in Hudson Bay, but has for many years been disregarded and its name applied to an entirely different bird, which, on the facts becoming evident, must now be known as the Lesser Canada Goose. Unfortunately the Committee on Nomenclature in the last Check-List of North American Birds saw fit to transfer the vernacular name Hutchin's with the scientific *hutchinsi* to this newly rediscovered form. This gives that name a meaning quite different from that associated with it for many years. This will inevitably cause confusion that might have been avoided if the name "Hutchin's" had been dropped for this newly rediscovered form and "Richardson's," in memory of its original describer, had been used instead. It must clearly be borne in mind that from now on the name Hutchin's Goose as applied by the Check-list refers to a bird entirely different from that which it has designated in the past.

A very small Canada Goose, by some regarded as an entirely distinct species. Wing 15 or under. Bill 1·35 or less (Figure 117c). Scarcely larger than a big Mallard duck, but coloured identically with the Honker or the Lesser Canada Goose. In size, like the Cackling Goose of the extreme west, but breast and underparts light and not mouse coloured. Breeding on the islands at the mouth of Hudson Bay and migrating in limited numbers through Manitoba. Of only casual occurrence east or west of that province.

### *Cackling Goose.* L'OUTARDE CANADIENNE MINIME

*Branta canadensis minima.* The smallest of the Canada Geese, by some regarded as an entirely distinct species, at times scarcely larger than a large Mallard: wing, 13·27 to 16·60; bill, 1·01 to 1·44 (Figure 117c). In colour like the preceding, but usually with dark mouse-coloured underparts. The most distinctive character, however, seems to be that the tarsus is slightly longer than the middle toe and claw. The voice is still higher and sharper than that of the Lesser Canada Goose, of a quality that has suggested the name "Cackling" and the local name of "Squealer" in California. The Cackling Goose is a west-coast bird. Its breeding range is not very well known, but thought to be in western Alaska near the Bering seacoast. It migrates mostly down the coast, but also in smaller numbers through the interior west of the coast ranges, and winters south of British Columbia.

The Canada Goose as a species is a watchful and a wary bird, usually spending the day well out on open water or in marshes, coming in at night to feed on the fields and stubble. While so engaged, there is always one long neck upstretched to survey the surroundings, and unobserved approach by the most expert stalker is next to impossible. On this account it has probably suffered less from hunters than some other members of its family, although its original numbers have been reduced. So long as its remaining breeding grounds in the far north remain uninvaded, and it is not seriously disturbed in its southern winter feeding stations, there is little danger of its extermination. In spite of this satisfactory condition of the species as a whole, the existence of the most desirable and interesting form of all, the Honker, is threatened, especially in the west.[1] This fine bird, breeding on the prairies in the midst of cultivation, is particularly exposed to the destructive influence of civilization and at the present rate of decrease it will be but a few years before we will speak of it as a prairie breeder in the past tense only. How far north these conditions will eventually extend there is no way to foretell, but the increase of populated areas in the Dominion probably means the eventual local extirpation of this species. Until we have a resident population that will permit such a fine bird as this to live, nest, and raise its young in unmolested proximity, the future of the Honker on the prairies is far from secure.

Even though it survives in the uninhabited north and still comes south to furnish its quota of sport, its disappearance as a resident in the settled communities would be a serious æsthetic and economic loss. It is a noble bird, a point of interest in any landscape. No one fails to thrill at sight of its long, V-shaped flocks flying overhead, or at the sound of its wild, barbaric music coming down through the twilight. Domestically, the Canada Goose is a model for man. Unlike ducks which mate for the season and then part, usually for ever, geese generally mate for life, mourn a lost mate, and are not easily comforted. Both sexes assist in the responsibilities

[1] For what seems at writing (1933) to be a serious condition for the species in the East *See* page 70.

of family life and if necessary share the supreme sacrifice in its behalf. We speak of the goose as the personification of foolishness, but the Canada Goose is one of the most intelligent and wiliest of birds and exhibits occasional bits of strategy that are astonishing.

What can be done to make these evidences of sagacity and devotion familiar to us all has been shown by Jack Miner, who has induced so suspicious a bird to come close about his house, inspired it with such confidence that it becomes as poultry about the back door, yet loses none of its wild ways or independence. Even more remarkable, he has overcome one of its strongest instincts, that of migration, and has induced it to winter far north of its natural wintering ground. If he can do this by means of simple protection and a little food, there is surely no reason, except our own indifference, for losing this magnificent bird from the prairies. Local sentiment can do more to apply practically Jack Miner's spectacular methods than can any law that may be passed, or enforced when enacted.

One of the great enemies of the geese is the automobile. On the prairie's level roads intersecting everywhere, and even with crosscuts across country possible, its untiring wheels follow the weary feeding flocks from pitch to pitch until, unrefreshed and hopeless of rest, they hurry off on their migratory way, refusing to tarry in the neighbourhood where they are so mercilessly harried. Nor are the results more satisfactory to the pursurers, as very few birds are taken in this way, and the survivors are so restless and uneasy that legitimate sport is spoiled for others. Without the development of a more sportsman-like spirit in the shooting public, it seems difficult or impossible to control this evil without laws more drastically curtailing our liberties than it seems possible or expedient to enforce.

173. **Common Brant.** LA BERNACHE COMMUNE. *Branta bernicla.* L, 26. Plate V A. A small, greyish brown goose, paler below, with a black head, neck, and upper breast interrupted only by a partly broken, narrow, white collar on the upper neck.

*Distinctions.* The black head without white face spots of any kind is characteristic of the Brant. Unfortunately, the term "Brant" has been applied throughout the Prairie Provinces to the White-fronted Goose, which is an inexcusable misuse of the name. On the Pacific coast and in the interior of British Columbia the term "Brant" is also misapplied to Lesser Canada and Cackling Geese.

*Field Marks.* A small, dark, or nearly black, goose with white V over the tail when flying, but without white face marks. Only to be expected on salt water.

*Nesting.* On the ground of the tundras.

*Distribution.* The northern hemisphere. In America, breeding across the Arctic coast and islands and migrating down both seacoasts. It appears inland or on fresh water only as a rare straggler. One record for Manitoba and occasional stragglers on the lower Great Lakes are the only authenticated occurrences in Canada away from the immediate vicinity of the sea.

*SUBSPECIES.* Two New World races are separated from that of the Old, as—The White-bellied Brant (la Bernache à ventre blanc) *Branta bernicla hrota* and the Black Brant (la Bernache commune noire) *Branta bernicla nigricans*, the latter being given full specific standing in the 1931 Check-list. The White-bellied Brant is identified by the underbody being light grey, sharply contrasting with the black breast. It is particularly an eastern bird migrating along the Atlantic coast and the Gulf of St. Lawrence. Occasional specimens and intermediates occur on the west coast. The Black Brant has a dark underbody blending imperceptibly into the black breast without sharp division. It is entirely a west coast species. The two breed in the high Arctics, meeting in the neighbourhood of Melville Island. Winters from New Jersey to the Carolinas and Vancouver to Lower California.

175. **Barnacle Goose.** LA BERNACHE NONNETTE. *Branta leucopsis.* L, 26. A medium-sized goose with a black neck and breast sharply defined against a light grey underbody and flank, and white forehead as well as white cheek and throat patches.

Figure 118
Barnacle Goose; scale, ¼.

*Distinctions.* Neck and breast solidly black, sharply defined against lighter underbody like the White-bellied Brant. Head black with prominent white cheek patches joined across the throat like the Canada Goose, but with extensive white forehead, leaving only a narrow black line from base of bill through eye.

*Field Marks.* Like a Brant, but with much white on face and forehead.

*Distribution.* Old World to northeastern Greenland. Casual in the eastern Arctics and the American Atlantic coast.

176. **Emperor Goose.** PAINTED GOOSE. L'OIE IMPÉRIALE. *Philacte canagica.* L, 26. A beautifully coloured goose of medium size. The head is white, with throat and foreneck of black fading into the breast. Whole body light slate grey, each feather of back, flanks, and breast with an edge of white and a subterminal band of black, giving a conspicuous effect of coarse scales or the appearance of a pale grey bird sharply barred all around with lines of black and white. The bill and feet are yellow. Juveniles and adults are similar.

*Distinctions.* The white head and neck, black throat, and light grey body with black and white scale marks are absolutely distinctive.

*Field Marks.* The general coloration should be distinctive at long distances.

*Nesting.* On the ground, on flat, marshy islets bordering the sea.

*Distribution.* Breeds locally on Bering seacoasts of Alaska and Siberia. Winters in north Pacific south to Sitka. A few records for southern British Columbia.

Figure 119
Emperor Goose; scale, ¼.

171. **White-fronted Goose.** SPECKLED-BELLY. L'OIE À FRONT BLANC. *Anser albifrons.* L, 27. Plate V B. A medium-sized goose, greyish brown, with a white patch at base of bill and speckled or irregularly black-spotted underparts.

*Distinctions.* The greyish brown body, brown head and neck, white forehead and bill patch, irregularly pied underparts, and yellow legs and feet make very distinctive characters for the adult. The juvenile is similar only to the young of the much rarer Blue Goose, but has yellow instead of pink feet and lacks the broad grinning patch characteristic of that species and the Snow Goose (Figure 120, compare with 121). The irregular blotching of black on the underparts may be almost or quite absent on young birds, but traces at least of the white face mark appear in most autumn birds.

*Field Marks.* A dark goose. Neck evenly brown with the body; without the cheek marks of the Canada Goose, but with a white patch surrounding the base of the bill. Legs yellow or orange. These marks can be seen on the adult at long range. The young bird when the usual white face patch is inconspicuous may be confused only with the juvenile Blue Goose which, except in special localities, is too rare to be often considered.

*Nesting.* On the ground of the tundra.

*Distribution.* The northern hemisphere. In the New World, central and western North America; breeding on the Arctic coast and islands and migrating through the prairies and along the west coast. Rarer in the interior of British Columbia. There are casual records for the lower Great Lakes and St. Lawrence River.

*SUBSPECIES.* The American White-fronted Goose *Anser albif ons gambeli* has been supposed to be the representative New World form of the species. Lately, however, it has been demonstrated that two forms of White-fronted Goose occur in America, and that *gambeli* is much the scarcer. Limited numbers of *gambeli* have been found wintering in California under the local name "Tule Goose," but most other specimens from this continent, and all Canadian specimens that have been examined, prove to be of the smaller race, the common White-fronted Goose *Anser albifrons albifrons*, which was previously considered confined to the Old World. The larger birds undoubtedly pass through on migration of the two, but so far Canadian specimens have not been brought to scientific notice.

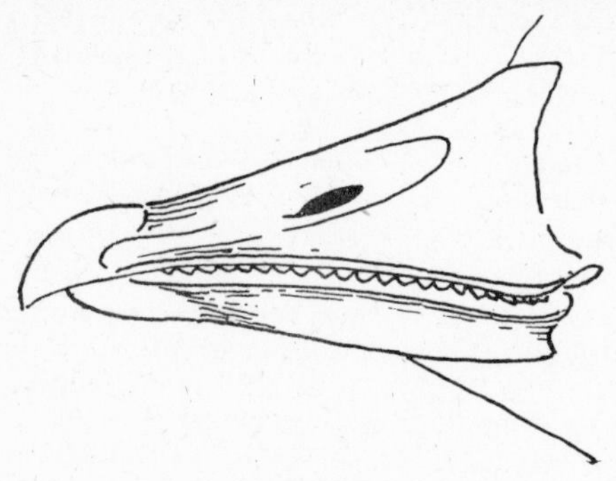

Figure 120

Bill of White-fronted Goose; natural size.

In certain sections of the prairie provinces this goose is popularly called "Brant." This is an unjustifiable misuse of a name otherwise applied, and has been the source of much confusion. (*See* under Brant, page 82.)

169. **Snow Goose.** WAVEY. WAVEY GOOSE. L'OIE BLANCHE. *Chen hyperborea.* L, 23. Plate V B. A medium-sized white goose with black primaries. Juveniles have

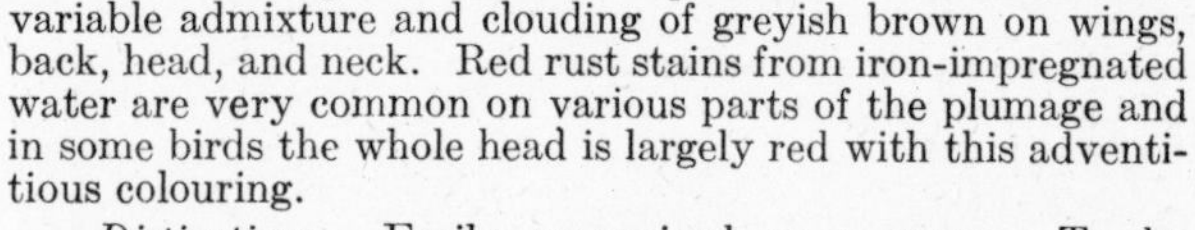

variable admixture and clouding of greyish brown on wings, back, head, and neck. Red rust stains from iron-impregnated water are very common on various parts of the plumage and in some birds the whole head is largely red with this adventitious colouring.

Figure 121

Bill of Snow Goose; scale, ½.

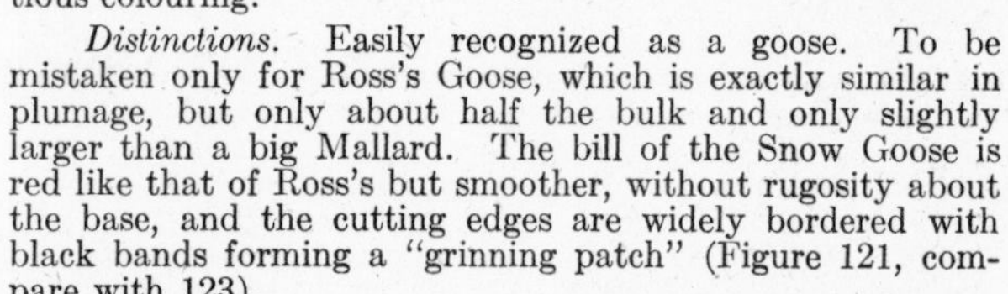

*Distinctions.* Easily recognized as a goose. To be mistaken only for Ross's Goose, which is exactly similar in plumage, but only about half the bulk and only slightly larger than a big Mallard. The bill of the Snow Goose is red like that of Ross's but smoother, without rugosity about the base, and the cutting edges are widely bordered with black bands forming a "grinning patch" (Figure 121, compare with 123).

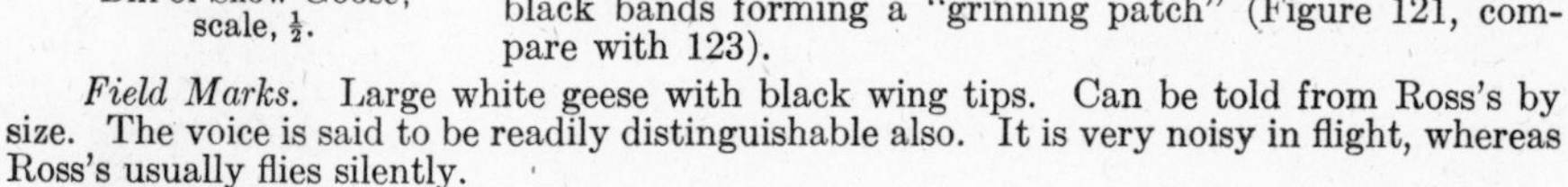

*Field Marks.* Large white geese with black wing tips. Can be told from Ross's by size. The voice is said to be readily distinguishable also. It is very noisy in flight, whereas Ross's usually flies silently.

*Nesting.* On the ground.

*Distribution.* Breeds on the islands and mainland of the American Arctic, migrates down through the interior and along the coasts, mostly west of the Great Lakes.

*SUBSPECIES.* The subspecies of Wavey common to the west is the Lesser Snow Goose (la Petite Oie blanche) *Chen hyperborea hyperborea*, the type form. The eastern race, the Greater Snow Goose (la Grande Oie blanche) *Chen hyperborea atlantica*, has been reported from the west, but without satisfactory evidence. The two differ only in size and so slightly and with so much individual variation that some doubt has been expressed as to the validity of the subspecific difference. So far as is known, the only flock of Greater Snow Geese extant winter off the Carolina coast and visit St. Lawrence River near Quebec on migration. Their breeding ground is in the northeastern Arctic Islands and northern Greenland. The probability of these birds occurring west of the Great Lakes, except by accident, is slight. One source of confusion to the general public may be the occurrence of Ross's Goose which seems to fulfil the requirements demanded by the name "Lesser," leaving the term "Greater" to be applied to the next larger, common white goose, the real Lesser. However, birds presumed on geographical grounds to be Lesser Snow Geese occur in sizes that agree well with dimensions for the Greater.

The name Wavey is a corruption of the Indian word "Wa-wa," meaning Wild Goose, and is the common name for the Snow Goose throughout the west. The Snow Goose migrates down through the prairies in immense numbers, turning the lakes and fields upon which it settles white as with snow. En route, the great flocks were formerly taken toll of by the Hudson's Bay Company's posts and the inhabitants of the northern unorganized territories, who killed large numbers to salt for winter use. Even under this great drain, their numbers did not seem to diminish as did those of other species. When they reach civilization, where they are actively hunted, they are so wary that few large bags are made within our territory.

Some twenty years ago, when seed was generally sown broadcast, the large flocks caused occasional serious damage and sometimes necessitated the replanting of crops. Settling on the newly sown fields the flocks progressed across them like drifting snow, the rear birds constantly passing over their fellows in front and leaving the ground clean of seed behind. Such immense flocks are seldom seen today, and present methods of drilling grain would prevent damage from them, as geese do not scratch as do chickens or grouse. Snow Geese are erratic in their choice of feeding grounds and seldom return to the same fields. It is because of this habit, and their extreme wariness, that methods suitable for hunting the larger Canada Geese mostly fail when used against this species.

169. 1. **Blue Goose.** L'OIE BLEUE. *Chen caerulescens.* L, 26. About the size of the Snow and the White-fronted Geese, but body slaty grey and brown, wave-marked with lighter feather edges on back and below. Wings and rump mostly slate colour; head and neck solid white. Juvenile is similar, but head and neck entirely brown. The bill is almost identical with that of the Snow Goose (*See* Figure 121).

*Distinctions.* The combination of white head and neck with darker body does not occur in any other American goose except the Emperor Goose, but that species has a broad, sharply defined band of black along the throat and foreneck, and is so widely separated in range from the Blue, that confusion is very unlikely. The brown-headed juvenile is very similar to the young White-fronted Goose, but has pink instead of yellow legs and feet.

*Field Marks.* The white head and neck and dark body can be distinguished at a great distance. Except for the flesh-coloured instead of yellow legs and feet, the juvenile can hardly be told by eye-sight observation from the young White-fronted Goose.

*Nesting.* On the ground of the tundra.

*Distribution.* Nesting on southwestern Baffin Island and the islands at the mouth of Hudson Bay, migrating through Manitoba to the Gulf coast. On the way it has few regular stopping places and the bulk of the species seem to make the journey from Louisiana and Texas coasts to southern Manitoba in a single flight. About the only place in settled Canada where it seems of regular occurrence in appreciable numbers is southern Manitoba. Here, on a narrow migration front, immense flocks are seen each spring, but it is seldom noted in the autumn. Elsewhere in Canada it is but an erratic straggler. The distribution and migration of this species have only lately been solved.

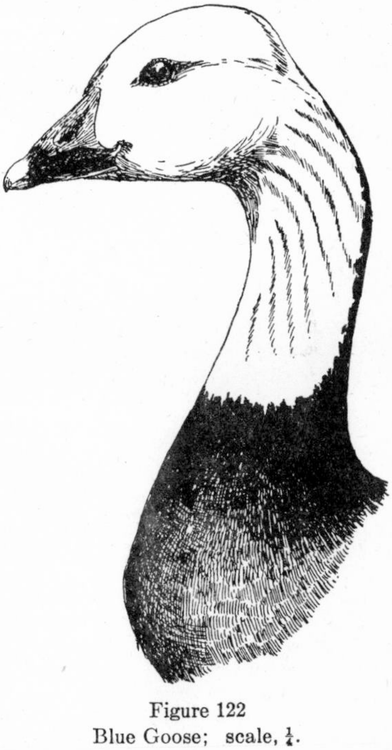

Figure 122
Blue Goose; scale, ½.

The Blue Goose in habit is so like the Snow Goose, with which it often associates, that for a long time it was regarded as the young of that species.

170. **Ross's Goose.** SCABBY-NOSED GOOSE. L'OIE DE ROSS. *Chen rossi.* L, 21. A small Wavey Goose, hardly larger than a big Mallard.

*Distinctions.* Likely to be confused only with the Snow Goose. Besides its decidedly inferior size, Ross's Goose lacks the black "grinning patch" of the Snow Goose, and the base of the bill in well-grown specimens is rugose and bluish, suggesting the popular name of "Scabby-nose" (Figure 123, compare with 121).

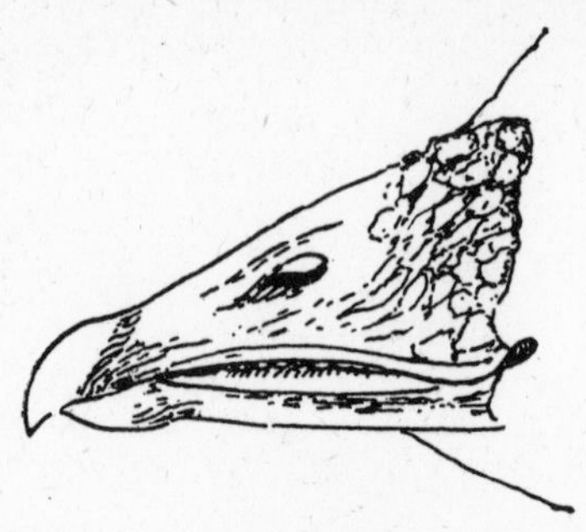

Figure 123
Bill of Ross's Goose; natural size.

*Field Marks.* A very small, white goose with black wing tips. In flight it is not as noisy as the Snow Goose.

*Nesting.* Unknown.

*Distribution.* A goose of interesting and problematical distribution. In the spring it passes in large numbers through the large lakes of Mackenzie district and vanishes towards the north. On the southward migration it comes down through the more western prairies and crosses the mountains of central Montana to the California coast. It occurs in British Columbia or Manitoba only as a straggler.

The general similarity of this species to the Snow Goose, and its small size, have probably suggested its identity with the Lesser Snow Goose and caused that species to be regarded as the Greater, an incorrect but rather natural conclusion for the non-technical observer.

178. **Bicolored Tree-duck.** LE MILOUIN BICOLORE. *Dendrocygna bicolor.* L, 20·5. A very long-legged duck, feet reaching beyond end of tail. Head, neck, breast, and underparts uniform, rich, yellowish brown (fulvous), paling on throat to cream, and darkening on crown and hindneck. A broad collar, incomplete behind, of dull white and dark brown stripes. Back, dark brown barred with slightly rusty feather borders. Tail, dark brown with white coverts above and below. Wing coverts, reddish chestnut.

*Distinctions.* The only duck so largely and evenly fulvous likely to be met. Legs long, feet large, toes extending well beyond tail.

*Field Marks.* General fulvous coloration and long legs. Too rare to be recorded in Canada on sight identification, except in the most favourable circumstances.

*Nesting.* On the ground or in hollow trees near water.

*Distribution.* Southwestern United States, Mexico, South America, South Africa, and India, north in America to central California. Only one record for Canada, from southern Vancouver Island.

*SUBSPECIES.* The above species has been determined as the northern race of this species the Fulvous Tree-duck (le Milouin du Mexique) *Dendrocygna bicolor helva.*

Figure 124
Skin of Fulvous Tree-duck, showing projection of feet beyond tail; scale, ⅛.

### Subfamily—Anatinae. River and Pond Ducks

*General Description.* Typical ducks with flattened spatulate bills, furnished with flat nail tip and straining laminæ or plates along the inner margins (Figure 111, page 68) instead of tooth-like projections (Figure 110, page 68). Feet with a small though well-formed hind toe, not modified into a flat lobe or fin-like appendage (Figure 125, compare with 164).

*Distinctions.* The bill will separate the River Ducks from the mergansers; and the hind toe as above from the Sea Ducks.

A. Harlequin Duck; scale, $\frac{1}{6}$

Male Female

B. White-winged Scoter; scale, $\frac{1}{6}$

Male Female

A. Red-breasted Merganser; scale, $\frac{1}{6}$

Female Male

B. American Goshawk; scale, $\frac{1}{6}$

Adult Juvenile

*Field Marks.* Under favourable conditions the general outline, rounded head, and shorter, thicker bill will separate these, and the Sea or Bay Ducks, from the mergansers. They rise more steeply from the water than either. When under way, the neck is inclined slightly upward from the body, and they lack the drawn-out appearance of the mergansers. The flock formation is usually irregular with little order or alinement. They are more difficult to distinguish from the Sea or Bay Ducks, but in general are longer and more shapely in appearance, with more slender necks. They are probably more easily recognized by species.

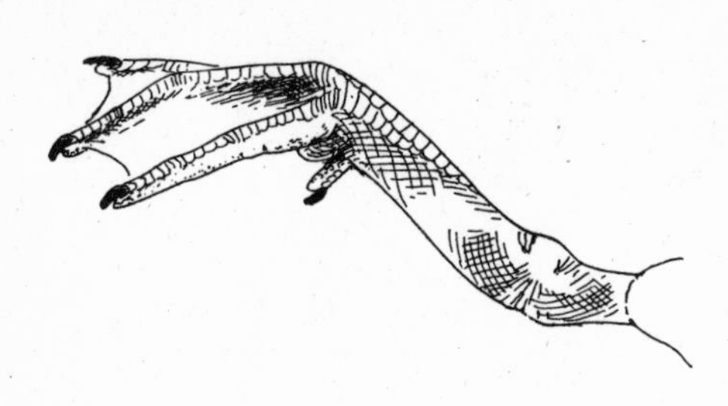

Figure 125
Foot of Surface-feeding Duck; scale, ½.

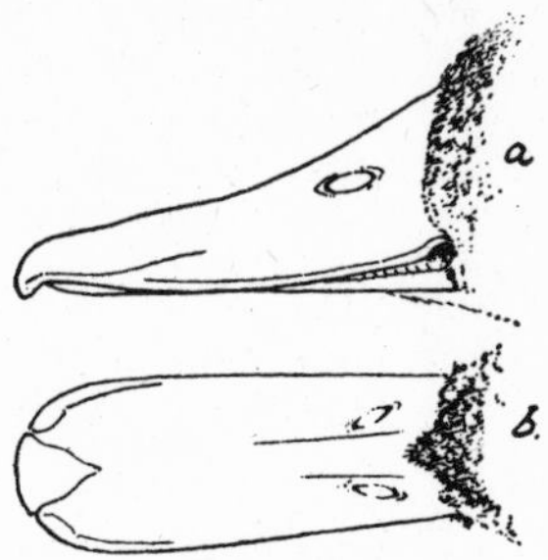


Figure 126
Bill of Surface-feeding Duck; scale, ½.

*Nesting.* Usually on the ground. Occasionally in trees.

*Distribution.* As a class the Pond and River Ducks are more abundant in the interior than on either coast.

As the names imply, the River and Pond Ducks frequent our smaller inland waters more than they do the larger ones. They feed from the surface by "tipping" and reaching under the water, and rarely dive. The food is gathered in the bill and the water squeezed out, the laminæ of the bills retaining the solid matter.

*Economic Status.* Being strictly water-birds and vegetable and insect feeders, their food habits generally are not harmful to human interests. It has lately been shown that ducks feed largely upon mosquito larvæ and that they may do surprising good in this direction. By actual experiment, a pair of ducks in a small pond did more to reduce these pests in it than a considerable school of goldfish. As game, they are of great importance, *See* pages 68-73.

132. **Mallard Duck.** GREEN-HEAD. LE CANARD ORDINAIRE. *Anas platyrhynchos.* L, 23. Plate VI A.

*Distinctions.* The male cannot be mistaken for any other wild duck, though many domestic strains approach it closely. The female is often referred to other species and is sometimes called "Grey Duck." There are several other ducks approaching her in coloration, but the purple speculum with the white bar both before and behind the speculum are good distinguishing marks (Figure 127).

*Field Marks.* Green head and white neck-ring are conspicuous recognition marks for the adult male. The speculum with its white bars will identify the female in life. The tail of both sexes shows a general whiteness in flight that is quite characteristic.

*Nesting.* On the ground usually; in high grass or reeds, occasionally at a considerable distance from water, and because of this it often thrives in sections from which other species have been driven away.

*Distribution.* Over practically the whole of Canada except in the far north, but less common in the extreme east. Breeds throughout Canada except where disturbed by settlement, but mostly west of Ontario.

This is the "Wild Duck" *par excellence*, and is known as such to the sportsman of the Old World as well as the New. It is the original stock from which our common domestic varieties sprang and nearly any mixed farmyard flock will show the green-black heads, white collar, or recurved uppertail-coverts denoting reversion to the original form. As well as being one of the best table-birds, it is one of the wariest of ducks.

The Mallard is a strong and virile bird and it crosses with other ducks more readily than any other. The results of such crosses are taken comparatively frequently, especially those with Pintail or Black Duck. It is interesting in such cases to note that the typical Mallard speculum is a dominant factor and is almost invariably inherited in all crosses with other species.

"The Mallard is the most important duck of the west and must be classed among the first two or three game birds of North America. It is a capable bird; a prolific multiplier, raising nine or ten young; hardy in the extreme; coming north at the break-up and remaining on the prairies until freeze-up; in the first rank as a table-bird; elusive and wary enough as game. It has taken to feeding on the fields to an extent approached by no other duck and the wheat or barley-fed Mallard is to the epicure the equal of any northern Canvas-back. Wondrous flights to the fields are seen on the prairies in places and sometimes in September damage is done to the wheat shocks. Large numbers of Mallards are shot on the fields and this has made the bird available as game to many hunters who cannot shoot upon the marshes. Only in the coastal west where, sometimes, on account of its habit of eating decomposing salmon and so becoming unfit for food, is the bird other than a favourite."

Figure 127
Wing of Mallard.

Figure 128
Wing of Black Duck.

133. **Black Duck.** BLACK MALLARD. DUSKY DUCK. LE CANARD NOIR. *Anas rubripes.* L, 22. Plate VI B. Very similar in general appearance to a very dark brown, almost black, female Mallard. In the male the general streakiness, though largely obscured by a uniform dark colour, persists strongly on the face. The same is true of the female to a less degree.

Figure 129
Black Duck (male);
scale, ½.

*Distinctions.* Besides the general dark coloration, the absence of white borders to the purple speculum fore and aft (Figure 128) is distinctive in any plumage. There is no danger of confusing it with any of the black Scoters, because of the speculum and mallard-like bill, the hind toe of the River and Pond Ducks, and the streaky coloration on the face.

*Field Marks.* Very dark, almost black, with a silvery sheen to the underwing surfaces. It is too rare a bird west of the Great Lakes to be recorded on sight identification.

*Nesting.* On the ground, near water.

*Distribution.* An eastern bird not generally found west of the Great Lakes. There are numerous Manitoba records, where it seems to be increasing during recent years, and one from Saskatchewan.

*SUBSPECIES.* Two subspecies have been recognized. The Southern Black Duck (le Canard noir du Sud) *Anas rubripes tristis* and the Red-legged Black Duck (Le Canard noir à pattes rouges) *Anas rubripes rubripes.* The latter has been postulated as the more northern breeder coming south late in the autumn, but the validity of the former is not well established or its breeding range well marked out.

Figure 130
Gadwall; scale, ¼.
Female Male

Figure 131
Wing of Gadwall;
scale, ¼.

135. **Gadwall.** GREY DUCK. SPECKLE-BELLY. LE CANARD CHIPEAU. *Chaulelasmus streperus.* L, 19·50. A streaked grey duck, white below, without much decided detail. Male: finely vermiculated crosswise on flanks and back; head and neck finely and evenly speckled (Figure 130). Female: streaked in much the same pattern as female Mallard. All plumages with large white speculum edged forward with dead black and with lesser wing coverts chestnut-red (Figure 131).

*Distinctions.* The large white speculum and chestnut-red upperwing-coverts are always distinctive. In females and juveniles the red is sometimes scattered and faint, but always present.

*Field Marks.* Male: a medium-sized duck of greyish colour without obvious red or much detail except strong black and white area on folded wing. Female: like a small Mallard with a white speculum. In flight, the white speculum spot of the secondaries on the rear of the wing makes best recognition mark. More likely to be confused with Baldpate than any other duck.

*Nesting.* On ground in grass or under bushes.

*Distribution.* Across the continent to north of Lake Athabaska. More common west, than east, of the Great Lakes.

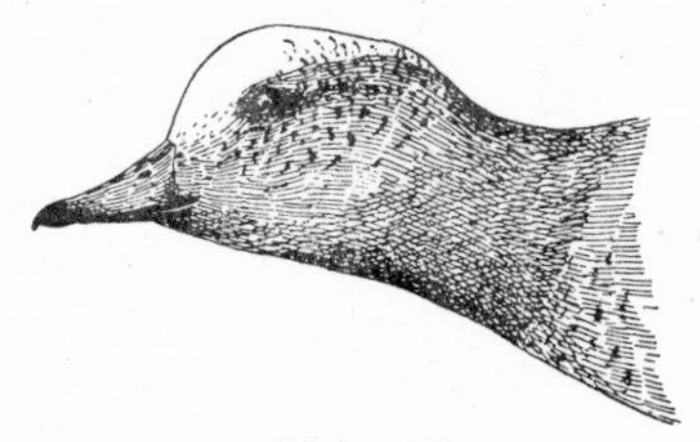

Figure 132
European Widgeon (male);
scale, ¼.

136. **European Widgeon.** LE CANARD SIFFLEUR D'EUROPE. *Mareca penelope.* L, 19. Male: like the Baldpate or American Widgeon, but the head solid brick-red from cream cap to base of neck. Female: hardly distinguishable from female Baldpate.

*Distinctions.* Red head of adult male distinctive. In other plumages probably only separated from Baldpate by having axillars thickly but finely speckled or marbled with grey (Figure 133) instead of being pure white, or very slightly marked or shaft streaked (*See* Figure 134).

*Field Marks.* The species is too rare to be distinguished on sight, except the male with its creamy cap and plainly red head.

*Distribution.* Northern part of eastern hemisphere. Occasional records in eastern United States and on the west coast north as far as Wrangell Island. In western Canada the only records have been from southern Vancouver Island. One of the interesting developments from bird-banding is the demonstration that the Occasional European Widgeon that occurs on our east coast originates in Iceland and is not American raised.

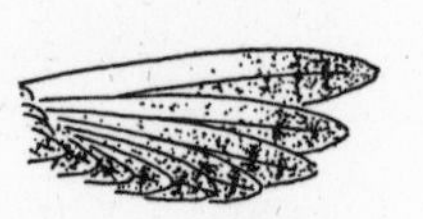

Figure 133
Speckled axillars of European Widgeon; scale, ½.

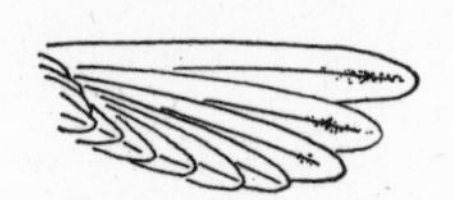

Figure 134
Plain axillars of Baldpate; scale, ½.

Figure 135
Wing of Baldpate; scale, ¼.

137. **Baldpate.** AMERICAN WIDGEON. LE CANARD SIFFLEUR D'AMÉRIQUE. *Mareca americana.* L, 19. Plate VII A.

*Distinctions.* The adult male with its white cap, from which the vernacular name is derived, and the pinky, vinaceous breast and flanks, is distinctive enough. In all plumages may be known from any other common duck by the white upperwing-coverts, some rather patchy, backed by a velvety black speculum (Figure 135, compare with 131). No red on wings as in the Gadwall. From the European Widgeon it may be distinguished in all plumages by its spotless or nearly immaculate axillars (Figure 134, compare with 133).

*Field Marks.* The male's white cap, vinaceous breast and flanks, and white patch on fore-wing. Both sexes when flying show a white patch on the forepart instead of rear edge of wing.

*Nesting.* On the ground in grass or under bushes.

*Distribution.* Ranges over nearly all of Canada. More common west than east of the Great Lakes. Breeds north to the mouth of the Mackenzie.

"This is a duck more characteristic of the extreme west, being much better known on the coast waters than on the prairies. It is a hardy species, wintering well northward, a bird of large waters rather than of sloughs and ponds. Large flocks of these handsome birds, their flashing white wing patches showing even at a distance, are a common sight to the coastal sportsman. Though a prolific breeder and one of the most numerous of western ducks it loses some popularity on account of its rather small size. Its flesh, however, ranks high and it apparently never becomes contaminated by fish-eating. It is one of the first of the coast ducks to mate and turn north in spring."

143. **Pintail.** SPRINGTAIL. SPRIG. LE CANARD PILET. *Dafila acuta.* L, 28. Plate VII B. A large-sized duck, of striking coloration, with long, slender neck and long, projecting centre tail feathers.

*Distinctions.* High plumage males are unmistakable. Females and juvenile males are like the female Mallard in general coloration, but without the prominent white-bordered speculum. Instead, the speculum is dull bronze, bordered in front by a narrow cinnamon line and behind by a narrow one of white.

*Field Marks.* In any plumage, even when without the long "spring tail" or "sprigtail," the long neck and wings and general slenderness of this bird are recognizable in any attitude, in addition the striking colour pattern of the male or the absence of strong speculum of female, make the best recognition mark of the species.

*Nesting.* On the ground, in some cases at considerable distance from water.

*Distribution.* Both continents of the northern hemispheres. In America north to Arctic coast. Nesting in Canada practically wherever found.

This is one of the widest ranging and most generally common of the ducks.

*SUBSPECIES.* The American Pintail (le Canard pilet d'Amérique) is now separated from the Old World form under the name *Dafila acuta tzitzihoa.*

Figure 136
Tail of Pintail; scale, ⅕.

"The Pintail is a duck of the prairies, the prairie slough being its ideal habitat. As a game bird it is less popular than the Mallard, mainly because it does not often feed on the fields as that duck does, and because it is smaller. The Pintail usually is the most numerous duck upon the prairie sloughs. It is often the first duck to arrive at the break-up in spring, but is not a late lingerer in the autumn, the largest flocks are seen in late August and September. A very early nester, raising large broods. A rather shy bird, speedy on the wing and capable of taking care of itself. This duck claims second or third place in the hearts of the plainland hunters."

138. **European Teal.** LA SARCELLE D'EUROPE. *Nettion crecca.* L, 14·5. Like the American Green-winged Teal, but without the white crescent in front of the wing and with a white scapulary line over the closed wing (Figure 137).

*Distribution.* Europe and Asia to Iceland and Aleutian Islands. There are old and unsubstantiated records for Labrador and Nova Scotia and it may eventually be detected on the coast of British Columbia.

American Green-winged Teal. Figure 137 (Both male) European Green-winged Teal.

139. **Green-winged Teal.** LA SARCELLE À AILES VERTES. *Nettion carolinense.* L, 14·50. Plate VIII A.

*Distinctions.* The smallest of our ducks. Size will always distinguish it from all others except the Blue-winged and Cinnamon Teals, and the Buffle-head. The brilliant green speculum will distinguish it from the latter and the absence of chalky blue on the fore-wing from the former two.

*Field Marks.* Small size. In any plumage lack of chalky blue on wings distinguishes from the two other teal, and the lack of white on the wings from the equally small Buffle-head.

*Nesting.* On the ground, near water.

*Distribution.* Across the continent, most common in the west except perhaps the southern mid-prairie sections. Breeds north to the mouth of Mackenzie River.

One of the daintiest of the ducks. Its habit of flying in large flocks and its great speed on the wing make it well known to sportsmen. The ease with which it attains such high speed while other species seem to labour so strenuously is notable.

"Teal, both Green- and Blue-winged, are birds of the smaller waters, especially of the shallow prairie sloughs. Of the two, the Green-winged is the more universal bird. It is the earlier migrant in the spring and remains north much later than its blue-winged relative in autumn. Most Blue-wings leave the prairies in September, the Green-wings remain into the next month. Both are much given to frequenting the shallows and congregating in sunning parties on mudbanks and sandbars. They are eagerly sought by sportsmen, for in spite of their very small size no other ducks are so fat and few so toothsome. Teal are shot much more easily than many other ducks on account of their manner of flying in compact masses and where their great speed gives them little advantage against the scatter gun."

140. **Blue-winged Teal.** LA SARCELLE À AILES BLEUES. *Querquedula discors.* L, 16. Plate VIII A.

*Distinctions.* One of the smallest of our ducks. Small size and large area of chalky blue on wing, characteristics shared only by the Cinnamon Teal and the Shoveller. The latter is a very much larger bird. The former in adult male is too dissimilar for any confusion, being solid cinnamon-rufous almost all over. Females of Blue-winged and Cinnamon Teals are so much alike that probably some specimens will be impossible of separation by any known test. As a rule the female Blue-winged is less heavily and less broadly streaked or overwashed on breast and flanks and the bill averages shorter and relatively slightly broader at the base.

*Field Marks.* Small size and large area of chalky blue on wings and white underwing surface like a Mallard, separate from all but the Cinnamon Teal. In adult males the difference in general coloration of these two species is too great for serious confusion. The females probably cannot be told apart in life and generally can be recognized only when accompanied by a mate whose identity is evident.

*Nesting.* On the ground amidst grass.

*Distribution.* Across the continent. Rather scarce in extreme east. Common through the prairie sections, rarer in the interior of British Columbia, and practically absent from the Canadian west coast. Breeds north to Great Slave Lake.

141. **Cinnamon Teal.** LA SARCELLE CANNELLE. *Querquedula cyanoptera.* L, 16. One of the four smallest of our ducks. Adult male: uniform rich cinnamon-red head, neck, shoulders, breast, and flanks. Green speculum. A large area of fore-wing chalky blue as in the Blue-winged Teal. Female: hardly separable from female of that species.

*Distinctions.* The male, with its strongly red coloration similar to the Ruddy Duck, but with wholly red head and blue wing patch, is easily recognized. The female can not always be separated from the female Blue-winged Teal. As a general rule it is more coarsely and heavily striped and overwashed with a richer brown on breast and flanks, and its bill is longer and more slender in proportion than in that species. These characteristics are not infallible and often it can only be identified by an accompanying mate. The common rust staining of the Blue, or even the Green-winged, Teal has often been the basis of records of this species.

*Field Marks.* Small size, general redness of body, white underwing surface like a Mallard, and chalky blue wing patches for the male. The female can hardly be distinguished in life from the female Blue-winged Teal.

*Distribution.* The west coast of southern British Columbia southward, and adjoining interior. There are a few substantiated records from Alberta, Saskatchewan, and Manitoba, where it should be looked for with care but females identified with caution.

*Nesting.* Nest of grasses, on the ground. In some cases at considerable distance from water.

142. **Shoveller.** SPOONBILL. LE CANARD SOUCHET. *Spatula clypeata.* L, 20. Plate VIII B. A good-sized duck with a widened, spoon-shaped or shovel-shaped bill (Figure 138).

*Distinctions.* The Shoveller bill, remarkably spatulate at end with fringe of long, comb-like laminæ on sides of upper mandible, is characteristic in any plumage. The contrasting coloration of the adult male is striking. The female is much like the female Mallard, but smaller, without any speculum or marked wing pattern, but always with at least a suggestion of pale blue on the forepart of the wings.

*Field Marks.* The striking coloration of the adult male is distinctive. The female is rather like the female Mallard, but without the strongly marked steely blue speculum. In any plumage and at considerable distance the slightly bulbous appearance of the bill is distinctly recognizable.

*Nesting.* On the ground, in the grass, but not always in the immediate vicinity of water.

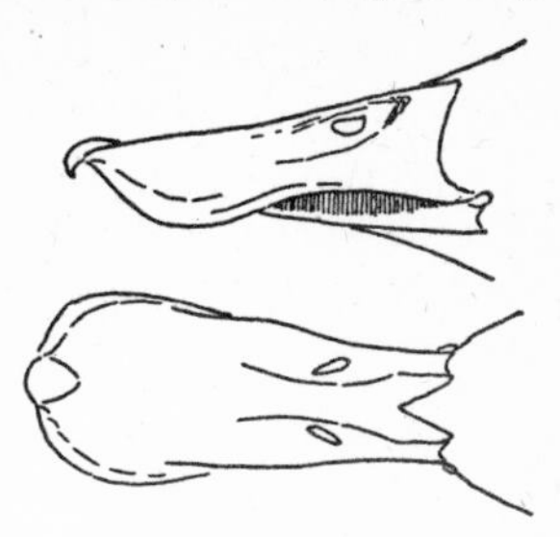

Figure 138
Bill of Shoveller;
scale, ½.

*Distribution.* Common to both Old and New Worlds. Occurs in America across the continent, north to mouth of Mackenzie River. Breeds throughout western Canada. Rare in the east.

"The Shoveller or Spoonbill is a lover of the mud, and consequently the shallow, muddy prairie sloughs are its favourite habitat. Like the Pintail it is a bird of the prairies. In flight, when the bulbous bill cannot be noted it much resembles the Mallard, and many sportsmen have presumably shot a Mallard and picked up a Spoonbill. There is some prejudice among western sportsmen against the bird, owing to its small size and to the slight inferiority of the flesh when compared with that of several other species. This duck is a late arrival in spring and migrates in September, and perhaps is seldom taken at its best in the north. The Shoveller, like the Pintail, sometimes joins the Mallards in their flights to the fields, but never alights with them to feed on dry land."

144. **Wood Duck.** SUMMER DUCK. LE CANARD BRANCHU. *Aix sponsa.* L, 18·50. Plate IX A.

*Distinctions.* A very characteristic bird in any plumage. Even in the dull eclipse plumage the male shows a shadowy suggestion of the peculiar face markings. Owing to the demand for this bird as a semi-domesticated duck on ornamental waters, dealers sometimes substitute the more easily procured female Mandarin Duck for that of this species. The males, though quite as gorgeous as the Mandarin, are perfectly distinctive, but the females are so similar that the substitution may not be immediately discovered. However, the Mandarin female lacks the long, fleshy bill process running up the sides of the forehead, and the feather line is consequently straighter than in the Wood Duck.

*Field Marks.* The down-hanging crest and the white throat of the male are often visible when all the rest of the bright coloration is lost in the distance or confused by the glare of the sun. The white eye-ring of the female is likewise quite conspicuous. When on wing the white underbody is sometimes quite distinctive, as this species seems to show more white than any other white-bellied duck.

*Nesting.* In hollow trees or stumps in the vicinity of quiet water.

*Distribution.* Across the continent, north barely into Canada. A woodland bird and hence rare or absent throughout the prairies, occasional in southeastern Manitoba, more common in the east and in southern British Columbia.

This is the brightest coloured and most beautiful duck in America and perhaps in the world. The only species that can approach it is the Mandarin Duck of China which is often seen in confinement with it. The Wood Duck was originally the "Summer Duck" of our southeastern borders and almost every woodland stream and backwater pond had at least one pair; but, since the clearing of the land, the farmer's-boy-shot-gun combination has been too much for it. Its bright colours, the relative conspicuousness of its nesting places, and the ease with which it can be stalked or "jumped" in its more or less wooded haunts, have made it an easy prey for even the inexperienced shooter and it was until lately in great danger of being exterminated. A duck that alights in trees is more or less paradoxical to most European sportsmen, but this species does so commonly. It builds its nest in a hollow tree some distance from the ground, usually overlooking a quiet oxbow pond or other dead water. How the young are brought to the ground is not known, and many conflicting reports are circulated regarding it—such as the old birds carrying their young in their bills or on their backs, or shoving them out to flutter to the ground and take chances with their little, unfledged wings. In some way they reach the ground at an early age and follow the mother about the reaches of the streams or other quiet waters. Later they seek the marshes, which they inhabit through the autumn, leaving for the south before the first frost has chilled the waters.

The Wood Duck takes readily to nesting boxes prepared for the purpose and its numbers could probably be increased in this way.

This is *not* the bird commonly called "Wood Duck" on the prairies and in the north. The birds generally so termed are the Golden-eye and the Buffle-head, both of which build in trees and seem fitted to the name.

The Wood Duck is a very beautiful bird and its disappearance would cause profound regret. The way in which its numbers have been reduced in the east indicates that it cannot withstand the dangers of modern sporting and other conditions as do hardier, shyer, and more inaccessible species. It never seems to have been, except in certain localities, as common as other ducks, even in British Columbia, and though its numbers there may not be dangerously reduced, today the sportsmen of that province and elsewhere would be well advised to confine their shooting to other more numerous and more commonplace species and thus extend the close season by a gentleman's agreement. In the east, a long, close season, and the stopping of spring shooting, appear to have had the desired effect of increasing the numbers of this species, but it seems to many of us that the great value of this wonderful little bird is as an object of beauty rather than of sport.

### Subfamily—Fuligulinae. Bay, Sea, or Diving Ducks

*General Description.* Heavily or compactly built ducks with typically flattened or spatulate duck-like bill sometimes swollen or high at base (Figures 155-160), but always with flattened nail at tip (Figures 140 and 142). Hind toe modified into a flat, paddle-shaped lobe (like Figure 139).

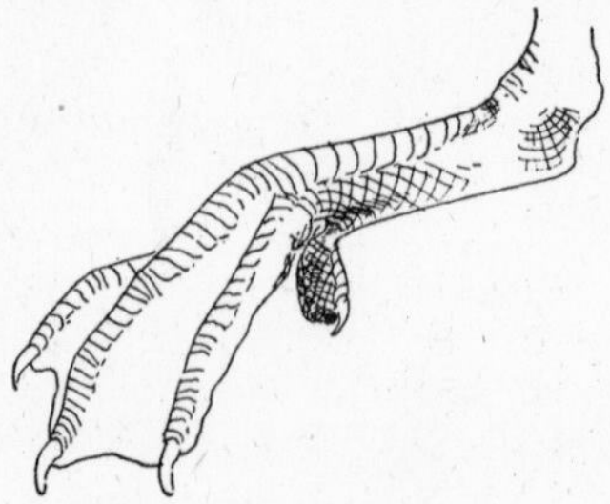

*Distinctions.* Bill will separate the Sea Ducks from Mergansers; and hind toe from River and Pond Ducks (Compare with Figures 168 and 169, and 125).

*Field Marks.* Rather difficult to distinguish from the River and Pond Ducks except as species. They are in general more heavily built, with thicker and usually shorter necks. They dive rather than tip in feeding; rise less steeply from the water, and alight more awkwardly.

*Nesting.* Usually on the ground, sometimes in trees.

*Distribution.* Cosmopolitan, common across the continent, but likely to be more numerous on the coasts than in the interior.

Figure 139
Foot of Diving Duck.

A. Sharp-shinned Hawk; scale, $\frac{1}{6}$

Juvenile Adult

B. Red-tailed Hawk; scale, $\frac{1}{6}$

Juvenile Adult

PLATE XIV

A. Red-shouldered Hawk; scale, $\frac{1}{6}$

Adult Juvenile

B. Swainson's Hawk; scale, $\frac{1}{7}$

A common light phase Dark phase

The Bay and Sea Ducks, though more at home on large waters, often frequent marshes and shallower waters for feeding or breeding. They are excellent divers, in some cases descending even to such depths as to become entangled in deeply set fish nets. The family includes some of our finest table-birds.

*Economic Status.* The direct economic importance of their food habits is as a rule even less than that of other ducks. Much said under previous subfamily, page 87, is true of these birds.

146. **Redhead.** LE MILOUIN À TÊTE ROUSSE. *Nyroca americana.* L, 19. Very similar in coloration to the Canvas-back, but slightly smaller and lighter in build.

*Distinctions.* A little smaller than the Canvas-back from which it differs only slightly. Compared with that species, the male has a slightly darker back and the red of the head does not extend to the shoulders. Females are almost identical with female Canvas-back, but somewhat darker, and can always be distinguished by the shape of the bill. In this species the culmen has a concave instead of a comparatively straight profile (Compare Figures 140 and 142). The female also bears a general resemblance to the female Scaup and Ring-necked Ducks, but is larger than either and has no white face mark. Large size and general coloration of male, when distinguishable, separate it from anything but the Canvas-back.

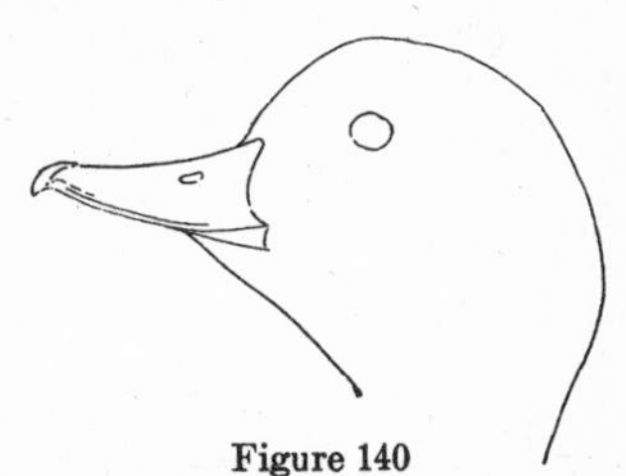

Figure 140
Head outline of Redhead; scale, ⅓.

*Field Marks.* Large size, and general coloration of male when distinguishable, will separate it from anything but the Canvas-back. The outline of the head with crown rising abruptly from the base of concave bill (Figure 140) gives a round-headed appearance that will distinguish it from the Canvas-back at a considerable distance. The brick-red of head stopping in mid-neck instead of continuing to shoulders is a good recognition mark at close range. Females are appreciably darker than female Canvas-backs, but probably cannot be told from them in life by colour alone under ordinary conditions. They resemble Scaups or Ring-necks, but are considerably larger, generally paler, without white face mark or white wing stripe.

*Nesting.* Nest of reeds lined with down, over water.

*Distribution.* Across the continent, most common in the interior, practically absent from the west coast. Breeds in the west north to Great Slave Lake.

The Redhead is so closely associated with the Canvas-back that discussion under that species will apply to both.

150. **Ring-necked Duck.** RING-BILLED DUCK. LE MORILLON À COLLIER. *Nyroca collaris.* L, 16·50. Like a very small Scaup with a black back and in highest plumage with a faint reddish or coppery band about the middle of neck and a light-coloured band encircling the bill.

*Distinctions.* Size and general scaup-like coloration in all plumages. The adult male has a solidly black back, a white ring on bill, coppery neck band, and grey spe ulum. The neck band is usually somewhat vague and partly suggested by a greyish or brownish one on the Scaups. The female and juvenile are very like comparable plumages of the Scaups. The grey instead of white speculum is the best distinction between them. The white lines or patches at base of bill, meeting across chin, will separate Ring-necks from most other ducks with grey speculum. Autumn females and young males bear close resemblance to parallel plumages of Redheads, but show no trace of white border to the speculum that is more or less evident in that species.

Figure 141
Ring-necked Duck; scale, ⅓.
Female Male

*Field Marks.* The male is like a small Scaup with a black back, but with the light grey flank feathers overlapping the wings and part of the back; in life it appears as a white-bodied bird. The head has also a fuller crest than the Scaups, giving an entirely different contour to the head. Other plumages probably can be separated from the two Scaups only by the grey instead of flashing white speculum.

*Nesting.* On the ground, near grassy ponds.

*Distribution.* Across the continent, but records of the Ring-necked are so confused with those of the Scaups that the ranges are not very well delimited. It appears to breed in the woodland regions north of the prairies, north at least to Mackenzie Valley, and in Cariboo district, British Columbia. More information is desired concerning the range and breeding habits of this bird.

147. **Canvas-back.** LE MILOUIN AUX YEUX ROUGES. *Nyroca valisneria.* L, 21. Plate IX B. Differing from the Redhead principally in slightly larger size and heavier build.

*Distinctions.* Slightly larger than the Redhead from which it differs only in small details. Compared with that species the male has a slightly lighter back, and the red of the head extends down to shoulders. Females are nearly identical with female Redheads, but somewhat lighter, and can always be distinguished by the shape of the bill. In this species, the culmen has a straight instead of a concave profile (Compare Figure 142 with 140). The female has also a general resemblance to the female Scaup and Ring-necked Ducks, but is larger and has no white face mark. The red eye from which the species obtains its popular French name is restricted to the adult male.

Figure 142
Head outline of Canvas-back; scale, $\frac{1}{3}$.

*Field Marks.* Large size. General coloration of adult male when distinguishable separates it from anything but the Redhead. The outline of head with heavy "nose," and crown slanting back from base of the straight bill, gives a long-headed appearance and is a characteristic by which it may be separated from any other species at considerable distance. The brick-red of head continuing to shoulders is a good recognition mark at close range. Females are appreciably lighter than female Redheads, but probably under ordinary conditions may not be told from them in life by colour alone. They resemble Scaups or Ring-necks, but are considerably larger, generally paler, and without white face mark or white wing stripe.

*Nesting.* Nest of reeds lined with down over water.

*Distribution.* Across the continent, common in the interior and on the west coast. Scarce on the east coast in Canadian waters. Breeds in the west north to Great Slave Lake.

"Canvas-backs and Redheads have more in common than mere appearance. They are both deepwater ducks and expert divers, and are found together frequenting the same lakes and marshes. Their principal food seems to be the tuberous roots of pond weeds and is secured at depths of from 2 to 10 feet. To many sportsmen the Canvas-back ranks first amongst the ducks and its praises have been sung for generations. To the western epicure, however, it is surpassed as a delicacy by the wheat-fed Mallard and it is probable that it does not reach its stage of especial excellence until fattened on the wild celery of the southern marshes. Both Canvas-back and Redhead make regular flights morning and evening and are constantly on the wing on windy days. They are shot either on flight ways, while passing from one slough to another, or over decoys on the water. The Canvas-back is one of the speediest of ducks on the wing, a hard target, hard to kill and difficult to retrieve, but the largest and heaviest when taken. It is probably because of these qualities that it has withstood the hunter much better than the Redhead."

148. **Greater Scaup Duck.** SCAUP DUCK. BLUEBILL. BROAD-BILL. LAKE BLUEBILL. LE GRAND MORILLON. *Nyroca marila.* L, 18·50. Like a larger edition of the Lesser Scaup Duck shown on Plate X A.

*Distinctions.* Difficult to separate from the Lesser Scaup, but larger. Male with greenish instead of purple reflections on head. In any plumage except occasional young birds, distinguished from the Lesser Scaup by the white to near-white on the outer webs of the inner primaries (Figure 143, compare with Figure 144). In the Lesser Scaup this light spot may be represented by a pale area, but it does not reach the clear white of this species. The females resemble the females of several other species, but can be separated from all except the female Lesser Scaup and the Ring-neck by the white spot at base of the bill, and from the latter, together with the Redhead and Canvas-back, by the white instead of grey speculum.

Figure 143
Wing of Greater Scaup Duck; scale, about $\frac{1}{3}$.

*Field Marks.* In general the adult male Scaups appear black for the front half of the body and white for the remainder, a colour pattern visible at a considerable distance. At rest, distinguished from the male Ring-neck by light instead of black back; in flight, in any plumage by white instead of grey speculum. An experienced eye can sometimes tell the two Scaups apart in life by the white on the primaries as above, otherwise, as small differences in size are very deceptive, they are probably inseparable in the field. The female is distinct from all white-bellied brown ducks except the Lesser Scaup and the Ring-neck by the white spot at the base of the bill, and from the latter and the Redhead and Canvas-back by the white instead of grey speculum.

*Nesting.* On the ground, near grassy ponds.

*Distribution.* Common to New and Old Worlds. In America, across the continent. Many of our breeding records for this species have been confused with the Lesser Scaup Duck, but this is a more northern species. We have no authenticated nesting record from the prairies or British Columbia where it seems to be a migrant only. Known to nest north at least as far as Churchill and Great Slave Lake. It is more common in migration on the coast than in the interior.

Much information founded on accurate specific identification is desired as to the occurrence, nesting, and migration of this species. It is more of an open or large water bird than the Lesser Scaup, earlier in spring and later in autumn.

149. **Lesser Scaup Duck.** BLUEBILL. BROAD-BILL. LITTLE BLUEBILL. MARSH BLUEBILL. LE PETIT MORILLON. *Nyroca affinis.* L, 16·50. Plate X A.

*Distinctions.* Difficult to separate from the Greater Scaup, though slightly smaller. Male: with purplish instead of greenish reflections on head. In any plumage except occasional young birds distinguished from the Greater by the absence of white or near-white on the outer web of the inner primaries (Figure 144, compare with 143). In this species this area may pale a little, but it does not achieve the whiteness of the Greater Scaup. The female resembles the female of several other species, but may be separated from all except the Ring-neck by the white spot at base of bill and from that species together with the Redhead and Canvas-back by the white instead of grey speculum.

Figure 144
Wing of Lesser Scaup Duck; scale, about $\frac{1}{3}$.

*Field Marks.* In general, male Scaups appear black for the front half of body and white for the remainder, a colour pattern visible at considerable distances. At rest, distinguished from the male Ring-neck by light instead of black back, and in flight, in any plumage, by the white instead of grey speculum. An experienced eye can sometimes tell the two Scaups apart in life by the colour characters of the primaries as above, otherwise, as size is a deceptive character, they are probably inseparable in the field. The female is distinguished from all other white-bellied brown ducks, except the Greater Scaup and the Ring-neck, by the white spot at the base of the bill, and from the latter as well as the Redhead and Canvas-back by the white instead of grey speculum.

*Nesting.* On the ground, near grassy ponds.

*Distribution.* Across the continent. Breeds throughout the Canadian west, north to near the Arctic coast.

This is the Scaup commonly breeding throughout the Canadian prairies and southern British Columbia. All records of the Greater nesting within this area have proved upon investigation to be this species.

"The Lesser is the most numerous Scaup on the prairies, as the Greater is on the coast. They are both deep water feeders, diving for their food much as do the Canvas-back and Redheads, and spend most of their time on the open water of the lakes or the shallow bays of the coast. The Lesser is most numerous on the plains and marshes just before the freeze-up and many migrate only when driven out by the freezing of the waters. Such birds are invariably very fat. Scaups are not very enthusiastically hunted in the west but are taken in the same manner as Canvas-backs, by both flight and decoy shooting. They are speedy flyers, but as they travel in straight lines and bunch compactly in the flock, they lose the advantage of their speed, and are easily shot."

151. **Common Golden-eye.** WHISTLER. WHISTLEWING. GREATHEAD. (*Incorrectly* WOOD DUCK.) LE GARROT COMMUN. *Glaucionetta clangula.* L, 20. Plate X B. The male is a striking black and white duck with yellow eyes. The female is light coloured, with sharply contrasted seal-brown head.

*Distinctions.* The adult male is too distinct in coloration to be confused with anything except Barrow's Golden-eye. The juvenile male and female can be distinguished from all similar birds by general lightness; back ashy grey rather than brownish, and seal-brown head sharply contrasting with a white neck. The adult male differs from the male of Barrow's Golden-eye in having greenish instead of purple reflections to head, oval instead of crescentic white face mark; flank, feather group with narrower black border and with considerably more white in wing and back pattern. Juvenile males and females can best be separated by the shape of the bill. In this species, the bill (Figure 145, compare with Figure 149) is larger, longer for its height, and of less stubby appearance. It is also of more even width with less tapering towards the tip. These bill characters may not be as well-marked in all specimens as shown in the figures but are generally recognizable. For further differences see Barrow's Golden-eye, the next species.

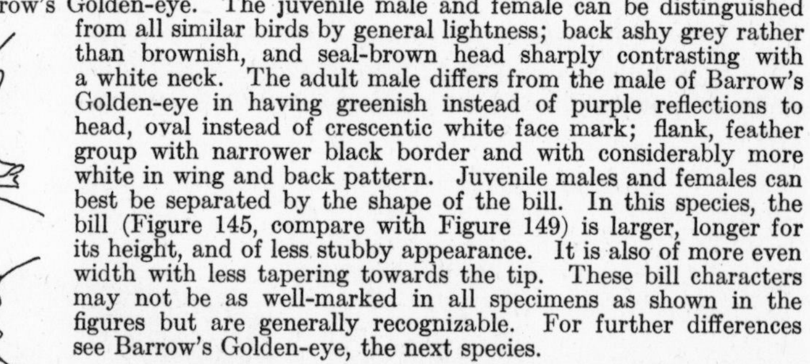

Figure 145
Bill outline of Common Golden-eye; scale, ½.

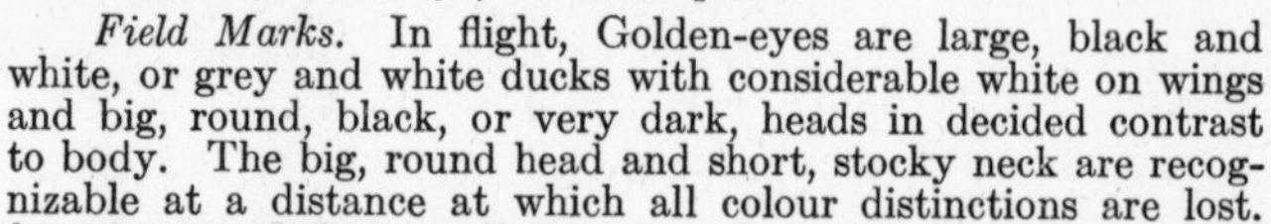

*Field Marks.* In flight, Golden-eyes are large, black and white, or grey and white ducks with considerable white on wings and big, round, black, or very dark, heads in decided contrast to body. The big, round head and short, stocky neck are recognizable at a distance at which all colour distinctions are lost. The loud whistling of the wings in flight is well known and suggests one of the most common popular names. The species is not likely to be confused with any species but Barrow's Golden-eye. Males may be distinguished from Barrow's by the round instead of crescentic white face spot, when that is visible, and, on the water, by the relative amount of black and white displayed. This species, having white flank feathers normally covering the edge of the wing and more white in back and wing, appears as mostly white on the body instead of mostly black as in Barrow's Golden-eye (Figure 146). Juveniles and females of the two species are not to be distinguished in life with any certainty, the larger amount of white on the lesser wing coverts of this species may be suggestive at times, though Barrow's Golden-eye usually shows a darker head with a higher forehead.

*Nesting.* In hollow stumps or trees, or even in openings in buildings.

*Distribution.* The greater part of the northern hemisphere. In America across the continent, nesting east and west as far north as suitable timber occurs.

*SUBSPECIES.* The New World form of this species is subspecifically separated from the Golden-eye of the Old World as the American Golden-eye (le Garrot d'Amérique) *Glaucionetta clangula americana.*

**Figure 146**
Field Marks of Common and Barrow's Golden-eyes.

The Golden-eye is one of the best-known ducks. The shrill whistling of its wings as it whirls by the blind makes it notable to the shooter and its habit of nesting in trees and other hollows has drawn the attention of others, and suggested the misnomer, "Wood Duck." Its fondness for nesting in various cavities leads at times to rather peculiar and interesting choice of locations. It sometimes comes through stovepipe or other holes into unused attics. In Camrose, Alberta, one persisted in using the chimney of a residence for its nest, until a false flue was substituted. In this case, the ducklings, when freed from the shell, scrambled in some way to the top of the chimney, and flinging themselves over the edge, rolled and bounced resiliently to the ground unhurt, there to be led away by the mother to the nearest water. In this case and in some others authentically reported of this species, the young were not assisted to the ground in any way.

"This is one of the first ducks to come north in spring and one of the last to leave in autumn. Though sparsely common everywhere, it is not regarded as good game in the west. On the prairies it is seldom eaten, and on the coast its flesh is often unfit for food in the autumn on account of the eating of dead salmon. Although it is prolific, large flocks of the species are seldom seen."

**Figure 147**
Windpipe of Barrow's Golden-eye.

**Figure 148**
Windpipe of Common Golden-eye.

152. **Barrow's Golden-eye.** LE GARROT DE BARROW. *Glaucionetta islandica.* L, 20. Plate X B. Closely similar in all plumages to American Golden-eye.

*Distinctions.* For distinctions from other ducks except the Common Golden-eye, see that species. The adult male differs from the Common in having purplish instead of greenish reflections to head; crescent-shaped instead of round white face spot; flank feather group edged on upper border with broad band of black, and considerably less white in wing and back pattern. Juvenile males and females can best be separated by the shape of the bill. In this species the bill (Figure 149, compare with Figure 145) is smaller, and shorter for its height, giving it a more stubby appearance. It is also of less even width, tapering more towards the tip. These characteristics may not be as well marked in all specimens as shown in the figures, but are generally recognizable. In young males a less apparent difference can be found. The forehead of Barrow's Golden-eye rises abruptly from the base of the bill, where a lump can be felt under the plumage by firmly stroking the forehead with the finger. Anatomically the males of the two species can be separated even in young birds early in the autumn by the enlargement of the windpipe. In the Common Golden-eye, there is an extraordinary bulbous enlargement of the windpipe between the arms of the merrythought. In Barrow's the whole pipe is gradually enlarged along the neck, but without any suggestions of a bulb (*See* Figures 147 and 148).

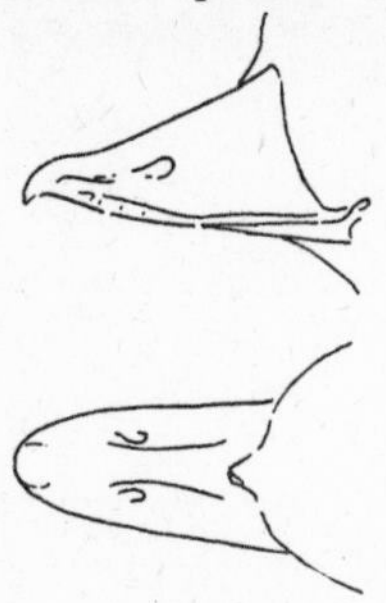

Figure 149
Bill outline of Barrow's Golden-eye; scale, ½.

*Field Marks.* For recognition marks as Golden-eyes, *See* previous species. From the Common Golden-eye, it may be known by the crescent-shaped instead of oval face spot, as far as that can be seen, and at greater distance on the water, by the relative amount of black and white displayed. This species, having the flank feathers that normally cover the edge of the wing widely bordered with black, and more black in back and wing pattern, appears as mostly black on the body instead of mostly white as does the Common Golden-eye. Juveniles or females can probably not be told apart in life with any certainty, though the less amount of white of the lesser wing coverts may be suggestive at times.

*Nesting.* In stumps or hollow trees when available, otherwise in rock cavities or on the ground.

*Distribution.* Northern North America. A bird of the extreme east and west, common on the Gulf of St. Lawrence, and through the mountains and on the coast of British Columbia, but absent in the country between.

In the far west this duck is a frequenter of the little mountain lakes near which it nests, and to which the young broods are brought as soon as they are out of the shell. Every little pool in the hills and mountain valleys in spring shows Barrow's Golden-eye bobbing and gesticulating in its courting ritual. Later the brown-headed female, with the brood of little black and white ducklings, occupies the scene, while the moulting males disport themselves elsewhere enjoying gay bachelor life. Where they disappear to at this season is not clearly known, but probably a search of the sea off the outer coasts, in summer time, would discover the missing birds.

153. **Buffle-head.** BUTTERBALL. SPIRIT DUCK. LE PETIT GARROT. *Charitonetta albeola.* L, 14·75. A very small duck, almost as diminutive as the Teal, but coloured in striking black and white. Male: white below and around base of neck; back black; head iridescent black, broken by large, triangular patches of pure white with apex below the eye, the base meeting its fellow across nape. The feathers of sides of head lengthened, making puffs on sides of face, hence the name. The female is white below, blackish or greyish brown above and on head, with softly margined white cheek spot extending back towards nape. The juvenile is like the female, but the throat is a little lighter and the cheek mark partly obscured.

Figure 150
Buffle-head; scale, ¼.
Male Female

*Distinctions.* The very small size and white speculum. Juveniles and females are rather like comparative plumages of Scaups, but much smaller and with a light cheek patch instead of a spot at base of bill. Somewhat suggestive of female Harlequin, but continuously white below, with one instead of two face spots, and a white speculum.

*Field Marks.* Male with conspicuous white triangle on black head is easily recognized. This species though it has a big-headed appearance similar to the Golden-eye is so much smaller that confusion can hardly result. Females and juveniles can best be recognized by their small size, single face spot, and white underparts and speculum.

*Nesting.* In stumps or hollow trees.

*Distribution:* North America, breeds in the west throughout the prairies, and in British Columbia, north through Mackenzie Valley.

The name Spirit Duck is given to this little species because of its remarkable diving, and ability to disappear when injured.

"Scattered commonly throughout the west, and in autumn sometimes met with in considerable flocks, the Buffle-head is one of the incidental ducks that come to bag without being specially sought. It is a diving duck and rarely found upon shallow, muddy ponds. Its flesh is good inland, though on the west coast often unfit for food from its habit of feeding on dead salmon."

Figure 151
Old-squaw; scale, $\frac{1}{4}$.

*a*, male in summer.
*b*, male in winter.
*c*, female.

Figure 152
Tail of Old-squaw (male); scale, $\frac{1}{5}$.

154. **Old-squaw.** COCKAWEE. LONG-TAILED DUCK. LE KAKAWI (le Canard à longue queue). *Clangula hiemalis.* L, 21. (Projection of two middle tail feathers beyond others 4·5-5·0.) A medium-sized duck showing a remarkable seasonal change of coloration. The adult male in spring and summer has head (Figure 151a), neck, breast, and back dark seal-brown, lower abdomen and flanks white. There is an almost white, mask-like patch including the eye and rusty-ochre stripes over the wings and at base of hindneck. In winter, the colours change entirely and it becomes a mostly white, instead of a mostly dark, bird (Figure 151b). Head and neck white with a light grey face and a large, dark, and rusty grey patch over cheeks and ears. White below, with a broad belt of dark seal-brown, nearly black, sharply defined against white base of foreneck above and abdomen below. Above, white of neck extended almost to shoulders; back black with spray of elongated pearl-grey feathers drooping from shoulders over wings. No speculum or wing marks. In both seasons the long, central tail feathers (Figure 152) are conspicuous. There is a band of orange or pink about the bill. The female is more obscurely coloured. Flanks and below white, with a dull breast-band. Above, dark brown with lighter feather edges. Head (Figure 151c) with dark brown cap extending down back of neck. Extensive brown cheek and ear patch suffusing over throat and down foreneck, leaving face in front of the eye greyish, and sides of neck white. There is no speculum, or white of any kind, on the wings in either sex or any plumage.

*Distinctions.* The male with its long "sprigs" or centre tail feathers can be mistaken only for the Pintail, but its entirely different colour and decidedly chunky build make confusion unlikely.

The female is less easily characterized. In general appearance it resembles the female Harlequin or Buffle-head. Its much larger size, lack of white wing spot, and presence of white on the neck, separate it easily from the Buffle-head; its white underparts and flanks, larger amount of white on head, and white neck are distinctive from the Harlequin.

*Field Marks.* The long tail of the male, along with chunky build and general coloration. In winter, it is mostly white with a conspicuous black patch on the side of the head. In summer it is mostly black, or very dark, with a white mask. The female is largely white, especially on flanks and underparts, the only such duck with solidly dark wings. The species is comparatively easy to recognize in life by these characteristics.

*Nesting.* On the ground, near water, hidden under bushes or grass.

*Distribution.* Common in winter on the seacoasts or the Great Lakes, rare in the interior. We have only occasional records for the species from the prairie sections. Breeds on the Barren Grounds across the continent. It is regularly only a winter visitor or migrant in our southern localities, but occasional subnormal birds summer on the southern coasts and the larger more northern lakes.

In the southern regions of Canada it is essentially a winter duck and a bird of the seacoasts. It winters there in enormous flocks and is a most expert diver, sometimes being taken from fish-nets at depths of 90 feet or more. It is considered nearly worthless as a table-bird.

155. **Harlequin Duck.** LORD AND LADY. ROCK DUCK. LA CANE DE ROCHE. *Histrionicus histrionicus.* L, 17. Plate XI A. A small duck, well named after particoloured Harlequin.

*Distinctions.* The male with its striking coloration is not to be confused with any other species. The female, however, is not unlike the females of several other species. Having no wing spot or speculum sets her off from all other comparable ducks except the Old-squaw, the Surf Scoter, and the Ruddy. From the Old-squaw she can be told by the evenly dark head and neck with two, sometimes three, white spots on the sides of the head and the dark flanks and undertail coverts. From the Surf Scoter, she is distinguished in hand by very much smaller size and the more delicate, un-scoter-like bill (Compare with Figure 159). From the Ruddy female she differs in having a small, narrow, instead of a large, flat, or spatulate, bill (Compare with Figure 161), and the brown areas are sooty and solid without suggestion of rusty or ochraceous vermiculation on the back. There is a slight general resemblance to the female Buffle-head (Figure 150), but there is no white on the wing.

*Field Marks.* As far away as colour details can be made out, the male Harlequin with its sharp, contrasting white spots on a dark ground is conspicuously identifiable. The crescent just in front of the wing is visible at a great distance. The female is more easily confused, especially with the Buffle-head, the Old-squaw, and the Surf Scoter. From the Buffle-head its larger size, general darkness of underbody, two or three instead of one vague light spot on the face, and lack of white on wing when flying will differentiate under most circumstances. From the Old-squaw, which is also without wing spot, it is probably best distinguished by its dark instead of light underparts and flanks, the small amount of white on the head, and the total absence of white from the neck. The round white spot on the side of the hind head is the most conspicuous of these facial marks and has quite a different appearance from the white streak back from the eye of the female Old-squaw (Figure 151c). In general coloration the female Harlequin is an almost exact small replica of the female Surf Scoter. When the great difference in size cannot be estimated, the more delicate bill and head outline is the best distinction from the heavy-billed, large-headed Scoter.

*Nesting.* On the ground, under rocks or driftwood or in hollow trees.

*Distribution.* A bird of peculiar, discontinuous distribution. Common on the northern Atlantic and the Pacific coasts and in the interior of British Columbia. Rather scarce through Slave River and Mackenzie River Valleys and never seeming to come south into the prairie sections except in the foothills or regions adjacent to the mountains. It breeds on the mountain streams, probably wherever found, and on south Baffin Island and adjacent Labrador.

*SUBSPECIES.* The western American and northeastern Asian birds of this species have been separated from our eastern birds by small details of colour, as the Western Harlequin Duck (la Cane de roche de l'Ouest) *Histrionicus histrionicus pacificus.*

A. Ferruginous Rough-leg; scale, $\frac{1}{6}$
Most common phase

B. Marsh Hawk; scale, $\frac{1}{6}$
Adult male — Juvenile

PLATE XVI

A. Osprey; scale, 1/10

B. Peregrine Falcon; scale, $\frac{1}{6}$

Juvenile    Adult male

This is a bird typical of the mountain torrents. Its summer home is the brawling glacial streams that descend the mountain sides, and the little pot-hole lakes that dot the higher valleys. The female raises her young in quiet, little glacial lakes, while the male, gay Harlequin that he is, betakes himself to the seacoast, where in company with others of his sex and some unmated or bereaved females, he spends the summer off rocky shores or on the kelp beds. The beauty of these wonderful little ducks has given them the name among prospectors and trappers of "Lord and Lady Duck," and their chosen haunts on the coast have suggested the term "Rock Duck."

156. **Labrador Duck.** LE CANARD DU LABRADOR. *Camptorhynchus labradorius.* L, 20. A good sized duck, now extinct. The male was strikingly pied with black and white with a distinct black ring around a white neck.

*Distinctions.* White head and neck with sharp black ring in the male. In the female, the broad bill probably curled up near the tip in old specimens. Any newly found specimen, however, should be identified with great care.

*Distribution.* East coast. As the species became extinct about 1875, before much was known about it, its distribution can only be inferred. It is known mostly from wintering specimens on the New England coast and probably bred somewhere on Labrador.

Figure 153
Labrador Duck; scale, ½.
Female Male

EIDERS

Though not forming a recognized systematic subdivision of the ducks, the Eiders are sufficiently similar to warrant special reference as a group in a popular work of this kind.

*General Description.* Large, sturdily built birds; with the scoters, the largest of our ducks. Males have broad masses of contrasting black and white, with sharp secant markings, and delicate suffusions of pale nile green and wine-coloured tints. The females are coloured in even shades of brown and are notable in being more or less extensively crossbarred, in some cases completely around the body, at others mostly across breast and flanks. The bills, except of Steller's and Spectacled Eiders, are stout, and much intruded upon by plumage at the base (*See* Figures 155 to 157).

*Distinctions.* In size and heavy build like the scoters, but the males have large amounts of white and the females are crossbarred in brown.

*Distribution.* Arctic and marine in distribution. Seldom coming down from their northern haunts, and only accidentally, if ever, on fresh water.

The Eiders are notable as the source of the eiderdown of commerce. It is the under, or body, down plucked by the bird itself for use as nesting material. Each nest is composed of a considerable mass of warm down on which the eggs are laid and with which they are covered when the parent leaves the nest. In Iceland, small amounts of down are gathered at regular intervals during egg deposition and incubation. This is gradually replaced by the bird as long as her supply lasts, after which she is left in peace until the eggs are hatched, when the remainder is also taken. After cleaning from adherent straws, grasses, and bits of moss the down is ready for sale and use. In that country land-holders have a proprietary right in the Eiders that nest on their lands. The birds are strictly protected and encouraged to nest close to the houses, where they become semi-domestic in their habits and furnish a regular and appreciable source of income.

157. **Steller's Eider.** L'EIDER DE STELLER. *Polysticta stelleri.* L, 17. The smallest and the least eider-like of any of the birds known under that name. Male: white, except for the following details—neck all around and back, iridescent blue-black. The head is peculiarly silvery in its whiteness, with a throat patch and spot encircling the eye of dead black. A small, dark, sap-green nape crest and a suffusion of same colour in front of eye (Figure 154). Below—abdomen to tail very dark, carbonized brown suffusing up flanks and breast in a lighter burnt vinaceous tint—as though the bird had squatted on a hot plate. A group of narrow feathers, striped iridescent black and white, falling in curved plumes over the secondaries on the closed wing. The female is rich dark brown, with suggestion of scorching below, more or less crossbarred with lighter on upper breast, neck, and face. Both sexes have an iridescent, blue-black speculum bordered each side with white like a Mallard (*See* Figure 127, page 88).

Figure 154
Steller's Eider; scale, ½.
Female Male

*Distinctions.* In the male the general coloration, especially the silvery sheen of the face and crown. In the female general dark brown colour, crossbarring on breast and face, and white-bordered blue speculum.

*Field Marks.* Probably, large amount of white on body, black neck and throat, and silver-white face and crown make as good field marks for adult male as can be given. Except within its natural range not to be recorded on sight identification.

*Nesting.* On the ground of the tundra.

*Distribution.* Coast of Bering Sea and adjoining Arctic Ocean. Occurs occasionally east to the Yukon coast, possibly beyond. More common on Siberian side of Bering Strait.

A distinctively beautiful bird to be expected in Canada only along the extreme western Arctic coast or as a possible rare straggler on the Pacific.

160. **Common Eider Duck.** LE MOYAC (l'Eider). *Somateria mollissima.* L, 23. Male: black below, cutting sharply against the white breast which is delicately suffused with vinaceous pink; white above; head white with nile-green suffusion from cheeks to nape; broad black on crown and through eye to hind head. Female: evenly coloured in a fine pattern of various browns, blacks, and light ochres arranged in broken bars around the body. Bill processes extending up either side of forehead in long, fleshy tongues.

Figure 155
American Eider Duck; scale, ¼.
Female Male

*Distinctions.* An eastern coast species. The male is mistakable for no other eastern species, but differs from the Pacific Eider in lacking the black V line on the throat. The female is much like that of the King Eider, but the feathering of the sides of the cheek extend forward to be in line with the nostrils instead of stopping well back from them (Compare Figures 155 and 156 with 157).

*Field Marks.* Size and general coloration.

*Nesting.* On ground, nest built entirely of down.

*Distribution.* The Eider Duck inhabits northern parts of Europe and eastern America. A strictly Atlantic bird breeding in the eastern Canadian Arctic and in Greenland.

*SUBSPECIES.* The American Eiders differ slightly from those of Europe and Greenland and are referred to two subspecies—the Northern Eider (Le Moyac du Nord) *Somateria mollissima borealis* with the bill processes sharp and pointed and inhabiting the northern waters from some place on Labrador northward, and the Southern Eider (Le Moyac du Sud) *Somateria mollissima dresseri* with broad, rounded bill processes, breeding from northern Maine to southern Labrador.

In Scandinavia and Iceland the Eiders are semi-domesticated and the down derived from their nests is an important source of revenue. Though on the Labrador and Gulf of St. Lawrence coasts there are immense flocks of these birds little attempt has been made to turn them to account except as food; but the numbers have been so rapidly reduced by reckless killing and egging that only a small fraction of the original number remains. On these bleak and desolate coasts where fresh meat is scarce the Eiders should be conserved for food if for nothing else. An intelligent and far-seeing policy would conserve the Eiders for all time to come, supply a liberal amount of flesh food and eggs, and at the same time produce a crop of down worth in the markets far more than the carcasses of the dead birds.

161. **Pacific Eider.** LE MOYAC DU PACIFIQUE. *Somateria v-nigra.* L, 24. A large eider. Like the American Eider but with a sharp, black V on throat. White above, black below, the latter cutting squarely and sharply against a white breast delicately tinted with vinaceous. Neck, throat, and cheeks, pure white; jet black cap extending to below eyes, split over the hind head by a wedge of white, nape washed with delicate nile-green that fades gradually away into cheeks and under eyes (Figure 156). Female: light brown, crossbarred on breast, flanks, and much of back with dark cream, and light rusty ochre crown and face finely streaked with dark.

*Distinctions.* The male likely to be confused only with the American Eider. To be distinguished from it by a black V with apex on throat under the gape and arms extending under cheeks (Compare with Figure 155). The eastern Eider, however, is not known to occur west of Hudson Bay. The female resembles the female King Eider, but may always be distinguished from it by the feathering of the sides of the bill extending as far as the nostrils (Compare with Figure 157). From the eastern American Eider, the species can be told by the shape of the long bill processes. In the Pacific-Eider these long, fleshy extrusions average thinner, narrower, and sharper and extend along the top of the forehead instead of slightly along the sides of the face.

*Field Marks.* White back, and head, with black cap, probably make the best field marks.

*Nesting.* On the ground of the tundra.

*Distribution.* The western Arctic coast and islands from Coronation Gulf to shores of Bering Sea. Occasional on lower Mackenzie and Great Slave Lake. One record reported from Washington coast. To be expected on inland waters or on our west coast only as a straggler.

Figure 156
Pacific Eider; scale, ¼.
Female Male

The largest of the western Eiders and to be looked for as an occasional winter visitor on the outer British Columbia coast.

162. **King Eider.** LE MOYAC REMARQUABLE (le Warnecootai). *Somateria spectabilis.* L, 23. A large Eider. Adult male: black below and mostly black on body above. Foreparts all white to head, the white falling like a cape over shoulders, narrowing to a point between the wings where it is sharply demarcated, and cutting sharply straight across lower breast, where it is tinged with warm vinaceous, against the black underparts. Wing-coverts, and a conspicuous spot on either side at the base of the tail, white. The head is very distinctive. The base of the bill on either side rises in high, broad, fleshy processes, coloured orange-yellow in life, and bordered by a narrow line of black velvety feathers. The cheeks are flushed with delicate nile-green and the crown and nape are chalky blue. The throat is marked with a black V, the apex being under the bill and the arms extending under the line of the cheek feathers (Figure 157). The female is similar to the female of the Pacific Eider, light brown, more or less finely streaked on head and neck and coarsely V-marked with dark and light on breast, back, and flanks.

Figure 157
King Eider; scale, ¼.
Female Male

*Distinctions.* The adult male in breeding plumage is unmistakable with his great yellow bill processes and general coloration. The juvenile and the female are so like parallel plumages of the Common and Pacific Eiders that the bill feathering is probably the only reliable distinction. In the King Eider the featheration on the sides of the bill does not extend nearly as far as the nostrils (Compare Figure 157 with 155 and 156).

*Field Marks.* The breeding male with its bright yellow bill processes can be recognized at long range. When this cannot be seen, the largely black, instead of largely white, back should distinguish it from any other eider with which it might be confused. Females and juveniles can probably be recognized only when in hand.

*Nesting.* On the ground of the tundras, or under driftwood on the seashore.

*Distribution.* Northern parts of both hemispheres. Breeds along our whole northern coast and the islands north of them. We have no records for the western interior or the west coast. In winter south on east coast to Nova Scotia. Occasional on Lake Ontario.

158. **Spectacled Eider.** L'EIDER À LUNETTES. *Arctonetta fischeri.* L, 21. A larger bird than Steller's, but smaller than any of the other eiders. Below—beginning sharply at base of white neck dark slate grey, shading to dark brown on abdomen and flanks. Above—largely white with spray of stiff, curved white feathers falling over closed secondaries. Head with yellow bill, white throat, sea-green cheeks, a hanging crest of stiff nile-green feathers on sides of nape. In front of eyes a spot of sap-green feathers of peculiar texture, resembling deep-piled velvet. The most striking feature of the face, however, is a circle of soft silvery white feathers about the eye, sharply bordered by a thin line of black that suggests the name "Spectacled." The female is light brown, darker above, with broken dark and rusty bars across breast, flanks, and on back. The head is light and finely streaked.

Figure 158
Spectacled Eider; scale, $\frac{1}{4}$.
Female Male

*Distinctions.* The coloration and spectacles of the male are unmistakable. The female is easily recognized as an Eider by its crossbarring, and as this species by the peculiar circle of finely marked and velvety brownish plumage about the eye, the equivalent of the similarly situated white eye spot of the male.

*Field Marks.* The white body and head, with dull, but not black, crown, and conspicuous white eye spot, should be recognizable at considerable distance. Females are probably not recognizable in life except under exceptional circumstances.

*Nesting.* On the ground of the tundras.

*Distribution.* Coast of Bering Sea and adjoining Arctic coasts. Regularly occurring in Canada only on the Yukon coast and the mouth of Mackenzie River, perhaps straggling farther east.

A very beautiful but locally distributed Eider that is to be expected only as a rare straggler away from the western Arctic coast.

## Scoters

The Scoters, comprising the genus *Oidemia*, are large, heavily built birds, and with the Eiders the largest of our ducks. Males are solid black with only small spots of white. The bills are swollen at the base and highly coloured. The females are coloured in heavy masses of dark brown or nearly black, without distinct pattern.

*Distinctions.* The males are the only ducks approaching solid black or with the peculiarly swollen bills (Figures 159 and 160). The females are the only solidly, dark-coloured ducks without definite pattern.

*Distribution.* Northern parts of both hemispheres.

Scoters are expert divers and feed largely on shells and crustaceans. In the summer, large flocks of males and non-breeding females gather in the middle of the larger waters and on the seacoast in the kelp beds. They seem to get most of their food from the bottom, even in water of considerable depth.

165. **White-winged Scoter.** LA MACREUSE À AILES BLANCHES. *Melanitta deglandi.* L, 22. Plate XI B.

*Distinctions.* Always easily recognizable in any plumage by the over-all black or dark coloration and the large white wing patch.

*Field Marks.* In any plumage, a large, black, heavily built duck with pronounced white wing patches.

*Nesting.* On the ground, under or among bushes, sometimes in the woods a long way from water.

*Distribution.* Across the continent. Breeding on the prairies northward. Though a common migrant and summering in large numbers off the coast we have no breeding records for British Columbia or the eastern provinces.

This is the commonest scoter throughout most of southern Canada. Though it breeds on the prairies from the southern boundary northward it is still an interesting problem where the vast numbers of scoters that frequent the two coasts at all seasons build their nests. Much more information is desired on this point.

166. **Surf Scoter.** BOTTLE-NOSED DIVER. SKUNK-HEAD. LA MACREUSE DU RESSAC *Melanitta perspicillata.* L, 20. Adult male: an all-black scoter with greatly swollen highly coloured bill and two sharply defined triangular white patches on head; one on the forehead, the other on nape and back of neck.

Female: light brown, lightening on cheeks and below, and a more or less well-defined dark cap.

*Distinctions.* The male with its solid blackness and two white head patches is easily recognized. The bill is unique. The base is much swollen at the sides behind the nostrils, and on this extruded surface is a sharply defined, irregular spot of black surrounded with white which shades into yellow towards the tip and into red on the culmen.

Figure 159
Surf Scoter; scale, ½.
Female Male

The female resembles the female American Scoter except that the lightness of the cheeks is usually broken into two vague spots. The best characteristic for separation of any plumage of the Surf from the American Scoter is the featheration of bill; the feathers of crown extending a considerable distance down the culmen instead of cutting off squarely at the forehead (Compare Figure 159 with 160).

*Field Marks.* Under some conditions, rather difficult to distinguish from the American Scoter. The lack of white wing patches separates it easily from the White-winged. The peculiar bill coloration and the white spots on forehead and nape are distinguishable at a considerable distance. The nape spot, however, is not permanent; the white feathers composing it are shed at times, leaving an area of black down in its place, discernible on close examination from the surrounding blackness by its velvety texture.

The female is probably not separable under ordinary conditions from the female American Scoter. The species is, however, identifiable in flight by the loud whistling made by its wings, audible at times, when in flock, for half a mile or more.

*Nesting.* In grass, near water.

*Distribution.* Across the continent, more common on the seacoasts than inland. Apparently it nests in the forest area north of the prairies in Mackenzie and Alaska, but substantiated breeding records are few, and there is none at all for British Columbia. Like some other ducks it is often present in large numbers throughout the summer off Vancouver Island coast, where thousands may be seen, without signs of nesting. This is an excellent example of presence in nesting season being insufficient evidence for breeding records.

163. **American Scoter.** BLACK SEA COOT. BUTTER-NOSED SCOTER. LA MACREUSE À BEC JAUNE. *Oidemia americana.* L, 19. Adult male: solid coal black with base of bill swollen and coloured bright yellow. Female: brown, lightening on throat, cheeks, and abdomen and with a rather sharply defined dark cap.

*Distinctions.* The solid black plumage of the male, unrelieved by any colour, and the yellow bill enlargement are very distinctive. The female resembles the female Surf Scoter very closely. The light colour on the face is more evenly distributed and not broken into patches as is usually the case in the latter species. The most reliable distinction seems to be the bill. In the female American, the forehead feathering does not extend down the culmen as it does in the Surf Scoter (Compare Figure 160 with 159).

Figure 160
American Scoter; scale, ¼.
Female Male

*Field Marks.* This is the smallest of the scoters. The solid blackness of the male, and yellow "butter-bill," are very distinctive. Both sexes show silvery on the under surface of the primaries in flight, but females looking solid black in the distance or against the sky may not always be separable from the Surf Scoter in life. The absence of white wing patches will always separate this species and the Surf Scoter from the White-winged.

*Nesting.* On the ground near water.

*Distribution.* Across the continent. Rare or absent from the interior. Breeds in northeastern Asia and northwestern Alaska. Nesting in Canada but little known.

167. **Ruddy Duck.** LE CANARD ROUX. *Erismatura jamaicensis.* L, 15. A rather small duck. Breeding male: rufous-chestnut on flanks, back, and neck. Below, white with a peculiar grebe-like, silvery sheen vaguely crossbarred with brown that becomes more pronounced on the breast. The crown is covered with a black cap and the face and chin are pure white. The bill is a bright sky blue. The bill colour fades after breeding season, but the vestiges of the ruddy breast persist through the autumn. The

Figure 161
Ruddy Duck; scale, ¼.
Female Male

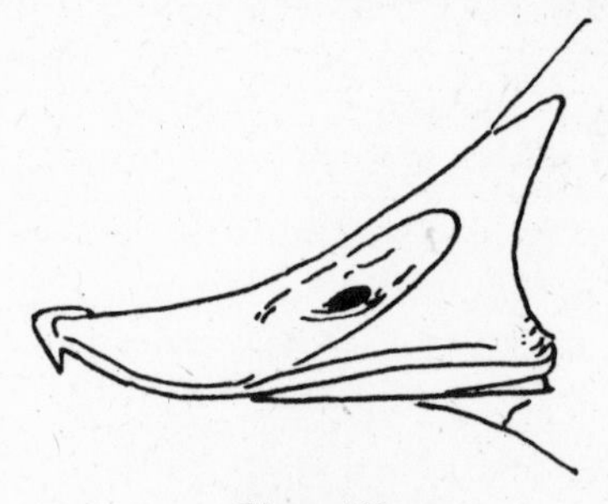

Figure 162
Bill of Ruddy Duck;
natural size.

female is a brownish bird, lighter below, with the same silvery sheen as the male. The cap is brown and the face with a vague light spot broken by a faint dark streak from the gape back over the ears.

*Distinctions.* The red male with contrasting black and white head is very distinctive. The female is in plain browns without sharply characterized markings anywhere. She closely resembles the female Buffle-head, but has no white wing spot, is not as white below, and the face mark is less distinct and of different pattern (*See* Figure 150, page 100). She has an even closer resemblance to the female Harlequin, but with different face pattern (*See* Plate XI A), and the back has a very fine pepper-and-salt, or semi-vermiculated, effect, with minute specks of rufous and ochre. The Ruddy can be separated in all plumages from any other duck by the distinctively dense plumage below, with its grebe-like sheen, the tail of stiff, spike-like feathers, and the broad, short bill with peculiar hook to the nail (Figure 163).

*Field Marks.* The red back, black cap, or white face patch of the male can be recognized at long distance. The round, chunky body, the short thick neck, and the habit of carrying the tail spread star-like over the back are also characteristic. The general chunky outline is probably the best recognition mark for the female in life.

*Nesting.* In reeds, over water.

*Distribution.* Across the continent, scarce eastward. Breeding in the prairies and southern British Columbia northward.

The Ruddy Duck is a unique little bird and does not seem very closely related to the other ducks. In the breeding season it is amusing to watch the male as he bustles importantly about his dull-coloured mate, cutting rippled circles on the water, bobbing and bowing, the erect, spread tail making him look still dumpier and shorter.

"The Ruddy Duck is not regularly hunted anywhere in the west. It is seldom found in the shallow sloughs and as it is not given to making flights, it can usually be shot only on the water."

### Subfamily—Merginae. Mergansers. Fish Ducks. Saw-bills

*General Description.* Fish-eating ducks with a more cylindrical, tapering, and less spatulate or flattened bill than the other ducks (Figure 163, compare with 126, page 87). The cutting edges of the mandibles have a series of serrations giving rise to the popular name "Sawbill." The nail on the tip of the bill forms a small but evident hook. The hind toe (Figure 164) is developed into a flat paddle or fin-shaped lobe similar to that of the Sea Ducks and quite different from the hind toe of the River Ducks (Compare with Figure 125, page 87). The males are brightly and strikingly coloured, mostly in black and white. The females are dull coloured, with reddish heads and necks. Most plumages have crests. In the females and most young birds, the crests, to the casual eye, are ragged, and without well-defined shape.

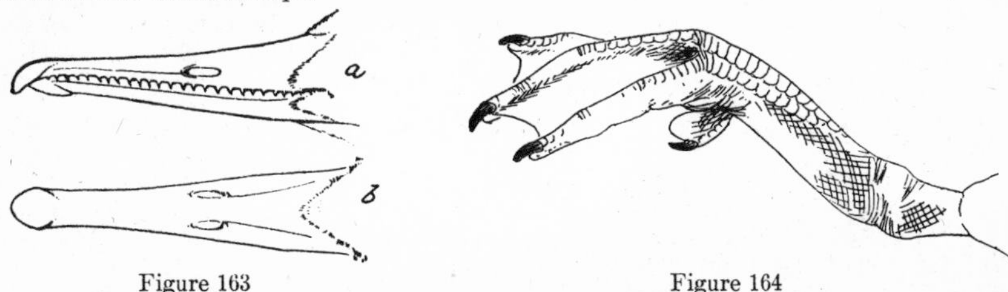


Figure 163
Bill of Mergansers.

Figure 164
Foot of Merganser; scale, $\frac{1}{2}$.

*Distinctions.* The saw-toothed bill easily distinguishes the Mergansers from the Sea Ducks which resemble them in the character of the hind toe.

*Field Marks.* Typical Mergansers are long, slender ducks with long, slim bills. The slenderness of general build and the long-headedness are apparent both at rest and in flight. When flying, the bill, head, neck, and body are carried in a straight line which gives a drawn-out appearance that is quite characteristic. Mergansers, except the Hooded, which is rather solitary, usually fly in long, single files or lengthened flocks approximating lines, rarely in irregular, indiscriminate bunches as do other ducks. They are seldom seen high in the air, but usually pass over the water low down and just above the surface. Scoters also have this habit, but are heavier in build and much blacker.

*Nesting.* Mergansers in the breeding season are mostly river haunters, nesting either on the ground, among rocks, or in hollow trees.

*Distribution.* A small family; most of its species inhabit the northern hemisphere.

Mergansers feed upon fish and shell-fish captured under water by diving; for this method of feeding their hooked and serrated bills are admirably adapted. They are, during the breeding season, mostly fresh-water frequenters, though they visit the seas sometimes in large numbers. They are not very desirable as food, though some young autumn birds, properly cooked, are not to be altogether despised.

76916—8

*Economic Status.* Mergansers eat fish and, in certain waters—such as at the heads of salmon streams—they may do appreciable harm. Ordinary trout streams are too small for these species and it is only in special circumstances that their depredations are serious. In waters that successfully withstand commercial fishing, the fish taken by even a considerable number of Mergansers may be disregarded. In streams where angling is the most important interest too many Mergansers may be a just cause of complaint. However, Mergansers, like other birds, tend to take the food most easily obtained. The fish most highly valued by sportsmen are those agile, game varieties that are seldom pursued by Mergansers or other feathered fish-eaters when less active ones are available. These birds should not be condemned on suspicion, circumstantial evidence, or individual examples, but only after thorough investigation and proof of their destructiveness. The Migratory Birds Convention, on proper application, affords relief against birds that are doing serious damage, and if an examination by qualified investigators shows that valuable interests are being seriously injured, permits for *necessary* destruction can be obtained.

131. **Hooded Merganser.** LE BEC-SCIE HUPPÉ. *Lophodytes cucullatus.* L, 17·50. The smallest of our Mergansers. The male is a most striking bird with great black and white "hood" and rich chestnut flanks. The distinctive hood is a flat, disk-like crest, coloured pure white with a narrow, black edge that rises from the forehead, makes a wide, circular arch over the head, and meets the neck at the nape. The female is much duller coloured, with brownish fuscous body, lighter below, and with a thin, fan-shaped, reddish brown crest.

Figure 165
Hooded Merganser; scale, ½.
Male Female

*Distinctions.* The male is unlike any other bird on the continent. The female can always be distinguished by small size for its subfamily, and its entirely different coloration from other Mergansers in Canada.

*Field Marks.* The male with its strong black and white coloration and big hood is easily recognizable. The female and juvenile male are small, dull-coloured ducks with thin crests. In flight, the contrasting black and white lanceolate striping of the tertials falling over the base of the wing can often be recognized when other specific details are not evident.

*Nesting.* In hollow trees.

*Distribution.* More or less common over all of Canada, north to tree limit. It probably nests wherever it can find suitable timber.

The Hooded Merganser is a bird of quiet ponds and woodland pools. It is the most edible of the Mergansers, which fact, as well as the clearing of the timber, and its nesting in easily accessible localities, has probably reduced its numbers.

*Economic Status.* It is doubtful if any serious charge can be proved against this little Merganser. Its chosen haunts are not those of game or food fish, and it probably consumes a smaller proportion of fish than either of its larger relatives.

129. **Common Merganser.** SAW-BILL. GOOSANDER. SHELDRAKE. SHELDUCK. LE HARLE COMMUN. *Mergus merganser.* L, 25.

*Distinctions.* Male: much similar to next species, but larger and of heavier build throughout, without crest or reddish breast-band and with more white less interrupted with black on flank, wings, and neck. The delicate salmon tint of the underbody is present

PLATE XVII

A. American Sparrow Hawk; scale, $\frac{1}{6}$

Male Female

B. Blue Grouse (Sooty Grouse); scale, $\frac{1}{6}$

Female Male (hooting)

PLATE XVIII

A. Spruce Partridge; scale, $\frac{1}{5}$

Female Male

B. Ruffed Grouse; scale, $\frac{1}{6}$

Grey phase Red phase

only in the highest plumage and quickly fades to white after death. Female and young male are alike and not distinguishable from parallel plumages of the Red-breasted Merganser except by careful study of details. The head is generally a deeper brown and stops with a sharp line where it meets the grey of the lower neck. The upper throat usually has a well-defined, pure white patch. The bill characteristics (Figure 168) are the only ones for absolute identification. The bill of the American is of heavier and less slender build, and the nostrils are set near the centre of its length instead of well within its basal half (Compare with Figure 169). These are distinctions that are evident only when both species are in hand for direct comparison. The feathering of the base of the bill gives an absolute distinction. In this species the feathering of the sides of the two mandibles extends forward an approximately equal distance, instead of the upper featheration decidedly over-reaching the lower.

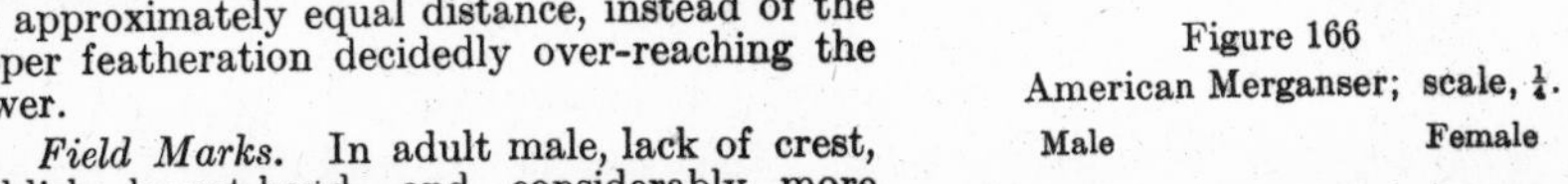

Figure 166
American Merganser; scale, ¼.
Male Female

*Field Marks.* In adult male, lack of crest, reddish breast-band, and considerably more white on sides, flanks, and wings. In flight, the large amount of white on the bend of the wing and outer scapulars. It is doubtful whether females may be distinguished in life, with certainty, from the Red-breasted Merganser. The darker brown of the head, its sharp ending on the neck, and the white throat are suggestive but not determinative characters.

*Nesting.* In hollow trees or rock cavities near water. Nest of grasses, etc.

*Distribution.* Common in New and Old Worlds, nesting throughout western Canada, north to limit of trees.

*SUBSPECIES.* Represented in America by the American Common Merganser *Mergus merganser americanus* (le Grand Bec-scie) a very close relative of the European form.

Figure 167
Appearance in flight of American Mergansers.

This is the larger of the two representatives of this genus, but generally frequents the smaller waters, streams, and lakes. It is less common than the Red-breasted on the larger lakes or the sea. Otherwise the two birds are similar in habit.

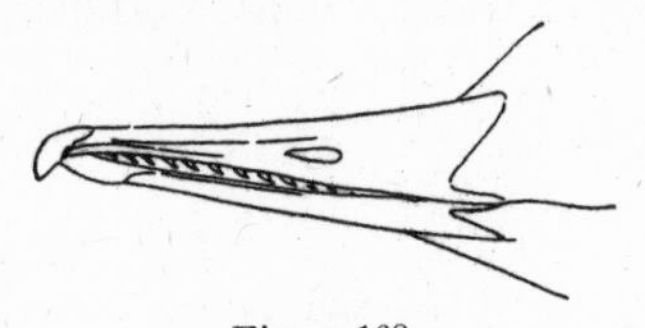

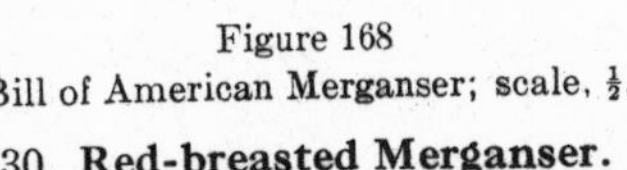

Figure 168
Bill of American Merganser; scale, ½.

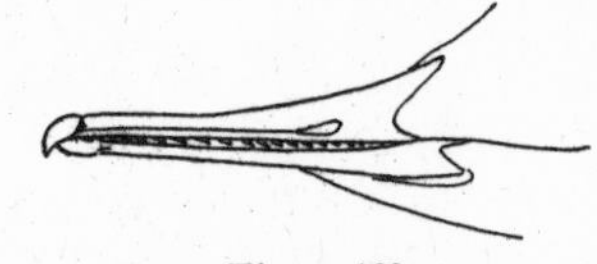

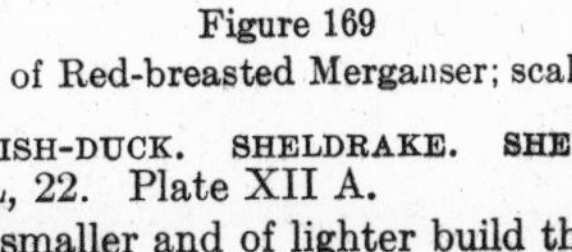

Figure 169
Bill of Red-breasted Merganser; scale, ½.

130. **Red-breasted Merganser.** SAW-BILL. FISH-DUCK. SHELDRAKE. SHELDUCK. LE BEC-SCIE À POITRINE ROUSSE. *Mergus serrator.* L, 22. Plate XII A.

*Distinctions.* Male: similar to last species, but smaller and of lighter build throughout, with crest and reddish band across breast and with less white more interrupted with black on flank, wings, and neck. The delicate salmon tint of the underbody is present only in highest plumage and quickly fades to white after death. Female and young are alike and not distinguishable from parallel plumages of the American Merganser without careful study of details. The head is generally a paler red and blends gradually into the grey of the lower neck. The reddish colour suffuses over the throat which is usually light, but it rarely has a decided white patch. The bill characteristics are the only certain identification. The bill of the Red-breasted is of lighter and more slender build and the nostrils are well within its basal half. These are comparative distinctions, only evident when both species are in hand for direct comparison. The feathering of the base of the bill is absolutely distinctive. In this species the feathering of sides of the upper mandible extends well forward of that on the lower (Figure 169).

*Field Marks.* Like the preceding species except—in adult male—presence of crest, immaculate white or pink underbody, dark breast-band, and less white on sides, flank, and wings. In flight, smaller amount of white on bend of wing and outer scapulars. It is questionable whether females can be distinguished in life with certainty from the previous species. The paler red of the head, its gradual blending into the lower neck and body colour, and the lack of decided white throat patch are suggestive but not determinative.

*Nesting.* On ground near water, sometimes in trees.

*Distribution.* More or less common throughout Canada, nesting north to Arctic coast.

In general habits similar to the preceding, but more often seen on the larger waters and comparatively rare on small streams and pools.

## Order—Falconiformes. Diurnal Birds of Prey

*General Description.* Flesh-eating birds with four well-developed toes, each armed with a strong, sharp claw or talon for seizing and holding prey. Bill is hooked, and the base covered with a swollen soft skin or cere in which the nostrils are situated (Figure 171, but *See also* 172, page 114). The Birds of Prey differ from the generality of birds in that the females are considerably larger than the males. This is probably due to the greater strain placed upon the female in feeding her young. This greater responsibility, demanding strength, weight, and endurance rather than fine technique, necessitates a higher development of these qualities in the female than in the male, who, although he may assist his mate, has not the final responsibility for the growing family.

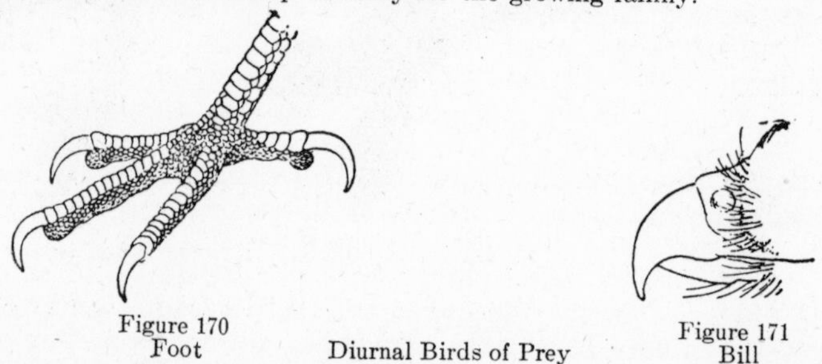

Figure 170
Foot

Diurnal Birds of Prey

Figure 171
Bill

*Distribution.* Raptorial birds are distributed over all the world except the Antarctic continent, where their place is taken by the Skua Gulls and other rapacious sea-birds.

Though for many years the Diurnal Birds of Prey have been closely associated with the Nocturnal Birds of Prey (Owls) by systematists, latest revisions have quite removed them from each other and the Owls have been given an order to themselves (*Strigiformes*). *Falconiformes* is divided into two Suborders: *Cathartae* American Vultures; and *Falcones* the Hawks, Eagles, etc.

*Economic Status.* Perhaps no birds are better known and at the same time so generally misunderstood in their economic relations as these. All know the flesh-eating propensities of the hawks, owls, and eagles, but few realize that amongst them are some of man's best friends and that the popular policy of killing them indiscriminately is a mistaken one. Some do considerable damage, but to include all in the condemnation merited by the few is a grave economic error. The first family, the Vultures, are repulsive birds, but as scavengers exceedingly useful, and no valid complaint can be lodged against them. Of the Diurnal and Nocturnal Rapaces, their mixed status is the cause of much misconception. Fortunately in regard to these birds we can speak with authority based upon actual data and not mere speculation. The United States Biological Survey made a thorough study of the food habits of American hawks and owls, basing its conclusions upon the examination of about 2,700 stomachs taken in all seasons of the year in various parts of the United States and Canada. The whole, with the data for its substantiation, is embodied in a report, "The Hawks and Owls of the United States," by Dr. A. K. Fisher.[1] Although compiled in and for an adjoining country all Canadian species are treated, and the results are as applicable to Canada as to the United States. As some of the less harmful species do not occur in Canada the following percentages should be slightly altered for our use, but not enough to modify perceptibly the general conclusions. Only six of the seventy-three species studied are injurious. Of these, three are extremely rare in Canada, and one is altogether a fish-eater. Of the remainder, 56 per cent of the stomachs examined contained mice and other small mammals, 27 per cent insects, and only 3½ per cent poultry or game-birds. Dividing the thirty-three raptorial birds of western Canada into groups according to their economic status we find that four species are wholly beneficial and absolutely harmless; seventeen are mainly beneficial, doing decidedly more good than harm; six are about balanced in their effect; and six are positively harmful. Only three of these six are common enough to warrant consideration and only two, the Sharp-shinned and Cooper's Hawks, are numerous enough in the thickly settled communities to be noticed. The Goshawk is a more northern species whose distribution overlaps the edges of settlement on the north or in the mountains.

In making these generalized estimates, it should be understood that they are based on averages of the whole country throughout the year. Local conditions, time of year, and the particular interests of the locality may modify the conclusions. For instance, the Red-tailed Hawk, in summer time on the open prairie, is just as efficient and indefatigable a gopher killer as the Ferruginous Rough-leg; in the autumn when gophers have holed up, and the young, inexperienced hawks are seeking easily captured prey, game and poultry may in some cases suffer slightly from their attack. The Bald Eagle is only a rare picturesque feature of the landscape over most of Canada, but on the coasts it is often seen in greatly increased number and may be a serious enemy of water-fowl. The Marsh Hawk is an inveterate mouser, but in early summer the abundance of young upland and marsh game has attractions for it. Just where to draw the line between generally beneficial and harmful species is thus sometimes difficult to decide.

Raptorial birds, like human beings, tend to subsist on that which is first to hand, and a generalization based on one set of conditions will not always hold good for others. It is a natural psychological fact that we ourselves feel a definitely known, concrete loss more keenly than we do a much greater one that we have unwittingly escaped. The loss of a single partly grown chicken to hawks is more keenly realized than the absence of some hundreds of gophers that never intruded themselves upon our consciousness. The one fact is taken as a calamity, the other as a matter

[1] See also "The Hawks of the Canadian Prairie Provinces in Their Relation to Agriculture"; Geol. Surv., Canada, Mus. Bull. 28 (1918).

of course. It is such warping of judgment that we must particularly guard against in estimating the real value of our Birds of Prey.

However, the so-called balance of nature has been profoundly disturbed by civilized man's appearance on the scene, and the new balance in process of establishment may not be altogether to his liking. Civilization itself is an unnatural condition, a disturbed balance, and to be retained only by constant interference with nature's attempt to return to a more primitive order. Such interference may be absolutely necessary, but, unguided by comprehensive understanding of the complicated action and reaction in nature's economy, it is likely to be bungling and, like prodding the works of a fine watch without understanding its mechanism, cause evil greater than that which it is intended to correct. When, however, a species increases to numbers detrimental to man's interest, it is expedient and justifiable to reduce them. But in doing so we should take heed of what we undertake and assure ourselves that worse evils will not follow. We have largely eliminated the coyote and fox as threats to our flocks, and have thereby removed an active check on the mice, gophers, and ground-squirrels. Some species of hawks do more damage than good to us and can well be destroyed, but care should be taken that discrimination be shown and that the harmless or useful ones, the remaining efficient natural control of rodent pests, be not involved.

The difficulties of recognizing the various species of hawks and discriminating friend from foe are considerable. However, two simple rules will assist. All black hawks are positively beneficial. Most summer hawks on the prairies are to be regarded as beneficial unless actually taken in a harmful act. Those of late autumn or winter may in the west be treated as harmful without much danger to innocent species. In the east this distinction does not work quite so well and a little more discrimination should be exercised.

## SUBORDER—CATHARTAE. AMERICAN VULTURES

This suborder is composed of the American Vultures which are systematically quite distinct from those of the Old World. One family only is represented in Canada, *Cathartidae* the Turkey Vultures. Vultures are carrion feeders, relying upon dead meat and not capturing living prey unless it is in the last stages of exhaustion. Ordinarily, they touch nothing but decaying flesh. This is usually regarded as a matter of choice, but may be a necessity, as their feet are not formed for grasping and the bill is comparatively weak. They may, therefore, be unable to break into large, sound carcasses and are forced to await the decay which renders the subject less refractory.

### FAMILY—CATHARTIDAE. TURKEY VULTURES

*General Description.* Large birds, nearly uniformly black in coloration. Bill is comparatively long and less strongly hooked than in remainder of the *Raptores* (Figure 172). Head and upper neck are bare of feathers and have a superficial general resemblance to those of the turkey, but are without wattles or warty excrescences. Feet resemble those of a chicken rather than of a hawk. Claws are blunt and the foot is poorly adapted for seizing or holding prey.

*Distribution.* Vultures are essentially birds of the warmer regions. They enter Canada only along the most southern boundaries.

Figure 172
Head of Turkey Vulture.

Vultures cannot be observed to best advantage in Canada. In the southern United States they may be seen every hour of the day floating on motionless wings high in the air, searching the country with telescopic eye for carrion. When an animal dies (or even before) it is sighted, and a black form drops beside it from the sky; shortly it is joined by another, and another, and soon where not a bird was previously to be seen, many are struggling about the unclean feast. The question as to whether vultures find their odoriferous food by scent or by sight is still a debatable one. Though formerly food finding was regarded as a visual function later observation has suggested that the elaborate nasal development found in the species is more serviceable in this direction than early experimentation indicated. The flight of the vultures is one of the wonders of the physicist. They hang suspended in the air or even rise beyond the limits of human vision, without visible effort. On motionless, outspread pinions they glide in great ascending spirals, mounting higher and higher, and then, still circling, maintain their positions for hours at a time, without a single apparent stroke of the wing. The act of thus rising in the air without visible expenditure of power was for long regarded as one of the mysteries of bird life until man, obtaining mastery of the air himself, found that he could do approximately likewise with soaring and gliding planes by taking advantage of hitherto barely suspected upward currents of air.

*Economic Status.* The vultures are not birds of prey in the usual acceptation of the term, for they do not kill what they eat but feed entirely on carrion. They have been accused, and perhaps justly, of accelerating death at times, but they never attack an animal that is not in the last stages of exhaustion. In Canada the species is of little economic importance, but in the south their scavenging is an important safeguard to the health of the more careless communities, and in many places they are rigorously protected by law for sanitary reasons.

325. **Turkey Vulture.** TURKEY BUZZARD. LE VAUTOUR COMMUN. *Cathartes aura.* L, 30. All dark, very nearly black, with head and neck naked or, in juveniles, covered with sparse, greyish brown, fur-like down.

Figure 173
Turkey Vulture; scale, $\frac{1}{20}$.
Appearance in flight.

*Distinctions.* Large size, all dark coloration, hooked beak with long, extensive cere, naked or downy head coloured red in the adult (Figure 172), and weak, chicken-like, rather than raptorial, claws mark it plainly as a vulture. The Turkey Vulture is the one most likely to be seen in Canada and the only species to be expected in the west. There is a record of the California Condor in southern British Columbia, but it seems to have an uncertain basis.

*Field Marks.* A large, black bird next in size to the eagles (Figure 174-1), usually seen sweeping around in great circles or soaring on motionless wings high in the air. Seen from below, the forepart of the wings and body is coal black and the flight feathers a shade or so lighter (Figure 173) giving an effect of black arms with silvery grey wings. The tail is comparatively long and round. Often the white bill or bare, red head and neck are seen as a flash of colour, making determination certain.

*Nesting.* On the ground, usually in a hollow log, or under an upturned stump.

*Distribution.* Only accidental in the Maritime Provinces. It occurs regularly in limited numbers in Lake Erie district of Ontario. From Manitoba to the west coast it occurs more commonly along the southern boundary north to Duck Mountains and Edmonton.

*SUBSPECIES.* The North American form is the Northern Turkey Vulture (le Vautour Commun du Nord) *Cathartes aura septentrionalis.*

*Economic Status.* Being a carrion feeder no harm can be charged against the species and after winters that have been unusually severe on the cattle of the plains, it may perform valuable services as a scavenger of dead animals.

326. **Black Vulture.** LE VAUTOUR NOIR. *Coragups Atratus.* L, 24. Very like the Turkey Vulture, but slightly smaller.

*Distinctions.* Distinguished from the preceding by the neck, head, and base of the bill being black instead of red or pink.

*Field Marks.* The general blackness of the bare head parts. From below the wings look all black except for a large, lighter spot involving the primaries. The tail is comparatively short and square. The bird is too rare in Canada to be recorded safely from sight observation except in the most exceptional circumstances.

*Distribution.* A bird of more eastern distribution than the Turkey Vulture. Regular from Virginia south, straggling across our borders occasionally in the Maritime Provinces.

Of too infrequent occurrence in Canada for more than passing mention. It is to be expected occasionally only in the Maritime Provinces.

## SUBORDER—FALCONES. HAWKS, EAGLES, ETC.

*General Description.* Bill strongly hooked from the base (Figure 171, page 112), where it is covered with a swollen cere or mass of yellow, waxy-looking tissue in which the nostrils are situated. This tissue is distinctly softer than the bill proper and usually yellow in colour. The feet are powerful and furnished with strong claws or talons for capturing and holding living prey (Figure 170, page 112).

*Distinctions.* The members of this suborder differ from the vultures in having the bill shorter and more strongly hooked and the head feathered instead of bare (Compare with Figure 172). The tarsus is usually bare and the toes are never feathered.

Two familes are represented in Canada: *Accipitriidae* the kites, hawks, and eagles, and *Falconidae* the Caracaras and true falcons.

### Subfamily—Perninae. The Swallow-tailed Kites, etc.

The kites are birds of southern distribution and only one species has ever been taken in Canada.

327. **Swallow-tailed Kite.** LE MILAN À QUEUE FOURCHUE. *Elanoides forficatus.* L, 24. (Projection of outer tail feathers beyond middle ones 8 inches.) A rather small hawk. Measures large because of the great elongation of its outer tail feathers which extend 8 inches beyond the middle ones. Wings and tail pure black; all remainder, including head, shoulders, and upper back, white. A bird strikingly coloured in intense black and white, with the deeply forked tail and long, pointed wings of a Barn Swallow. It is hardly possible to mistake this for any other species.

*Distribution.* Tropical and semitropical America, appearing very rarely along our southern border. The only records for Canada are based on a few old observations in southern Ontario, southern Manitoba, and adjoining parts of Saskatchewan. Under the conditions of a former abundance, it evidently wandered north more frequently than it does today.

Figure 174
Flight silhouettes of (scale, about $\frac{1}{16}$):
1, Turkey Vulture.
2, Bald Eagle.
3, Osprey.
4, Rough-legged Hawk.

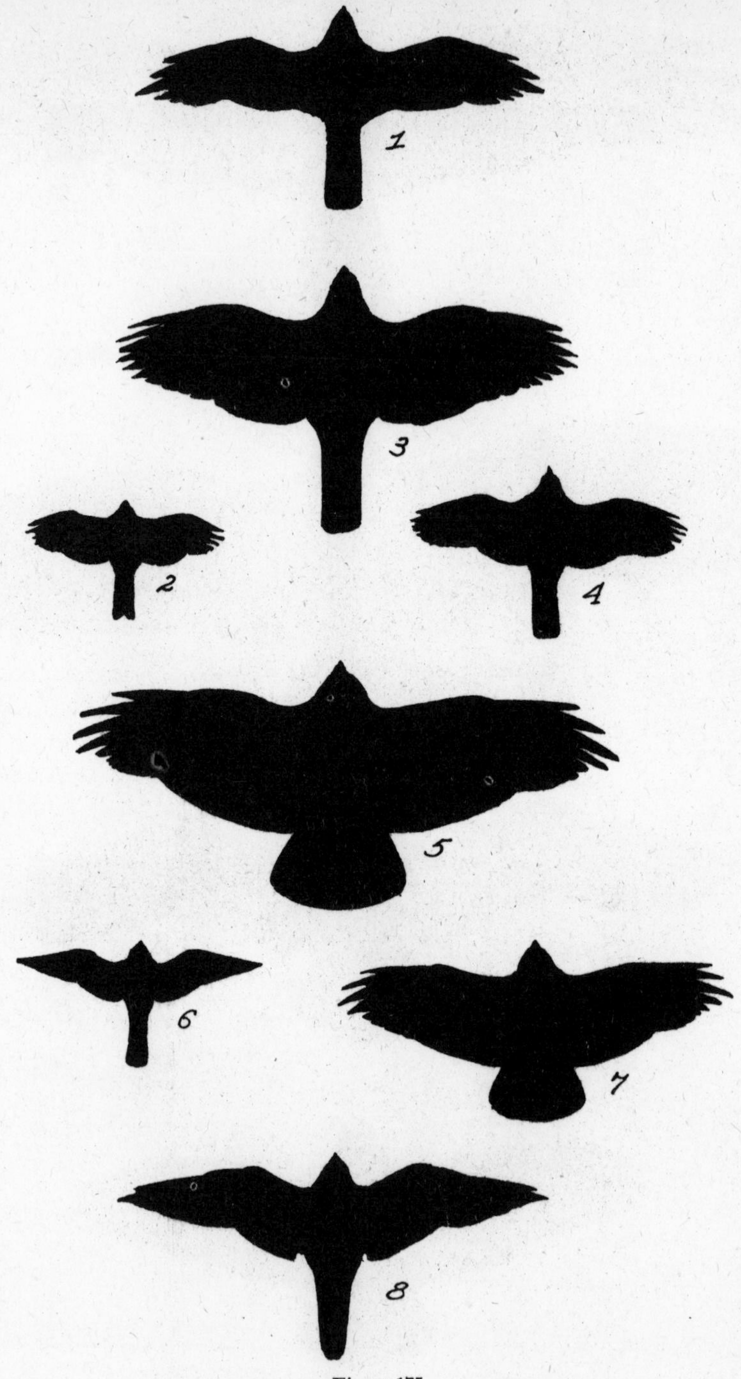


**Figure 175**

Flight silhouettes of (scale, about $\frac{1}{18}$):

1, Marsh Hawk.
2, Sharp-shinned Hawk.
3, Goshawk.
4, Cooper's Hawk.
5, Red-tailed Hawk.
6, Sparrow Hawk.
7, Broad-winged Hawk.
8, Peregrine Falcon.

A. Sharp-tailed Grouse; scale, $\frac{1}{6}$ Prairie Chicken; scale, $\frac{1}{6}$

B. Bobwhite

Female Male

PLATE XX

A. Sandhill Crane; scale, 1/20

B. Sora Rail; scale, 1/4

Juvenile Summer adult

A most beautiful species, but too rare in Canada to receive more than passing reference here.

*Economic Status.* Its principal food is insects, snails, and reptiles; it never touches mammals or birds.

**Subfamily—Accipitriinae. The Short-winged or Bird Hawks**

*General Description.* Very small to large hawks with short, rounded wings, long tail (Figure 175—2, 3, 4) and untoothed bill (Figure 177, compare with 211, page 143). Under surface of primaries and secondaries regularly barred to tip. The five outer primaries emarginate (*See* Figures 178 and 182).

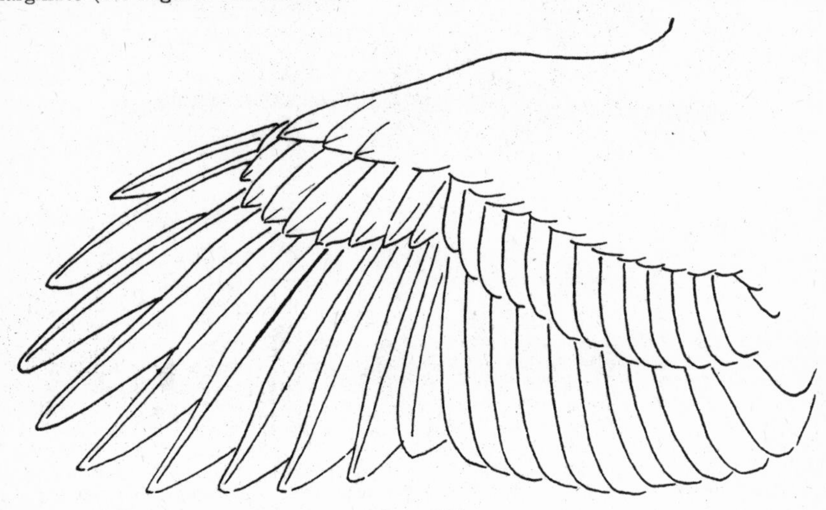

Figure 176
Round wing of Accipiter, upper surface.

The Accipitrine Hawks are woodland birds that beat about the tree tops or along the edges of the woods; they do not habitually soar high in the open. They take their prey by surprise and quick attack rather than by open pursuit. Their short wings (Figure 176) and long tail give rapid bursts of speed and flexibility of manœuvre, but are not suited to long-sustained effort.

*Economic Status.* These are the only common species of Canadian hawks for which little good can be claimed. They are active and spirited and though without the great strength and endurance of the true falcons do far more real damage than their larger and heavier relatives. The term "Chicken Hawk" popularly applied to any small hawk receives its meaning from these birds. They never eat carrion, but make fresh kills, rarely returning to partly devoured prey. They are pre-eminently bird-eating hawks and seem to prefer feathered to furred food. Fortunately the two commoner species are small and their capacity for damage is slight in consequence. The one large and powerful member of the group, the Goshawk, is of more limited distribution and, except in unusual winters, is less commonly seen in the more settled parts of southern Canada, except in the mountains where elevation brings northern conditions within easy flight distance of agriculture.

Figure 177
Untoothed bill of Accipiter.

334. **American Goshawk.** BLUE PARTRIDGE HAWK. HEN HAWK. L'AUTOUR D'AMÉRIQUE. *Astur atricapillus.* L, 22. Plate XII B. A large hawk, smaller only than the big Buteos (Figure 175–3), striped brown and white when juvenile like several other species, but, when adult, uniform light grey almost all over, finely vermiculated with dark or lighter below.

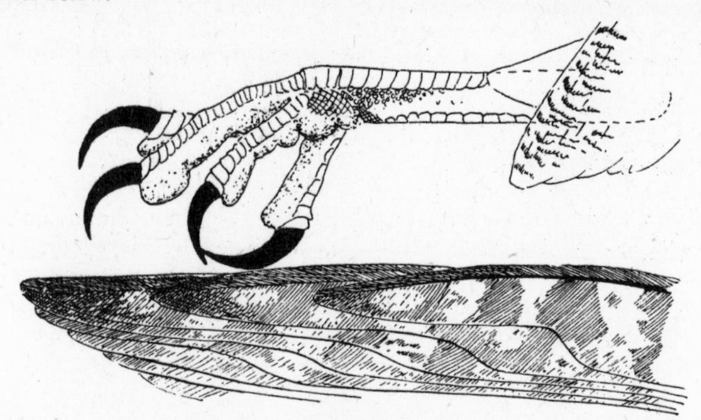

Figure 178
Specific details of Goshawk; scale, $\frac{1}{2}$.

*Distinctions.* The adult is, by its distinctive blue-grey colour, unmistakable. The juvenile resembles a number of other species, from all of which, except its next relative, the Cooper's Hawk, it can be separated by its five emarginate instead of three or four (Compare Figure 178 with 184 and 188, pages 124 and 129) primaries, regularly, though sometimes faintly, barred below to the tips (Figures 178, 179). From the Cooper's Hawk, that approaches it in size, by the feathering of the leg which extends one-half or more of the length of the tarsus (Compare Figures 178 and 182). However, an Accipiter over 19 inches long will almost certainly be this species. The Goshawk also often has the whites of the underparts tinged with buffy, which never occurs with the Cooper's Hawk.

*Field Marks.* The largest of the Accipiters, next smaller to the large Buteos, the Red-tail, and Swainson's Hawk (Figure 175–3). Rounded wings, regularly barred below, and long tail as an *Accipiter* (Figure 179). Large size and, when adult, general slaty grey colour indicate a Goshawk.

*Nesting.* In trees.

*Distribution.* Breeds in the northern wooded sections across the continent. Sometimes in winter it comes down into the prairie and southern sections in considerable numbers.

Figure 179
Goshawk (juvenile); scale, $\frac{1}{12}$.
Appearance in flight.

*SUBSPECIES.* The type form, the Eastern Goshawk (l'Autour de l'Est) *Astur atricapillus atricapillus*, is the common subspecies over the greatest part of its range. Some migrants into southern British Columbia and southward are more overwashed with buffy in the juvenile, and have been separated as the Western Goshawk (l'Autour de l'Ouest) *Astur atricapillus striatulus*. We know very little of the geographic distribution of this form, but presume that it breeds somewhere on the northwest coast. The fine vermiculation of the underparts usually given as the distinctive character of this race is but an indication of full maturity.

The American representative of the Old World Goshawk or "Goose Hawk," which seems to have been the original name, was the only short-winged hawk regularly used in ancient falconry. It was flown at hares, partridges, and such ground-game, which its long tail and short wings allowed it to follow through rapid turnings and twistings, whereas its size allowed it to kill quite large game. It was not, however, regarded as a thoroughly sportsmanlike bird as it lacked the spirit and energy of the long-winged falcons and its use lacked the excitement and interest aroused by the use of "Noble Hawks."

*Economic Status.* Fortunately this bird is only an irregular winter visitor to our most thickly settled sections. Otherwise it would be a serious menace to the poultryman. Of 20 stomachs examined: 9 contained poultry or game; 2, other birds; 10, mammals; 3, insects; and 1, a centipede. Of the 10 mammals, 3 were rabbits and 1 a grey squirrel, both of which can be regarded as useful. This gives a total of 15 harmful food items against 9 useful and 1 neutral. There can be no question as to the harmful status of this species. Its size gives it ample power to take pullets and even well-grown hens, and such large game as Ruffed Grouse is its favourite food. Though the real home of the Goshawks is in the more northern forests, once they establish themselves near a farmyard they are likely to visit it daily. They dash suddenly over or around a building into the middle of the poultry flock, seize their victim, and are off with it before the owner can protect his property.

332. **Sharp-shinned Hawk.** CHICKEN HAWK. L'ÉPERVIER BRUN. *Accipiter velox.* L, 11·25. Plate XIII A. The smallest of the Accipiters. About the size of the Sparrow Hawk and Pigeon Hawk (Figure 175—2). Similar in colour and plumage sequence to Cooper's Hawk. In juvenility: striped with dark brown and white; adults: back dark blue and breast barred with dull reddish and white.

*Distinctions.* By small size to be confused only with the Sparrow Hawk, Pigeon Hawk, and Cooper's Hawk. Easily separated from the first by lack of red on back and tail and from it and the Pigeon Hawk, which are both true falcons, by its short, rounded wings and untoothed bill (Figures 176 and 177, compare with 210 and 211). Usually separated from the Cooper's Hawk by its smaller size, but a large female may measure closely to the size of a small male of that species. A bird under 14 inches long should be a Sharp-shinned; over 16, a Cooper's. The tarsus of the Sharp-shinned is comparatively longer and more slender than that of Cooper's and the tail is square or slightly forked when closed (Figure 181) instead of rounded (Figure 182).

*Field Marks.* Short, round wings regularly barred below; long tail (Figure 180); and flight—when not under a burst of speed a series of alternating, quick, even strokes and short sails—will mark this species as an Accipiter. Very small size and square instead of round tail will separate it from Cooper's. The lack of red on back and tail is an additional distinction from the pointed-winged Sparrow Hawk.

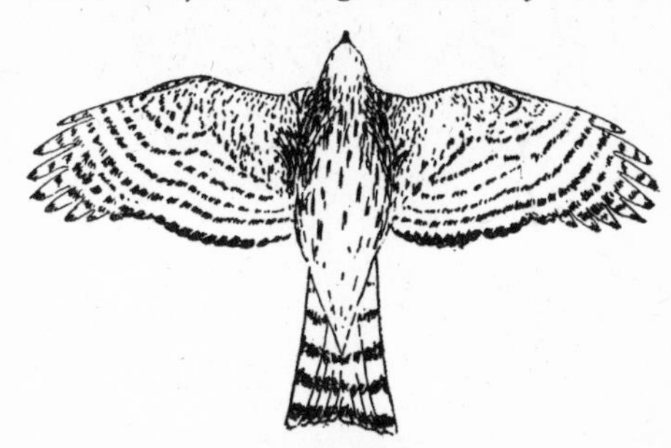

Figure 180
Sharp-shinned Hawk (juvenile); scale, $\frac{1}{5}$.
Appearance in flight.

*Nesting.* In trees, usually conifers.

*Distribution.* Nests in most of the wooded sections of Canada except in the more southern parts, north to the tree limit. A common migrant nearly everywhere.

This is one of the smallest hawks we have. It has not the sustained strength or persistency of the "Noble Falcons," but it is active and agile. It makes bold dashes at its prey, but on missing the stroke seldom follows it up by pursuit and almost never strikes on the wing, as the falcons do.

*Economic Status.* This is the species that should have been called "American Sparrow Hawk" instead of the little falcon that has been so named. It is a close relative, and the American representative of the European Sparrow Hawk, which is also an *Accipiter*. The name would suit this bird excellently as sparrows and other small birds are its favourite food.

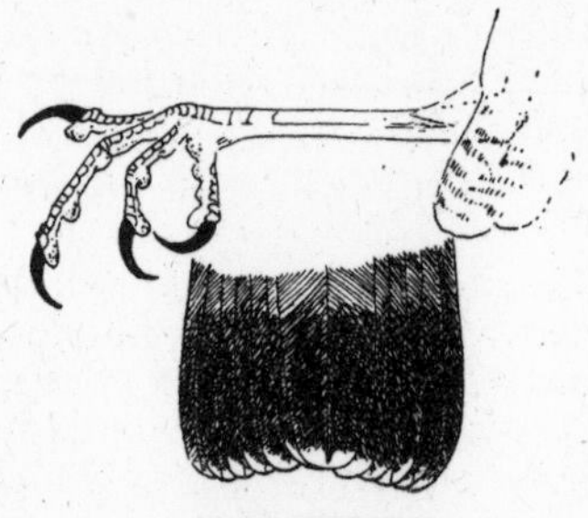

Figure 181
Specific details of Sharp-shinned Hawk; scale, ½.

Of 107 stomachs examined, 6 contained poultry or game-birds; 99, other birds; 6, mice; and 5, insects. This gives 105 harmful food items against 11 good ones. The mice consisted of no more than 9 individuals, but the small birds numbered 115, from Kinglets to a Mourning Dove in size. This makes a strong case against this otherwise rather interesting species. One good word can be said for this little hawk; it is fond of the English Sparrows and takes toll of their flocks about the smaller towns and cities.

333. **Cooper's Hawk.** CHICKEN HAWK. L'ÉPERVIER DE COOPER. *Accipiter cooperi.* L, 15·50. A rather small hawk, between the Sharp-shinned and Goshawk in size (Figure 175—4). Almost exactly similar in colour and plumage sequence to the Sharp-shinned Hawk (*See* description of that species), but larger.

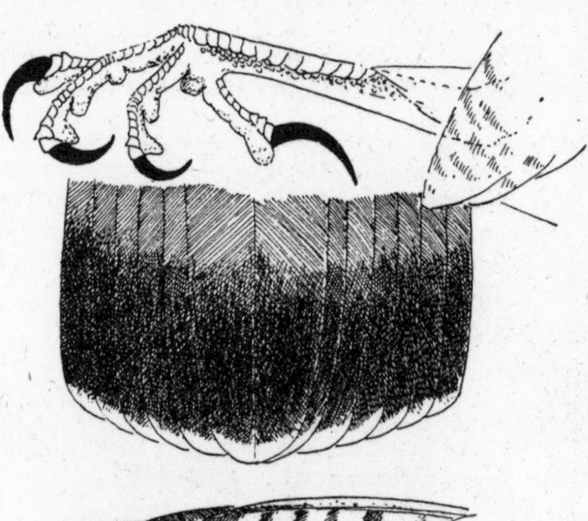

Figure 182
Specific details of Cooper's Hawk: foot and tail, scale, ½; wing tip, scale, ¼.

*Distinctions.* Easily separated from the smaller falcons, the Sparrow Hawk, and the Pigeon Hawk, by its accipitrine characters of round wing and untoothed bill (Figures 176 and 177, compare with 210 and 211). Most likely to be confused with the Sharp-shinned or Broad-winged Hawks. Usually separated from the Sharp-shinned by larger size; but a small male may measure closely to the size of a large female of that species. A bird over 16 inches should be this species; under 14, a Sharp-shinned. The tarsus of Cooper's Hawk is heavier and the tail is rounded instead of being square or slightly forked when closed (Figure 182, compare with 181).

Occasional very large females may approach a small Goshawk in size. A bird 19 inches or under should be a Cooper's Hawk. In no plumage does it resemble the adult Goshawk, but juveniles of the two species have a very similar coloration. The best distinction other than size is the feathering of the leg. In Cooper's Hawk, less than one-half of the tarsus is feathered, in the Goshawk, one-half or over (Compare Figures 182 and 178). The Cooper's Hawk is also similar in size and colour to the Broad-winged Hawk. The latter, however, is a *Buteo* and not an *Accipiter*, with a deeper wing and a chunkier build. The best colour distinction, however, is the under-wing surface. In Cooper's Hawk it is sharply and regularly barred to the primary tips, in the Broad-winged it is mostly creamy white with but suggestions of bars. In Cooper's Hawk the first five primaries are emarginate, in the Broad-winged but three (Compare Figures 182 and 188).

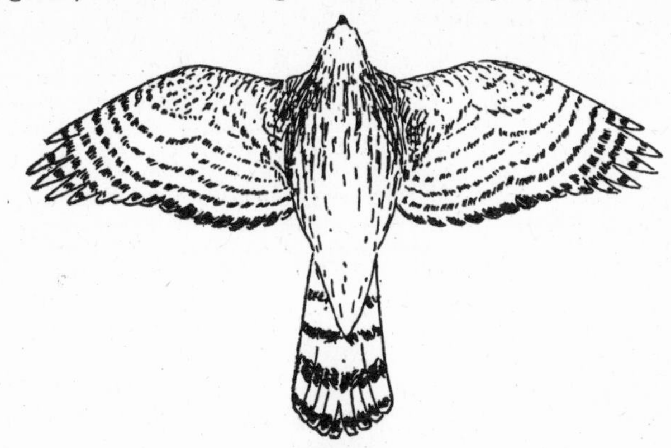

Figure 183
Cooper's Hawk (juvenile); scale, $\frac{1}{6}$.
Appearance in flight.

*Field Marks.* A small hawk between the Sharp-shinned and Broad-winged in size (Figure 175—4). Short, round wings regularly barred below, long tail (Figure 183), and flight—when not under a burst of speed, a series of quick even strokes and short sails—will mark this species as an *Accipiter*. Small size will separate from comparable plumaged Goshawks and the round instead of square tail from the Sharp-shinned.

*Nesting.* In trees, much like the Sharp-shinned, but seldom in conifers.

*Distribution.* Breeds in most of the southern wooded sections of Canada, south over the United States. A few winter on southern Vancouver Island.

An even more harmful species than the Sharp-shinned, as its larger size gives it greater power and capacity for damage. Showing an almost equal spirit it seeks larger prey and even a fairly well-grown chicken is not safe from it. Adult fowls are rarely attacked unless feeble.

*Economic Status.* Of 94 stomachs examined: 34 contained poultry or game-birds; 52, other birds; 11, mammals; 1, frog; 3, lizards; and 2, insects. The mammals consisted of rodents, mostly harmful, but one a grey squirrel; making a total of 87 food items against the species, 12 in its favour, and 4 neutral. As it is a comparatively common hawk throughout much of the settled parts of the country, it is certainly a menace and is responsible for much of the popular ill-repute of the order as a whole.

### Subfamily—Buteoninae. The Buzzards and Eagles, the Mammal Eaters

#### True Buzzards

Heavily built hawks of medium or very large size (Figures 174—4, and 175—5 and 7). Bill without notches or tooth-like projections (like Figure 177, compare with 211). The wings are round like the *Accipiters* (Figure 176), but broader. The tail is long, full, and generally carried spread out in a broad semicircle (Figures 185 to 202). The first three or four primaries are emarginate (Figures 184, 188), and with the exception of the Red-shouldered Hawk, which is confined to eastern Canada, these feather groups are usually solidly coloured, with little barring and, from underneath, with more or less of a white area at their bases. Most western representatives of this group show remarkable dichromatism, one extreme of which is very dark brown, almost black, and substantially alike in all species affected. The two Rough-legs and one species of eagle have tarsus feathered to the base of the toes (Figures 190 and 196).

*Field Marks.* Round, broad wings; broad, full tail (Figures 174—4 and 175—5 and 7), and habit of soaring high in the open make the best field marks for the buzzards.

These are the true buzzards. The Turkey Vulture is incorrectly called "buzzard" in the south. Buzzards lack the dash, speed, and spirit of either the *Accipiters* or the falcons and specialize on less active game. They often feed on insects and occasionally on carrion. They are the common high-flying hawks of summer, and can be seen circling high in the air or perched sentinel-like on fence or telegraph pole, scanning the open landscape. They are birds of the open, as the *Accipiters* are of the brush, and are not given to quick dashes through the shrubbery like their agile relatives. They are the hawks that build the great, bulky nests in the larger trees of the prairie bluffs, in the coulées, or on the ground on steep hillsides.

*Economic Status.* As a class the buzzards are the most useful as well as the largest of our hawks. Some of the largest of them have scarcely a black mark against them. They live throughout the summer almost entirely on rodents. Although there is a slight reservation in the approval with which the Red-tailed Hawk is regarded in the east, there is no doubt as to its usefulness throughout the prairie region, as it is amongst the foremost of gopher destroyers. Wherever rodent vermin is an important agricultural factor, this group of hawks may be regarded as valuable allies of the farmer. Its members have a marked preference for furred, over feathered, game, and their large size and capacity ensure that their activities are on sufficient scale to be of value.

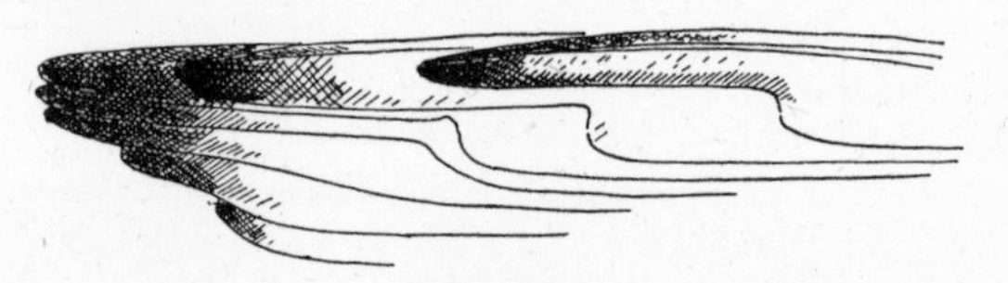

Figure 184
Four notched primaries of Red-tailed Hawk; scale, ½.

337. **Red-tailed Hawk.** HEN HAWK. LA BUSE À QUEUE ROUSSE. *Buteo borealis.* L, 20. Plate XIII B. One of our two largest buzzards. Characteristic adults have brick-red tails, but western birds are so variable that this or any colour character make uncertain criterion for identification. Though in the east the Red-tailed is practically constant in coloration, its only marked variation being two age-plumages, in the west the case is quite different. In the east the adult is a brown hawk largely white or cream coloured below, with a solidly red tail. The juvenile is similar, but blacker and whiter and the tail is barred with lighter and darker colours of the back. The western bird not only shows similar two age-plumages, but also appears in two distinct colorations, one of which is solidly near-black, with many intermediates between it and a much whiter opposite extreme, thus making an almost infinite number of colour variations. As three other western species of comparable size show a similar dichromatism and are inseparable from the Red-tailed by colour in the dark phase, the difficulty in distinguishing the species is great. Fortunately there are other characters besides colour to assist in identification.

The Red-tail plumage that is most common in western Canada is hardly distinguishable from the eastern bird. The juvenile above is solidly dark brown, almost black, from crown to tail inclusive, the latter being barred regularly with still darker shades. All below is white, with sides of breast, flanks, and a broken area on upper abdomen striped with dark. Some intermixture of white or cream can be expected on crown and back. The adult of this juvenile is, in general, similar, but redder above, more creamy below, with less and ruddier streaking and almost immaculate pantaloons. The tail is an even brick-red with more or less of a narrow, black, subterminal band and a faint, faded, or creamy tip. Many western birds differ from this type only by irregular mixtures of red in the tail of the juvenile, more heavily barred thighs or pantaloons, and the addition of more or less complete dark bars across the red tail of the adult.

The extreme dark phase is almost entirely dark brown, nearly black (like the dark Swainson's Hawk), with a dark-barred, grey-mottled, or red tail that may be either barred or not. Between these two phases is every possible intergradation and some very peculiar piebald mixtures occur. On the other hand, some specimens run to an extreme of whiteness that approaches albinism.

Figure 185
Red-tailed Hawk; scale, $\frac{1}{12}$.
Appearance in flight.

There may be large amounts of white or cream mixed with the dark of the back, and the head may be largely white. The tail may be cream to white, with or without dark barring. These differences, not due to sex, age, or season, have suggested the division of the species into numerous subspecies, but the more the species is examined the less claim do these irregular variants seem to have to special treatment, any more than do those of Swainson's Hawk and the Rough-legs that show similar variants but are not subspecifically divided on that basis.

*Distinctions.* Size will separate the Red-tailed Hawk from all hawks except Swainson's and the two Rough-legged Hawks. The bare instead of feathered tarsus will easily distinguish it from the latter two (like Figure 178 instead of Figure 190). The birds average larger than Swainson's, but there is considerable variation in size and they are best distinguished from it by wing characters. In the Red-tailed the first four instead of the first three primaries are sharply emarginate and the third, fourth, and fifth are about equal in length, but longer than the rest, and thus form the point of the wing (Figure 184). Though both species are so variable in colour that some plumages are difficult or impossible to separate on that basis, there are certain distinctions that can usually be observed. In the Red-tailed the dark areas aggregate across the abdomen instead of across the breast, leaving the upper the lightest part of the front. In Swainson's the converse is the case, the lightest spot being below the breast. This distinction is less pronounced in light juveniles and, of course, is absent in the extreme solidly black phase. Small, juvenile Red-tails may be confused with the Red-shouldered Hawk, common in eastern but rare or absent in western Canada.

*Field Marks.* A large buzzard, practically the same size as the Rough-leg and Swainson's, only noticeably inferior to the osprey and the eagles (Figure 175—5). Wings round and broad. Of wide range in colour, from near-black and white, with or without varying amounts of cream and reddish, to solid and complete dark brown, almost black. A reddish tail when present is always determinative of this species. Separated from Swainson's Hawk by slightly rounder, less-pointed wing tips, and by the breast being lighter instead of darker than the abdomen. From the two Rough-legged Hawks, the Red-tailed is separated with greater ease as a rule. It is never as evenly dull ochre on the breast, nor has it the decided, sharply defined, black, abdominal band of the characteristic American Rough-legged (Figure 191). It is rarely as solidly white below, nor are the pantaloons in as deep rufous contrast as is usual in the Ferruginous. The tail, except in the *Kriderі* phase (*See* following), is not as white, and even in that form it never whitens towards the base, nor are there white spots on either side of the rump. Another point of distinction is that although the inner webs of the primaries lighten towards their bases, they do not separate in any normal flight attitude to show a flash of white from above as they do in the Rough-leg even in the blackest phase (Figure 194).

*Nesting.* In bulky nests in tree tops.

*Distribution.* Across the continent as far north as the tree limit. More common in breeding season in the wooded than in the prairie sections, but common throughout the latter in migration.

*SUBSPECIES.* The Red-tailed Hawk in the A.O.U. Check-list has been divided into several races. The Eastern Red-tail (la Buse à queue rousse de l'Est) *Buteo borealis borealis* extends westward through Ontario; but, beginning with the prairie sections in Manitoba, it intergrades, intermixes, and interbreeds so thoroughly with the Western Red-tail (la Buse à queue rousse de l'Ouest) *Buteo borealis calurus* that there is great difficulty in defining the distinctive characters or saying where one begins and the other leaves off. Almost typical eastern birds can be found westward to the mountains and the most common plumage of the prairie is only slightly different from that of the eastern birds. Mixed with, and even mated to, these indeterminate birds, are those of unmistakable *calurus* character—larger amounts of black below, the dark tail of the juvenile more or less mixed with red, and the red tail of the adult more or less barred with dark. Strangely, the particular type of coloration upon which the name *B.b. calurus* is founded, a black-phased bird with a black-barred red tail, although common farther south, is very rare in Canada. In British Columbia a redder type occurs. It is a heavily coloured plumage, with a reddish tendency across the breast. This coloration is not often seen on our prairies.

Besides these two forms, *borealis* and *calurus*, there are two others recognized by the Check-list that present peculiar problems to the Canadian ornithologist—Krider's Hawk *Buteo borealis kriderі* and Harlan's Hawk *Buteo borealis harlani*. These are so variable that it is difficult to say just what are their distinguishing characters or whether after all they are not respectively just the light and dark extremes of the Western Red-tail.

Krider's Hawk (la Buse de Krider) *Buteo borealis kriderі* is like a whitened *Buteo borealis* with much white on head, tail, and intermixed on the back in variable amount and distribution. The tail of the adult may be pale red, cream colour, or even pure white, and may be sharply barred or nearly immaculate. This form is not common anywhere, but is most numerous from Iowa to Manitoba and occurs irregularly west to the mountains. Birds of *kriderі* appearance occur sporadically throughout the west, north even to the Yukon. The present writer is not decided as to whether *kriderі* is entitled to full subspecific status or is only a light colour-variant of other *Buteo borealis* races.

Harlan's Hawk (la Buse de Harlan) *Buteo borealis harlani* is the name usually given to a plumage form that occurs most regularly in migration in southern Manitoba and across the Prairie Provinces to the southern Yukon. Most characteristically it is in full black phase, but also occurs with a white underbody. In the adult the tail is curiously and variably mottled, or marbled, or clouded with shades of black, grey, and reddish, or any combination of these colours. The juvenile has a dark, black-barred tail and is not plainly, if at all, distinguishable from black-phased *calurus* of similar age. There is no unanimity among authorities as to what are the essential characters of this race or the systematic relation it bears to other forms of the species. This author is not certain whether to regard it as a distinct species that hybridized freely with *Buteo borealis* or merely a colour-variant of *calurus*. Its breeding range seems to centre about southern Yukon Territory where it interbreeds freely with *calurus* and *kriderі*, but individuals with *harlani* characters are found nesting south to western Alberta.

*Economic Status.* Nearly everything said of Swainson's and the Rough-legged Hawks (which see) applies to this bird. Its record is not quite so satisfactory, but it is almost captious to raise objections. It is a hardy bird, and may remain with us later in the season than the others; often a few linger after the gophers have holed up for the winter. Then, of necessity, it must turn to other prey, and for a short season may give some offence to the poulterer or the game protectionist, for it is powerful if not very agile, and has been known to kill birds as large and vigorous as ravens. Depredations are usually committed by young and inexperienced birds in search of easy prey, but the fact that the species has already spent months industriously hunting ground-squirrels and gophers and will do so another

PLATE XXI

A. American Coot; scale, $\frac{1}{6}$

B. Killdeer; scale, $\frac{1}{4}$

PLATE XXII

A. Black-bellied Plover; scale, ¼

Summer adult    Autumn juvenile

B. American Woodcock; scale, ¼

season if spared, should more than counterbalance any injuries it may inflict in the meanwhile. Where rodents are a serious economic problem, as in the west, the Red-tailed Hawk is too valuable to be destroyed except under severe provocation.

339. **Red-shouldered Hawk.** LA BUSE À ÉPAULETTES ROUSSES. *Buteo lineatus.* L, 18·30. Plate XIV A. Smaller than the Red-tailed or Swainson's Hawks, but larger than the Broad-winged. The juvenile is coloured much like the young, light phases of those birds. Adults are solidly light tawny rufous below, more or less softly barred with lighter, and lined with fine, dark, shaft streaks. Tail and wings are barred with dark and light, decidedly so in the adult, less in the juvenile.

Figure 186
Red-shouldered Hawk (juvenile); scale, $\frac{1}{12}$.
Appearance in flight.

*Distinctions.* Separated from all comparable hawks except the Red-tailed by having four instead of three first primaries emarginate (like Figure 184). In nearly all plumages, the shoulders or lesser wing-coverts are strongly rusty.

*Field Marks.* Only to be expected in the east where the Red-tail, which it may resemble in size, is the most serious cause of confusion. The best field mark when soaring, as it is most commonly seen, is the white or translucent spot at the base of the primaries. The juvenile is more evenly and sharply striped on the body than any Red-tail and, besides being larger, the wings and tail are more sharply and narrowly barred than the Broad-wing (*See* Figure 186, compare with 185 and 187). In the adult the strong, rufous underparts and the red shoulders when seen are distinctive from either of the above. Too rare in western Canada to be identified there by sight.

*Distribution.* Eastern North America, north to the spruce forest. West to western Ontario. Also the Californian coast. Its presence in Manitoba has been suspected but never demonstrated. Sight records of its occurrence on the southern British Columbian coast have been reported, but are withdrawn by the observer and may be disregarded. It should be looked for carefully, especially in Manitoba, but identified with caution.

*SUBSPECIES.* The eastern and California members of this species, though entirely isolated from each other, are yet listed as subspecies of a single species. The western form, known as the Red-bellied Hawk (la Buse à poitrine rouge) *Buteo lineatus elegans*, differs from the Northern Red-shouldered (la Buse à épaulettes rousses du Nord) *Buteo lineatus lineatus* in being considerably richer and brighter in colour and seems to have different habits and bearing. It is described as being owl-like in flight, which cannot be said of the eastern bird, and the two forms may yet prove to be specifically distinct. It has been listed as a British Columbian species, but its occurrence there is extremely doubtful.

This is probably the most common hawk in eastern Canada. It is similar in habit to the Red-tailed except that it does not insist upon deep woods for its nesting habitat but will build in almost any little patch of woodland, sometimes in surprising proximity to settlement.

*Economic Status.* This species is, fundamentally, very similar in its food habits to the Red-tailed, but being a much smaller and lighter bird the damage it can do is proportionately less, whereas its good offices are scarcely if at all impaired. Of 206 stomachs examined: 3 contained poultry; 12, other birds; 102, mice; 40, other mammals; 20, reptiles; 30, batrachians (frogs, etc.); 92, insects; 16, spiders; 7, crawfish; 1, earthworm; 2, offal; and 3, fish. It will thus be seen that its diet is varied. Whether the shrews, frogs, reptiles, and spiders are to be counted for or against the species is open to some doubt, but the large number of mice and insects against 3 of poultry and 12 birds obviously acquits the species of the charge of doing much damage.

343. **Broad-winged Hawk.** LA PETITE BUSE. *Buteo platypterus.* L, 15·89. The smallest of the *buteos* (Figure 175—7). Similar in size to Cooper's Hawk. Juvenile, dark brown above; white below, striped on sides of breast, flanks, and abdomen with dark. Much like a small, juvenile Red-tailed of the eastern or light type. Adult, above, dark, without any bluish tinge. Tail, dark, with two or three conspicuous light bars across. Below, dull rufous brown irregularly barred with white, the reddish more uniform towards the breast. Occasional melanotic or black specimens occur, but are exceptional and do not form a regular phase of the species.

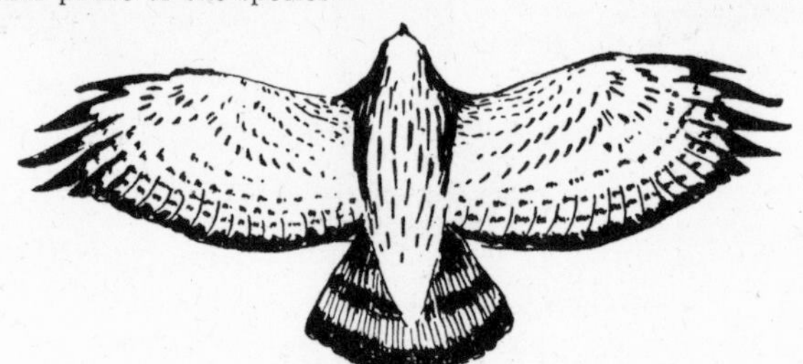

Figure 187
Broad-winged Hawk (juvenile); scale, $\frac{1}{12}$.
Appearance in flight.

*Distinctions.* Very much smaller than any other *Buteo.* Likely to be confused only with Cooper's Hawk, but has three outer primaries emarginate (like Figure 188), instead of five as in Cooper's and the other *Accipiters* (Figures 180 and 183). In spite of its reddish-barred underparts, the adult is easily distinguished from the adult *Accipiters,* by having no shade of bluish on the back, and the two to three prominent light tail bars considerably narrower than the intervening dark spaces and very pale brown without any greyish suggestion.

*Field Marks.* A small hawk, somewhat larger than Cooper's, but of evident *Buteo* outline (Figure 175—7). Its call, a fine, long drawn-out squeak, like that of a rusty hinge, is very characteristic. The wings have a black border as if in mourning and the tail is very broadly barred (Figure 187).

*Nesting.* In trees in the woods.

*Distribution.* Eastern North America, westward in Canada through the wooded sections north of the prairies to near the Rocky Mountain foothills about latitude 55 degrees. A bird of the birch-poplar and hard woods rather than of the dense spruce forest. A scarce migrant across the prairies.

*Economic Status.* This is a bird of the open forest and bush-lands, fairly common in the east but hardly numerous enough in western Canada except, perhaps, in the wooded parts of Manitoba, to have economic importance.

Of 57 stomachs examined: 2 contained small birds; 15, mice; 13, other mammals; 11, reptiles; 13, batrachians (frogs, etc.); 30, insects; 2, earthworms; 4, crawfish. Without further analysis this evidence is sufficient to free this species from any stigma of being harmful.

342. **Swainson's Hawk.** LA BUSE DE SWAINSON. *Buteo swainsoni.* L, 20. Plate XIV B. Nearly equal in size to the Red-tail. Although it has a light and dark phase and shows an equally bewildering variety of coloration it never has a red tail. A common

juvenile plumage is very similar to many young Red-tails; above, dark brown; below, white slightly tinged with buff, and variably striped with dark on flanks and across breast. Perhaps the most characteristic adult coloration shows mostly light below, whitest on throat, with a broken, or continuous darker band of some shade of brown across the breast. The dark phase, when complete, is uniform dark brown similar to the corresponding plumages of the Red-tailed and the Rough-legged.

*Distinctions.* Separated from the Rough-legged by the bare instead of feathered tarsi (like Figure 178, instead of 190). Distinguished from the Red-tailed by slightly smaller average size and by having three instead of four first primaries emarginate, and the third and fourth (not the fifth) equal and longest, forming the tip of the wing and making the wing slightly more pointed than that of the Red-tailed (Compare Figures 188 and 189 with 184 and 185). Though both species are so variable in colour that some plumages are difficult to separate, there are certain distinctions that can usually be observed. In the Swainson's Hawk the dark markings are concentrated or aggregated across the breast instead of across the abdomen, leaving the latter the lightest part of the under surface (Compare Figures 189 and 185). In the Red-tailed the converse is the rule. This distinction is less pronounced in juveniles and, of course, is entirely absent in the extreme solid black phase.

Small juveniles can be distinguished from the Red-shouldered Hawks by their having three instead of four emarginate primaries.

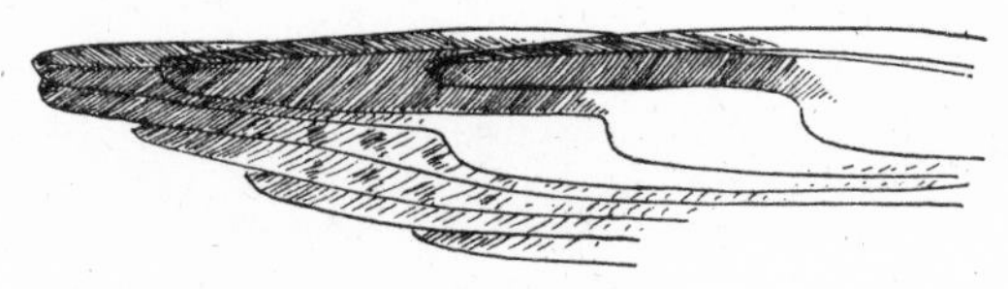

Figure 188
Three notched primaries of Swainson's Hawk; scale, $\frac{1}{2}$.

Swainson's Hawk is much larger than the Broad-winged and the emargination of the primaries will separate it from the larger *Accipiters*, such as the juvenile Goshawk which has five feathers emarginated (Compare Figure 188 with 185).

*Field Marks.* A large buzzard hawk with wings slightly more pointed than the Red-tailed (Figure 189). Wide range in colour, from near-black and white with varying amounts of cream, dull ochre, and reddish to solid and complete near-black. Usually with

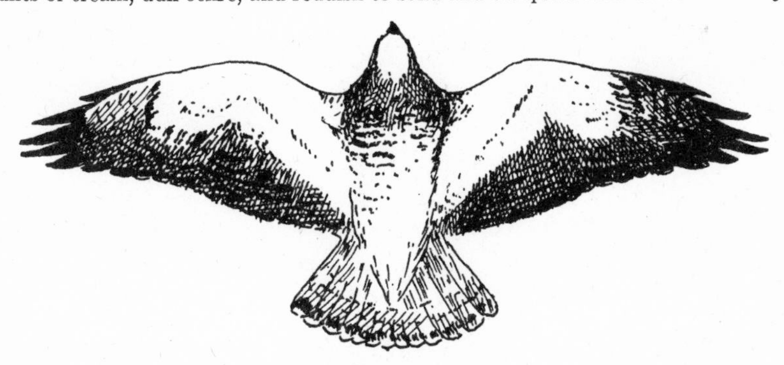

Figure 189
Swainson's Hawk; scale, $\frac{1}{12}$.
Appearance in flight of most characteristic plumage.

more or less of a darker breast-band making the abdomen the lightest part of the under surface. It is rarely as extensively white below as the lightest of the Ferruginous Rough-legs, nor are the pantaloons as deeply rufous. The tail is never markedly white or red and is usually somewhat regularly barred. Another point of distinction from the Rough-legged Hawk is that the base of the inner webs of the primaries do not lighten enough to show white on the upper surface of the wing in any normal flight attitude (*See* Figure 194).

*Nesting.* A bulky nest of sticks in trees.

*Distribution.* Western North America. In Canada, from Manitoba westward to the coast, north to the tree limit. Most common on the prairies. Migrates to South America. It is our only hawk that regularly retires entirely from the North American continent in winter.

Swainson's is the common hawk of the prairies. Nearly all the larger bluffs and most of the wooded coulées contain one or more nests from which the birds beat out over the cultivated and waste places carrying destruction into the ranks of ground-squirrels and gophers. Though the Red-tailed Hawk may take an occasional chicken or grouse, instances of Swainson's Hawk doing so are unusual enough to cause surprise. It varies its rodent food with grasshoppers caught on the ground with clumsy gravity, making heavy hops with waving wings and short runs hither and thither as it grabs the nimble insects with talons that look absurdly big and formidable for the purpose. Though its effect on insects is not to be disregarded, its highest usefulness is obviously directed against small mammal pests. Early and late it is at work supplying its own needs and those of its hungry offspring, and the number of gophers consumed by a single family of this hawk throughout the season reaches an important total. The prairie farmer can scarcely raise better paying stock than a few broods of Swainson's Hawks. The value of this system of gopher control is that it is always working and is not confined to the premises that are kept clear of vermin by dint of the owner's efforts, but is spread over those of his more careless neighbour whose land is a constant source of reinfestation to surrounding localities.

## Rough-legs

The Rough-legged Hawks are buzzards principally characterized by having legs feathered to the base of the toes (Figure 190). They are hawks

Figure 190
Feathered tarsus of Ferruginous Rough-legged Hawk;
scale, ½.

of the very largest size, but their feet are comparatively small and weak for so large a bird, and they are obviously too lightly armed for attack on vigorous prey. They restrict their diet to small mammals and insects, being particularly efficient grasshopper destroyers. They obtain their name from the "rough" or feathered tarsus. There are two species of Rough-legs in Canada, one nesting commonly in the southern prairies, the other a summer inhabitant of the far north, passing through settled Canada only on migration. Both species are dichromatic and occur in light and dark phases with intermediate plumages.

**347. Common Rough-legged Hawk** LA BUSE PATTUE COMMUNE. *Buteo lagopus.* L, 22. One of the largest of our hawks, slightly smaller than the Ferruginous Rough-leg and comparing in size very closely with the Red-tailed. It occurs in a light and a dark phase, and has intermediate plumages. The commonest coloration (Figure 191), the light phase, probably a juvenile plumage, is brown above, with much blended cream, or rusty ochre feather edgings that become more extensive on head. The base of the tail is cream, changing to dark for final half. Below—cream or dull light ochre, with practically solid and complete dark brown abdominal band, usually sharply defined at upper line. Face, foreneck, and breast more or less striped with brown. The dark phase is solid, near black like the corresponding plumage of the other buzzard hawks. Adult and intermediate plumages have a peculiar speckled appearance of mixed brown or black, without systematic pattern. The only constant characters of plumages are the lightening or whitening of the basal half of the tail.

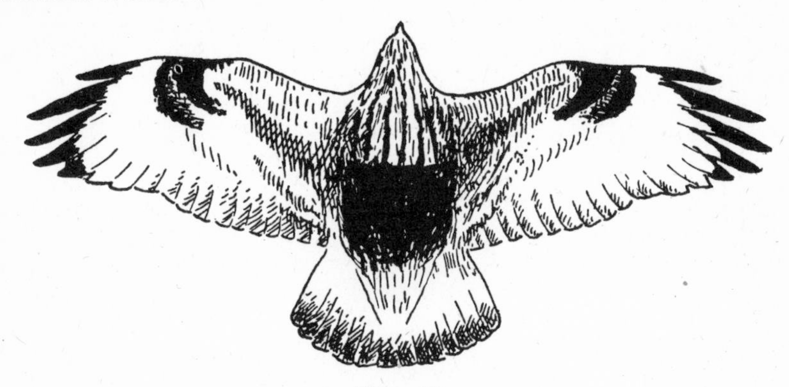

Figure 191

American Rough-legged Hawk; scale, $\frac{1}{12}$.

Appearance in flight of most characteristic plumage.

*Distinctions.* With its feathered tarsus (like Figure 190), to be confused only with the Ferruginous Rough-leg. In the dark phases the two are absolutely alike in colour, but this species never has the large amount of pure white that the ordinary plumage of that species shows. In the pale phase the ochraceous breast and head and the conspicuous dark abdominal band (Figure 191) are distinctive. In the adult and intermediate plumages, the Ferruginous never seems to have the irregular spotted or speckled mixture of this species. In the complete dark phase, the bill shape that is distinctive in any plumage is probably the best criterion. In this species, looking at the bill from above, it is narrow and constricted towards the gape (Figure 192) instead of being broad and "frog-mouthed" (Figure 195).

*Field Marks.* Recognizable by its outline and high soaring habits as a buzzard.

Except in characteristic plumage with extensive dull ochre breast and sharply defined dark abdominal patch, it is difficult to separate it from several similarly appearing hawks. The under surface of the wing usually has a much more pronounced "thumb-mark" of dark near base of primaries than other comparable species, and the tail, white at base and dark at end, shows a much wider, broader, and more pronounced tail band than in any other similar bird (Figure 191). The American Rough-leg has the same light spot at the base of the primaries on the upper surface of the wing as the Ferruginous (Figure 194).

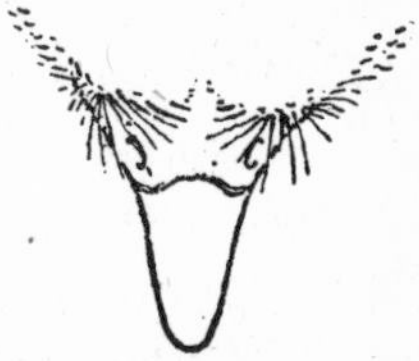

Figure 192

Narrow bill of American Rough-legged Hawk (from above); natural size.

*Nesting.* On the ground, on rocky ledges, or in trees.

*Distribution.* Northern parts of Northern Hemisphere. A bird of the far north. In America nesting on the barren grounds across the continent. Wintering from British Columbia and Minnesota southward. Only a migrant, almost a winter visitor, in cultivated sections of Canada.

*SUBSPECIES.* The American Rough-leg (la Buse pattue d'Amérique) *Buteo lagopus sancti-johannis* is separated from the European Rough-leg by being double instead of single phased, and thus presents an analogous case to that of the Eastern and Western Red-tailed Hawks where the same distinction occurs.

This is an early spring and late autumn visitor to our marshes where it is to be seen beating up and down over the sere surface, dropping occasionally into the grass, and then resorting to some nearby fence-post or other little elevation to devour its catch. More commonly, however, it is noted circling in large, loose flocks, so high in the air as to be seen with difficulty, and slowly drifting north or south on its migrations.

*Economic Status.* Its talons are small and weak for so large a bird, and it confines its attentions to small mammal game. It may sometimes pick up a wounded bird left by the shooters, but occasions of its taking anything of economic value are practically unknown.

Though one of our largest hawks, it is among the three least harmful. Of 45 stomachs examined: 40 contained mice; 5, other mammals; 1, lizard; 1, empty. A record like this is enough to condemn the indiscriminate killing of hawks. It is a mouse-hawk *par excellence*. It also feeds on grasshoppers and has been known at times to do most excellent work controlling plagues of these destructive insects.

348. **Ferruginous Rough-leg.** SQUIRREL HAWK. GOPHER HAWK. CHAP-HAWK. LA BUSE PATTUE COULEUR DE ROUILLE. *Buteo regalis.* L, 24. Plate XV A. A characteristic light plumage is shown in the plate. There is also a complete "black" phase, that is inseparable in colour from the dark Swainson's Hawk. A lighter coloration has all the underparts pure, uniform white, very slightly streaked, and the pantaloons or thighs white, or heavily barred with dark rusty in striking contrast with the white abdomen and breast. The whole tail may be white, but usually darkens slightly towards the tip (Figure 193).

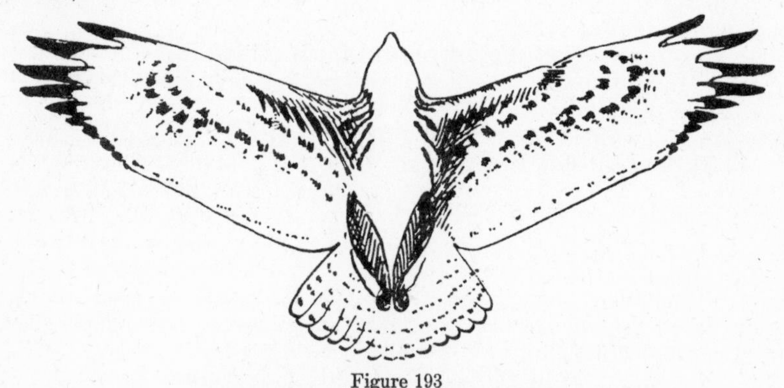

Figure 193

Ferruginous Rough-legged Hawk; scale, $\frac{1}{12}$.

Appearance in flight of extreme light phase.

*Distinctions.* Easily recognized as a Rough-leg by its feathered tarsi (Figure 190). The breast shows a large amount of pure white, which the American Rough-leg never does, and it never has the general ochraceous tone nor the sharply defined, dark, abdominal band of that species. The tail is white, often gradually darkening towards tip, but never with well-defined, dark, terminal band. In no plumage has it the patternless intermixture of black and light seen in the adult American Rough-leg. The most certain and final distinction, however, between these two species, is the shape of the bill. That of the Ferruginous when examined from above is wide and heavy at the base instead of narrow and constricted, and presents a "frog-mouth" appearance (Compare Figures 195 and 192).

*Field Marks.* A very large buzzard, the vulture, eagle, and osprey only being larger (Figure 174—4). Separated from the most characteristic American Rough-leg plumage by white breast and abdomen, and absence of dark terminal band to tail (Compare Figure 193 with 190). Rough-legs summering on the southern prairies are almost certain to be this species, and are likely to be confused only with the Red-tailed or Swainson's Hawks. The ruddy coloration of the back, white underparts with little marking, contrasting thighs, and white tail, or tail gradually whitening towards base, make the best distinction from those species. The black phase is very difficult to recognize except by the white bases of the primaries that often show as a flash of white on the upperwing surface when that member is extended to its fullest (Figure 194), a character that is not visible in the normal flight attitudes of the other comparable species except the American Rough-leg.

The typical Ferruginous Rough-leg in flight, seen from below, shows a dark V-mark with apex under the tail, formed by the deeply coloured thighs and tarsi brought together at the closely held feet.

Figure 194

Wing of Ferruginous Rough-legged Hawk (viewed from above, showing white at base of primaries); scale, $\frac{1}{5}$.

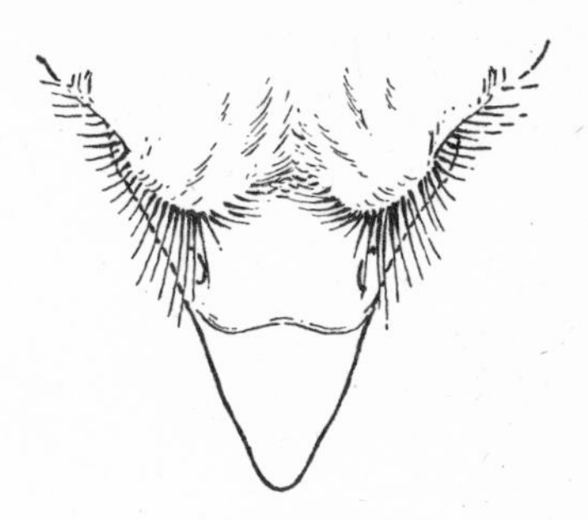

Figure 195

Wide bill of Ferruginous Rough-legged Hawk; natural size.

*Distribution.* Western North America, a bird of the prairies. In Canada, breeding on the southern prairies and southward. Not yet satisfactorily identified in British Columbia, though it has been noted in the state of Washington and occurs regularly in California.

The largest but the least harmful and most beneficial of our hawks. It builds immense, bulky nests in the cottonwoods and poplars in the coulées, on shelves and pinnacles of the bad lands, or even on steep, smooth hill-sides. These nests are repaired and added to year after year until they assume enormous proportions. One such was noted on a sloping bank in the Red Deer River bad lands, built to a height of about 10 feet. The base was old, rotten, and compressed, and seemingly of great age; the top was loose, fresh, and in occupation. Some nests are in such easily accessible situations that the wonder is—how they can escape the depredations of the ever-prowling coyote. Perhaps they do not, for though many old nests are encountered in such positions, most of them are small, denoting short occupation, and few are in current use.

This is a magnificent bird, and should be far more numerous than it is. In out of the way localities it is still common, but it is not particularly wary and disappears more rapidly than other hawks when its habitat is invaded by settlement. It is to be seen often enough on the great grazing leases, but in agricultural communities, where it is most necessary, it seems doomed to disappear before the ill-judged prejudice against hawks in general.

The Ferruginous Rough-leg is the Ground-squirrel or Gopher Hawk *par excellence* and well deserves the name. The number of these pests destroyed by them is astonishing. We have no evidence that, through the period of their stay in this country, they ever touch anything but small mammals, and their record is absolutely clear. One nest examined by the writer in the bad lands of Red Deer River contained the fresh remains of several gophers, and in a small hollow immediately under the nest was nearly a bushel of fragments of similar prey, dried bits of furry skin, tails, and feet, and such small discards from innumerable meals. The number was not counted, but must have represented several hundred animals, yet they were but the pieces that happened to fall just in this particular direction from the nest. A conservative estimate of the requirements of a family of these large hawks is surprising in its total. Two adults, from spring arrival to the birth of young, three months, consume not less than a gopher a day, 90 in all. After the young are out, four in the brood, and for two months at least, the family requirement can not average less than three gophers a day, or 180. Thereafter for one month, the six practically adult birds, though four are still growing, probably will require one gopher each a day, or 180 more. A single gopher, in favourable circumstances, destroys at least one bushel of wheat. Supposing that one-tenth of this can be charged against the average gopher, we still have thirty-five bushels of wheat as the value of this one family of large hawks for a single season. This can be translated into dollars and cents by multiplying by the current price of wheat, and makes a sum that is well worth considering.

With the reduction of coyotes, foxes, and other natural enemies of gophers on the prairies, these large buzzard hawks, the Red-tail, Swainson's, and Rough-legs, should be encouraged in every way to take their places.

## Eagles

The Eagles are our largest Birds of Prey. Size alone will differentiate them from the hawks. Any bird of prey over 30 inches long, or 6 feet in extent, is an eagle. They are typically large buzzards, and have a similar outline in flight, but with a longer though equally round-tipped wing, and the tail broad but not so long (Figure 174—2). A very distinctive character of the eagles in life is the shape of the head and bill. The bill is rarely as long as the head itself but shows a particularly massive and characteristic appearance that can be recognized as eagle-like at a considerable distance. We have only two species in Canada.

**349. Golden Eagle.** L'AIGLE DORÉ. *Aquila chrysaëtos.* L, 30. A large, dark brown Eagle, the hindneck suffused with an ochraceous cast suggesting the name "Golden" (Figure 197), and the basal half of tail dark, with indistinct broken bars or speckles of greyish. Tarsus feathered to the base of toes.

*Distinctions.* In all plumages very similar to the juvenile Bald Eagle, but quite different from the adult. The mature Golden is all black or very dark brown, with hindneck dull ochre. The end of the tail is dark, but beneath the coverts at the base it is

**Figure 196**
Feathered tarsus of Golden Eagle; scale, ⅓.

Figure 197
Golden Eagle; scale, ⅓.

Plate XXIII

A. Wilson's Snipe; scale, $\frac{1}{4}$

B. Upland Plover; scale, $\frac{1}{4}$

PLATE XXIV

A. Spotted Sandpiper; scale, $\frac{1}{4}$

Adult Juvenile

B. Willet; scale, $\frac{1}{4}$

Winter adult Summer adult

obscurely mottled or barred. The juvenile is similar, but the basal half of the tail is largely, or entirely, white. The most distinctive feature for this species, however, is the tarsus; it is feathered to the base (Figure 196) of the toes in all plumages, instead of being bare as in the Bald (*See* Figure 200).

*Field Marks.* Recognizable as an eagle by its large size; to be confused only with the juvenile Bald Eagle. The juvenile Golden shows as a black bird with a prominent white spot at the base of the primaries, visible on both upper and lower surfaces in flight. The tail is largely white with a broad, black border (Figure 198). The adult is all evenly black below (Figure 199). The young Bald Eagle has considerable grey on the underwing surface, becoming more pronounced towards the body, and the tail is either all dark or gradually lightens from the tip without showing a pronounced terminal band (*See* Figures 201, 202).

*Nesting.* Nests of sticks on ledges of cliffs, occasionally in trees.

*Distribution.* Northern part of Northern Hemisphere. In America, across the continent, north to the Arctic Ocean, and breeding in Canada irregularly in the wilder localities. More common in the western mountains than elsewhere.

Figure 198
Golden Eagle (juvenile); scale, $\frac{1}{18}$.
Appearance in flight.

Figure 199
Golden Eagle (adult); scale, $\frac{1}{18}$.
Appearance in flight.

In summer, the Golden Eagle is a bird of the mountains, as the Bald is of the coast and large waters, but it spreads out over the country in late autumn and winter. It is a far more spirited and noble bird than the more common Bald Eagle, being a less habitual carrion feeder than that species, and capturing more of its prey by strength and pursuit.

Except in the mountains of British Columbia, or the prairies in autumn, the Golden Eagle is a rare sight in Canada, and the majority of the popular reports of the species are based on the juvenile Bald Eagle. Its principal food is the big mountain marmot, but many a foolish Blue Grouse, nesting out on the bare mountain shoulders, is picked up by it, and its attacks on the lambs of mountain sheep, or the kids of the mountain goat, are not few or bootless. Probably if the mother is at hand, the bold raider is usually beaten off, but its assault is so sudden and unexpected that often the bleating prey is seized before maternal assistance can prevent. The charge has been made, and with considerable evidence in support, that this bird and the mountain lion are the two serious enemies of these alpine animals. How serious the depredations are remains to be demonstrated, but away from the immediate neighbourhood of high mountains little objection can be taken to the species. Even in the mountains, the damage it does can be easily overestimated, as marmots, rabbits, and gophers are undoubtedly its staple food, the other supplies being probably the result of hoped-for opportunity rather than habitual seeking. On the prairie sloughs it pursues ducks to some extent, but is a most persistent hunter of jack rabbits. Stories of children having been carried off, or other similar popular tales, are to be largely discounted. Such things may possibly have occurred, but are too extraordinary and most accounts too poorly substantiated to be regarded without suspicion. On the whole, except where special interests and conditions prevail, the Golden Eagle is a harmless and picturesque feature of the landscape.

351. **Gray Sea Eagle.** LA PYGARGUE ORDINAIRE (l'Aigle gris). *Haliaeetus albicilla.* L, 35. Much like the Bald Eagle, with white tail when adult but with head and neck greyish, blending into the body colour instead of being sharply defined white.

*Distinctions.* The adult is like the Bald Eagle except for differences indicated above. Juveniles are more striped below than in that species, but the distinctions are so fine that careful comparison and good judgment are essential to identify with certainty.

*Distribution.* Northern parts of eastern hemisphere and southwestern Greenland. It has been reported from Cumberland Sound, eastern Baffin Island, on uncertain evidence.

352. **Bald Eagle.** AMERICAN EAGLE. L'AIGLE À TÊTE BLANCHE. *Haliaeetus leucocephalus.* L, 33. Adult: a large, dark brown (nearly black) eagle with white head and tail. Juvenile: all dark brown. Tarsus bright yellow, bare for half its length (Figure 200).

*Distinctions.* The adult Bald Eagle, with its conspicuous white head, neck, and tail is too distinctive to be mistaken. The juvenile is so like the Golden that it has often been confused with it. It never has the golden ochraceous hindneck. The tail lightens towards the base with age, but always gradually, and never shows a definite tail bar as does the young Golden Eagle. The final distinction is the feathering of the tarsus which is bare for half its length instead of being feathered to the base of the toe (Compare with Figure 196).

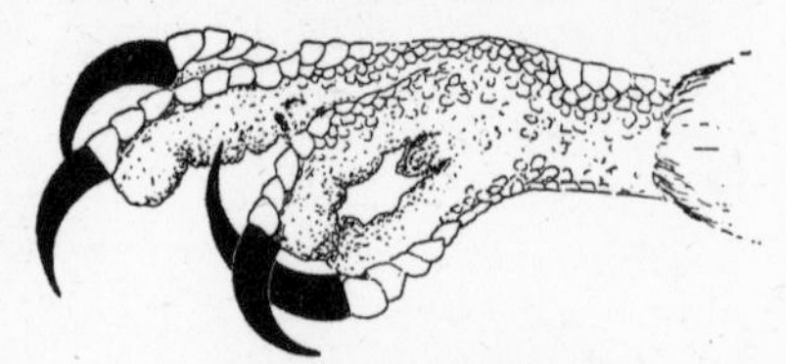

Figure 200
Bare tarsus of Bald Eagle; scale, $\frac{1}{3}$.

*Field Marks.* The adult with white head and tail is unmistakable (Figure 201). The juvenile is very similar to the Golden Eagle. It does not show a white spot at base of the primaries on the spread wing, but the under surface is largely greyish towards the body. The tail may lighten from the tip towards the base, but gradually, and never so as to show a definite terminal bar (Figure 202, compare with Figures 198, 199).

*Nesting.* Usually in large nests of sticks in tops of tall, isolated trees.

*Distribution.* North America, from northern tree limit south to Mexico. In Canada, across the continent, more common on the seacoasts than elsewhere.

*SUBSPECIES.* The Canadian bird is the Northern Bald Eagle (l'Aigle à tête blanche du Nord) *Haliaeetus leucocephalus alascanus*, separable from the southern subspecies by slightly larger size.

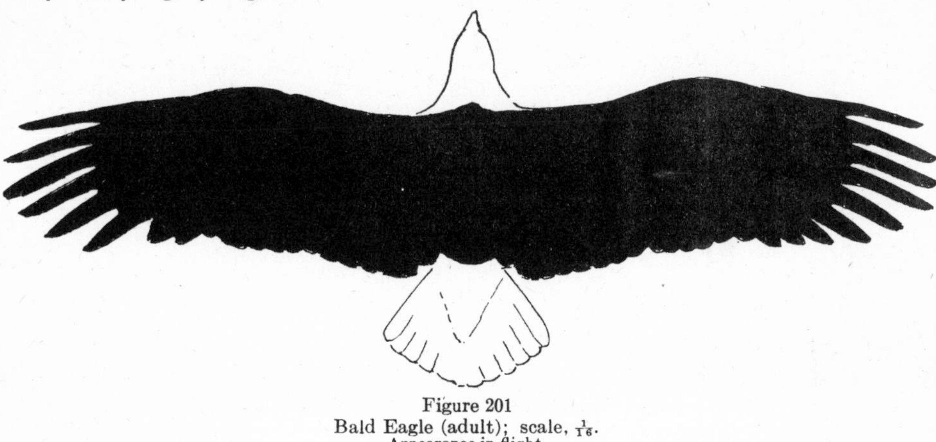

Figure 201
Bald Eagle (adult); scale, $\frac{1}{16}$.
Appearance in flight.

Figure 202
Bald Eagle (juvenile); scale, $\frac{1}{16}$.
Appearance in flight.

Throughout Canada, except on the seacoasts, the Bald Eagle is nothing more than a rare, interesting, and picturesque feature of the landscape. It is greatly to be regretted that it is usually a target for every gun when it comes within range.

*Economic Status.* Of 15 stomachs examined: 1 contained game; 5, mammals; 9, fish; and 2, carrion. In examining these data it is observable that the 6 stomachs containing mammals and game are winter specimens and, except one, were taken at a distance from water. Had the natural breeding and summer grounds of the Bald Eagle been the source of the specimens here studied, the mammals and game would probably have been replaced by fish, for this forms the great bulk of its food. The food is taken in various ways. The bird can dive for fish in true Osprey manner when necessary, but it usually picks them up dead from the shore or, where ospreys are common, takes the fish from them by force. To do this it pursues and badgers the successful fisher until it drops its prize, which by a lightning-like swoop is caught in the air and carried away in triumph. The Bald Eagle is, as a rule, hardly energetic enough to capture the quicker birds, but wounded or hurt ducks or game are eagerly picked up from the marshes. When opportunity offers the Bald Eagle eats offal without compunction.

On the seacoasts, where unusual numbers of eagles occur, and different conditions prevail, certain reservations to these conclusions have to be made. The principal food of the Bald Eagle is undoubtedly fish when available, and most of it is waste and offal, but when the salmon are crossing the bars into the mouths of rivers, or making their way up the riffles to spawn, the eagles attack them energetically. It is not only the fish actually killed and eaten that cause uneasiness, but the more numerous ones that tear themselves away from the great talons and die without having accomplished the propagation of their species. These are at times considerable. When the west coast salmon die after spawning, the Bald Eagles gorge themselves on the stranded bodies, and are too well fed and lazy to attack living game. When this time of abundance is over, however, the eagles turn to more energetic methods of living, and waterfowl then may suffer severely. Once on the wing such birds are comparatively immune from attack, for the Bald Eagle rarely, if ever, attacks from the wing, but, if surprised on the water and cut off from the air, the fate of birds even as large and hardy as geese and loons is practically sealed. The fowl dive at the swoop of the enemy, but in the clear coastal waters they cannot hide, and when they come to the surface again for air, there is the pursuing eagle awaiting them. A gasp is all that is allowed them before another dodge and dive. This goes on for but a few minutes when, exhausted and helpless, the victim is carried off, or towed in triumph to the shore. Where eagles are only ordinarily numerous, these attacks may be looked upon with equanimity as being of no serious harm to the species affected, but where, as on certain parts of the seacoast, dozens of eagles may be seen perched on commanding stubs overlooking the bird grounds, their attacks may be serious. At least, their constant harrying keeps the species in question so stirred up and nervous that they are unable to feed in peace, and linger no longer in the vicinity than is absolutely necessary. That eagles, even under these conditions, make serious inroads on the multitudes of wild fowl or fish of the coast, is questionable, but that they are always deserving of full protection can also be disputed. Any method designed to keep their numbers more in harmony with human demands should be applied and limited to the localities where they are an adverse economic influence, and where it does not destroy the picturesque features of the interior landscape, which the nature lover cannot well spare.

### Subfamily—Circinae. The Harriers

#### Harriers

The Harriers are long-winged, long-tailed birds of prey of light, slender build and with partly feathered eye-ring somewhat suggestive of owls (Figure 203). Their habitat is the open meadow and marsh, and mice are their principal prey. We have but one species in North America.

331. **Marsh Hawk.** MARSH HARRIER. LE BUSARD DES MARAIS. *Circus hudsonius.* L, 19. Plate XV B. Adult male: coloured like a gull, light slate-blue above, white below, black wing tips. Juvenile: mostly reddish brown, striped with lighter below. Adult female: like juvenile, but paler and less red.

Figure 203
Marsh Hawk (adult male); scale, ½.

*Distinctions.* A partial and incomplete feathered eye-ring, merely suggestive of those of the owls, is distinctive of the species. The general gull-like colours of the adult male and the warm reds of the juveniles are characteristic.

*Field Marks.* A medium-sized hawk of long, slender build. Slighter than a Broad-wing, smaller than a Coshawk, and larger than Cooper's (Figure 175—1). General coloration and the white rump, which shows conspicuously in flight, are the best field marks. Its long wings and tail (Figure 204) give it a somewhat falcon-like outline in flight, but its action is entirely different. The Marsh Hawk when soaring holds its wings decidedly elevated above the body instead of almost on a level with it, as do most hawks (Figure 205).

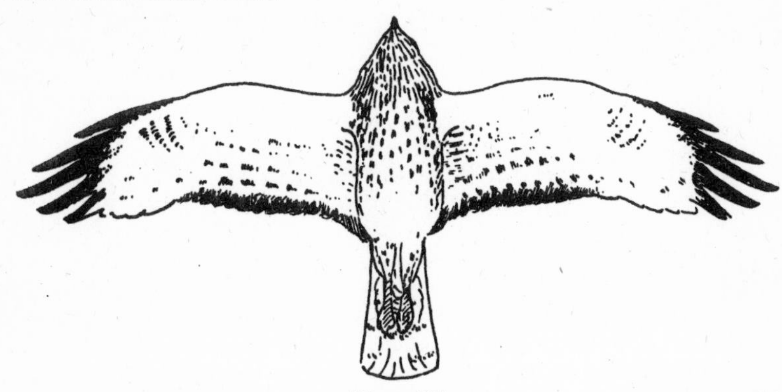

Figure 204
Marsh Hawk (adult male); scale, $\frac{1}{10}$.
Appearance in flight.

Figure 205
Field marks of Marsh Hawk.
Note angle of wings when flying.

*Nesting.* On the ground in a dry spot of the marshes, or in a hayfield.

*Distribution.* The whole of the United States and Canada north to near the Arctic Breeds throughout its range in Canada.

One of our commonest hawks found almost anywhere in Canada. It haunts the open marshes, meadows, and fields and is to be seen beating up and down, quartering and covering the ground like a well-trained bird-dog. For an instant it hovers over its intended prey and then drops upon it, rising a moment later to alight on a fence-post or other similar slight elevation to devour its captive. The young are unsuspicious, but the blue adults are amongst the wariest of birds and fall to the gun comparatively seldom.

*Economic Status.* Of 116 stomachs examined: 7 contained poultry or game-birds; 34, other birds; 57, mice; 22, other mammals; 7, reptiles; 2, frogs; 14, insects; and 1, indeterminate matter. Thus of 144 food items 41 were harmful, 93 useful, and 10 neutral. Of the 41 harmful items, only 3 were domestic fowl, and the remainder wild stock, consisting of 46 individuals of considerably less value than the domestic varieties. The mice and other mammals included about 117 individuals. The insects were mostly locusts, grasshoppers, and beetles. The balance is evidently in favour of this species, which is incapable of taking any fowl but small ones and then only when they wander into its habitat. Keeping spring chickens close about the premises is an almost perfect protection against this bird. Haunting marshes, grassy meadows, and tangled dry sloughs, as it does, it is the natural enemy of field-mice and probably does as much to keep their numbers within bounds as any other single natural influence.

Probably on the whole, and certainly in strictly agricultural country, the Marsh Hawk is considerably more beneficial than harmful. For a few weeks in early summer, when the marshes throng with small ducks and the young Prairie Chickens are on the uplands, it often engages in questionable pursuits and considerable numbers of half-grown game-birds become its prey. However, as soon as these immatures become too large and sturdy for so light a raptore to handle, it once again turns to mice and lesser game. Except where game is the most valuable crop, its presence is to be encouraged and shooting resorted to only where its depredations are particularly serious.

### Subfamily—Pandioninae. Ospreys

The Fish Hawks or Ospreys constitute a sub-family of raptorial birds subsisting entirely upon fish, which they capture in shallow water by diving. Other members of the order eat fish, but usually only as scavengers or by stealing from fish-catching birds. As there is only one species of Fish Hawk in America, no general discussion of the family is necessary here.

364. **Osprey.** FISH HAWK. L'AIGLE-PÊCHEUR (l'Orfraie). *Pandion haliaeetus.* L, 23·10. Plate XVI A. A very large, dark brown (nearly black) and white hawk, very white below without other markings than sometimes a vague, disconnected band of suffused, light brown spots across the breast.

*Distinctions.* A large brown and white hawk, with pale blue feet, the soles of which are covered with sharp, horny processes for grasping slippery fish (Figure 206). Head, largely white with contrasting black ear coverts, and a loose crest of white, dark-tipped feathers, from the hindhead.

*Field Marks.* A very large hawk (Figure 174—3), very white below, with a long wing expanse, almost eagle-like in outline, but with wing tips less broadly rounded (Figure 208).

Next smaller than the eagles. The facial markings are quite distinctive, white throat, black bar over ears, and white nape and sides of rear head with distinct occipital crest (Figure 207). Habits of hunting over broad shallows and diving from the wing.

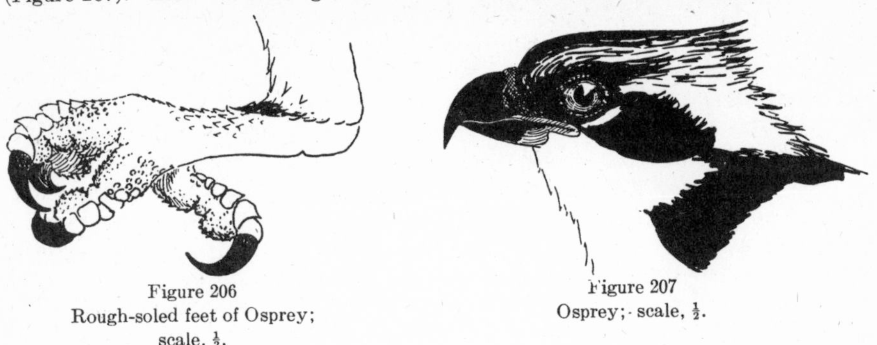

Figure 206
Rough-soled feet of Osprey;
scale, $\frac{1}{2}$.

Figure 207
Osprey; scale, $\frac{1}{2}$.

*Nesting.* Enormous nest of sticks in isolated tree tops, rarely on, or near, the ground. Nests are added to year after year and may assume the size of small haycocks.

*Distribution.* Nearly cosmopolitan. In the New World, North and South America. In Canada, across the continent, north to the tree limits, breeding locally and irregularly anywhere except in the open prairie country.

*SUBSPECIES.* The American Osprey (l'Aigle-pêcheur d'Amérique) ***Pandion haliaetus carolinensis*** is separated from the Old World form on the grounds of slightly larger size and small difference in colour.

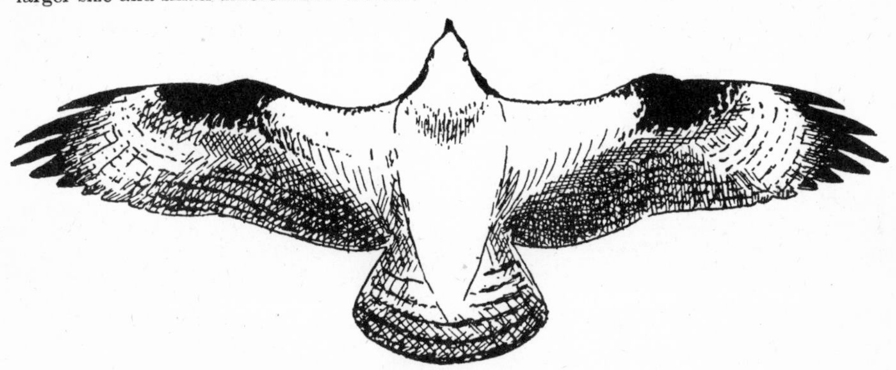

Figure 208
Osprey; scale, $\frac{1}{13}$.
General appearance in flight.

The Osprey is a most picturesque feature of the broad shallows of inland waters, or the tidal flats of the sea. Sailing at a considerable height over the water, it pauses a moment on hovering wings, and then drops suddenly. It falls, not straight down like a Kingfisher, but in a long spiral, striking the water feet first, with wings raised high over its back. There is a splash of white spray and, for a moment, the bird, except for the black wing-tips, is entirely hidden from view; then, with a heave of its powerful shoulders, it raises itself clear of the water and with one or two strong strokes rises in the air, a fish clasped in its rough talons, and returns to its aerie.

The term "osprey," as applied by the millinery trade, has nothing to do with this bird. The graceful plumes called ospreys are the product of a heron or egret, and the origin of the use of this confusing name for them is somewhat obscure.

The Osprey frequents broad, shallow, tidal flats, shallow bays, and clear water, where the fish on the bottom are exposed to view, and not too deep for capture. In the interior, the species is constantly growing rarer, but it seems to hold its own much better on the seacoast. Its great, bulky nest upreared conspicuously, and added to year after year, constantly invites attack from the human nest robber, who imagines that because the osprey is a hawk and eats a few fish it can claim no consideration at his hands. Next to man its worst enemy is the Bald Eagle which pursues and forces it to drop the hard-earned result of its fishing. With a clever swoop the bold raider catches the fish in the air as it falls, and makes off with his booty.

*Economic Status.* Though the food of the Osprey is entirely fish the antipathy that fishermen have for it is rather exaggerated. Feeding as it does in shallow waters it takes few fish of economic importance. On the coast, flounders, tomcod, and other small species form the bulk of its food. On the freshwater lakes, sunfish, perch, and suckers seem to be its staples. The number of game or marketable fish it catches is undoubtedly small. In eleven stomach examinations there was none. Trout streams are not attractive to the species and most of the valuable fish, such as bass and pickerel, usually lie too deep for it to catch.

### FAMILY—FALCONIDAE. CARACARAS AND FALCONS

This family is divided into two subfamilies, one of which, *Poliborinae* the Caracaras, has been represented in Canada by a single stray specimen. In general they can be described as hawks that have turned vulture.

362. **Common Caracara.** LE CARACARA COMMUN. *Polyborus cheriway.* L, 23. A vulture-like hawk with long cere and both mandibles bare of feathers to beyond eye. The talons, although strong and well developed, are not decidedly curved for holding struggling prey. Strongly black and white, with shoulders distinctly and sharply barred.

*Distinctions.* Plainly characterized as above.

*Distribution.* The warmer parts of North and South America. A single specimen was taken years ago near Port Arthur, Ontario.

*SUBSPECIES.* The North American form is Audubon's Caracara (le Caracara d'Audubon) *Polyborus cheriway auduboni,* ranging from Lower California to Florida.

Figure 209
Audubon's Caracara; scale, ⅓.

### Subfamily—Falconinae. True Falcons

The falcons were known to the old falconers as the Noble or Long-winged Hawks, and on account of their great spirit, strength, and address, were the chosen birds for use in hunting. Their long wings give them great speed and their endurance permits them to maintain it. They are bold and strong and capture their prey by sudden swoops when possible,

A. Greater Yellow-legs; scale, $\frac{1}{4}$
Juvenile

B. Least Sandpiper; scale, $\frac{1}{4}$ Semipalmated Sandpiper; scale, $\frac{1}{4}$
Both young in autumn

Plate XXVI

A. Marbled Godwit; scale, $\frac{1}{4}$

B. Wilson's Phalarope; scale, $\frac{1}{4}$

Male Female

but unlike the *Accipiters* are not discouraged when their stroke misses. They first rise above their prey by means of a long, spiral climb. Once above, they drop like a bullet, striking with their powerful talons as they do so.

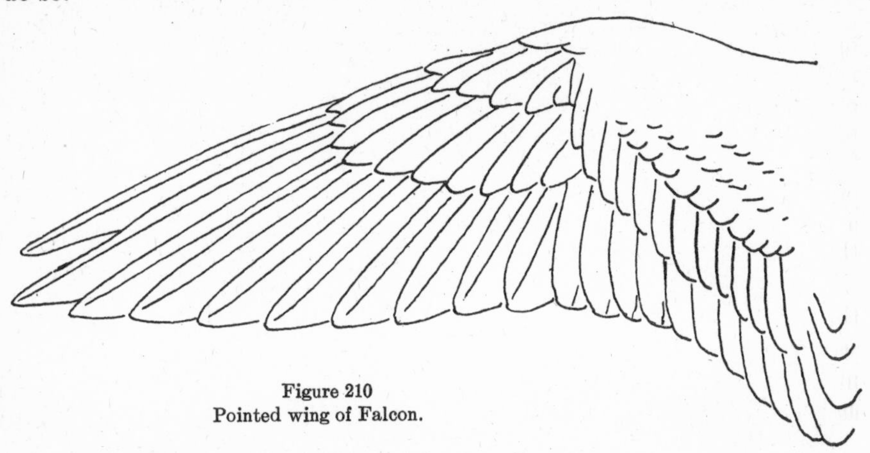

Figure 210
Pointed wing of Falcon.

The flight of falcons is quite recognizable—pointed wings (Figure 210) and quick strokes with very little sailing. Seen in the hand, the upper mandible furnished with a tooth and a small "doll's head" process within the nostrils (Figure 211) will always separate the falcons from other hawks. Fortunately, none but the smallest and least harmful of the subfamily is common within cultivated areas, and those that size makes important are either very rare or are more or less confined to the wilder wastes where their depredations can do the husbandman the least harm. Even those that do occur occasionally about cultivation are generally wary enough to keep away from the immediate vicinity of the habitations.

Figure 211
Toothed bill of Falcon.

## Gyrfalcons

*General Description.* The largest of the falcons, 20 to 22 inches in length; usually of light coloration, in some cases nearly pure white, others almost black. They are most

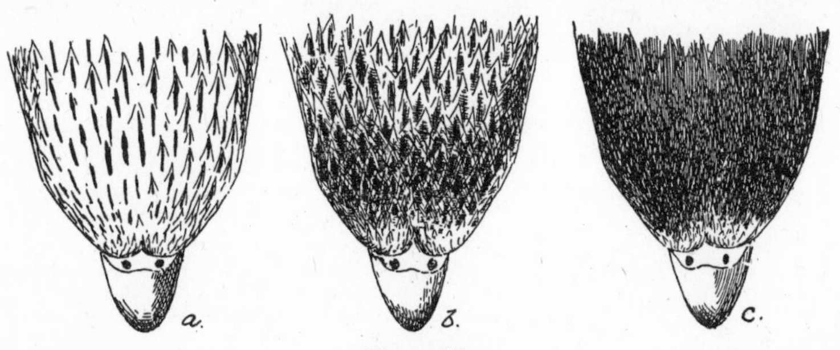


Figure 212
Crowns of Gyrfalcons.
*a.* White Gyrfalcon. *b* and *c.* Variations of American Gyrfalcons.

easily distinguished from the other falcons by their large size, but are otherwise characterized by the tarsus being feathered for one-half its length instead of only one-third, and the first primary being equal to or shorter, instead of equal to or longer, than the third.

The Gyrfalcons were most highly regarded for hunting by the falconers of old and by the exacting laws of the times their use was restricted to persons of the highest rank. They combined all the spirit and hardihood of the smaller species with greater size and strength and hence were adapted for the largest game to be taken with hawks. The Gyrfalcons are of far northern distribution in Canada and are very rare within the limits of settlement, rarely troubling poultry yards or game coverts; otherwise a war of extermination would probably have to be waged against them as they undoubtedly can be very destructive.

There is considerable difference of opinion about the relationship of the various forms of Gyrfalcon and no arrangement of them so far advanced seems to meet with general approval. The last Check-list (1931) recognizes only a single species in the New, and the Old, Worlds, instead of two as heretofore.

353. **Gyrfalcon.** LE GERFAUT. *Falco rusticolus.* L, 22. A large falcon. Mostly white, sometimes almost immaculate; almost solidly black or anything intermediate between these. Adults may have a decidedly barred back, but juveniles are much softly striped below and extensively feather edged with light above.

Figure 213
Gyrfalcon; scale, $\frac{1}{5}$.

*Distinctions.* As a falcon, by toothed bill and pointed wings. As a gyrfalcon, by large size and, in one subspecies, by general whiteness.

*Field Marks.* A very large falcon, said to resemble a goshawk in action. May be very black or very white. In the latter case may have a strong resemblance to a Snowy Owl, but note small head.

*Distribution.* The Arctic regions of both hemispheres. In winter may appear almost anywhere in Canada.

*Nesting.* On cliffs, or in trees.

*Subspecies.* The Check-list recognizes three subspecies in America. The White Gyrfalcon (le Gerfaut blanc) *Falco rusticolus candicans.* Predominantly white, sometimes almost immaculate, with sparse or scattered dark flecks on wing tips, wings, or back, and a sharply shaft-streaked crown (Figure 212a). The lack of markings on the undertail-coverts separates this from other races with which it may almost intergrade. It breeds in the eastern Arctics to western Europe. All other American Gyrfalcons are ascribed to the Black Gyrfalcon (le Gerfaut noir) *F. r. obsoletus,* and the Asiatic Gyrfalcon *F. r. uralensis;* the latter appearing in western Alaska and wandering occasionally south to Washington. It may occur on our west coast. The Black Gyrfalcon includes the birds covered in former editions of this work as *F. r. obsoletus, F. r. gyrfalco,* and *F. r. rusticolus.* The wisdom of this course may be questioned and the writer in inclined to restrict *F. r. obsoletus* to the very black birds of Labrador and to include the others under *F. r. rusticolus.*

355. **Prairie Falcon.** LE FAUCON DES PRAIRIES. *Falco mexicanus.* L, about 18. Like a pale or faded Peregrine. Much like the juvenile of that species, but more white below.

Figure 214
Prairie Falcon; scale, 1/5.

*Distinctions.* Recognizable as a falcon by toothed bill (Figure 211) and pointed wing (Figure 210). Rather variable in size, but, considering above distinctions, likely to be confused only with the Peregrine Falcon. Similar in colour pattern to that species, but exhibits little change due to age. In any plumage the darker colours are in faded or light browns instead of dark brown, black, or bluish grey. Below, the dark markings are less extensive, and never predominate over the white. Like the much rarer and larger Gyrfalcon, the first primary is shorter than the third, instead of being equal to or longer.

*Field Marks.* Recognized as a falcon by sharp, triangular wings, fairly long tail, seldom spread in flight, rapid wing beat without sailing, and the repetition of a single harsh note when agitated. Very much like the Peregrine Falcon in size, outline, and action (*See* Figures 175—8 and 215), from which it is best distinguished in life by its pale, sandy coloration. In flight the underwing surface shows a decided, dark patch formed of the dark or smoky axillaries.

*Nesting.* On cliffs, in crevices, or under overhanging ledges, in the most arid localities.

*Distribution.* Western North America, south to southern Mexico. In Canada, the prairie regions of Saskatchewan and Alberta and the valleys of southern British Columbia.

The Prairie Falcon is the prairie and desert representative of the Peregrine and resembles that species in many ways. It has the same bold dash and gallant hardihood, but shows more inclination to prey on small mammals, instead of birds. On occasions it even turns seriously to grasshoppers and the crop of at least one specimen examined by the writer was filled with these insects. Of 8 other stomachs examined: 3 contained game-birds; 5, other birds; 2, mammals; and 2, insects. The above is not a very reassuring record for the species, but the Prairie Falcon is a bird of the arid wilds and except in the neighbourhood of typical bad lands is rarely numerous enough to have any decided economic effect. The greatest complaint that can be normally laid against it is its tendency to visit the vicinity of grain elevators on the edges of prairie towns, and prey upon the domestic pigeons attracted by the spilled grain.

356. **Peregrine Falcon.** LE FAUCON PÈLERIN. *Falco peregrinus.* L, about 18. Plate XVI B. Adult: slaty blue above, slightly barred and lightest on rump, darkening to black on crown and tip of tail. Below, white to cream, sharply barred with black on abdomen, flanks, and thighs.

Juvenile: dark brown above, slightly feather-edged with lighter. Below, dark brown, with broad feather-edges of cream, producing a striped effect but tending to bars on flanks. Breast, flanks, and upper abdomen with dark predominating; throat and lower abdomen lighter.

*Distinctions.* Recognizable as a falcon by toothed bill (Figure 211) and pointed wing (Figure 210). Rather variable in size, but with above distinctions only likely to be confused with the Prairie Falcon. The juvenile Peregrine, however, is a dark brown, instead of a sandy, coloured bird, and the underparts may approach a solid brown, relieved by feather-edge stripes of cream to rufous-buff, instead of white or cream ground, with sparse brown spots or stripes.

The adult is distinctly slaty colour on the back, lightest on rump, darkest to nearly black on head and tail tip—colours that never occur on the Prairie Falcon. The faces of these two falcons are distinctive, with a dark bar down each side of the face from the gape, a detail that can be seen for considerable distance. The first primary, when full grown, is usually longer than the third, sometimes equal to it, but very rarely shorter.

Figure 215
Peregrine Falcon.
Showing characteristic wing action and outline in flight.

*Field Marks.* Recognized as a falcon by sharp, triangular wings, fairly long tail seldom spread in flight, rapid wing beat without sailing, and wings descending on the down stroke as far as they ascend on the up beat (Figure 215). The note when agitated is a rapid repetition of a harsh "*Kack-kack-Kack-etc.*" Hardly distinguished from the Prairie Falcon by size, outline, or action, but of stronger, darker coloration, nearly black above instead of sandy in adult, and the dark predominating in the underparts of the juvenile. In flight the underwing surface is of general uniform tint without any decidedly differentiated masses of colour.

*Nesting.* On cliff ledges, but not under shelter of strong overhangs, or in clefts; and always (?) in the immediate vicinity of water.

*Distribution.* The greater part of the northern hemisphere, south in winter to Africa and South America. In Canada, across the continent north to the Arctic Islands, nesting wherever there are steep cliffs in the vicinity of water. On migration, more common about water than elsewhere.

*SUBSPECIES.* The American form of the Peregrine Falcon, the Duck Hawk (le Faucon pèlerin d'Amérique) *Falco peregrinus anatum*, is separated from the Old World representatives of the species by small details of colour. There is another race, Peale's Falcon (le Faucon pèlerin de Peale) *Falco peregrinus pealei*, from the northwest coast of Queen Charlotte Islands and northward, that is distinguished by its average darker colour.

The Peregrine Falcon was, next to the Gyrfalcon, the most desirable hunting hawk of the falconers of old, and is still used for this purpose by a few enthusiasts in the Old World, who keep up ancient traditions. In our imagination it is still associated with royal functions and mediaeval surroundings. Though of very wide distribution, it is nowhere common, and usually nothing more than a rare and picturesque visitor.

*Economic Status.* The size of the prey that this bird can take is remarkable. Even the Mallard is often struck down and successfully brought to land to be eaten. Near one nest the writer found the remains of several full-grown Ruffed Grouse, which must have been carried to it, but on the prairies Franklin's Gull seems to be its favourite prey. An examination of the stomach contents of 16 specimens gave the following results: 7 contained poultry or game-birds; 9, other birds; 1, mice; and 2, insects. It is one of the few large hawks that show a preference for feathered, over furred, food. Fortunately for itself, it is as wary as it is spirited, and rarely comes close to man's residence or his poultry yards. Its favourite hunting grounds are the mud-flats frequented by shore birds, or the marshes where ducks congregate. An accomplished killer of wild fowl, the Peregrine is a thorough sportsman in its hunting, and captures its game by direct, irresistible attack, or straight pursuit, instead of craft surprise, and, as a sportsman and an historical character, can claim some indulgence from human rivals. There should be enough game in the country to support so picturesque a character without arousing the jealousy of other hunters.

**357. Pigeon Hawk.** AMERICAN MERLIN. LE FAUCON ÉMÉRILLON D'AMÉRIQUE. *Falco columbarius.* L, 10. A small falcon, very similar in size and coloration to the Sharp-shinned Hawk. Adult male: back, pale slate blue (almost gull-blue), dark slate, or bluish black, shaft-streaked with black. Tail, barred with the same blue, and with black in varying proportions. Below, white or cream more or less heavily streaked with ochre and brown, heaviest and darkest on flanks. Throat, pure, or nearly pure, white, immaculate or nearly so. Thighs, strongly tinged with warm buff, more or less brown streaked.

Figure 216
Pigeon Hawk (adult male); scale, ⅓.

Adult female resembles the juvenile, with sometimes an approach to the blue back of the male.

Juvenile: back brown or sandy brown, to nearly black, slightly shaft-streaked. Tail, uniform dark, or barred with dark of back and greyish or buffy-white, the dark areas being wider than the light. Below, cream or deep buff, more or less heavily streaked with dark or sandy brown. Throat, light to white, sometimes immaculate, usually sparsely streaked.

*Distinctions.* Recognized as a falcon by pointed wings and toothed bill (Figures 210 and 211). Distinguished from other falcons except Sparrow Hawk by smaller size. Easily separated from that species by extensive entirely different coloration, especially the absence of any red (Compare with Plate XVII A).

*Field Marks.* By small size, to be confused only with the Sparrow Hawk and the Sharp-shinned. Separated from the former by habits, habitat, and lack of extensive red in plumage, and from the latter by pointed instead of rounded wings, and falcon-like outline and action (similar to Figure 215, compare with 180).

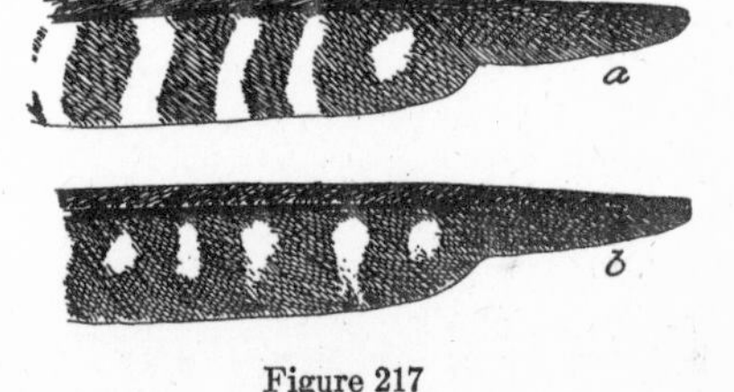


Figure 217
First primaries of Pigeon Hawks; scale, ½.
a, Common Pigeon Hawk and Richardson's Merlin.
b, Black Merlin.

*Distribution.* Northern North America. In winter, as far south as northern South America. In Canada, across the continent, north to tree limit.

*SUBSPECIES.* The Pigeon Hawk is divided into four geographical races. The Eastern Pigeon Hawk (le Faucon émérillon de l'Est) *Falco columbarius columbarius* is the medium dark bird, breeding in the forest sections throughout eastern Canada. Richardson's Merlin (le Faucon émérillon de Richardson) *Falco columbarius richardsoni* is a pale extreme nesting on the prairies; the Black Merlin (le Faucon émérillon noir) *Falco columbarius suckleyi* is a dark form of the west coast. In migration, both Richardson's and the Black Merlin occasionally wander into the interior valleys of southern British Columbia, and the Eastern Pigeon Hawk occurs commonly within the ranges of both the others. Another race, *Falco columbarius bendirei*, the Western Pigeon Hawk (le Faucon émérillon de l'Ouest), has been postulated for British Columbia interior and the northwest.

Richardson's Merlin is very distinct from the Eastern subspecies, being very considerably paler and more like the Old World Merlin *Falco aesalon* than the Eastern Pigeon Hawk *Falco columbarius columbarius.* The blue of the back of the adult male may be described as gull-blue, being the same pearly shade as the mantle of some of those birds. Below, the stripings are pale, rather soft instead of sharp, and the white or cream ground plainly predominates. The back of the juvenile is light brown with blended rusty-ochre feather edges, giving a soft colour-effect like wet sand, instead of dark mud. Although the distinction from *columbarius* is not so great below, the darks never predominate over the whites, creams, or ochres of the ground colour. Probably the most distinctive character of this race is the crown: that of the Eastern Pigeon Hawk is always decidedly dark, having the effect of dark brown feathers with faintly lighter edgings; in Richardson's Merlin, the crown is lighter, having an effect of rusty-ochre feathers with soft, dark median lines.

In the Black Merlin all the dark colours are sootier, and more extensive. The back of the adult male is much like that of the Eastern Pigeon Hawk, but blacker, and that of the juvenile is nearly black instead of dark brown. Below, in all plumages, the dark stripes are deeper in colour, broader and sharper in outline, and predominate over the lighter ground. The throat is generally plainly streaked instead of immaculate. The pattern of the first primary is usually a good test for this subspecies. In the Eastern Pigeon Hawk the light barrings are sharp and clear, and extend to the outer edge of the vane; in the Black Merlin they are smaller, sometimes almost lacking, and do not run to the edge of the web (Figure 217). The Western Pigeon Hawk is described as intermediate between *suckleyi* and *richardsoni*, but the present writer fails to see that specimens from the postulated localities are recognizably different from *columbarius* and cannot substantiate it.

In courage and spirit this species is a miniature of the Peregrine Falcon. It is more of a woodland bird, and is usually seen under less falconine conditions, dashing about the edges of copses, more like a Sharp-shinned Hawk, but when observed in straight-away flight in the open its falcon characters are plain.

Of 51 stomachs examined: 2 contained young chickens; 41, small birds; 2, mice; and 16, insects. It is apparent from this record that the Pigeon Hawk is destructive to small birds, and on occasions will take small poultry. Though more common than the larger falcons, it is still far from numerous; this, together with its natural wariness, prevents it from becoming a serious pest to the poultryman. It often follows the shore bird flocks on migration, and seems particularly fond of the Black-bellied Plover. Though, individually, it has considerable possibility of harm to wild life, the species as a whole has little economic effect.

360. **American Sparrow Hawk.** AMERICAN KESTREL. KILLY HAWK. LE FAUCON CRESSERELLE D'AMÉRIQUE. *Falco sparvarius.* L, 10. Plate XVII A. A small falcon of very distinctive coloration. The only small Canadian hawk showing much red.

*Distinctions.* The coloration is very distinctive, especially the red back and tail of the male, the general redness of the upper parts of the female, and the characteristic black and white face marking, which is common to both sexes.

*Field Marks.* The falcon characters of pointed wings and long tail, small size, ruddy colour, and habits of hovering stationary in the air and of pumping its tail up and down immediately after alighting.

*Nesting.* In holes in trees, usually a flicker's deserted nest in the top of a high stump.

*Distribution.* North and South America. In Canada, across the continent, north to the tree limit. Common nearly everywhere.

*SUBSPECIES.* The Sparrow Hawk of Canada is the Eastern Sparrow Hawk (le Faucon cresserelle de l'Est) *Falco sparvarius sparvarius.* The Desert Sparrow Hawk *F.s. phalaena* was once accredited to the west but has been dropped from the Canadian list.

This is the only common falcon we have, and fortunately the one to which the least blame can be attached. It is a beautiful little bird, and the gayest coloured of our hawks. The open fields, slashes, or brûlés are its hunting grounds, and the tallest of dead trees in the open its chosen observation post. It beats about over meadows, occasionally stops and hovers for a moment on quickly beating wings like a kingfisher, and then drops upon its quarry.

Calling this bird a "Sparrow Hawk" is a slanderous misnomer. That name, by right of description and association with Old World forms, belongs to the Sharp-shinned Hawk, which is a confirmed small bird killer and a close relative of the European Sparrow Hawk. Grasshopper Hawk would be a far better descriptive term for this little falcon, for grasshoppers are its favourite food.

*Economic Status.* Although a true falcon, this bird is one of the most efficient and valuable protectors of the farm. Of 291 stomachs examined: 1 contained a game-bird (Quail); 53, other birds; 89, mice; 13, other mammals; 12, reptiles or batrachians (frogs, etc.); 215, insects; and 29, spiders. Of the birds examined, 43 were taken in the winter months, from December to April. Of specimens taken in seasons when insects are available only 10 stomachs contained birds. This record shows that birds are killed by this falcon from necessity rather than choice. The "other mammals" were mostly harmful rodents, with a very few shrews. The insects are usually grasshoppers which do great damage and are difficult to control. From the above evidence it is obvious that the Sparrow Hawk is beneficial and should be protected.

This is a bird that could be advantageously and successfully attracted about the prairie farms and ranch houses. Dependent as it is on flicker holes or similar cavities for nesting sites, its normal breeding is limited to the vicinity of trees of considerable size. However, it is very adaptable, and has followed the Flicker out along the telegraph lines into the most open country, utilizing for nesting the premises of the original excavator. Suitable bird-houses erected on poles on the bare prairie would probably be found and utilized by it.

## Order—Galliformes. Gallinaceous Birds, Scratching Birds

As the name implies, these birds are adapted for securing their food by scratching the ground. The best popular representatives are the common barnyard fowl. They are found in almost every country in the world. In North America we have native only one division of the group.

### SUBORDER—GALLI. FOWL-LIKE BIRDS

*General Description.* This suborder is composed of birds with strong, compact feet, four toes, and blunt claws adapted for scratching the ground (Figure 218). Legs and feet may be heavily feathered to end of toes (*See* Ptarmigan, Figure 198). Though best adapted

Figure 218
Typical foot of scratching bird.

Figure 219
Typical bill of scratching bird.

for terrestial life they perch readily in trees and often feed and roost there. Bills short, horny, and with strongly arched culmen (Figure 219); nostrils set in a soft feathered or bare intrusion into the base of the bill; wings short and round. These birds rarely take wing except for short flights or to avoid immediate danger. The body plumage has pronounced aftershafts, small plumes growing from the base of the main feather (Figure 220).

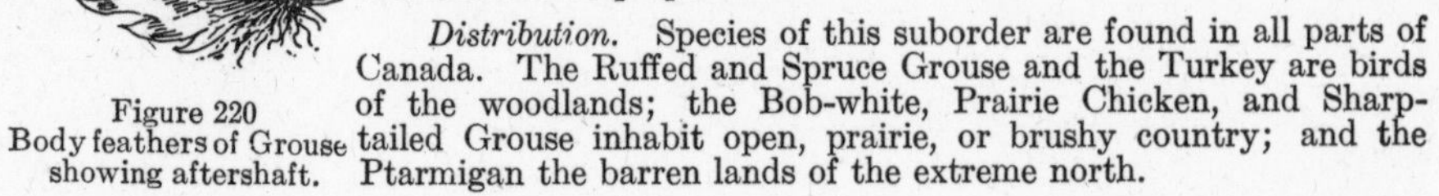

Figure 220
Body feathers of Grouse showing aftershaft.

*Nesting.* On the ground, eggs laid on the dead grass or leaves with little or no preparation.

*Distribution.* Species of this suborder are found in all parts of Canada. The Ruffed and Spruce Grouse and the Turkey are birds of the woodlands; the Bob-white, Prairie Chicken, and Sharp-tailed Grouse inhabit open, prairie, or brushy country; and the Ptarmigan the barren lands of the extreme north.

*Economic Status.* Their food is both insect and vegetable—grains, buds, leaves, fruit, and insects being equally acceptable to them. As several species frequent cultivated fields their economic status is of interest to the husbandman and has been the subject of considerable investigation, the results of which show that some of them are among the most useful birds on the farm. The insect part of the food of some species is decidedly important and very little objection can be made to the other items, which are mostly waste or wild material of little or no consequence to the agriculturist.

Like most of our larger birds they have been greatly reduced in number, and should be strictly protected and the killing of them limited to the natural annual surplus, leaving an ample permanent breeding stock untouched.

Most, if not all, members of the order in this country are subject to great fluctuation in number, and a gradual increase over a period of years followed by a sudden decrease is to be expected. The causes of this are various and complicated. A winter of unusually heavy snowfall that covers the food and fills the shelter coulées full of drifts will destroy much potential breeding stock. When a thaw or sleety weather is followed by a cold snap, it puts an impenetrable crust on the snow and prevents the getting of food or the burrowing for shelter. A long, cold, wet spring is disastrous to young birds, which are particularly susceptible to such conditions.

The welfare of these birds is linked somewhat closely with that of the rabbits and hare, not only of their own locality, but of the far north. The rabbit is the mainstay of all the carnivora—weasel, fox, coyote, lynx, Goshawk, and Great Horned and Snowy Owls. Other animals are eaten on occasion and even commonly, but rabbits are the staple food supply. When rabbits are plentiful, all the wilderness life waxes fat and numerous; the small mice, moles, and birds that find their enemies engaged in more profitable hunting, the fur bearers that revel in an abundance of easily caught food, and the trappers, even the great fur companies themselves, reap a rich harvest. When rabbits diminish in numbers, as they do periodically, owing to a little understood recurrent epidemic, starvation faces the greatly augmented forces of the rabbit-eaters that lately found life so comfortable and increase so easy. The numbers must be adjusted to a reduced food supply and thousands die by starvation and attendant evils, but not until every possible source of food supply is exhausted. Fat hunters grow lean and turn their attention to game and to hunting methods that in times of plenty are regarded with indifference, and everything of food value suffers accordingly. Competition becomes keen; raptores

A. Glaucous-winged Gull; scale, $\frac{1}{8}$

Adult in winter

B. Herring Gull; scale, $\frac{1}{9}$

Summer adult — Juvenile

A. Bonaparte's Gull; scale, $\frac{1}{6}$
Adult in winter (flying)
Summer adult
Juvenile

Franklin's Gull; scale, $\frac{1}{6}$
Adult in winter (flying)
Summer adult
Juvenile

B. Forster's Tern; scale, $\frac{1}{6}$
Summer adult — Juvenile

hunt farther afield, trespassing upon their neighbours' preserves, and the stress is intensified. Many wander far in their hungry search and invade localities where they do not normally appear. The keenest pinch naturally occurs in winter and then the resident grouse and upland game birds suffer severely. On our prairies may be an influx of coyotes, goshawks, and large owls from the north, which, with the usual resident vermin, turn to the Prairie Chicken, Sharp-tailed, and other grouse as the most available food supply, and hunt them with systematic persistence. The grouse naturally suffer proportionately, and by the time their enemies are reduced to normal numbers, may be sadly depleted. When the tide turns, however, it does so decisively. Rabbits are astonishingly prolific and increase faster than all their enemies combined. The enemies, now tremendously reduced in numbers, again turn their attention to their natural furry prey; the food supply exceeding the demand, the wandering raptores return to their former ranges. The resident vermin have been reduced by the bitter competition with the visitors and the grouse are again free from intensive persecution. Life becomes comparatively easy and undisturbed for them. Only the strongest and most vigorous have survived, large clutches of eggs are laid, and unless other deterrent circumstances arise they soon regain their wonted numbers.

Besides these climatic and raptorial influences, probably, as is the case with the rabbits, epidemic disease and parasites play no small part in the vicissitudes of the grouse and their allies. These birds are to a large extent gregarious, and disease can be readily communicated. Some seasons we find many birds infested with parasitic worms, and showing other evidences of diseases that doubtless have much to do with their sudden reduction in number. How many of these diseases have been introduced by our domestic poultry it is difficult to say, but such an origin is probable.

Recent investigation suggests that some, perhaps all or most, of our native grouse are particularly intolerant of common poultry disease, have not yet acquired resistance to the imported organisms that cause it, and cannot long exist in health in contact with domestic fowl. Perhaps the common practice of feeding wild coveys during hard winters with the poultry in the barn yard is a mistaken kindness that may disseminate disease in the ranks that we are trying to conserve.

Shooting should not be overlooked as a cause of great reduction, but the fact that in notoriously poor grouse years the birds are as scarce in un-shot as in well-shot covers, indicates that it is not always a primary, though it may often be a contributing, cause. No species, however numerous, can successfully withstand persistent, unregulated, or excessive shooting, but just what constitutes excessive shooting varies with the locality, the season, and passing conditions. Shooting that barely keeps a numerous thrifty species in reasonable control will annihilate it when it is already depleted by other causes. Consequently, laws for the protection of grouse have to be continually altered and adjusted to conditions, but even in spite of the best of laws thoroughly enforced in both letter and spirit, upland game must be expected to fluctuate in numbers and years of plenty be followed by scarcity, at which times every endeavour must be made to assist recuperation.

Of this suborder there are four families in Canada: *Tetraonidae* the grouse; *Percinae* the partridges and quails; *Phasianidae* the pheasants (introduced); and *Meleagridae* the turkeys.

## FAMILY—TETRAONIDAE. GROUSE

The grouse have the nostrils hidden in feathers that occupy an intrusive space at the sides of the base of the bill (Figure 219). The tarsus is either completely or partly feathered; in the ptarmigan the feathering includes the toes. The toes when unfeathered, in winter, are bordered on each side by a small fringe composed of individually horny scales or pectinations (Figure 225, page 155), which are shed in midsummer. Many species, especially in breeding season, have fleshy erectile combs over the eyes, coloured yellow or red. The grouse comprise the bulk of our upland game birds and are great favourites of sportsmen. The sexes are nearly alike, show slight seasonal variation in plumage, except in the ptarmigan, and the birds do not usually migrate. The ptarmigan, which directly reverse each of these statements, are so well characterized otherwise that no confusion is probable. All species nest on the ground, making little preparation for the eggs. They lay unusually large sets of eggs, six to eighteen, and the young, chicken-like, follow the parent as soon as out of the shell.

### Blue Grouse

In the western mountain districts are two species of large, slate-blue grouse that can be combined under the colloquial term Blue Grouse. Until lately they were regarded as subspecies of a single species, but in the latest Check-list (1931) they are given distinct specific standing.

297. **Dusky Grouse.** LE TÉTRAS SOMBRE. *Dendragopus obscurus.* L, about 21. Plate XVII B. A large grouse, the male an even, dark, slaty grey below, the female confusedly patterned or barred with ochres and browns but abdomen dull slate. Very similar in either sex to next succeeding species.

*Distinctions.* Far western range; size, considerably larger than a Ruffed Grouse; and general slatiness of the male. The female is patterned much like the female Spruce or Franklin's Grouse, but is decidedly larger and the centre of the abdomen is evenly slaty without evident barring. These details will separate from all grouse but the closely allied Sooty Grouse. The most obvious distinction in Canadian birds between these two is the well-defined terminal grey tail band in the male (Figure 221, compare with 222). It is a rather variable character, however, and birds intergrading in this character occur. Females are even more difficult to separate and in many cases geography makes the only test.

*Field Marks.* A far western woodland species. Large size, general leaden greyness of the male, and general sandy duskiness of the female. The solidly coloured tail will distinguish from the Ruffed Grouse and the unbarred breast and underparts from the female Spruce or Franklin's Grouse that may inhabit the same territory. To be distinguished from the Sooty Grouse by its geographical distribution east of the Coast Range, and its more subdued hooting, given from the ground and audible for only a hundred yards or so, instead of from trees and carrying a mile or more.

*Distribution.* The western mountain region and their eastern foothills. In Canada, British Columbia east of the Coast Range, southern Yukon, and parts of Mackenzie Valley.

*Nesting.* On the ground.

*SUBSPECIES.* Though the characters of the Canadian races of Dusky Grouse seem to be satisfactorily understood, the nomenclature of them offers difficulties as to which proposed name should be applied. Two races occur: a dark, northern form and a paler, southern one that crosses the International Boundary from the south. According to the latest information, the former is referable to Fleming's Grouse (le Tétras sombre de Fleming) *Dendragopus obscurus flemingi,* the latter to Richardson's Dusky Grouse (le Tétras sombre de Richardson) *Dendragopus obscurus richardsoni,* of which the Pallid Dusky Grouse *Dendragopus obscurus pallidus,* recently described, is a synonym.

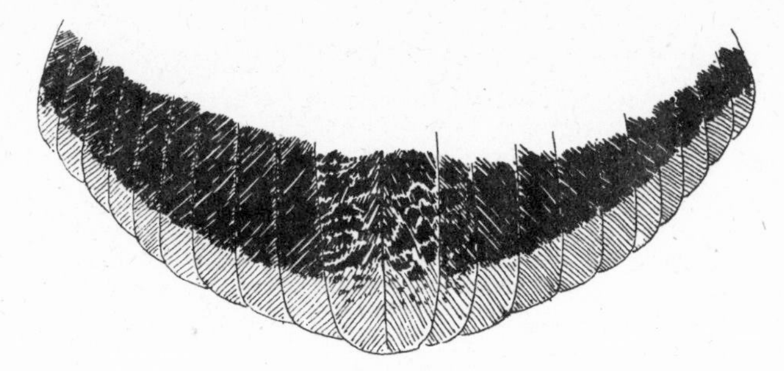

Figure 221
Tail tip of Dusky Grouse; scale, ½.

Figure 222
Tail Tip of Sooty Grouse; scale, ½.

297a. **Sooty Grouse.** LE TÉTRAS COULEUR DE SUIE. *Dendragopus fuliginosus.* L, about 21. Like the previous species except tail with faint or no terminal grey bar.

*Distinctions. See* previous species.

*Distribution.* Northwest coast of North America from the base of the Alaska Panhandle to southern Nevada. In Canada, British Columbia, west of the Coast Range.

*SUBSPECIES.* Two subspecies are recognized in Canada. The type form the Northwest Coast Sooty Grouse (le Tétras du Nord-Ouest) *Dendragopus fuliginosus fuliginosus,* of most of the above range, and the Sitka Sooty Grouse (le Tétras de Sitka) *Dendragopus fuliginosus sitkensis,* slightly darker in the male and decidedly redder in the female, inhabiting Queen Charlotte Islands and the islands of southern Alaska.

298. **Spruce Grouse.** CANADA GROUSE. FOOL HEN. LE TÉTRAS DES SAVANES. *Canachites canadensis.* L, 15. Plate XVIII A. A small grouse. The male coloured in black, grey, and white with small red comb but little other colour. Female irregularly barred all around body with the same colours, but with large admixture of rusty-brown.

*Distinctions.* Size will distinguish from any other grouse but the very closely allied Franklin's Grouse of British Columbia and the mountains, and the ptarmigan of the north and higher elevations. Easily distinguished from the latter by the unfeathered toes (Compare with Figure 226). The male is distinguished from Franklin's by the rusty-ochre tips to the tail feathers and the absence of broad white tips to uppertail-coverts (Figure 223, compare with 224). Northwestern birds, the Alaska Spruce Grouse, sometimes have white at the end of tail-coverts, but never on the tip of tail itself, which is a common character in Franklin's of either sex. Females are more difficult to distinguish and may at times be inseparable from Franklin's. The rusty tail tip and the absence of broad white tips to uppertail-coverts in this species are the best distinctions.

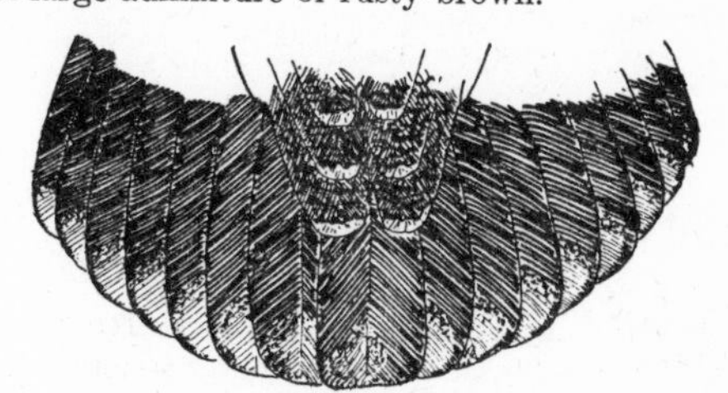

Figure 223
Tail tip of Spruce Partridge; scale ½.

*Field Marks.* Small size, and general black, grey, and white coloration and red comb of male. Female is a small, reddish brown grouse strongly banded all around body. Unless terminal rusty tail band is observed in flight probably not separable by sight from Franklin's Grouse.

*Distribution.* The northern spruce forests across the continent. In the Prairie Provinces south to the edge of the continuous forest, but not extending far southward in the mountains. In British Columbia not reaching the Canadian National Railway tracks nor the coast anywhere.

*SUBSPECIES.* The Spruce Grouse is divided into several recognized subspecies, all much better characterized in the female than in the male.

The Hudsonian Spruce Grouse (le Tétras des savanes Hudsonien) *Canachites canadensis canadensis* occupies most of the northland from Labrador west to the base of the Rocky Mountains near Jasper Park. There is also an apparently isolated community on the southwest coast of Alaska; for which a separate name has been proposed. The Alaska Spruce Grouse (le Tétras des savanes de l'Alaska) *Canachites canadensis osgoodi* occupies central Alaska, the Yukon, northern British Columbia, and Mackenzie Valley. Manitoba, north to the head of the big lakes, is inhabited by the Canada Spruce Grouse (le Tétras des savanes du Canada) *Canachites canadensis canace*, which is also the southern Ontario and Maritime Province form. These races are too slightly defined, however, to warrant consideration by any but the expert with a large series of specimens for comparison.

The Spruce Grouse, though colloquially and often officially called "partridge," is a true grouse misnamed through general but careless usage. It is a bird of the northern woods. Its over-confiding nature has given it the name of "Fool Hen" as, where not much disturbed, it can be killed with sticks or stones. For this reason it is one of the first birds to disappear before settlement and it is rapidly vanishing from all but the most retired and lonely localities. Owing to its feeding largely upon spruce or evergreen buds its flesh in late or middle winter is usually too strong for the ordinary civilized palate and it can not be listed as a legitimate game bird.

299. **Franklin's Grouse.** FOOL HEN. LE TÉTRAS DE FRANKLIN. *Canachites franklini.* L, 15. Almost exactly like the Spruce Grouse, with tail black to the tip or else with narrow white termination and generally with conspicuous white tips to uppertail-coverts (Figure 224, compare with 223).

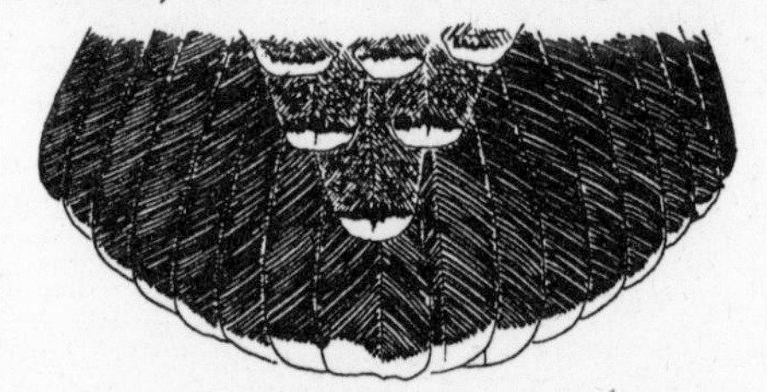

Figure 224
Tail tip of Franklin's Grouse; scale, ½.

*Distinctions.* Size will distinguish from any bird but the very closely allied Spruce Grouse of northern British Columbia and the Prairie Provinces, and the ptarmigan of the far north and high elevations. Easily distinguished from the latter by the unfeathered toes (Compare with Figure 226). The male is distinguished from the Spruce Grouse by the lack of rusty-ochre tips to the tail feathers, or its replacement by a narrow line of white, usually with pronounced white tips, on the uppertail-coverts. This last character sometimes occurs in the Alaska form of the Spruce Grouse which, however, has not the white tail tip common to both sexes of Franklin's. Females are more difficult to distinguish and may at times be inseparable from the Spruce Grouse. The lack of rusty in tail tip and the presence of broad white tips to uppertail-coverts are the best distinctions. Specimens approaching intermediate may occur. Slight traces of rusty on tail tip may occur in Franklin's Grouse, but never anything like a terminal bar. This difference never seems quite bridged over and is, therefore, regarded as fully specific.

*Field Marks.* Small size and general black, grey, and white coloration and red comb of male. Female, a small, reddish brown grouse strongly banded all around body. Probably inseparable in life from the Spruce Grouse unless the terminal tail characters are evident. There are, however, but few places where their ranges overlap.

*Distribution.* The mountains of northern Oregon to central British Columbia from the Coast Range to the eastern slopes of the Rockies in Alberta.

All that is said of the Spruce Grouse is equally true of this species.

300. **Ruffed Grouse.** PARTRIDGE. BIRCH PARTRIDGE. LA GELINOTTE DES BOIS FRANCS (La Perdrix). *Bonasa umbellus.* L, 17. Plate XVIII B. A large, woodland grouse coloured in wood-browns and greys. Broad, soft, black feathers making "ruffs" on sides of neck, and lower back feathers with small, fine eye-spots. Female similar but

with ruffs smaller. Occurs in two phases, regardless of age, sex, or season. A red form with the light parts of the tail brick-red, the browns elsewhere tending towards reddish rather than grey, and with copper-coloured (or black) ruffs. In the grey phase, the ground colour tail is ashy grey, there is much grey overwash on the back and elsewhere, and the ruffs are steely black. There are various intergrading and mixed plumages.

*Distinctions.* The soft, black ruff feathers on the sides of the neck, the broad, ample, many-barred tail, and the small eye-spots on lower back make this an easily distinguished species. The legs are more sparsely feathered than in other grouse and the lower half of the tarsus is bare (Figure 218). In winter the toes are edged with a row of fine pectinations suggesting snow-shoes. In midsummer these are shed and the toes are clean (Figure 225).

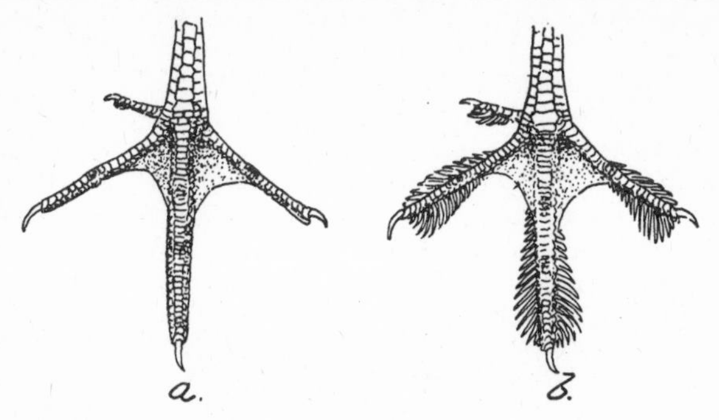


Figure 225
Foot of Ruffed Grouse: *a*, summer; *b*, winter.

*Field Marks.* Size, general coloration, ruffs, and especially the broad grey or red, many-barred tail which is very conspicuous when the bird is flushed.

*Distribution.* Wooded regions of Canada and the northern United States. In Canada absent only in a few localities of the most southern arid prairies.

*SUBSPECIES.* The Ruffed Grouse is split into a number of recognized subspecies. The Canada Ruffed Grouse (la Gelinotte des bois francs du Canada) *Bonasa umbellus togata* and the Nova Scotia Ruffed Grouse (la Gelinotte des bois francs de la Nouvelle-Ecosse) *Bonasa umbellus thayeri* are the east Canadian forms, the latter confined to the extreme east and the former extending across the continent into southern British Columbia and to the east slope of the Coast Range. The Grey Ruffed Grouse (la Gelinotte grise des bois francs) *Bonasa umbellus umbelloides* occupies the interior of British Columbia. It has considerably more grey veiling on back and elsewhere and the red phase is scarcer. The Yukon Ruffed Grouse (la Gelinotte des bois francs du Yukon) *Bonasa umbellus yukonensis* is a newly recognized form of Alaska and Yukon. It carries the general greyness still farther than the previous forms. The Oregon Ruffed Grouse (la Gelinotte des bois francs de l'Oregon) *Bonasa umbellus sabini* is the bird of the Pacific coast, west of the Coast Range. This is a very red bird with little or no grey anywhere. The back is in general a warm rufous-brown and the breast and underpart are heavily and broadly barred. The extreme grey phase is scarcely greyer than some of the red birds of other subspecies.

Owing to the dichromatism and great individual variation in this species these races, except *sabini*, are difficult to separate and considerable confusion prevails amongst authorities as to their relative distribution. Typical birds of the *umbelloides* type can be found intermixed with good *togata* far east on the prairies and south near the boundary of British Columbia, and vice versa, *togata* specimens crop up in *umbelloides* regions. Probably only in the extreme ranges will the forms be found pure and unmistakable, and most local races can only be determined by average characters that leave room for wide variation in personal opinion. With such areas of overlapping it is hardly safe to be dogmatic. The above ranges give the present opinion of the writer based upon quite considerable material, but this does not agree with the American Ornithologists' Union

Check-list which extends *togata* west only to Manitoba and extends *umbelloides* over the prairies and southern British Columbia, referring the Alaska and Yukon birds to *yukonensis*.

The Ruffed Grouse is the "Partridge" of most Canadian sportsmen. Where it has learned its lesson of wariness, as in old centres of settlement, it offers probably the best sport of any of our upland birds. Lying close in the dense underbrush and bursting from the tangle like a miniature explosion, attaining full speed almost instantly, and hurtling away in the shadowy aisles of the bush, it tests the alertness and the skill of the finest marksman. However, all birds have not learned the lessons so necessary to existence and shooting Ruffed Grouse in the north and west is a severe test of sportsmanlike ideals. Too often it degenerates into pot-hunting and shooting on the ground or from trees. Such methods may fill the bag but are no more sportsmanlike than killing poultry with an ax.

The Ruffed Grouse is a bird of the bush and is seldom seen away from timber. Through the prairies it is to be found in most of the larger poplar bluffs and in the wooded valleys of the rivers. Its drumming is a sound well known to all frequenters of the woods. It is a series of reverberating throbs made by rapidly beating wings and has a peculiar all-pervading intensity that makes the direction of its origin difficult to locate. The beats begin slowly with measured frequency, gradually increasing in speed until at the end of perhaps five seconds they run into each other and die away in a confused whir. The male is usually strutting on a favourite fallen log when he pauses to drum. During the drumming the bird displays all his ornaments—tail, crest, and ruff—and his wings are lost to sight in a haze of speed. There has been much discussion as to how the sound is produced. The action is so quick that it confuses the eye, and conflicting explanations have been given by eye witnesses. Slow moving pictures, however, have shown that the beat is produced by the forward stroke of the wings against the air in front of the bird. The similarity of the sound of the wings as the bird suddenly rises to wing is evident. The action is, probably, the call of the male to the females as is the display of the Peacock or the Turkey gobbler. Spring is the proper season for drumming, although it is indulged in regularly in the autumn also, probably in sheer exuberance of spirits, for there is no sexual activity accompanying it and the females appear to give it no particular attention.

## Ptarmigan

*General Description.* Ptarmigan are Arctic Grouse and notable for their remarkable seasonal change in plumage. In winter they are, except for certain details in some species, pure white; in summer, they are barred or vermiculated with various shades of red, brown, and ochre, with irregular white feathers and patches remaining from winter. The moult seems practically constant throughout the summer, and as they have an autumn as well as a summer plumage, some very puzzling plumage mixtures occur. In the same bird white feathers of the previous winter may still persist when similar ones of the coming winter season are appearing together with a mixture of both the summer and the autumn plumages. The principal characteristic of the summer plumage is generally a distinct and coarse cross-barring and that of the autumn is fine vermiculation and an intimate pepper and salt mixture of colours. In summer, irregular patches of white may persist and the wings are always white. The feet are feathered to the toes (Figure 226). With these decided characteristics

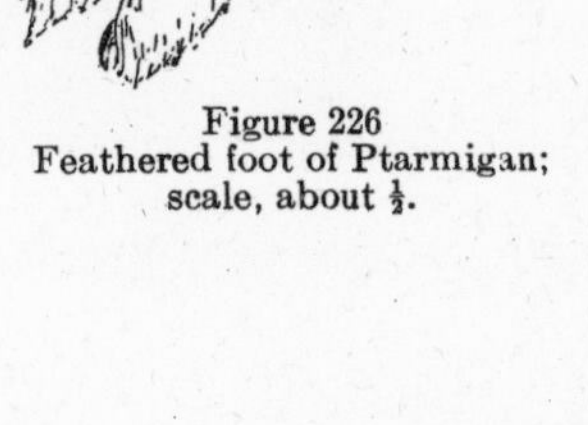

Figure 226
Feathered foot of Ptarmigan; scale, about ½.

A. Common Tern; scale, $\frac{1}{4}$

Summer adult

B. Marbled Murrelet; scale, $\frac{1}{6}$

Young in winter

Summer adult

PLATE XXX

A. Band-tailed Pigeon; scale, $\frac{1}{4}$

Male

B. Mourning Dove; scale, $\frac{1}{4}$ Passenger Pigeon; scale, $\frac{1}{4}$

there need be no mistaking this group. In midsummer the toes in moult may seem bare, but the worn feathers remaining and the incoming pin feathers always show that this is but an intermediate condition. Under certain conditions the nails, and to some extent the bill, overgrow in a remarkable manner.

Ptarmigan are circumpolar and like many other Arctic forms they extend southward along the mountain tops where high elevation carries northern conditions into more southern latitudes. The northern individuals make long, seasonal migrations, walking much of the way but flying occasionally, and are capable, when necessary, of making passage of quite wide stretches of water, as between the Arctic Islands. Those of more southern habitat move down the mountain sides to find milder conditions.

There are three species of ptarmigan in America, one of which, the White-tailed, is peculiar to the Rocky Mountain region. The Red Grouse of Scotland is an interesting ptarmigan that has lost its ability to turn white in winter.

Our three ptarmigan have been split up into various races, but individual and seasonal variations are so great and the racial differences are so slight that none but an expert, with large experience in the group and ample specimens, is competent to separate many of them.

301. **Willow Ptarmigan.** LE LAGOPÈDE DES SAULES. *Lagopus lagopus.* L, 15. The largest of our ptarmigan. In winter all white excepting the tail which is black (Figure 227). A scarlet comb over the eye is prominent in spring and may persist more or less at other seasons.

Figure 227
Specific details of Willow Ptarmigan; natural size.

The summer plumage is rarely complete and, mixed with the white of winter, first appears on the head spreading to breast. In the male, the plumage is nearly uniform maroon-brown to almost black on throat and breast, with barring on crown and hindneck. The autumn coloration of these parts is considerably lighter, no darker than rich chestnut, and the upper parts are markedly barred with shades of reddish ochre and dark brown, with comparatively little of the fine vermiculation that is such a striking feature of the autumn plumage of the other species.

The females are heavily barred with dark brown and ochre, the latter being predominant. They are not nearly as red in general effect as is the male.

*Distinctions.* A small grouse. Feet feathered to toes (Figure 226) and white wings distinguish them as ptarmigan. The black tail always separates the Willow from the White-tailed Ptarmigan, and the larger bill from the Rock Ptarmigan. The greatest difficulty of separation will be from summer and autumn plumages of Rock Ptarmigan. The male is recognizable by colour in summer or autumn by the more general reddish effect, especially the large masses of almost even red on neck and breast; neither sex ever shows the fine pepper and salt vermiculation that is so characteristic of the autumn plumage of the other two species. Females in the summer plumage are difficult to separate by colour characters from the parallel plumage of the Rock Ptarmigan; size, especially of the bill, which is larger and less slender, makes the most reliable criterion (Compare Figures 227 and 228). The bills may be variable in size, but no Rock Ptarmigan has the bill quite as heavy as the lightest of this species.

*Field Marks.* As ptarmigan, in winter, by nearly complete whiteness and in summer by white patches on body plumage and white wings. From White-tailed at any season by black tail. Probably rarely separable in life from the Rock Ptarmigan except in the case of good maroon-breasted males.

*Distribution.* Northern parts of northern hemisphere. In America across the continent mostly north of tree limits in summer, migrating occasionally to northern edge of prairies in winter. Also occurring at some elevation south to central British Columbia.

*SUBSPECIES.* The generally recognized race of Willow Ptarmigan throughout most of western Canada differing from the type form of Europe is the Black-shafted Ptarmigan (le Lagopède à ailes noires) *Lagopus lagopus albus.* Alexander's Ptarmigan (le Lagopède d'Alexander) *Lagopus lagopus alexandrae,* a southern Alaskan coast form, has been reported from Porcher Island, British Columbia, near the Alaska-British Columbia boundary. Another form has lately been described, the White-winged Ptarmigan (le Lagopède à ailes blanches) *Lagopus lagopus leucopterus,* lacking the black shafts to the primaries, from the Arctic Islands, and *Lagopus lagopus alleni* Allen's Ptarmigan (le Lagopède d'Allen), characterized by dusky clouding of the primaries, inhabits Newfoundland.

302. **Rock Ptarmigan.** ARCTIC PTARMIGAN. LE LAGOPÈDE DES ROCHERS. *Lagopus rupestris.* L, 13. The intermediate in size of the three ptarmigan. In winter, all white except a black tail and usually a black bar through eye to the base of bill (Figure 228). A scarlet comb over the eye is prominent in spring and may be present to a lesser degree at other seasons.

The summer male is decidedly barred with dark and ochre with little white intermixed, the dark being predominant. In autumn plumage the same colours are present, but generally lighter and vermiculated with a fine pepper-and-salt effect, the ochre predominating and with more white than in summer, which gives a greyish overcast.

Females are coarsely barred, showing much more light colours than the male. The autumn plumage has the barring reduced and is somewhat less finely vermiculated than the male.

*Distinctions.* A small grouse. Feet feathered to end of toes (Figure 226) and white wings distinguish it as a ptarmigan. The black tail separates it from the White-tailed Ptarmigan, and in winter the black streak through the eye, sometimes reduced, occasionally obsolete, from the Willow. The greatest difficulty of separation will be from summer Willow Ptarmigan. The male is recognizable by colour in either summer or autumn plumage by the lack of any mass of red and the presence of pronounced crossbarring. In the autumn plumage both sexes show a pronounced, fine vermiculation foreign to the Willow. Females in summer plumage are difficult to separate from similar plumage of the Willow Ptarmigan by colour characters, and size, especially of the bill which is lighter and slenderer as well as smaller, makes the most reliable criterion (Compare Figures 228 and 227). The bill may be quite variable, but no Willow Ptarmigan ever has the bill quite as slight as the heaviest of this species.

*Field Marks.* Considerably smaller than the Willow Ptarmigan, and with more slender bill. With few exceptions recognizable in winter by a black area in front of eye.

*Distribution.* A more Arctic form than the Willow or the White-tailed. Northern North America and Greenland. In America, across the continent farther north than the Willow and seldom if ever coming down into civilization even in winter. Occurs in some of the mountain tops as far south as central British Columbia.

*SUBSPECIES.* A number of subspecies are recognized, several being credited to Alaska. Over most of the continental mass the Southern Rock Ptarmigan (le Lagopède

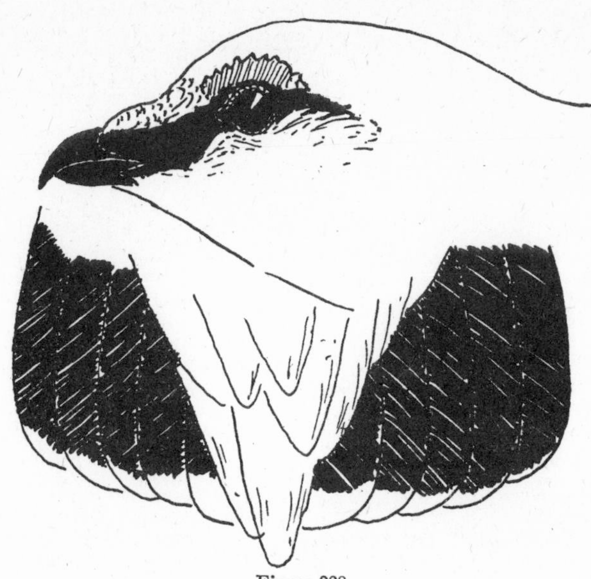

Figure 228
Specific details of Rock Ptarmigan; natural size.

des rochers du Sud) *Lagopus rupestris rupestris*, a generally greyish bird, is the prevailing form. In the higher Arctic Islands and the far northwest the Northern Rock Ptarmigan (le Lagopède des rochers du Nord) *Lagopus rupestris kelloggae*, a yellower bird, is found. Some authorities still refer the Newfoundland Rock Ptarmigan to Welch's Ptarmigan (le Lagopède de Welch) *Lagopus rupestris welchi*.

304. **White-tailed Ptarmigan.** LE LAGOPÈDE À QUEUE BLANCHE. *Lagopus leucurus*. L, 12·50. The smallest of the ptarmigan. In winter all white, including face and tail (Figure 229). A scarlet comb over eye is prominent in spring and may persist to a less degree at other seasons.

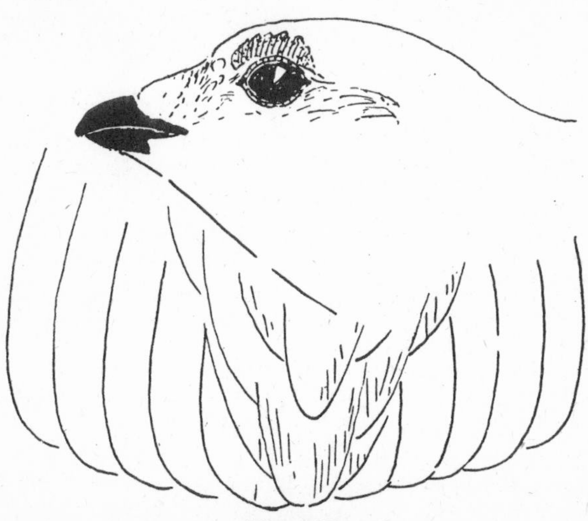

Figure 229
Specific details of White-tailed Ptarmigan; natural size.

The summer male is coarsely barred (or blotched) with black in throat and breast and the back finely barred with black and ochre. In autumn plumage the black of the breast and foreparts is replaced by (or intermixed with) finely vermiculated black and white and ochre in approximately even proportions. The back is uniformly vermiculated with the same colours in fine pepper-and-salt effect, the ochre predominating as in the Rock Ptarmigan, but with even more greyish overwash.

Females are more coarsely and regularly barred than males, but with less ochre, and are more of a black and white appearance than any of the other ptarmigan. The autumn female shows much fine vermiculation, but is always more barred, especially on breast, than the male.

*Distinctions.* A small grouse. Feet feathered to toes and white wings distinguish as ptarmigan. The white tail separates it from either of the other species.

*Field Marks.* As a ptarmigan, in winter, by complete whiteness. In summer by white patches on body plumage and white wings and tail. As a White-tailed in any plumage by white tail.

*Distribution.* Mountains of Alaska, British Columbia, and adjacent Alberta southward to new Mexico. A mountain bird rather than an Arctic one. Only regularly found above timber-line, and of somewhat erratic and discontinuous distribution.

*SUBSPECIES.* Two subspecies are recognized in Canada. The Northern White-tail (le Lagopède à queue blanche du Nord) *Lagopus leucurus leucurus*, of Alaska, Yukon, and northern British Columbia, and the Southern White-tail (le Lagopède à queue blanche du Sud) *Lagopus leururus altipetens*, of southern British Columbia and southward. The latter is buffier and less grey in the autumn plumage.

305. **Prairie Chicken.** PINNATED GROUSE. SQUARE-TAIL. LA POULE DES PRAIRIES. *Tympanuchus cupido.* L, 18. Plate XIX A. A large prairie grouse with a short, rounded tail, a group of stiff, straight feathers covering an inflatable sac on sides of neck; body heavily barred in brown and white. Tarsus feathered, but toes bare.

*Distinctions.* To be mistaken only for the Ruffed or the Sharp-tailed Grouse. Easily distinguished from the Ruffed by the short, solidly dark tail, the lack of small eye-spots on back, and the replacement of the soft ruffs on sides of neck by stiff, straight feathers. Separated from the Sharp-tailed Grouse, with which it is most often confused, by the stiff feather neck ornaments and by being regularly and completely barred all below instead of V-marked; and the tail evenly rounded instead of ending in a soft, flaccid point.

*Field Marks.* Easily recognized from the Ruffed Grouse by open instead of woodland habitat, short, evenly dark tail, and stiff, straight feathers instead of soft ruff on neck. From the Sharp-tailed Grouse recognized by heavy barring all below, and short, evenly rounded tail.

*Distribution.* Central North America from Canada south. Not an original inhabitant of Canada, but it has come in within historical times. It is now common throughout the prairies of Manitoba and is gradually spreading westward through Saskatchewan and Alberta. Originally of at least occasional occurrence in southern Ontario, especially along the Michigan border, in which state it still occurs locally and in limited numbers.

*SUBSPECIES.* The Greater Prairie Chicken (la Grande Poule des prairies) *Tympanuchus cupido americanus* is the only form recognized in Canada. The Heath Hen *Tympanuchus cupido cupido*, of Massachusetts and adjoining localities—once extremely abundant, now, with the death of the last bird on Martha's Vineyard, extinct—was a subspecies of Prairie Chicken.

Considerable confusion accompanies the name of "Prairie Chicken." This, however, is the bird to which the name applies correctly both historically and by habitat. It is a true bird of the open and not a brush species like the Sharp-tailed Grouse, which in Canada has largely usurped the title. It is a bird that, given fair protection, thrives near settlements, and evidently has followed the great grain fields northward. It is migratory and moves southward in the winter. In the spring it resorts to its dance grounds, such as a bare knoll or some similar spot of not very evident qualifications, but which is used for the purpose year after year and by generation after generation as though it had some special and unique attraction. The early morning is the time of activity and large numbers of birds gather and execute a most elaborate and interesting mating ritual. The male has, under the stiff plumes, large inflatable sacs on each side of the neck, coloured bright orange and capable of enormous distention, swelling out like a small orange on either side of the throat. With these inflated, the stiff plumes over them spread finger-wise upwards and outwards, and the tail opened over the back, the bird struts and utters a succession of low, intense, hollow sounds that can be heard for miles. All spring and early summer this dull, reverberating sound can be heard near its haunts, filling the air with a heavy throb, but difficult of location as to direction or distance. The species is a good strong flyer, lies well to a dog, and is wary enough to satisfy exacting sportsmen.

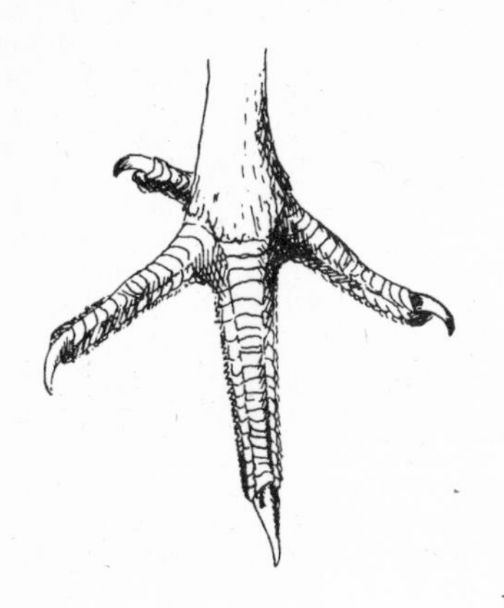

Figure 230
Feet of
Prairie Chicken in winter. Sharp-Tailed Grouse in winter.
Scale, ½

308. **Sharp-tailed Grouse.** (*Incorrectly* PRAIRIE CHICKEN.) LA GELINOTTE À QUEUE FINE. *Pedioecetes phasianellus.* L, 17·50. Plate XIX A. A large grouse palely coloured in browns, ochre, and white, with many sharp, dark V-marks on breast and flanks and with a soft, pointed, almost white tail. No particular neck ornaments or plumes.

*Distinctions.* The general lightness of colour, short, sharp tail, and distinct V-marks on breast are too characteristic to be confused with any other bird. Most like the true Prairie Chicken, the Pinnated Grouse, or Square-tail. The nearly white tail with upper coverts lengthened, projecting, and brought to a fine taper produce the effect of a sharply pointed tail; this, the profusion of sharp V-marks on breast and flanks, and the absence of any specially developed feather groups on the side of the neck are absolute distinctions from the dark, round tail, heavily barred breast, and stiff feather-neck ornaments of the Prairie Chicken proper. Tarsus feathered to between the toes (Figure 230).

*Field Marks.* A light-coloured grouse, sharp-tailed; very light below, with many dark V-marks on breast and flanks and no special neck plumes or ornaments.

*Distribution.* The more open spots in the spruce woods across the continent. In Ontario and western Quebec from the vicinity of the Canadian National Railway tracks northward to James Bay. In the west, across the prairies and British Columbia from southern Yukon Territory to south of the International Boundary.

*SUBSPECIES.* Several subspecies of Sharp-tailed are recognized. The Northern Sharp-tail (la Gelinotte à queue fine du Nord) *Pedioecetes phasianellus phasianellus*, a slightly dark form, ranges across the north woods from Quebec to Alaska. The Prairie Sharp-tailed (la Gelinotte à queue fine des prairies) *Pedioecetes phasianellus campestris,* a generally creamy-coloured bird, occupies the prairies, and the Columbian Sharp-tailed (la Gelinotte à queue fine de la Colombie) *Pedioecetes phasianellus columbianus*, a slightly greyer bird, is the form of southern British Colombia. The boundaries between the northern and the southern forms have not been quite accurately defined.

This is the common grouse of the Canadian prairies and in consequence, as stated under the previous species, has been consistently misnamed "Prairie Chicken," a title already pre-empted by another species. The Sharp-tail is a bird of the brush and light timber rather than the prairie, but is not a deep woods species like the Ruffed, nor a mountain one like the Blue.

In the autumn it gathers in large flocks and has been blamed for eating grain in the stook and doing some damage. Careful investigation shows that unless the ground is covered with snow the birds prefer feeding on waste grain in the stubble to that in the stooks. They like to perch on such small eminences to enjoy the sun or for outlook when the flock is feeding in the stubble. The larger proportion of food in the crops of a number of birds shot in seemingly incriminating circumstances in freshly stooked wheat fields, consisted of weed seeds, especially bindweed, waste fruit, and vegetation, showing that they are not partial to grain when other food is available. On the other hand, both this and the previous species are notable grasshopper devourers and probably in this capacity are worth many times the loss they inflict. On the whole this is a most valuable bird from both sporting and agricultural standpoints.

309. **Sage Hen.** LA GELINOTTE DES SAUGES. *Centrocerus urophasianus.* L, 26. A very large grouse finely marked in dull white and browns without much evident pattern, giving a general creamy-brown effect, with a dark brown abdominal spot and a rounded, variegated tail of sharply pointed feathers (Figure 231).

Figure 231
Tail of Sage Grouse; scale, about ⅓.

*Distinctions.* Large size, general colour effect of the Sharp-tail, but with finer and less decided pattern, all tail consisting of sharply pointed feathers, and a dark abdominal patch. Unmistakable for any other species.

*Field Marks.* Large size, general pale brown coloration, with blackish abdomen and tail like a section of a many pointed star.

*Distribution.* Across the sage brush plains from the Canadian border south to New Mexico. This species occurs in Canada only along the southern borders of western Saskatchewan and eastern Alberta. At one time it occurred as a straggler in the southern part of Okanagan Valley, British Columbia.

This fine big grouse occurs on the sage brush plains of the higher arid prairie steppe. Much of the ground it inhabits is useless for anything but grazing and this is probably all that has saved it to us. The species still exists in limited numbers in out of the way localities. In general the large ranch holders have shown an admirable spirit of protection towards it and have done much to perpetuate the species. As a table bird the Sage Hen is not very desirable as it is apt to be too strongly impregnated with sage to be palatable. In the spring the male Sage Hen, like many other grouse, executes a most interesting mating dance. In it the star-shaped tail is opened to its fullest extent and thrown over the back, so as to give the appearance of a many rayed flower, and the under coverts are fluffed. A throat sac is inflated and the body is bowed down to the ground. It is to be hoped that the few individuals of this most interesting bird remaining in Canada may be preserved.

### FAMILY—PERDICIDAE. PARTRIDGES AND QUAILS

This family includes the smaller of our upland game birds, which are easily distinguished from the grouse by the horny or fleshy scale over the nostril instead of the nostril being practically concealed in the feathering (Figure 232, compare with 219). The legs and toes are bare of feathers. From the pheasants they are easily distinguished by their much smaller size—the wing being under 7 inches instead of 9 or over. There is little specialization in the way of combs or air sacs. They do not indulge in ritualistic mating dances nor do they boom, hoot, or crow, as do species of many of the other families.

*Introduced:*

**Gray Partridge.** EUROPEAN GRAY PARTRIDGE. COMMON PARTRIDGE. HUNGARIAN PARTRIDGE. LA PERDRIX D'EUROPE. *Perdix perdix.* L, 12·6. Considerably smaller than our commoner grouse, but considerably larger than any of our so-called quail. A very fine, vermiculated intermixture of black, white, rusty, and cream on back, neck, and breast; more rufous on lower back and nearly clear black and white with a general greyish effect on breast. Wing coverts sharply shaft-streaked with cream. Flanks barred with white and chestnut. Face, throat, and superciliary line of tawny chestnut (Figure 233). A conspicuous double spot or horseshoe mark of rich chestnut occupies the upper abdomen. Sexes similar in coloration, but female in duller tones.

Figure 232
Nostril concealed under scale.

Figure 233
Hungarian Partridge; scale, ½.

*Distinctions.* The only partridge-like bird with such fine vermiculation, reddish throat, and chestnut abdominal patch.

*Field Marks.* In localities to which it is likely to extend it cannot be mistaken for any other bird, the ptarmigan being the only grouse-like bird of similar size or fine vermiculations. In flight it is dull, obscurely coloured, and shows a large amount of rufous brown in tail.

*Distribution.* Europe and west-central Asia. Introduced into Alberta near Calgary about 1908 and by 1923 had extended its range north nearly to Edmonton, south to the International Boundary, and east to the central parts of Saskatchewan. Within this area it thrives and good bags are being made in season. Introduced into southern Manitoba in 1924 and appears to be doing well there.

It was also introduced on southern Vancouver Island and the adjoining mainland about 1905. Here, it met with varying fortune, but on the whole has become well established and is now present in fair numbers. It has also spread north from the State of Washington into Okanagan district where it is increasing and spreading radpidly.

The objection to the importation of foreign species does not apply as strongly to game birds as to others. Species that are systematically hunted for economic use are in very little danger of becoming too plentiful; the problem in such cases is one of conservation rather than of control as, should it be necessary, there are plenty of sportsmen ready to reduce their number without bounty, bonus, or other artificial incentive. If the shooters were to pursue the House Sparrow, Crow, or other vermin as assiduously as they do game birds, the problem of their control would soon be solved. Even so, there is one thing to be borne in mind—that we cannot have foreign species except at the expense of competing native ones. It is notable that wherever this or other introduced species have increased to any marked extent, the resident grouse and Prairie Chicken have decreased in a similar degree. Sportsmen and the game departments of the various provinces should face this fact squarely and decide whether they prefer foreign to native game; they cannot well have unlimited numbers of both in the same area.

289. **Bob-white.** QUAIL. AMERICAN QUAIL. LE BOB-WHITE. *Colinus virginianus.* L, 10. Plate XIX B. A very small partridge or quail-like bird. Above—coloured in warm shades of pinkish or vinaceous brown, with dark brown mottlings, and a few lines of ochre or cream. Below—mostly white, decidedly barred with sharp black vermiculations. Flanks streaked with a pinkish brown which is also suffused evenly over the breast. A black gorget across upper throat, extending to cheeks and face, invades the reddish brown crown. A sharply defined, white throat. White, superciliary line extends down neck and breaks into fine white spots along sides of lower neck. The female is similar, but with duller, more blended colours, no black on face and neck, and an ochre instead of white throat and superciliary line.

*Distinctions.* The only pinkish coloured partridge or quail-like bird of its size likely to occur in the area covered by this work.

*Field Marks.* Quail-like appearance, very small size, and ruddy coloration. Its clear, whistled call of "Bob-white" is unmistakable.

*Distribution.* Eastern North America, from just north of the Canadian boundary along Lake Erie to Texas and Mexico. It has been introduced in southern Vancouver Island, Fraser Valley, and Ashcroft and Vernon districts, British Columbia. For a time it throve in the last two localities. Later it was almost killed off by severe winters, but a few may still be found in the districts mentioned. It is not as hardy as the California Quail. A further attempt at introduction was made near Victoria in 1922, but with what success is not yet known.

*SUBSPECIES.* There are several subspecies of the Bob-white recognized, but as the source of the introduced birds is unknown and no originally native specimens are available for examination it is impossible to say to what race they belong.

*Introduced:*

294. **California Quail.** LA PERDRIX DE LA CALIFORNIE. *Lophortyx californica.* L, 10·50. Above—olive-grey blending into olive-brown on wings and flanks, greying on tail and neck; breast, clear blue-grey. Abdomen—peculiarly scale-marked with sharply defined black borders on white, ochre, and light chestnut ground. Flanks sharply streaked with white. Jet black throat patch with white border and white superciliary line. Forehead, light ochre. A cape of beautifully white-speckled, black-margined grey feathers falling from crown to shoulders. The most distinctive feature, however, is a plume of several scimitar-shaped, black feathers an inch or more in height, springing from the crown with the tips pointed forward (Figure 234). Female similar, but plumes much smaller and colours reduced and blended.

Figure 234
California Quail; scale, ½.

*Distinctions.* With scimitar-shaped plumes, white-bordered black throat, and scaled abdomen unmistakable for any other bird in Canada.

*Distribution.* Originally, Pacific coast from Oregon to southern Lower California. Introduced into British Columbia.

Probably introduced into the State of Washington near Seattle about 1874, and on Vancouver Island shortly after. Here, they appear to follow the broom-plant, which affords them shelter from vermin and weather as well as food. They suffer under occasional heavy snowfalls in winter, but soon recuperate. The centre of abundant occurrence is still southern Vancouver Island, but they occur at least as far north as Comox. Attempts to introduce them into Fraser Valley have not been successful, but about 1900 they were introduced into the southern Okanagan Valley where they have done remarkably well.

*SUBSPECIES.* The typical form, the Coast Quail (la Perdrix cotière) *Lophortyx californica californica*, seems to be the race to which our birds should be referred. It is unfortunate that importers are careless as to the origin of their introductions. Where restocking of covers has been numerous, the stock has in many cases become hopelessly mongrel. Restocking should be in the hands of responsible authorities, careful records kept, and the purity of the strain maintained.

*Introduced:*

292. **Painted Quail.** LA PERDRIX ÉLÉGANTE. *Oreortyx picta.* L, 11·50. Pale, olive-grey on back, lightening to clear, light, slate-grey on head, neck, and breast. Flanks conspicuously barred with dark brown alternating with white, between two bands of rich chestnut. The throat has a sharply defined chestnut patch, black edged, and bordered by a white crescent. The most striking ornament, however, is a long, black, pencil-like plume springing from the crown and falling over the back (Figure 235). The sexes are almost alike.

*Distinctions.* Rich chestnut throat, flank bars, and the long pencil plume.

*Field Marks.* Size, long, slender black plume, and chestnut on flanks.

*Distribution.* Originally the Pacific coast from the State of Washington south into California. Probably the first attempt at introduction into Canada was made on Vancouver Island about 1865 with birds from San Juan Island, where the species was indigenous, but it was not successful. About 1872 another attempt was made with birds from the same locality and the species is, in consequence, today fairly common locally in Victoria and Sooke regions, Vancouver Island, and has been noted as far north on the island as Duncan.

Figure 235
Mountain Quail; scale, ½.

*SUBSPECIES.* Several subspecies of Painted Quail are recognized. The subspecies native to the lower levels west of the Cascades where our stock probably originated in Washington is the Mountain Quail (la Perdrix élégante des montagnes) *Oreortyx picta*, and our birds are probably the same, though in the various introductions that have been made in Washington, a strain of the Plumed Quail (la Perdrix à panache) *Oreortyx picta picta* from the higher levels adjacent may have been intermixed.

## FAMILY—PHASIANIDAE. PHEASANTS

A large, Old World order with no native American representative. Many species take kindly to domestication and have been carried by man all over the world. The most familiar example of this family is the common domestic poultry. The pheasants are often brilliantly coloured with metallic sheens, and run to remarkable sexual specializations in the way of tail, wing, and other feather ornaments. The nostril is hidden under a fleshy scale like that of the partridge and quail, but the only species that has been naturalized under wild conditions is so much larger than any of that family that there can be no chance of confusion.

*Introduced:*

**Common Pheasant.** CHINA PHEASANT. LE FAISAN ORDINAIRE. *Phasianus colchicus.* L, 35. A large, game-cock-like bird. Male: strikingly and magnificently coloured, with narrow, gracefully pointed tail about 15 inches long. Back, beautifully variegated in complicated pattern with deep maroon, cream, ochre, black, and shades of emerald green, many of them metallic. The back is mostly green, the wing-coverts mostly maroon, and the cape mostly ochre. Breast, solid, rich burnt sienna, with violet reflections and scale, marked with black feather edges, abdomen black and rich ochre, on flanks spotted with purple-black. Head and neck, except crown, brilliant, steely black with conspicuous white collar about base. Face largely bare red skin, and crown metallic greenish ochre with white superciliary line. Short, steel-black ear tufts (Figure 236). The tail is largely dull olive-ochre barred with black. The female is entirely unlike the male. Variegated in dull, earthy ochres and rich dark brown markings. The ochre is clear on the breast, the markings heaviest on back, growing smaller and finer towards the head. The tail is about half as long as that of the male.

*Distinctions.* No other wild bird is found in Canada with such a long, tapering tail, or such a wonderful mixture of showy colours. Many of these birds have crossed with the English Pheasant (Le Faisan d'Europe), an impurely bred *Phasianus colchicus* crossed with *torquatus*. The two are very similar in coloration, but *colchicus* is without the white ring on the neck. The mantle is fiery orange and there is less greenish ochre on the crown.

The Mongolian Pheasant (le Faisan de Mongolie) *Phasianus colchicus mongolicus* was introduced into British Columbia from Shantung province, China, in 1909, and has hybridized with the above and still further obscured the specific characters of the birds of the British Columbia mainland and Vancouver Island. It has a white neck-ring like *torquatus* but interruped in front, and the lower back and rump are orange-red mixed with dark green more like *colchicus*. On the whole the pheasants of British Columbia are so hopelessly mongrel that it takes an expert quite familiar with the various species to estimate the mixed relationships of individuals.

*Field Marks.* Long, sweeping tail, seen on no other bird except some other pheasant that may have escaped from confinement.

Figure 236
Ring-necked Pheasant; scale, ½.

*Distribution.* Eastern China, Manchuria, and Mongolia. Introduced in a number of places in Canada at various times, but only in southern British Columbia and southern Ontario with marked success. On southern Vancouver Island and on the mainland along Fraser River and the southern valleys adjoining it has become well established and is one of the regular game birds.

It makes a magnificent object of sport to the upland shooter. Being wild, wary, and well able to take care of itself, it satisfactorily tests the hardihood and skill of the hunter. When brought to bag, the cock is a magnificent trophy and large enough to furnish an appreciable addition to the table. Some complaints have been made as to its effect on certain crops and its belligerent attitude towards native grouse. How well-founded these complaints are, experience alone can decide. One thing is certain, that we cannot have such a fine, large bird without a complementary loss of other native, competing species. Just how far we want to go in this replacement of native by foreign forms is a question that a community cannot solve for itself without considering the welfare and wishes of its neighbours, as species once successfully established spread indefinitely and refuse to be confined by county, provincial, state, or national boundaries.

FAMILY—MELEAGRIDIDAE. TURKEYS

The largest of our scratching birds and so familiar from its domesticated form that it requires no detailed description. There is only one species in Canada.

**310. Wild Turkey.** LE DINDON SAUVAGE. *Meleagris gallopavo.* L, 48·50. So nearly like our domestic Bronze Turkey as to require no special description.

Figure 237
Turkey. Domesticated male in display.

*Distinctions.* The only bird from which it is necessary to separate the Wild Turkey is the tame or domestic variety. The latter originated from Mexican stock and in consequence always shows a little white at the tip of the tail. The tail of the Wild Turkey ends in wood-brown.

*Distribution.* Originally distributed over the whole of eastern North America to Maine and southern Ontario.

*SUBSPECIES.* Several subspecies of Wild Turkey are recognized. The type form is found in Mexico. The Canadian bird is the Eastern Wild Turkey (le Dindon sauvage de l'Est) *Meleagris gallopavo silvestris.*

The turkey as a wild form occurred in Canada only in southern Ontario and has been extinct for many years. At present the Wild Turkey remains only in the most out-of-the-way wooded localities of the wilder southern states and even there it promises to vanish soon. There is probably considerable native wild blood in the domesticated turkey flocks along Lake Erie and a number of specimens of so-called Wild Turkeys are obviously at least half-bred with domestic birds.

The bird so commonly called "Wild Turkey" in the Prairie Provinces is not a turkey at all, but a crane of the order *Cruiformes* and an entirely different bird (*See* page 171). The true Wild Turkey has never been recorded in Canada west of southern Ontario.

## Order—Gruiformes. Cranes, Rails, etc.

Consisting in Canada of two families, *Gruidae* cranes, and *Rallidae* rails, gallinules, and coots.

### FAMILY—GRUIDAE. CRANES

*General Description.* Large, heron-like birds; dull, slaty blue with or without rusty overwash; or pure white, with black primaries. All colours are in even, over-all tints and

Figure 238
Foot of Crane showing elevated hind toe.

Figure 239
Appearance of Crane in flight.

there are no plumes or crests.

*Distinctions.* Distinguished from the herons by having the forehead as well as the space about the eyes bare, or with a sparse sprinkling of peculiarly modified, hair-like feathers (*See* Figures 240 and 242), and by the lack of pectinations on middle claw. The bill is shorter proportionately than that of the heron, but more heavily built, in both material and shape, there is no septum within the bill between the nostrils, and the hind toe is elevated above the others (Figure 238).

*Field Marks.* Cranes fly with outstretched neck instead of with head drawn into the shoulders as do the herons (Figure 239, compare with 100), and contrary to the habits of herons they often feed in flocks on upland fields.

So far as Canada is concerned, this family may be called the "Large Marsh Birds," a term, however, that has no other warrant than that of convenience. In this suborder, as in some of the swans, the windpipe enters a hollow in the keel of the sternum and has similar complicated convolutions (*See* Figures 241 and 243).

204. **Whooping Crane.** WHITE CRANE. LA GRUE BLANCHE. *Grus americana.* L, 50. A very large, white, heron-like bird with black primaries and bare, dull red lores, crown, and face streak (Figure 240). Juveniles have not as much colour on the bare parts of the head and face but are more or less completely overwashed with rusty, strongly resembling the iron that stains the white parts of adults and many water birds.

*Distinctions.* There is no other white, crane-like bird of equal size with which it can be confused.

*Field Marks.* A great white crane with a red face, standing about 4 feet in height. In flight, the outstretched neck and legs are distinctive for a crane, and the great size and the white plumage with black wing tips, for this species.

Figure 240
Whooping Crane; scale, $\frac{1}{4}$.

*Nesting.* On the ground, in the midst of wide marshes.

*Distribution.* North America, in Canada west of the Great Lakes to the foothills, breeding throughout its regular range. Now very rare and verging on extinction.

It is a regrettable fact that increased wariness and native vigilance never quite compensate for the handicap of large size in a wild bird or animal in its struggle for existence with civilization. The Whooping Crane is amongst the wariest of birds. It frequents the bare prairies and open sloughs where its great height from the ground gives it every opportunity to note approaching danger; yet from being a fairly common bird on the prairies it has been practically exterminated within the last thirty-five years. Today in our Prairie Provinces we know of but a few scattered breeding pairs. It is a serious question whether the species can be preserved to posterity. When a species becomes too low in numbers it succumbs to the weakened condition induced by inbreeding in spite of every protection that can be offered. Whether this is the case with the Whooping Crane remains to be seen. At present it is listed among the birds that are protected at all times, and it is to be hoped that this protection has not come too late. The last chance of preserving this, probably the most spectacular

PLATE XXXI

A. Yellow-billed Cuckoo; scale, $\frac{1}{3}$
Black-billed Cuckoo; scale, $\frac{1}{3}$

B. Screech Owl; scale, $\frac{1}{4}$
Grey phase
Red phase

PLATE XXXII

A. Great Horned Owl; scale, $\frac{1}{8}$

Arctic Horned Owl    Dusky Horned Owl

B. Hawk Owl; scale, $\frac{1}{6}$

bird of the prairies, depends entirely upon the people of the prairies. All localities cannot be watched by wardens, and no game laws are capable of 100 per cent enforcement. If occasional birds are killed there, it will matter little to the species that the offender is caught and punished, for the irreparable damage will have been done. Laws can do little for a case like this, but an aroused public opinion is much more efficient. Many may brave the laws on occasion but hesitate before doing that which will bring the condemnation of their personal friends and neighbours. It is to be hoped that no community will permit of the killing or disturbance of these birds without the expression of its displeasure as well as the infliction of the utmost penalty the law allows.

The deep, sonorous trumpeting of this bird is probably due to the great length of the windpipe that lies coiled up within the keel of the sternum in a complicated convolution (Figure 241). The windpipe enters the forefront of the keel and reaches directly back to the rear of the sternum, there it bends back sharply, enters into a double coil in the front end of keel, and emerges through the same orifice by which it entered. The folding and looping of the windpipe are much more complicated than either that of the Sandhill or Little Brown Cranes next described (Compare with Figure 243).

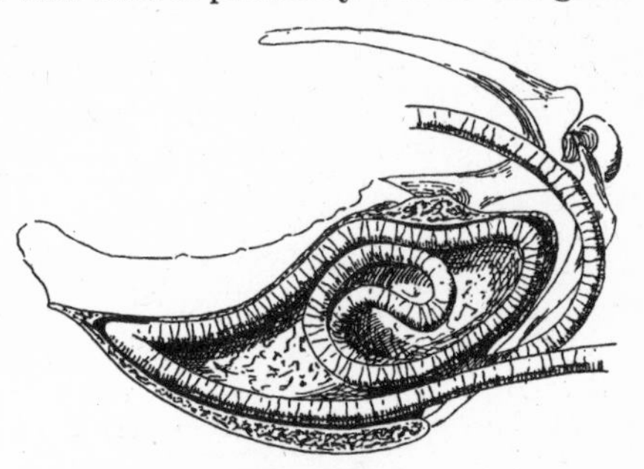

Figure 241
Longitudinal section through sternum of Whooping Crane; scale, about ⅓.

205. **Sandhill Crane.** (*Incorrectly* "Turkey".) LA GRUE GRISE D'AMÉRIQUE. *Grus canadensis*. L, 36–40. Plate XX A. A large, evenly light slate-coloured, heron-like bird with bare face and forehead coloured bright red. Old birds may show much adventitious rust colour and young ones have a wash of about the same colour naturally.

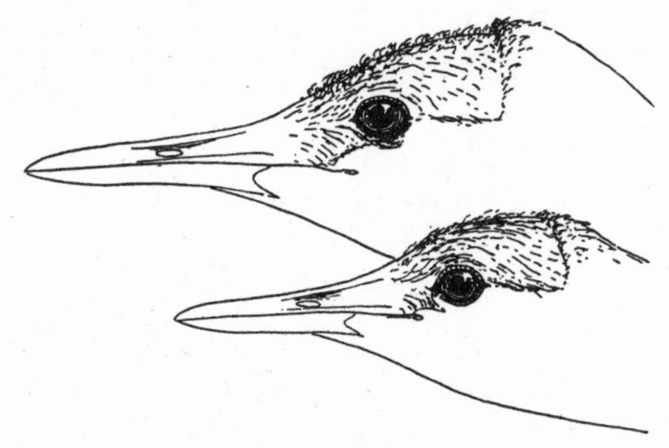

Figure 242
Heads of Sandhill Crane, Little Brown Crane, showing average comparative size; scale, ½.

*Distinctions*. With large size only to be confused with the Great Blue Heron, which is also often popularly called "Blue Crane." Easily distinguished, however, by the hind toe raised above the level of the others, the bare forehead, face red in adult, and the nostrils pierced through from one to the other. The crane never has any of the fine plumes on breast, crown, and back that are such prominent features of the Blue Heron in spring dress.

Many specimens show considerable overwash of rusty red on back and up neck. This, except in juveniles that are naturally rusty, is an adventitious coloration due to iron rust from the water and is not a specific character.

*Field Marks.* Easily recognized as a crane by heron-like outline, dull, even grey, or grey overwashed by rusty, red forehead and crown, and in flight at any distance by flying with head and neck outstretched (Figure 239)

*Nesting.* On the ground in wet spots of the marshes or tundra.

*Distribution.* Western north America, breeding in Canada west of the Great Lakes from below our boundaries northward into the Arctics.

*SUBSPECIES.* Until lately our two cranes have been regarded as two distinct species, but the 1931 Check-list has united them as of only subspecific distinction. The Little Brown Crane that may now be called the Lesser Sandhill Crane (la Petite Grue grise) *Grus canadensis canadensis* differs only in being of smaller size, usually under 39 inches, bill 5·5 inches or under, and tarsus less than 8·25. It is the more northern race breeding in the Arctics, south probably to about Great Slave Lake, migrating through the prairies and British Columbia to Mexico. The Greater Sandhill Crane (la Grande Grue grise) *Grus canadensis tabida* is larger, measurements greater than above. It nests throughout the Prairie Provinces and southern British Columbia indefinitely northward. The dividing line between the breeding ranges of the two forms is not known, but birds from Great Slave Lake have been referred to the Little Brown. South in winter to Mexico.

The rattling, tinny trumpet note of these birds is one of the notable sounds of the west. It can be heard for miles. Far away and softened by the distance it reaches the ear; a glance around reveals no sign of life, then far off on the pale prairie horizon a few specks heave into sight, they grow into birds with wide-waving pinions, heads outstretched on slender necks as if reaching forward. Hoarse horn answers horn louder and clearer back and forth, throughout the long-drawn line, and they come on with stately measured beat at a pace that eats the miles. A neighbouring hill attracts them, they circle it to see that the coast is clear, and then settle on its top, silhouetted in black against the sky. For a moment the trumpetings redouble as they stand at full height and survey the country for possible dangers, then the sounds cease, one by one the heads drop, the necks gracefully curve as they search the ground about with delicate grace, picking up a morsel here or making a quick reach there with an agile step or two after a fleeing grasshopper. Should the observer show himself the quick eyes note at once, the trumpet is blown, and all are drawn up to attention again. Often, the flock quietly edges over the hilltop where with body hidden from view the birds observe the suspicious object intently, only the head showing periscope-like above the round swell of the hill. They veritably hide behind mountains and peer over the peaks.

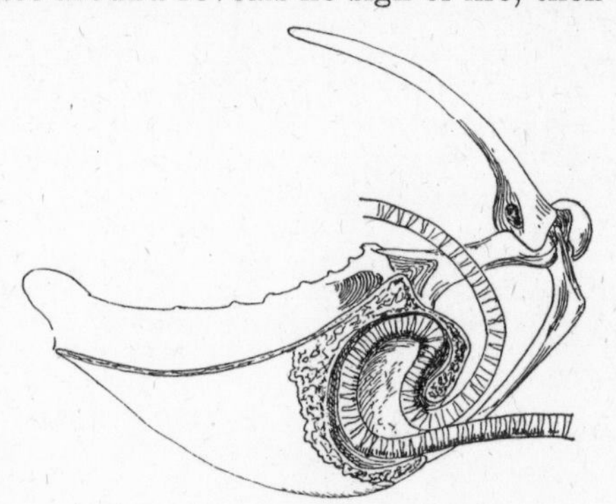

Figure 243
Longitudinal section through sternum of Sandhill Crane; scale, $\frac{1}{4}$.

In mating season they perform strange dances, with jumping, bowing, and gesticulations, the long legs angling stiffly and on occasion the wings waving wildly. Sometimes the ritual culminates in raising a stick or fragment from the ground, and tossing it high in the air. The nest is solitary, situated usually in the middle of a wide, wet, marshy slough, a 6-foot platform of reeds where the two downy red youngsters are hatched, under the solicitous attentions of both parents, for they make an ideal pair, sharing the household duties and responsibilities and probably mating for life. Throughout the summer, groups of unattached, non-breeding birds cruise about from slough to slough; pass the nights on mud-bars far out in the lakes and, mornings and evenings, their trumpeting flocks can be heard as they pass over or back. These flocks are probably composed of juveniles not ready to breed, or of adults that have lost their mates and have not paired again. They show remarkable attachment to certain localities and a single old bird will return year after year to its old home grounds, calling and trumpeting to others passing over, associating with visiting migrants as they pause on their way, but returning to its own lonely grounds again when they continue their journey.

In late summer, when the old birds and the season's young gather in flocks, together with migrant Lesser Sandhill Cranes, they frequent the grain fields and, occasionally when in great numbers, do considerable damage to the stooks. How much of the damage should be attributed to the Lesser Sandhill Crane it is difficult to estimate, probably the greater part, because the Greater Sandhill is becoming regularly scarcer every year as advancing cultivation and attendant dangers are encroaching on and rendering its old breeding grounds untenable. Cranes are protected now throughout the year, but, unless the legal fiat is assisted by general public opinion, the sandhill is doomed to extinction. At present Saskatchewan is the only province where cranes are seen in anything like their former number, but it is believed that the majority of these are not resident but are smaller migrants from the north.

These two cranes have long been locally known throughout the west as "Turkeys." To see one in the specimen arouses wonder that a long-legged wader should ever have been confused with our well-known table-bird; but in life the resemblance is not so remote as might be imagined. The red face resembles the red wattled head of the turkey and it is interesting to note that another bird, the Turkey Vulture, has evidently been associated with the same species for a similar reason. In feeding, the crane carries its body low and its head down as it works over a field, when, with its long legs partly hidden in the grass and vegetation, it has considerable resemblance to the turkey.

## FAMILY—RALLIDAE. RAIL-LIKE BIRDS

*General Description.* Toes long and slender to cover a large area of soft, uncertain footing. The pedal characters are somewhat like those of the shore birds, but the hind toe is long, as well developed as the others, and inserted on a level with them instead of being slightly elevated (Figure 244, compare with Figure 290, page 202). In this respect they resemble the herons, but may be distinguished from them by their un-heron-like build and their feathered lores. In one species, the coot (Figure 249, page 175), the toes are edged with scalloped flaps.

They are typical marsh birds, skulking in the long grass and reeds, running swiftly over yielding masses of half-floating vegetation, and preferring to hide rather than fly at the approach of danger. They all swim, habitually or on occasion. The family is divided into three subfamilies: *Rallinae*, the true rails; *Callinulinae*, Gallinules or Mud-Hens; and *Fulicinae*, Coots.

### Subfamily—Rallinae. True Rails

*General Description.* Very flat-bodied birds, compressed laterally, adapted for slipping between close-growing reeds and grasses; wings small, rounded, and comparatively weak. The whole structure of the bird is loose, giving the flexibility needed by habit and habitat, but not adapted for prolonged or strenuous effort.

*Distinctions.* Most easily recognized by negative characteristics; rail-like birds as described above that are not coots or gallinules (without frontal shield on forehead: compare with Figures 248 and 249, pages 174, 175).

*Field Marks.* Rails rise from the grass at one's feet with a loose, feeble flight, legs dangling and neck outstretched. They rise with evident and hurried difficulty, fly weakly a short way over the marsh, and then suddenly collapse into it again.

The rails are skulkers and expert hiders in the grass. They thread the narrow runways between the clumps with mouse-like dexterity and speed. They rely on their ability to hide more than on flight to escape danger and will often allow themselves to be caught in the hand rather than take wing. A rail will flush once in a seeming panic, but safely down again it can rarely be forced to wing a second time and in a small, isolated clump of cover will seldom be again detected except by a dog's keen nose. Rails can and do swim, but only occasionally and only for a short distance, as when passing from one grass clump to another they find the water too deep for wading.

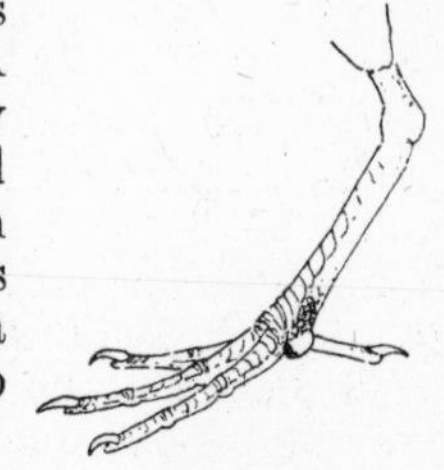

Figure 244
Foot of Rail; scale, ½.

Rails are very noisy, especially at night. Even in the daytime a sudden and unexpected noise will bring forth a chorus of their loud, harsh cacklings from the marsh, though not a bird may be seen.

Our western Canadian rails can be included in two divisions, a long-billed (Figure 245) and a short-billed (Figure 246) type. The first is represented by the King and Virginia Rails; the second by the Sora and Yellow Rails.

208. **King Rail.** LE RÂLE ÉLÉGANT. *Rallus elegans.* L, 15. A long-billed rail so like the Virginia (which see) except in size as to hardly require further description, the only appreciable difference in colour being in having rufous instead of grey cheeks.

*Distinctions.* Size, 15 inches instead of 9·50, is a perfect distinction.

*Field Marks.* As given for Virginia Rail but very much larger. Too rare in Canada, except in the more southern parts of Ontario, to be recorded on eye-sight alone.

*Nesting.* In wet marsh, in nest of grass.

*Distribution.* Eastern North America. Only regular in Canada in the most southern parts of Ontario. Once reported from Manitoba.

212. **Virginia Rail.** LE RÂLE DE VIRGINIE. *Rallus limicola.* L, 9·50. A long-billed rail (Figure 245). Foreneck, breast, and flanks cinnamon-rufous; back brownish black, each feather broadly margined with an ochraceous shade of breast colour; flanks barred black and white. Cheeks slate grey, almost black in front of eye, and with partial white superciliary line. Bill largely red and legs reddish brown. Juvenile similar but colours veiled with black.

Figure 245
Virginia Rail; scale, ½.

*Distinctions.* Distinguished from any other rail likely to be met with in western Canada by its long, decurved bill and general rufous coloration. Young birds, much clouded with black, have been taken for the Black Rail, but the long bill is distinctive. The King Rail is almost exactly similar in colour, but so decidedly larger (L, 15) as to cause no confusion.

*Field Marks.* Obvious rail appearance and habit, size, general reddish coloration, and long red bill.

*Nesting.* In wet marsh, nest of grass.

*Distribution.* North America. Breeds across Canada throughout the prairies, perhaps north of them, and in British Columbia into Cariboo District; the northern limit of range is not well known.

This rail is not quite so common as the Sora, but like it more often heard than seen. Its characteristic notes are a hard, dry, cackling laugh and a calm whistle given in an ascending scale.

214. **Sora Rail.** SORA. CAROLINA RAIL. LE RÂLE ORTOLAN. *Porzana carolina.* L, 8·5. Plate XX B. A short-billed, chunky, little rail without any shade of rufous on it. About the same size as the Virginia, but measuring less because of the short bill (Figure 246). The black throat and clear, grey breast are not present in juveniles.

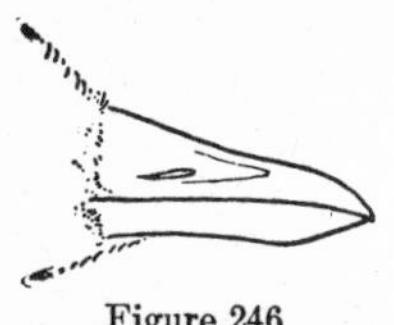

Figure 246
Short bill of Sora Rail; natural size.

*Distinctions.* The short bill, grey breast, and slightly olivaceous coloration of the back distinguish the Sora from the Virginia Rail. From the Yellow Rail, its larger size; the hint of olive rather than ruddy ochre in its general coloration; the back being striped rather than crossbarred with white, and the all-dark secondaries.

*Field Marks.* Loose, dangling flight as it rises and mouse-like skulking in the grass proclaim it a rail. Short, yellow, instead of long, red, bill and lack of rufous coloration separate it from the Virginia; larger size and lack of white patch in wing distinguish it from the Yellow.

*Nesting.* In wet marshes, nest of grass.

*Distribution.* North America. Across the continent, north to southern Mackenzie, breeding in Canada wherever found.

This is the most common rail of the prairie sloughs, at least it is the one most often seen, for it is not quite so inveterate a skulker as are the Virginia and Yellow Rails and perhaps its apparent abundance is due to its greater readiness to flush. It is probably not quite as common as the Virginia in southern British Columbia. It is more often heard than seen and its notes are a soft whistle, a piercing squeak, and rapid whistling cackle of a high pitch in a descending scale, the last being its love song.

215. **Yellow Rail.** LE RÂLE JAUNE. *Coturnicops noveboracensis.* L, 7. A short-billed rail (*See* Figure 246), smaller than the Sora. The coloration is similar in general pattern, but the slight olive cast on back and sides of the Sora is replaced in this species by a warm ochraceous tint, mixed with dark brown, and the back is barred with fine white lines. The breast is brownish ochre; throat light. The wings show prominent white patches on the secondaries in flight.

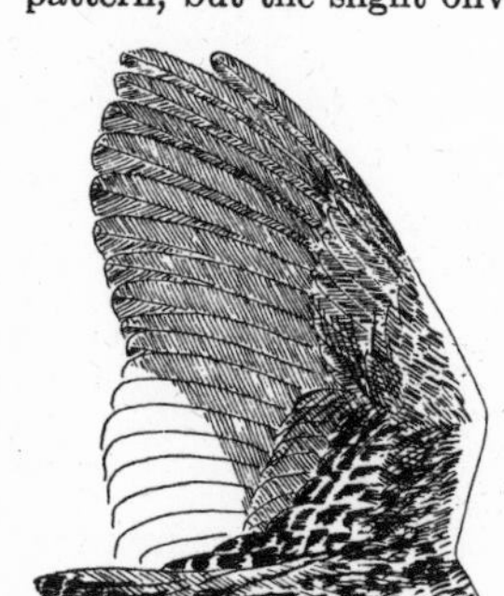

Figure 247
Wing of Yellow Rail; scale, about ½.

*Distinctions.* To be mistaken only for the Sora, but considerably smaller. The sharp, fine, white crossbarring of the back and white secondaries are determinative.

*Field Marks.* A very small, brownish rail with white wing patches prominent in flight (Figure 247).

*Nesting.* On the ground in damp edges of marshes, nest of grass.

*Distribution.* Eastern and central North America, and indefinitely north. Probably the most northern rail in summer distribution. Although noted in all our eastern and Prairie Provinces, has not been recorded in British Columbia.

This is the most expert of the rails in skulking and hiding. As it is almost impossible to flush, it may be far more common than we suspect.

According to actual records, it is one of the rarest birds in Canada. Its habits do not seem to differ much from those of the other rails, except that it does not require as much water in its habitat, and is more often found on the shoreward, grassy sides of marshes than in wet, reedy locations. Its notes are said to be like the sound of two stones tapped together, with a very plain rhythm—*tick, tick—tick, tick, tick—tick, tick, tick—tick, tick*—and so on in alternate twos and threes.

216. **Black Rail.** LE RÂLE NOIR. *Creciscus jamaicensis.* L, 5·50. A very diminutive rail, hardly larger than a sparrow. Nearly black in coloration; head, breast, and below dark slate-grey, darkest, to nearly black, on crown. Above, dark woody brown with many small, white, round spots. A rich rufous blended band across shoulders and lower neck.

Unsubstantiated records of this minute little rail have come from the Prairie Provinces, and southern Ontario and Quebec, but it is even more difficult to observe than the Yellow. Some of the specimens reported from southern Ontario have proved to be juvenile Virginia Rails. Very little is known of its distribution. The rail to be expected is the Northern Black Rail (Le Râle noir du nord) *C. j. stoddardi.* It may possibly occur in Manitoba, or its close relative, the Faralone Rail *C. j. coturniculus*, on the coast of southern British Columbia.

*Distinctions.* Very small size, extremely dark colour, and fine speckles of white on the back.

217. **Corn Crake.** LE RÂLE GENÊT. *Crex crex.* L, about 10·25. Considerably larger than any of our other short-billed Rails and with much distinct ochre on back and ruddy on wings.

*Distinctions.* As above.

*Distribution.* Europe and northern Asia. There are a few records for Greenland and the eastern American coast. Its status as a Canadian bird rests on a single erratic specimen taken on southern Baffin Island.

### Subfamily—Gallinulinae. Gallinules or Mud-hens

Rather large, duck-like birds with long toes without webs. Bill extending up forehead and usually brilliantly coloured in adult. Much like Coots, but note webless toes.

218. **Purple Gallinule.** LA POULE D'EAU POURPRÉE. *Ionornis martinica.* L, 13. Like the Florida Gallinule (*See* next species), but deep purple breast and neck and shining olive-green on back.

*Distinctions.* Like the Florida Gallinule, but more highly coloured in blues, purples, and greens. Juvenile usually with enough traces of colour for recognition and without any white on flanks. Easily separated from the coot by foot characters (Figure 248, compare with 249).

*Field Marks.* Gallinule or Mud-hen outline, decided blue iridescence, yellow legs, and all white undertail-coverts.

*Distribution.* Tropical and subtropical America, south regularly to the Carolinas. There are casual records for the eastern provinces and southern Ontario.

219. **Common Gallinule.** RICE-BIRD. MUD-HEN. RED-BILLED MUD-HEN. LA POULE D'EAU ORDINAIRE. *Gallinula chloropus.* L, 13·50. An almost evenly coloured, slate-blue bird; darker on head and a little lighter below, tinged with slightly iridescent reddish brown above; conspicuous white flank streaks and a small edging of the same under tail; bill and frontal plate (Figure 248) bright red; legs green with red garters just below the feathering.

*Distinctions.* Distinguished from Purple Gallinule by the characters mentioned above; from the Coot, which it closely resembles, by red instead of white bill and frontal plate, white flank lines, brownish back, and clean, unwebbed toes.

Figure 248
Details of Florida Gallinule; scale, ⅓.

A. Pygmy Owl; scale, $\frac{1}{6}$

B. Burrowing Owl; scale, $\frac{1}{6}$

Plate XXXIV

A. Barred Owl; scale, 1/7

B. Long-eared Owl; scale, $\frac{1}{6}$

*Field Marks.* Red bill and frontal plate, white flank streaks, brownish back, and all dark secondary tips when flying.

*Nesting.* Usually on a slight eminence such as an old muskrat house in watery marshes, in nest of waste vegetable fragments.

*Distribution.* More northern than the Purple Gallinule, and regularly common in Canada only along the lower Great Lakes. There is one record for southern Manitoba.

This is the best known Mud-hen of southeastern Canada. Its fairly large size and palatable flesh, due to its fondness for wild rice and other marsh seeds, renders it an object of pursuit by the sportsman. It requires more open water than the rails, but in general resembles them in habits. It is a rather noisy bird, especially at night; and during the day joins the rails in their chorus of surprise at unusual and unexpected disturbances. At times one bird will suddenly utter a volley of cackles, answered immediately by another, and another, and for a few moments the apparently deserted marsh is a small pandemonium of unexpected bird sounds.

*Economic Status.* Except as a quasi-game bird the gallinule is of little account economically.

### Subfamily—Fulicinae. Coots

*General Description.* Rather large, duck-like birds, but with long toes furnished with membranous lobes; bill extends up on forehead in a dead white plate or shield (Figure 249).

*Distinctions.* Scallop-webbed toes and frontal shield on forehead.

220. **Black Coot.** LA FOULQUE NOIRE. *Fulica atra.* L, 16. Like the American Coot from which it can be distinguished only by small details.

*Distinctions.* Slightly larger and more heavily built than the American Coot. Under-tail-coverts black instead of white; toes considerably longer, middle one over 2·75 inches instead of under; bill larger and heavier; frontal shield considerably broader, to 0·65 inch instead of 0·35 inch, broad, decidedly club-shaped, and without brown spots.

*Distribution.* Northern parts of eastern hemisphere. There are individual records for the Labrador coast and Newfoundland, but none that is strictly Canadian.

221. **American Coot.** MUD-HEN. LA FOULQUE D'AMÉRIQUE. *Fulica americana.* L, 15. Plate XXI A. An evenly coloured, dark, slate-grey, duck-like bird with a white bill and white frontal shield on the forehead, a dark reddish brown spot at base of frontal shield, and similar smaller flecks near the tips of both mandibles. Legs green with scalloped flaps (Figure 249).

*Distinctions.* The even grey coloration, blackening to head, white bill, and brown-based frontal shield; scalloped webs on toes are absolutely distinctive.

*Field Marks.* Size, slate-grey coloration, and conspicuous white bill and frontal shield. In the distance on the water coots resemble ducks, but have a smaller, rounder head and a more slender neck, that gives a characteristic silhouette. As it walks it has a graceful bobbing of the head in time with the step.

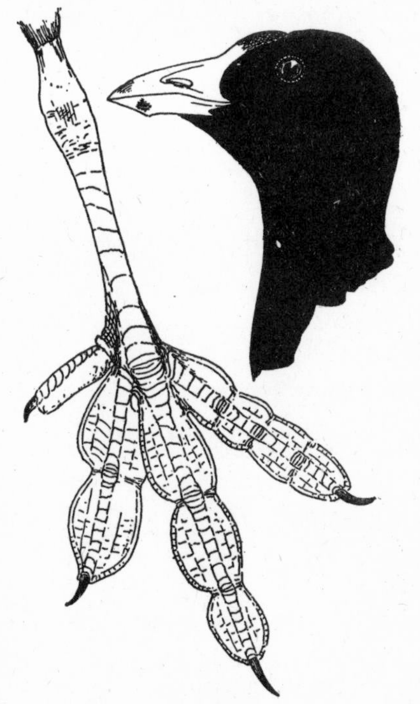

Figure 249
Specific details of Coot; scale, ½.

*Nesting.* Usually some slight eminence, such as an old muskrat house, in watery marsh in nest of waste vegetation.

*Distribution.* North America. Nesting in Canada across the continent, north to the Mackenzie and throughout Cariboo District in British Columbia.

The coot is a common bird on all our southern waters. In the autumn immense flocks gather on the lakes, often bedding out in the open water in black, raft-like masses. They are not generally regarded as desirable game birds and their large flocks have been blamed at times for exhausting the food for more valuable species.

*Economic Status.* The coot is a vegetable feeder, but, owing to its habitat, cannot be of economic importance except as a second-rate object of sport.

## Order—Charadriiformes. Shore Birds, Gulls, Auks, etc.

A rather composite order composed of many superficially diverse suborders. No popularly recognizable diagnosis of the order can be given and the members can be best recognized by the various suborders. These are: *Charadrii* the shore birds; *Lari* the skuas or jaegers, gulls, and terns; and *Alcae* the auks, murres, and puffins.

### SUBORDER—CHARADRII. SHORE BIRDS, SNIPES, SANDPIPERS, PLOVERS, ETC.

*General Description.* Shore birds constitute an order comparatively easy to recognize but difficult to describe briefly. All snipe-like or plover-like birds are included in this order. They have moderately, to extremely, long, delicately formed legs for wading in shallow water and pond edges, and length of neck and bill to correspond. The toes may be either three or four in number, and are poorly adapted for perching. They may be without webs entirely (Figure 290, page 202), or with partial webs situated either at the bases of the toes (Figure 296, page 206), or forming scalloped or entire edgings to them (Figures 306 and 308, pages 212, 213). The hind toe when present is small, weak, and slightly elevated above the rest. The wings are long and pointed and the tertials next to the body are lengthened (Figure 250).

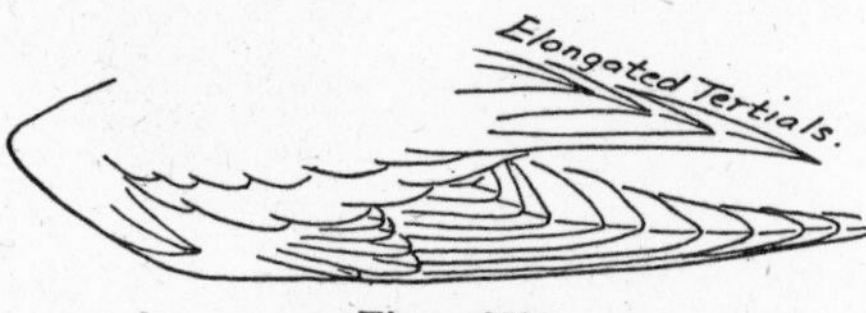


Figure 250
Wing of shore bird showing elongated tertials.

*Distinctions.* Some shore birds show superficial resemblance to the rails, whereas others (curlews) in certain characteristics may be mistaken for either ibises or herons, but may be distinguished from them by the small and elevated, or absent, hind toe and the feathered lores in front of the eye.

*Field Marks.* General outline, habit, habitat, and flight, characteristics which are usually quite diagnostic.

*Nesting.* On the ground, except in one species.

*Distribution.* The order, shore birds, is cosmopolitan and there are few areas in the world that some of its members do not occupy. The Old and New World forms of the northern hemisphere are closely related; some are identical, many are subspecifically related, and a few, such as the Turnstone, are found all over the world. Most of our northern species breed in the far north, some of them as far as land extends, though a few nest along, and across, our southern borders.

The shore birds, in the days of their original abundance, were, in the east and south, favourite game; now, since their numbers have been so greatly reduced, they are seldom systematically hunted, and are shot only incidentally. Of the shore birds of Canada, the woodcock and Wilson's Snipe are the most interesting game.

*Economic Status.* Most of the members of the order inhabit waste land and have little economic effect; others, frequenting cultivated fields, are of greater importance, and will be discussed under their specific headings. On the whole, the order is either harmless or actively helpful to man.

Shore birds have never been regarded as desirable game in the west, where larger and more prized objects of sport were available. Now, since they have become so greatly reduced, shore birds, except for a few species, are seldom hunted anywhere. Woodcock and snipe shooting still have their devotees who care more to exercise their skill than to obtain heavy bags; but woodcock are too rare west of the Great Lakes to be seriously considered as game and snipe shooting has been largely confined to eastern sportsmen. It was, therefore, little hardship to the western shooter when the majority of these species were given a continuous close season under the Migratory Birds Convention Act. Though the *Limicolae* as a group never seriously suffered in our western provinces, some of its species were not so fortunate. Large waders like the avocet, godwits, curlew, and willet, which commonly nested in what are now settled communities, have suffered greatly, though not so much from the legitimate sportsman as from the pot-hunter. The Migratory Birds Convention Act came none too soon to save them, and although the future of the vast hordes of lesser waders that nest far to the north seems reasonably secure, that of these larger ones is still doubtful. Those that so hang in the balance include some of the most attractive wild bird life of the prairies, they add a grace to many otherwise monotonous landscapes, and their long, clear, cool, flute-like whistles are amongst the imponderables that give character to the wide open of the great west.

The representatives of the suborder in Canada are divided into several families: *Haematopodidae* oyster-catchers; *Charadriidae* plovers, turnstone, and surf-birds; *Scolopacidae* woodcock, snipes, and sandpipers; and *Phalaropodidae* phalaropes.

### FAMILY—HAEMATOPODIDAE. OYSTER-CATCHERS

*General Description.* Large shore birds more heavily built than is usual in the order; bill stout and horny, extraordinarily flattened laterally (sideways) at tip (Figure 251). There are two species in Canada, one restricted to the east coast and the other to the west coast.

286. **American Oyster-catcher.** L'HUÎTRIER D'AMÉRIQUE. *Haematopus palliatus.* L, 19. Head, neck, and upper breast, black; back, olive-brown with contrasting white wing-patch and rump. All underparts, pure white; bill, large, bright red.

*Distribution.* Atlantic coast north to Virginia. Formerly to New Jersey, and accidental in New Brunswick. Probably breeds throughout its range.

The northern range of this striking bird was once on our southern sea coasts. It has long been exterminated (?) in Canada and there is little prospect of its occurring there again.

287. **Black Oyster-catcher.** L'HUÎTRIER NOIR. *Haematopus bachmani.* L, about 17. A large, all black bird, with long, extraordinarily flattened red bill and pink legs.

*Distinctions.* Not to be mistaken for any other species.

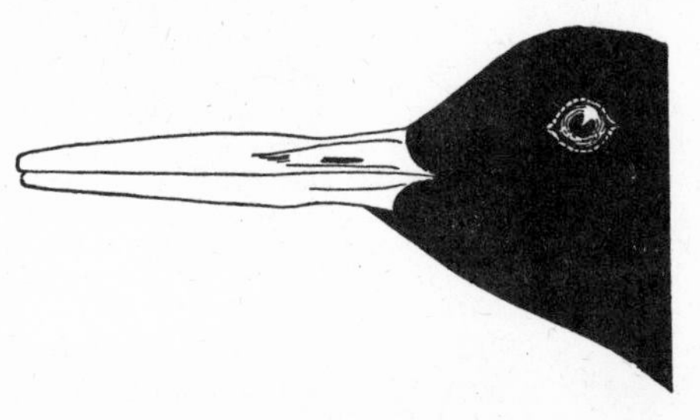

Figure 251
Oyster-catcher; scale, about ½.

*Field Marks.* Large, black bird, nearly as large as a crow, with conspicuous long, red bill.
*Distribution.* Pacific coast of North America, from Aleutian Islands to Lower California, breeds throughout most of its range. Winters from British Columbia southward.

This big, showy bird is found along most of our west coast and prefers rocky shores and the boiling surf to mud or sandy flats.

### FAMILY—CHARADRIIDAE. PLOVERS, TURNSTONE, AND SURF-BIRDS

This family is divided into four subfamilies: *Vanellinae* the lapwing; *Charadriinae* the plovers; *Aphrizinae* surf-birds; and *Arenariinae* turnstones.

#### Subfamily—Vanellinae. Lapwing

A single lapwing is of only casual occurrence on our eastern coast. With its long, pointed crest it is easily recognizable.

269. **Lapwing.** LE VANNEAU HUPPÉ. *Vanellus vanellus.* L, 13. A rather large black and white, plover-like bird with long, upstanding crest plume.

Figure 252
Lapwing (male); scale, ½.

*Distinctions.* With above description quite distinctive and unlike any other species it is likely to be confused with.

*Distribution.* Europe, east to China. Known in America only by a few, casual, wandering specimens until the winter of 1927 and 1928, when a large number appeared on our east coast only to perish in inclement weather. It is interesting to note that one of these wandering or storm-blown birds bore a band that had been placed upon its leg in Cumberland, England, and this definitely locates the point of origin of at least part of the flight.

### Subfamily—Charadriinae. Plover

*General Description.* The plover are rather more stoutly and compactly built than the snipe-like birds. Their bills are shorter, soft at the base, but ending in a hard, horny tip (Figure 253). Hind toe lacking in all species except black-bellied in which it is very small and almost rudimentary (Figure 262).

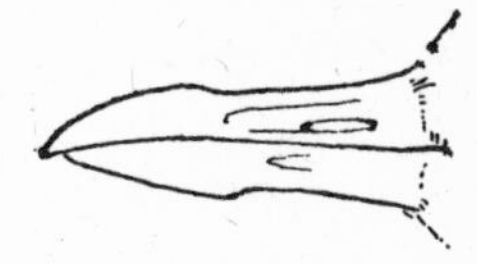

Figure 253
Bill of Plover; enlarged.

*Distinctions.* With the above description the plover are not likely to be confused with other families.

*Nesting.* On the ground in a slight depression, usually lined with scanty grass, moss, waste vegetation, or pebbles.

*Distribution.* The family, in closely related or nearly identical forms, is circumpolar in distribution, breeding mostly north of present settlement.

The plover are well known to the sportsman. They average larger in size than the snipe and some of them that feed in upland fields offer considerable sport.

*Economic Status.* As a family they frequent cultivated land more than other shore birds and hence are of somewhat greater economic interest. They are actively helpful to man.

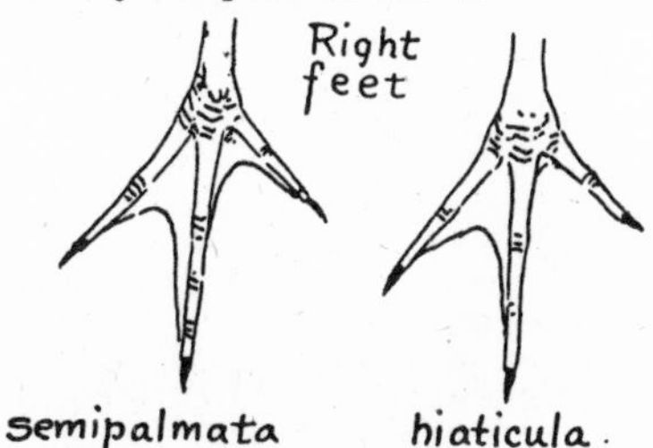


Figure 254
Feet of American and European Ringed Plover; natural size.

275. **Greater Ringed Plover.** LE GRAND PLUVIER À COLLIER. *Charadrius hiaticula.* L, 6·75. Like the Semipalmated Plover, but *See* distinctions.

*Distinctions.* So like the Semipalmated Plover that it can be separated from it only by close examination of the foot webbing. In this species there is no web between the inner toes, whereas the Semipalmated carries small webs deep in the angle (Figure 254).

*Distribution.* The Old World and Greenland. In Canada reported only from the eastern Arctics—eastern Baffin Island northward.

277. **Piping Plover.** LE PLUVIER SIFFLEUR. *Charadrius melodus.* L, 7·10. Very much like the Semipalmated Plover in pattern and size, but much lighter and with no black bar through face. Legs and base of bill orange-yellow. Tip of bill black (Figure 255, compare with 257).

*Distinctions.* Ordinarily mistaken only for the Semipalmated Plover, but much less common and less generally distributed. Above—even, light, ashy grey, the colour of dry, instead of wet, sand. Adult: no black bar through face and the juvenile with faintly greyish cheeks instead of brown. The breast-band may be broken in the middle or, in juvenility, very poorly defined.

*Field Marks.* A small, "peep"-like wader (*See* page 201), with very short bill and a more or less well-defined breast-band. Very much paler than the Semipalmated, especially about the face. Its melodious little whistle has suggested the specific name *meloda.* This is the only small Ringed Plover breeding in Canada south of semi-arctic conditions.

*Distribution.* Eastern North America, west across the southern parts of the Prairie Provinces but scarce west of Manitoba and not recorded from British Columbia. Breeds wherever found in Canada.

A small, delightful shore bird, tuneful as well as beautiful. It is decidedly a sand-beach bird and is never seen in grassy or marshy situations.

Figure 255
Piping Plover; scale, ½.

278. **Snowy Plover.** LE PLUVIER NEIGEUX. *Charadrius nivosus.* Similar in size and general coloration to the Piping Plover. It has a slight black bar, back from the eye, but no breast-band, just a single black spot on either side of the shoulders where such a band would begin. The bill is all black (Figure 256).

It has been taken in the State of Washington and may occur at any time in parts of British Columbia. There is a single record for southern Ontario.

Figure 256
Snowy Plover;
scale, ½.

274. **Semipalmated Plover.** AMERICAN RINGED OR RING-NECKED PLOVER. LE PLUVIER À COU BLANC. *Charadrius semipalmatus.* L, 6·75. A very small plover almost as small as a "peep," of general resemblance to the Killdeer (Plate XXII B), but with one instead of two black breast-bands (Figure 257, compare with Plate XXI B) and without the ochraceous rump and tail. Autumn birds are similar, but the colours are washed out and faded, especially the blacks about head. Legs and base of bill warm yellow. Tip of bill black.

*Distinctions.* The smaller size would prevent any confusion with the Killdeer even if the single, instead of double, breast-band and the dark rump and tail were not determinative. Can be confused with the much rarer Piping Plover which resembles it in both colour and size. Considerably darker than that species, the back being the colour of wet, instead of dry, sand. Adult with black bar from base of bill to cheeks (Compare Figure 257 with 255). Juvenile with cheeks brown instead of faintly greyish as in the case of the Piping Plover.

*Field Marks.* Often accompanying Least and Semipalmated Sandpipers and resembling them in size, but distinguished from them by the decided breast-band. The dark coloration, especially of the cheeks, of the adult, will separate from the Piping.

Figure 257
Semipalmated Plover;
scale, ½.

*Distribution.* North and South America. Breeds in the southern Arctics, across the continent south to Magdalen Islands, Churchill, southern Mackenzie, the Yukon, and Queen Charlotte Islands. Migrates throughout southern Canada.

A pretty little plover frequenting both mud-flats and sandy beaches. In the autumn, the early migrating adults with their sharply defined markings are distinctly noticeable in contrast with the duller, more blended juveniles that come later. Closely related to the Ring Plover of Europe from which it may be separated only by smaller size and a few minor details (*See* that species).

280. **Wilson's Plover.** LE PLUVIER DE WILSON. *Pagolla wilsonia.* L, 7·75. A rather large, ring-necked plover, much like a small Killdeer, with a single breast-band.

*Distinctions.* Like a Semipalmated Plover, with complete breast-band and black and white forehead bar, but with a black spot in front of the eye. Bill decidedly larger and heavier than in any similar species, equal to or longer than the middle toe and claw instead of being decidedly shorter (Figure 258).

*Distribution.* Southern North America. There is a single old record for Nova Scotia.

281. **Mountain Plover.** LE PLUVIER DES MONTAGNES. *Eupoda montana.* L, 7·25. Smaller than the Killdeer, but much larger than either of the little Ring Plovers, which it resembles in coloration.

Figure 258
Wilson's Plover; scale, ½.

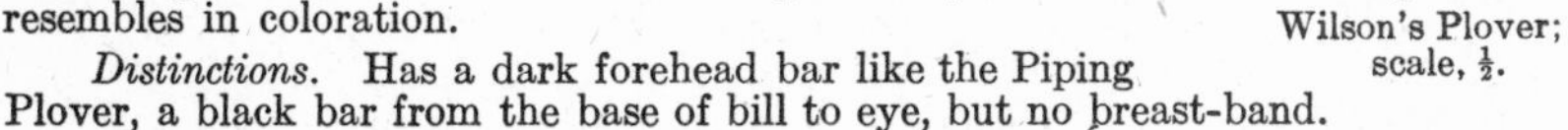

*Distinctions.* Has a dark forehead bar like the Piping Plover, a black bar from the base of bill to eye, but no breast-band.

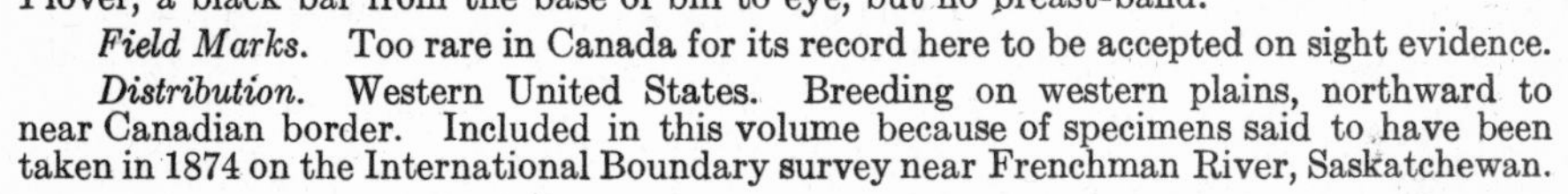

*Field Marks.* Too rare in Canada for its record here to be accepted on sight evidence.

*Distribution.* Western United States. Breeding on western plains, northward to near Canadian border. Included in this volume because of specimens said to have been taken in 1874 on the International Boundary survey near Frenchman River, Saskatchewan.

A bird of the dry uplands, almost independent of water. Occasional birds may possibly be noted in southern Saskatchewan and Alberta, as they were originally not uncommon in central Montana and still occur there.

273. **Killdeer Plover.** KILLDEER. LE PLUVIER KILDIR. *Oxyechus vociferus.* L, 10·50. Plate XXI B. A medium-sized shore bird commonly frequenting the uplands. Pure white below, with two black breast-bands and a large amount of rusty yellow on rump and tail.

*Distinctions.* The double black belt across the breast and the large amount of rusty yellow on tail and rump are distinctive. It is the largest of the belted plover.

*Field Marks.* Size, white underparts, and double black breast-belt, large amount of rufous on rump and tail, and loud, strident voice represented as *"Kildee, Kildee"* often repeated.

*Distribution.* North and South America. Breeding commonly in Canada across the continent except on the east coast; in the west, north to Mackenzie and Yukon Valleys.

A common bird over most of Canada. It nests in pastures and cultivated fields, as a rule at some distance from water. When its young are hatched it leads them to the nearest water, often the merest surface pool, where they dabble about the muddy edge until they are grown.

The species is well named *vociferus*, as it is amongst the noisiest of the noisy. One cannot approach its chosen haunts without it springing an immediate alarm that puts all within hearing at nervous attention. *"Kildee Kildee,"* it cries stridently, and makes off in frantic alarm, only to return and tell it again and again to the intruder and the whole community. It alights and runs about the object of its alarm with an aggravatingly repeated *"Cry ba-by-cry, cry ba-by ba-by"* rising to a shriek of excitement as it plays "broken wing" and makes patently misleading attempts to hide behind quite inadequate grass clumps. There may or may not be young or nests nearby. It may or may not have a proprietary interest in the ground invaded, but it acts the same in either case and is not content when at last it decoys or drives away its adopted enemy, but follows for long distances to prolong the agony and spoil his game whatever it may be. To the naturalist bent on studying some of the shyer denizens of the sloughs the Killdeer is an aggravation indeed, and at times considerable restraint is required to refrain from blowing the interfering busybody to bits and silencing its plaguing racket. However, at other times, its characteristic notes and the pretty way in which it alternately runs on twinkling little feet and pauses to look around like a robin hunting angle worms on the lawn are very attractive. It is interesting, also, to see the different ways in which it deals with various enemies. When real danger threatens, such as a horse straying too close and threatening to plant its great hoof upon the nest, its behaviour is not the same as when a dog ranges near. Into the face of the former it flies with a sudden start and loud calls in a manner that makes the great creature jump backward or to one side in startled fright, which accomplished, the bird returns to her brooding without more ado. With a dog, however, such tactics are useless, and the plover flies shrieking away from the nest on foot, wings dragging brokenly, legs trailing helplessly, and all in a flutter of terrified helplessness. The dog dashes at the apparently disabled bird which only just escapes the snap of the excited jaws. Another dash is also seemingly miraculously evaded and the bird manages to flutter a few rods away, to repeat the manœuvre again and again, always leading away from the nest and each time nearly but not quite caught. When the enemy is thus by false hopes decoyed far from the nest the Killdeer gets suddenly well and strong and leaves her would-be devourer to dine elsewhere whilst she returns to her duties. It is an old, old game, yet ever new, not altogether peculiar to the Killdeer, and so nearly always successful that the species persists and thrives in spite of dog, fox, coyote, or cat.

272. **American Golden Plover.** LE PLUVIER DORÉ D'AMÉRIQUE. *Pluvialis dominica.* L, 10·50. In general coloration and appearance much like the Black-bellied Plover (*See* Plate XXII A), but slightly smaller.

Figure 259
Specific details of American Golden Plover; scale, ½.
*a*, dark rump; *b*, dark crown;
*c*, no hind toe; *d*, grey axillars.

*Distinctions.* Likely to be confused only with the Black-bellied Plover whose plumage sequence it follows closely, with the following differences. In spring, decidedly more black than white above and the light speckles strongly golden yellow. Crown almost solid black instead of nearly pure white. Below, the black includes the undertail-coverts. The adults in winter are very similar to the juvenile which is generally quite yellow on back, the colour suffusing over face and breast. The markings above are considerably

A. Nighthawk; scale, $\frac{1}{8}$

B. Chimney Swift; scale, $\frac{1}{7}$

PLATE XXXVI

A. Ruby-throated Hummingbird; scale, $\frac{1}{2}$
Female Male

B. Rufous Hummingbird; scale, $\frac{1}{3}$
Male
Female

finer and sharper than on the Black-bellied, and those on breast and flanks tend towards faintly suggested bars instead of stripes. In any plumage, the Golden Plover is to be known from the Black-bellied by its rump, unicoloured with the back, dark tail, grey instead of black axillars, and the absence of even a rudimentary hind toe (Figure 259, compare with 262).

*Field Marks.* In spring the Golden Plover with extensive black underparts can be mistaken only for the Black-bellied. Its dark crown and back make the best distinctions when the bird is still. When it is on the wing the axillars, evenly grey with the under surface of the wing, and absence of white rump, are quite conspicuous (Figure 261).

In the juvenile, the faint indications of barring on breast, and the underwing and rump marks are the best field marks. The notes are also quite different, but must be heard before the difference can be appreciated.

*Distribution.* North and South America. Breeds along most of the Arctic coast and migrates more or less commonly throughout southern Canada. It is supposed that the spring migration is mostly through the interior of the continent and the autumn migration off the coast well out to sea. In the east, a continuous flight from Nova Scotia to Brazil is postulated, but certainly numbers of juveniles take a far more commonplace route, and in the autumn are seen in the interior.

Figure 260
Golden Plover; scale, ½.
(Juvenile or Winter)

*SUBSPECIES.* The American Golden Plover is divided into two subspecies—the Eastern Golden Plover (le Pluvier doré de l'Est) *Pluvialis dominica dominica*, covering most of the continent and migrating to the pampas of Brazil and the Argentine; and the Pacific Golden Plover (le Pluvier doré du Pacifique) *Pluvialis dominica fulva*, confined to the west coast, breeding in northwestern Alaska and adjoining Asia and migrating to China, Oceania, and New Zealand. It is slightly smaller and, especially in autumn, is more heavily and generally washed with yellow and buff.

Figure 261
Field marks of: *a*, Black-bellied; *b*, Golden Plover.

The American Golden Plover is very closely related to the European Golden Plover that has the lining of wings white. Within the memory of living sportsmen large flocks were regularly seen in the east, but now only occasional birds are met with. It is doubtful if it was ever numerous in the west, either in the interior or on the west coast.

270. **Black-bellied Plover.** BULLHEAD. LE PLUVIER À VENTRE NOIR. *Squatarola squatarola.* L, 11. Plate XXII A. In spring and summer—above, checked black and white; below, face, throat, and breast, solid black. Crown mostly white. Juvenile: above to crown, a dark ashy brown ground, finely speckled with cream or yellow; all below white; flanks, breast, foreneck, and face, softly striped with greyish brown. Adult birds in winter wear a plumage somewhat similar to that of the juvenile, but in early autumn are still partly in the summer coat. Most of the white may be worn off the upper parts and the black below is dull and mixed with the white of the incoming winter plumage.

Figure 262
Specific details of Black-bellied Plover; scale, ½.
*a*, white rump; *b*, black axillars; *c*, rudimentary hind toe.

*Distinctions.* Like the Golden Plover, but somewhat larger. At all seasons it resembles that species in colour, but differs as follows: in spring, decidedly more white than black above, especially on crown which may be nearly immaculate, instead of the converse. The white of the back at this season is not at all yellow. Below, rear abdomen and under-tail-coverts, white instead of black. The juvenile is never as yellow above as the typical Golden Plover and the markings are considerably coarser and more blended. The breast pattern is in faintly blended stripes, never with the suggestion of crossbarring as in the Golden. In any plumage, may be distinguished from the Golden by white or very light rump; black, instead of grey axillars, and the presence of a rudimentary hind toe (Figures 261 and 262, compare with 259).

*Field Marks.* In spring, the Black-bellied Plover, with extensive black underparts, may be confused only with the Golden. Its whiter head and back make the best distinctions when the bird is still. On the wing, the black axillars stand out plainly against the grey ground of the underwing, and the white rump is conspicuous. In juveniles and autumn birds, the striped instead of faintly barred breast, black axillars, and white rump are the best field marks (Figure 261). The notes are quite distinctive, but must be heard before the difference can be appreciated.

*Distribution.* Nearly cosmopolitan. In America, breeding along the Arctic coast west of Hudson Bay. Migrates throughout all southern Canada.

This is one of the finest plovers.

### Subfamily—Aphrizinae. The Surf-Birds

The surf-birds are described by Dr. Coues as being plover masquerading under the guise of sandpipers. As there is but one species, a general description will be given under it.

282. **Surf-bird.** L'OISEAU DU RESSAC. *Aphriza virgata.* L, 9·50. A rather large shore bird. Bill, plover-like with enlarged horny tip, longer and more slender than usual with that family; short legs and fleshy feet with small but well-developed hind toe (Figure 263). Adult: in spring, greyish brown above with some creamy feather edges and an irregular admixture of chestnut, working into stripes at the neck and crown and over the face and foreneck. Below, on flanks and breast, white heavily spotted and V-marked with greyish brown. Spots more or less veiled and coalesced on breast. Base of tail and rump white, remainder of tail dark. The juvenile is coloured very much like a juvenile Knot; greyish slate above, white below with foreneck and breast heavily streaked. Rump white.

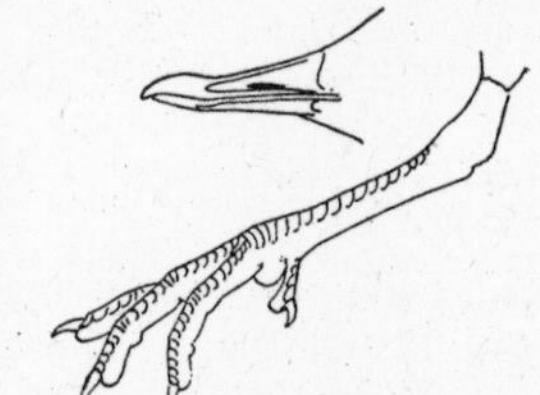

Figure 263
Bill and foot of Surf-bird; scale, ½.

*Distinctions.* Spring plumage more like the spring Wandering Tattler (page 194) than anything else, but the grey is browner and distinctly marked on back and breast instead of plain; below decidedly spotted instead of barred. Juvenile in general colour is half-way between the autumn Knot and the Wandering Tattler. Back, evenly grey, tending towards the ashy of the Knot and with similar fine, white, semicircular feather edge markings. The breast is more heavily striped and spotted than in either, and the white rump is distinctive.

*Field Marks.* A medium-sized wader with bill as short as the head, considerable white on inner secondaries and white rump. In spring, breast and underparts coarsely and heavily spotted. In autumn, a grey and white wader with decidedly but softly streaked breast and foreneck.

*Distribution.* Pacific coast of North and South America. Breeds in the interior of west Alaska and Yukon. Nest only lately discovered. Winters on the outer coast of Vancouver Island and the coast of southern South America.

As its name implies, it is a bird of the surf. It is found on the shores of rocky islets that receive the full heave of the open sea, amidst the spume and spray of the breakers.

### Subfamily—Arenariinae. Turnstones

Medium-sized shore birds, coloured in striking and pronounced pattern. Bill moderately short, slightly turned up and horny for terminal half. The tip is slightly flattened in horizontal plane, but not distinctly enlarged as in the plovers (Figure 264, compare with 259 and 263).

283a. **Common Turnstone.** CALICO PLOVER. LE TOURNE-PIERRE COMMUN. *Arenaria interpres.* L, 9·50.

*Distinctions.* A strikingly coloured bird. Back in rather broad masses of dull red, black, and white more or less intermixed. Rump and head white, the crown striped with brown or black. Underparts pure white, with black breast-band extending up side of neck to face where it makes a circle through the eye and around a white loral spot (Figure 265). Autumn birds have the colours subdued and the back coloration lost or only faintly represented, but enough of the face and breast markings always remain to suggest the above diagnosis.

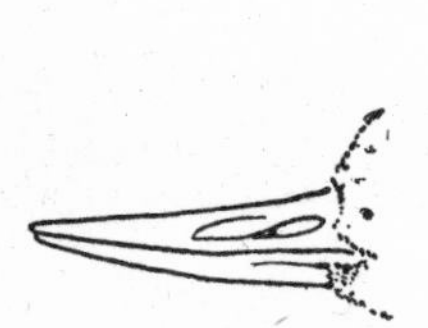

Figure 264
Bill of Turnstone;
natural size.

Figure 265
Turnstone; scale, ½.

*Field Marks.* The peculiar pied coloration in red, black, and white of the spring plumage. In the autumn the white lower back and uppertail-coverts separated by a dark bar.

*Nesting.* Depression in the ground lined with a few dead leaves or vegetable fibres.

*Distribution.* The turnstone as a species has one of the widest distributions of any bird, there being few countries where it has not occurred. The American subspecies, the Ruddy Turnstone, breeds from the Arctic coast west of Hudson Bay northward, and is more common on the Atlantic than the Pacific coast. Migrates throughout most of southern Canada except the interior of British Columbia. Rather scarcer in Saskatchewan and Alberta than in Manitoba and on the coasts.

*SUBSPECIES.* The turnstone is represented in America by the Ruddy Turnstone (le Tourne-pierre Roux) *Arenaria interpres morinella,* rather smaller than the European form, *Arenaria interpres interpres,* more red above and legs less intensely vermilion. The latter subspecies may occur on the British Columbia coast.

A bird of sandy, muddy, or rocky shores, but preferring the sand. It is named from its habit of turning over small stones and pebbles on the beach in its search for food, and it is astonishing what comparatively large stones it can move. It inserts its bill under the edges, gives a little fillip, and away goes the stone rolling or skidding over the beach to a considerable distance.

284. **Black Turnstone.** LE TOURNE-PIERRE NOIR. *Arenaria melanocephala.* L, 9·50. A black and white turnstone, more black than white. All above, except lower back and base of tail, solid black with green iridescence. Head, throat, foreneck, and breast the same, cutting sharply against pure white flanks and underparts. Narrow bar of black between white base of tail and lower back. Considerable white tipping on ends of upperwing-coverts and inner secondaries. In highest plumage, fine, sparse, white streakings on face, down sides of neck and across breast, aggregating into a vague forehead bar, superciliary line, and loral spot (Figure 266). These white specklings absent in many cases. In autumn and winter the black duller, and juveniles with faint white edgings on back feathers.

Figure 266
Black Turnstone; scale, ½.

*Distinctions.* A black and white wader in uniform over-all masses; can be mistaken for no other species.

*Field Marks.* A black and white wader coloured in broad masses. Has the same white rump and lower back and uppertail-coverts separated by black band as has the Ruddy Turnstone. Shows considerable white in wings in flight.

*Distribution.* Pacific coast of North America. Breeds in northwest Alaska and migrates down the coast, wintering from British Columbia to Lower California. Never met with inland.

The Black Turnstone occurs in great flocks along our west coast from late summer until the following spring. It is the commonest and most generally distributed wader of the coast. It frequents stony and rocky shores rather than sand or mud.

FAMILY—SCOLOPACIDAE. SNIPE-LIKE BIRDS. TIP-UPS, SANDPIPERS, ETC.

*General Description.* Small to medium shore birds, the curlew being the largest species. Feet never entirely webbed nor toes furnished with web-flaps or web-margins. Some species have small webs between the base of the toes, giving rise to the term "semipalmated" or half-webbed. All but one species, the Sanderling, page 210, have four toes. The bills are long, slender, and tapering; usually straight (Figure 267, and others); but some down-curved (Figures 270-272, pages 189-191); occasionally, as in the godwits, very slightly upcurved (Figure 300, page 208); rather flexible and usually slightly enlarged and sensitive at the tip.

*Distinctions.* Shore birds, usually recognized by the above popular names. Bill does not taper to fine, sharp point, like that of the phalaropes and avocets (Figures 305, 306, and 309, pages 212-214), and without the pronounced enlarged horny tip of the plover (Figure 253, page 179), is soft and rather flexible throughout its length (Figure 294, page 204, is typical), in contrast with the horny bills of the turnstones and oystercatchers (Figures 264, page 185, and 251, page 177).

*Nesting.* All except one species, the Solitary Sandpiper, page 194, nest on the ground, in slight hollows lined sparsely with waste vegetable matter.

*Distribution.* The greater number nest in the far north, though a few species south, even into the United States. They migrate down our coasts or through the interior according to species and distribution. Some of them have most interesting migration routes.

Among these birds are the woodcock and snipe of the wet woods and marshes; the tip-ups, teeters, and sandpipers seen along the shores and streams; and the curlew of the uplands. These species formed the great bulk of the wonderful flocks of shore birds that once thronged our shores.

Breeding mostly far beyond the confines of cultivation the occupation of their nesting grounds by settlers has had only the slightest influence upon their numbers. The great reduction must be blamed upon indiscriminate shooting. As they fly in dense flocks they offer an easy target and eighty or more have been known to fall at one discharge of the gun, so that it is not surprising that they are now comparatively scarce. It is a source of pleasure to know that the western sportsmen are not responsible for the decrease in numbers. A few of the larger forms such as the curlew and the godwit have suffered from the pot-hunter, but other species as a rule have not been regarded in our west as objects of sport. The removal of them from the list of game birds by the Migratory Birds Convention Act has not inflicted as much hardship on the western sportsman as it has on the eastern, but it has done much to conserve the birds in other quarters of their range outside Canadian jurisdiction.

*Economic Status.* Either perfectly harmless or actively useful according to habitat.

228. **American Woodcock.** LA BÉCASSE D'AMÉRIQUE. *Philobela minor.* L, 11. Plate XXII B. A rather large wader similar to the European Woodcock, but smaller and without any crossbarring below. All above coloured with an intricate pattern of various shades of rich wood-browns; below, a soft, uniform ruddy ochre. Eyes large and set very high in the head.

*Distinctions.* Large size, general uniform ochraceous colour below, mottled wood-browns above, and eyes set higher in head (Figure 267). Can hardly be confused with any other species. The first three primaries are peculiarly narrowed (Figure 268), a characteristic not present in any other similar species.

*Nesting.* On the ground, in the woods, amidst the dead leaves, with which its plumage harmonizes so well.

Figure 267
American Woodcock; scale, ½.

Figure 268
Emarginate primaries of American Woodcock; scale, ½.

*Distribution.* Eastern North America north to southern Canada. It has occasionally been reported from Manitoba without confirmatory evidence, but as it occurs in Minnesota, close by, its occurrence in the southern parts of that province would not be remarkable.

Woodcock haunt moist or wet shrubbery, alder or hazel thickets, or the tangled edges of damp woods. They spring suddenly from the ground on being disturbed, rise erratically on peculiarly whistling wings, and passing just over the tops of the underbrush drop suddenly into concealment again a few rods beyond. Woodcock may still be legally hunted under the terms of the Migratory Birds Convention Act, though the privilege is of little importance in the west.

The Pileated Woodpecker, Cock of the Woods, sometimes called "Woodcock" (page 280), is an entirely different bird and should not be confused with the real Woodcock. It cannot be legally hunted at all.

229. **Common Old World Snipe.** LA BÉCASSINE ORDINAIRE DU VIEUX MONDE. *Capella gallinago.* L, 11·25. Practically indistinguishable from Wilson's Snipe except that the axillars and under wing surface contain more white. The blackish barring of the axillars is reduced to distinctly less than the white, or is nearly absent (Figure 269).

*Distribution.* Northern parts of Eastern Hemisphere. There are no strictly Canadian records, but it has been taken at Mokkovik, Labrador.

Figure 269
Axillars of: *a*, Wilson's Snipe; *b*, European Common Snipe; scale, ½.

230. **Wilson's Snipe.** AMERICAN JACK SNIPE. LA BÉCASSINE DE WILSON. *Capella delicata.* L, 11·25. Plate XXIII A.

*Distinctions.* A sandpiper-like bird, with a very long bill (2·5 and over), dressed in wood-browns, ochre, and white. The brick-red tail barred with black and whitening on the outer feathers, will distinguish it if necessary. The dowitcher is the only wader of similar size having so long a bill, but its rump and back are largely white.

*Field Marks.* Grassy meadow habitat, long bill, and peculiar cork-screw flight as it rises with harsh "*scape, scape,*" note, together with size, general coloration, and reddish tail.

*Nesting.* On the ground, in grassy meadows.

*Distribution.* Across the continent. Breeds throughout the Canadian west except perhaps in the most southern parts.

Wilson's Snipe, commonly, though incorrectly called "Jack Snipe" or just "Snipe," is one of the sportsman's favourites. Its appearance on the scene with the first keen frosts, in considerable numbers, with its lying well to a dog, and having an irregular, twisty flight, make a combination of qualities that endear it to the true sportsman who desires a test of dexterity rather than food.

It is still permissible under the terms of the Migratory Birds Convention Act to hunt this snipe.

Throughout most of the prairies in spring and early summer the hollow, rapidly repeated, dull whistle of its love flight can be heard at all times of the day, while its author circles about so high as to be hardly discernible with the naked eye. It has been demonstrated that this sound is made by the air against the stiffly held outer tail feathers and can be exactly imitated by inserting these feathers in opposite sides of a cork and whirling the same about at the end of a string.

230. 2. **Jack Snipe.** LA BÉCASSINE SOURDE. *Lymnocryptes minimus.* L, 7·5. Very much like Wilson's Snipe but much smaller, wing scarcely over 4 inches. The back with iridescent streaks along the inner edge of the tertials and the tail solid dusky without crossbarring.

*Distribution.* Eastern Hemisphere. There are no strictly Canadian records, but it has been taken at Mokkovik, Labrador.

264. **Long-billed Curlew.** SICKLE-BILLED CURLEW. LE COURLIS À LONG BEC. *Numenius americanus.* L, 24. The largest of our waders, varying considerably in length owing to the growth of the long, decurved bill. All below pale, pink-buffy, lightening to cream on throat and face. Flanks lightly striped with brown which extends sparsely across breast and more thickly and finely up and around neck to face and crown. Above, dark brown and the same pink-buffy of the lower parts in complicated mottling and barring.

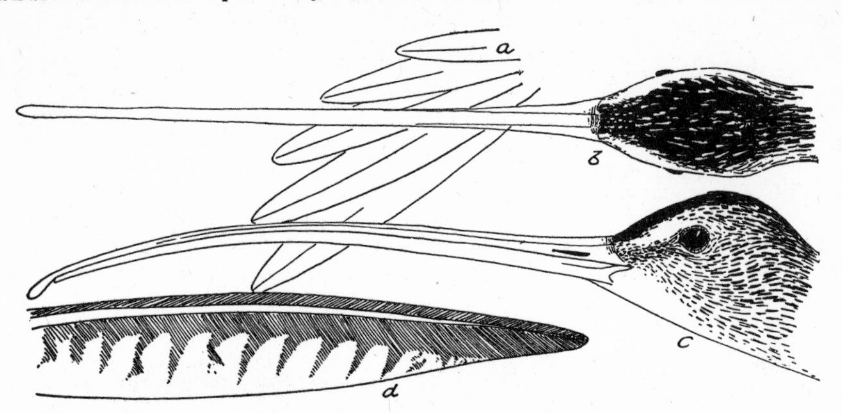


Figure 270

Specific details of Long-billed Curlew; scale, ½.

*a*, plain axillars; *b*, crown without median stripe;
*c*, profile of head; *d*, tooth-marked first primary.

*Distinctions.* The long, decurved bill and buffy coloration are distinctive of the curlews. Too large to be confused with the Eskimo Curlew, but very similar and at times nearly intergrading in length with the Hudsonian. Its distinctive characters are plain, unbarred, pink-buff axillars, which separate it from both the other curlews; saw-tooth markings on the primaries separate it from the Eskimo; and plain unbarred axillars distinguish it from the Hudsonian (Figure 270, compare with 271 and 272). As the bills of curlews continue to grow for some time after apparent maturity, they are rather variable in length, but any curlew with a bill over 4 inches long is probably this species.

*Field Marks.* Large size, buffy colour, and long, decurved bill for a curlew. Size is the best criterion in distinguishing the Long-billed Curlew in life from the Hudsonian. In general, it is more pink in colour, especially under the wings, the Hudsonian being more of an olive-brown. Anywhere in southwestern Canada the summer curlew is the Long-billed, the Hudsonian being only a spring and autumn transient.

*Distribution.* North America. Breeds along our southern border and southward from the interior of British Columbia to Manitoba. Has almost disappeared from eastern and western extremes of its range and only locally common elsewhere. We have several records from the British Columbia coast.

The finest of the shore birds. Not so spectacular in colour as the pink and white avocet or the banner-winged willet, but with a picturesque distinction of its own, and of sufficient size to make it conspicuous. The powerful flight on long, pointed wings; the clear-cut, distinctive outline, long sickle-bill extended and legs trailing; and the exultant, care-free whistles, clear, musical, and prolonged, unite to make this a notable bird that embodies the spirit of the open range more than does any other bird, and one that cannot fail to arouse enthusiasm in the sympathetic observer.

The commonest call-note is a clear "*Pil-will*," so nearly like that of the willet that it can not always be distinguished from it. Other notes resemble those of the Upland Plover. One especially delightful is a long-drawn "*Curl-e-e-e-e-u-u-u*," sparklingly clear and rising in the middle about five notes, then dying gradually away, lowering in scale and volume.

The entire call lasts about three seconds of time. As these birds alight they run along the ground a few yards, with their ample wings still raised straight over their backs, uttering their long whistle. Like the godwit they build their nests on the uplands at some distance from water and it is not until the young are hatched that they seek the edges of the pools and resume wader-like habits.

Whether we can retain such a large and conspicuous bird in settled country remains to be seen; this rests largely with the popular feeling of the communities they inhabit. Much said on this subject under the headings Avocet, Godwit, and Willet applies equally well to the curlew.

267. **Whimbrel.** LE COURLIS CORLIEU. *Phaeopus phaeopus.* L, 17. A curlew much like the Hudsonian, but more heavily striped and with a white rump. Axillars barred, but with white and brown instead of buffy and brown.

*Distribution.* Eastern Hemisphere. It has occurred, probably in territorial waters, near Sable Island, Nova Scotia.

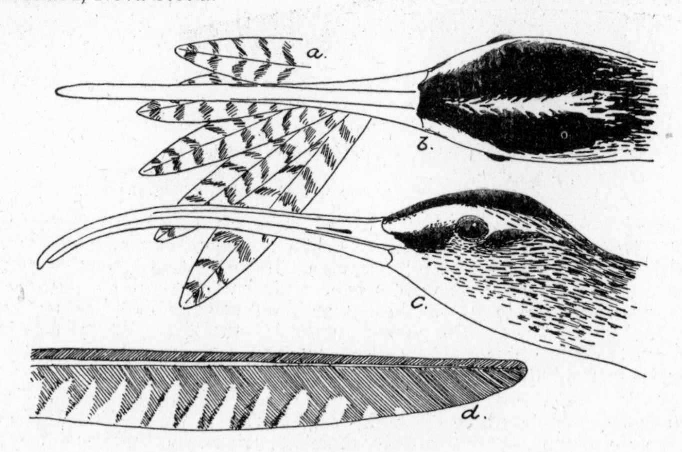


Figure 271
Specific details of Hudsonian Curlew; scale, ½.
*a*, barred axillars; *b*, median crown stripe;
*c*, profile of head; *d*, tooth-marked first primary.

265. **Hudsonian Curlew.** LE COURLIS HUDSONIEN. *Phaeopus hudsonicus.* L, 17. A smaller curlew than the last, but a larger one than the next. A very large shore bird of general buffy colour with long, decurved bill. It varies considerably in over-all length, owing to growth of bill. Buffy below, creamy rather than pinkish, whitening on throat and face. Above, rather faded brown, more or less intermixed with the buffy of below. Brown barring the flanks and striping the breast up the neck to face.

*Distinctions.* With the Eskimo Curlew superficially distinguished from the Long-billed by being more olivaceous than pinkish in general east and more heavily striped on breast and throat. The Hudsonian Curlew has saw-tooth markings on the primaries like the Long-billed; barred axillars like the Eskimo, but with a pronounced light median crown stripe, absent in either of the others (Figure 271, compare with 270 and 272). This combination of characters is always determinative. A curlew with bill under 4 and over 2·4 is likely to be this species.

*Field Marks.* Large size, buffy colour, and long, decurved bill for a curlew. Owing to distribution not likely to be mistaken for any other species, as it does not occur commonly in Canada where Long-billed may be expected. It is, however, a smaller bird than that

PLATE XXXVII

A. Belted Kingfisher; scale, $\frac{1}{4}$

Female (diving) Male

B. Yellow-shafted Flicker; scale, $\frac{1}{4}$

Male Female

PLATE XXXVIII

A. Pileated Woodpecker; scale, $\frac{1}{7}$

Female Male

B. Red-headed Woodpecker; scale, $\frac{1}{4}$

Adult Juvenile

species; less pink and more olive-brown. The colour characters are especially conspicuous on the underwing surface in flight. The Eskimo Curlew is too rare a bird today and too similar to be separated from the Hudsonian in life, by field observation.

*Distribution.* North and South America. Breeds on the northwest coast of Alaska and the coast of Mackenzie east to Hudson Bay. Migrates through the big lakes of Mackenzie and eastern Canada and along the Atlantic and Pacific coasts. Not noted, as yet, in the interior of British Columbia and only a few times in the Prairie Provinces.

266. **Eskimo Curlew.** LE COURLIS DES ESQUIMAUX. *Phaeopus borealis.* L, 13·50. The smallest of our curlews, almost identical in general form and colour with the Hudsonian.

Figure 272
Specific details of Eskimo Curlew; scale, ½.
*a*, barred axillars; *b*, crown without median stripe;
*c*, profile of head; *d*, plain first primary.

*Distinctions.* Like the Hudsonian but smaller, crown mottled but without well-defined median stripe, primaries plain without saw-tooth pattern, and axillars barred (Figure 272, compare with 270 and 271). This combination of characters is determinative. A curlew with bill under 2·25 is probably this species.

*Field Marks.* Like a very small Hudsonian Curlew, but too rare today to be recorded on field identification.

*Distribution.* North and South America. Breeds on the Barren Grounds of Mackenzie, migrates through eastern Canada and down the Mississippi Valley. We have no actual records for our Prairie Provinces, but these curlews have been taken on Great Slave Lake and were once numerous in Missouri River region.

Once noted for their vast numbers, and Audubon compared the flocks with those of Passenger Pigeons. Now nearly extinct. No doubt market hunting in the southern States was an important factor in their depletion, as they were marketed from the Gulf Coast regions by the hundreds of dozen brace. As in many such cases the bird seemed to disappear suddenly, about 1892, and it was not until it was practically gone that any general alarm was expressed concerning it. We often do not note the gradual depletion of any species, or if we do observe it we are prone to ascribe it to local instead of general conditions and it is not until many observers begin to compare notes that the true conditions are realized. All species have their bad and good seasons, epidemics, and other periodical setbacks. When there is a large natural reserve of numbers, such checks make no permanent inroad on the strength of a thriving species, but when a steady, even, though slow, reduction is in progress, checks, normally of minor importance, become catastrophic.

261. **Upland Plover.** BARTRAMIAN SANDPIPER. QUAILY. LA MAUBÈCHE DES CHAMPS. *Bartramia longicauda.* L, 11·50. Plate XXIII B. A rather large, ochraceous shore bird inhabiting the upland fields and prairies.

Figure 273
Upland Plover; scale, ½.

*Distinctions.* About the size of a Greater Yellow-legs, strongly ochraceous in colour, with a bill rather shorter than the head. It can hardly be confused with any other species. The first primaries are saw-toothed marked with dark on a ground of white (Figure 274). The much larger Long-billed and Hudsonian Curlews are the only other shore birds with this wing-quill saw-toothing (*See* Figures 270, 271), but the ground colour is buff instead of white.

*Field Marks.* A rather large, buff-coloured wader with bill about as long as head, much smaller than either the curlews or the godwits. Unlike other shore birds, it inhabits high ground. On the ground it has a short-legged, round-headed appearance and an action that suggests a young Prairie Chicken rather than a wader.

*Distribution.* North and South America. Breeding irregularly and locally across the continent, from far south of the border north to Alaska and southern Mackenzie.

Though the name "plover" is commonly accepted, this species is a true sandpiper, aberrant in habit, having deserted the shores and mud-flats for the dry uplands. The term Bartramian Sandpiper is a more satisfactory name, honouring a great ornithologist and expressing the true relationship of the bird. It is one of the most attractive of the prairie inhabitants. It has long, loud, clear whistles, variously modulated, which

Figure 274
First primary of Upland Plover, from below; natural size.

it gives in the spring and early summer. Sometimes these notes are accompanied by a remarkable dance flight; at other times they are given from the ground or some slight elevation such as the top of a fence post, where, with wings raised over the back, it poses in statuesque grace. It is a confirmed grasshopper destroyer and is probably worth much more in that capacity than as an article of food.

263. **Spotted Sandpiper.** PEWIT. PEET-WEET. TEETER. TIP-UP. LA MAUBÈCHE TACHETÉE (Alouette branle-queue). *Actitis macularia.* L, 7·50. Plate XXIV A.

*Distinctions.* Adults have decidedly round breast spots and a slight greenish lustre on the back. Young autumn birds resemble the Solitary, but are distinguished by white instead of barred axillars (Compare with Figure 276).

*Field Marks.* Size and distinct round spots on breast. When flying it may be distinguished from the Solitary Sandpiper, which it most resembles, by the white line along the ends of the secondaries and the much smaller amount of black and white barring on the tail. The Spotted Sandpiper teeters constantly, whereas the Solitary nods commonly, and teeters only occasionally. In this queer, spasmodic action, which seems more or less involuntary, the legs are momentarily flexed and the forepart of the body is jerked down as the tail is jerked up. This action is indulged in continually. Standing at ease on a stone at the water's edge it teeters; every pause in its little excursions is filled with a succession of teeters; and it stops even in full career to punctuate with a teeter. Its wing stroke is distinctive; its stiffly held, down-curved wings at the bottom of each stroke being very different from the long, flowing beat of any other similar wader.

*Nesting.* Slight hollow in ground at no great distance from water in the shelter of a clump of shrub or bunch of grass.

*Distribution.* Breeds over the whole of Canada north to tree limit. Common throughout its range.

This is the commonest summer sandpiper in Canada; occasional pairs are to be found along the smallest streams. It frequents all kinds of ground; sand beaches, gravelly reaches, mud-flats, or rocky shores. Almost any small sandpiper seen in summer near our waters may be provisionally put down as this species unless there are good grounds for other identification. Its habit of bobbing its body up and down occasionally, even when apparently at rest, or more rapidly when excited, has given it the common name "Tip-up." Its white-barred wings, peculiar flight, with a few quick beats followed by a short sail on decurved wings, and its loud, triumphant "*Pewit-pewit-pewit*" as it alights on the stream margin well ahead of the observer are familiar to all. One can chase it from point to point for some distance from its home ground, when, joined by its mate, it will circle well around the disturber and return to the place from which it started.

The French-Canadian well-known folk song "Alouette" is said to refer to this species. Of course, this is a popular misapplication of an Old World name to a New World form, for the Spotted Sandpiper is not even distantly related to the lark which is the real meaning of the French word.

Figure 275
Field marks of:
*a*, Spotted Sandpiper; *b*, Solitary Sandpiper.

*Economic Status.* Though normally frequenting water edges it is often seen in the adjacent fields, running between the furrows of newly turned earth or rows of growing crops. Its food consists mainly, if not entirely, of insects; hence it is beneficial to the farmer. The species has not suffered from shooting, probably because of its small size and non-flocking habits, and it seems to hold its own even in the most cultivated sections.

256. **Solitary Sandpiper.** LE CHEVALIER SOLITAIRE. *Tringa solitaria.* L, 8·40. A small Sandpiper of same general colour design as the Yellow-legs but much smaller; back darker, less mottled with light; rump same colour as back, less white in tail.

Figure 276

Barred axillars of Solitary Sandpiper; natural size.

*Distinctions.* Back dark brown, almost black with slight green sheen, but finely speckled with white, ochre, or rusty-ochre spots. The best specific distinction is barring of the axillar feathers under the wing (Figure 276), which occurs in no other comparable species.

*Field Marks.* A small black and white sandpiper with the same nodding habits as the two Yellow-legs (which see), but not the constant body-teetering of the Spotted Sandpiper, with which it is most likely to be confused. It nods continually but teeters only occasionally, instead of the contrary. It is also without the white bars on the wing that are so conspicuous in that species in flight, but shows more white barring on the tail (Figure 275b). The flight is a long, sweeping wing-beat more like that of the Yellow-legs than with stiff, down-curved wings like the Spotted.

*Nesting.* The nesting of this species was unknown until it was discovered recently that it builds in old nests of robins and other birds in bushes at some distance from the ground, as does the Green Sandpiper of Europe.

*Distribution.* North and South America. Presumably breeding across the continent, but actual nesting instances are rare. Northern and western Alberta and northern Saskatchewan have the only well-substantiated records. In migration more or less common throughout southern Canada.

Figure 277

Marbled primaries of Western Solitary Sandpiper, from below; natural size.

*SUBSPECIES.* Two subspecies of the Solitary Sandpiper are recognized. The Eastern Solitary Sandpiper (le Chevalier solitaire de l'Est) *Tringa solitaria solitaria* occupying most of the continent and the Western Solitary (le Chevalier solitaire de l'Ouest) *Tringa solitaria cinnamomea* from the eastern sides of the mountains west. In migration both forms occur throughout British Columbia and Alberta and the breeding distribution of the two forms is not well defined. The Western Solitary is characterized by slightly larger size; white spotting on back being more or less tinged with rusty-ochre in juvenility, and white marbling or blotching on base of under surface of first primaries (Figure 277). This latter, although it may not be present in all *cinnamomea,* never occurs in Eastern *solitaria.* None of these subspecific characteristics is absolutely determinative and an average of them should be sometimes taken in identification.

As implied by the name, this species is a rather solitary bird, being found, even in migration time, in individuals or pairs rather than in flocks. It is a mud haunter and is the only wader except the Spotted Sandpiper that is commonly seen about such small waters as drainage ditches, or along the edges of flooded woods.

259. **Wandering Tattler.** LE CHEVALIER ERRANT. *Heteroscelus incanus.* L, 10·50. A rather large, grey wader. The adult is an even slate-grey above, from tail to crown, without pattern or design. Below and flanks white, closely crossed with irregular bars of the same colour as the back, changing to fine stripes up foreneck and sparse speckles on throat. The juvenile is similar, but the barring below is replaced by a suffusion of even light grey on flanks, across breast, and up foreneck.

*Distinctions.* In spring the heavy grey barring below is mistakable for no other species. The Stilt Sandpiper is the only other wader with breast so barred, but it is much smaller and the colour is warm brown instead of slate-grey. In juvenility, the Wandering Tattler is rather like an autumn Knot, but the grey is decidedly darker, plumbeous rather than ash-grey, with practically no pattern, and the rump is the same colour as the tail and back. The autumn Surf-bird has also a general resemblance to the autumn Tattler, but has a white rump, considerable white in the wings, a well-streaked throat, and a closely spotted or striped breast.

*Field Marks.* A rather large grey wader; adult heavily barred below. Juvenile, white below with faint breast suffusion, but no other conspicuous characters. Bill rather longer than head.

*Distribution.* Rocky coasts and islands of the Pacific. It breeds in interior of Alaska and the Yukon, but its nest has only lately been found. It migrates down our British Columbia coast, but never occurs inland except as noted above. A purely maritime species except in the breeding season when some at least seem to go inland to nest; at other times it is confined to rocky shores.

Figure 278

Wandering Tattler; scale, ½.

**Adult** **Juvenile**

258. **Willet.** LE CHEVALIER À AILES BLANCHES. *Catoptrophorus semipalmatus.* L, 15. Plate XXIV B. A large, grey shore bird with white rump and pale tail and a conspicuous white bar across the wings.

**Figure 279**

Field marks of Willet.

*Distinctions.* There is no other species with which the Willet is likely to be confused. The general greyish and white colour and conspicuous black and white wings are perfectly distinctive even if the large size of the species be not sufficient identification.

*Field Marks.* A large grey and white wader with white rump and tail, and in flight with a flaring white bar across black wings (Figure 279).

*Distribution.* North and South America. Breeding from Nova Scotia in the east and the prairies in the west, southwards. Only a single record, from near Victoria, for British Columbia.

*SUBSPECIES.* The Eastern Willet (le Chevalier à ailes blanches de l'Est) *Catoptrophorus semipalmatus semipalmatus* occurs on the Atlantic coast and the Western Willet (le Chevalier à ailes blanches de l'Ouest) *Catoptrophorus semipalmatus inornatus*, slightly paler, in the interior and westward.

The case of the Eastern Willet has furnished us with a good object lesson in what may be accomplished by practical conservation. Up to a few years ago the Willet was deemed extinct north of Virginia. About 1916 the existence of a few breeding pairs on the Nova Scotia coast was called to our attention. Efforts to preserve them were made by special officers, admirably seconded by local residents, especially the late H. A. P. Smith, of Digby. The birds began to increase immediately and the future of this once depleted eastern race is hopeful. The Western Willet is not an uncommon bird on our prairies today, but, like the Godwit and the Long-billed Curlew, it offers great temptation to the occasional pot-hunter, and unless he can be controlled it is doubtful how long the Willet will survive in appreciable numbers. It is one of the three big waders that are so characteristic of the great prairies, the other two being the Marbled Godwit and the Long-billed Curlew. It loves to stand on the edge of the muddy water, and raise its striking black and white wings, banner-like, over its back, and pose spectacularly. Passing by in the bright sunshine, its white barred wings flash like a heliograph message. The most characteristic note is a long, musically whistled *"Pill-will-willet."* Sometimes this is heard on a still night, and when broken and softened by distance it sounds remarkably like the mournful plaint of the Whip-poor-will.

254. **Greater Yellow-legs.** GREATER TELL-TALE. LE GRAND CHEVALIER À PATTES JAUNES. *Totanus melanoleucus.* L, 14. Plate XXV A. A large, graceful wader, practically black and white in fine pattern, with long yellow legs.

*Distinctions.* Size, long yellow legs, and the lack of any buffy or rusty anywhere mark the yellow-legs. In autumn, the breast marks may be veiled and indistinct. Almost identical in coloration with the Lesser Yellow-legs, from which it is best separated by size. The bill of this species, especially the lower line of the under mandible, is very slightly upturned, but that of the Lesser is straight (Figure 280, compare with 281).

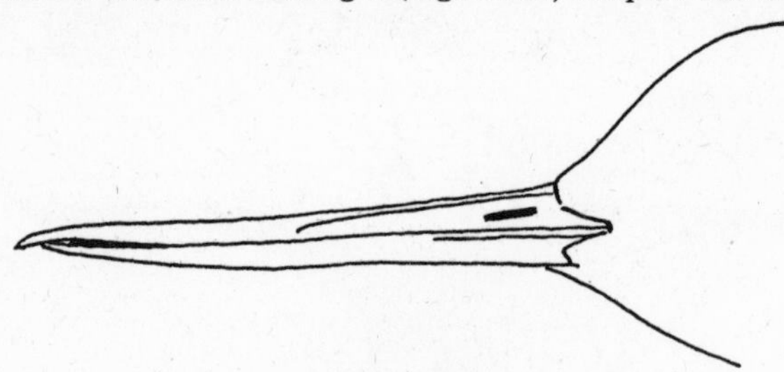

**Figure 280**
**Bill of Greater Yellow-legs; natural size.**

*Field Marks.* Long, slender, yellow legs entire lack of ochraceous or warm brown colours, and the large amount of white on tail and rump. When once acquainted with it, its flight is quite recognizable and its musically whistled notes are distinctive. The two yellow-legs are separable by size and by the slightly up-turned bill of this species. Both yellow-legs, together with the Solitary Sandpiper, have the strange habit of nodding and teetering. This consists, at irregular but frequent intervals, of a quick, spasmodic nodding of the head, or a momentary flexure of the legs and a simultaneous tilting upward of the tail. The nodding in these species is far more common than the teetering. It is indulged in at all times and in nearly all circumstances. Even when in repose, ever so often a slight nodding movement of the head can be observed; but when excited and nervous, scarcely a movement can be made without being preceded by an involuntary dip, and in pauses between action or in moments of irresolution the nodding becomes almost frantic.

*Distribution.* North and South America. Breeds across the continent, from the Gulf of St. Lawrence, the north edge of the prairies, and central British Columbia northward. Much less common than the Lesser Yellow-legs. Migrates throughout southern Canada.

The Greater Yellow-legs is one of the best known shore birds. Owing to its size and comparative numbers it is sought by sportsmen and it seems to have withstood their attacks better than many other apparently equally well-adapted species. It prefers marshy shores and mud to open sand and may be seen far out on the flats, wading about thigh deep, in water too deep for smaller waders. Its clear, flute-like, tremolo whistle in a descending scale is a sound to accelerate the pulse of any true sportsman or bird student. This species does not seem so numerous as, and is certainly more wary than, the Lesser Yellow-legs; otherwise this description will do for both.

255. **Lesser Yellow-legs.** LITTLE TELL-TALE. LE PETIT CHEVALIER À PATTES JAUNES. *Totanus flavipes.* L, 10·75. Almost exactly like the Greater Yellow-legs, but smaller in size.

*Distinctions.* Ordinarily, distinguished from the Greater Yellow-legs only by smaller size. Careful comparison will show that the bill is perfectly straight, whereas that of the Greater is very slightly up-turned (Figure 281, compare with 280).

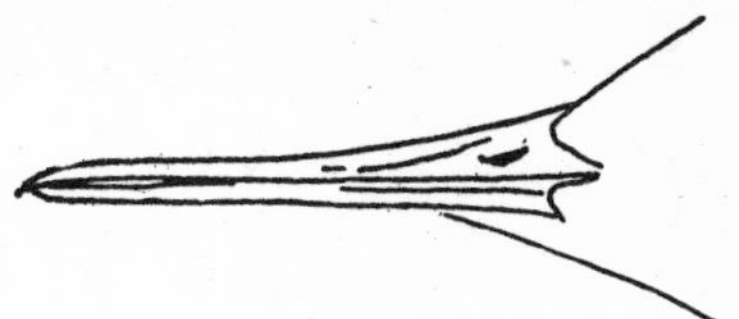

Figure 281
Bill of Lesser Yellow-legs; natural size.

*Field Marks.* Long, slender, yellow legs; entire lack of ochre or brown in coloration and large amount of white in tail and on rump will identify it as one of the two Yellow-legs; smaller size and perfectly straight bill as the Lesser. The Lesser Yellow-legs has the same nodding and teetering habits as the Greater, which see.

*Nesting.* On the ground.

*Distribution.* North and South America. Breeds from the Gulf of St. Lawrence, the northern edge of prairies, and probably central British Columbia northward. Migrates throughout southern Canada. The breeding ranges of these two yellow-legs are not very well delimitated. *See* previous species.

234. **Knot.** RED-BREASTED PLOVER. ROBIN SNIPE. LA MAUBÈCHE À POITRINE ROUSSE. *Calidris canutus.* L, 10·50. A medium-sized sandpiper. Spring adult, brick-red

Figure 282
Knot; scale, ½.
Adult

Figure 283
Bill of Knot; natural size.

throat and breast; abdomen and undertail-coverts, white. Above, finely mottled with black, greys, and light ochre running into stripes on crown. Uppertail-coverts, not including lower back, white, barred with black. Autumn birds entirely different; pale ashy grey above from crown to rump with very little pattern; feathers of back slightly edged with white, usually backed by fine black line giving an impression of a series of pale semicircles. All white below; faintly and obscurely striped across breast and up throat.

*Distinctions.* Spring birds can be confused only with the similarly red-breasted Dowitcher, but are easily distinguished by shorter bill (Figure 283, compare with 294). In autumn, by short bill; lighter, more even grey above, with the faint semicircles on back and grey rump. The breast-band is faint, being formed of fine stripes instead of an over-all clouding.

On the west coast in autumn it may be confused with the Wandering Tattler and the Surf-bird, both of which have the same general coloration, including suggestions of light semicircles on the back. The bill, between 1 and 1½ inches long, is shorter than that of the Tattler and longer than that of the Surf-bird (Figure 263). The grey of the back is more ashy than either, especially of the Tattler which is inclined towards bluish grey. The breast is intermediate between the two—faintly striped instead of heavily marked as in the Surf-bird, or evenly bluish grey as in the Tattler. The best distinctions, however, are the uppertail-coverts. In the Knot these are white, irregularly barred, and marked with dark; in the Surf-bird they are pure white, and in the Tattler grey, the same colour as the back.

*Field Marks.* In spring, red breast, and bill not much longer than head. In autumn, even light grey coloration above, without definite white spots or lines, and a short bill. Rump light in general effect but not white, as in the Surf-bird, and not extending up the back as in the Dowitcher.

*Nesting.* On the ground.

*Distribution.* Northern and southern hemispheres. In America, across the continent, breeding on the Arctic Islands, migrating throughout the prairie interior and the coasts, but more common on the latter. A bird of extraordinary range, wintering in South Africa, Patagonia, and New Zealand.

235. **Eastern Purple Sandpiper.** WINTER SNIPE. ROCK SNIPE. LA MAUBÈCHE DES ROCHES DE L'EST. *Arquatella maritima.* L, 9. A rather small sandpiper. Adult in spring: above, dark brown variegated on edges and tips of feathers with pale buff or white, sometimes a little rusty ochre; below, white with broad breast and upper abdominal band of ashy grey with indefinite or blended brown spots extending along flanks and in fine streaks up throat. Rump dark, inner secondaries largely white. Legs dull orange to olive ochre. In autumn and winter: above, black with purple iridescence, feather edged with greyish; below, white with broad breast-band of ashy grey.

Figure 284
Atlantic Purple Sandpiper; scale, ½.

*Distinctions.* A strictly maritime east coast species. The darkest of the eastern grey sandpipers. General irregular blotchiness of the breast in spring and the even greyness in the autumn and winter. Similar to the winter plumage of the Red-backed Sandpiper, but darker, and a distinct purplish sheen to the black feather centres of the back.

*Field Marks.* General dark colour and short, yellowish legs. In flight with considerable amount of white on inner secondaries. It comes on the southeastern Canada coast very late in autumn and in winter on rocky, surf-beaten shores where no other species of shore bird is to be expected.

*Nesting.* On the ground amongst the rocks.

*Distribution.* Atlantic regions of northern hemisphere. Nests on the Arctic Islands, winters on our eastern sea coast. Very few records away from the sea.

A. Lewis's Woodpecker; scale, $\frac{1}{3}$

B. Yellow-bellied Sapsucker; scale, $\frac{1}{3}$

Female Male

PLATE XL

A. Red-breasted Sapsucker; scale, $\frac{1}{3}$

B. Hairy Woodpecker; scale, $\frac{1}{3}$

Harris's Woodpecker Northern Hairy Woodpecker

Both males

235b. **Western Purple Sandpiper.** LA MAUBÈCHE DES ROCHES DE L'OUEST. *Arquatella ptilocnemis.* L, 9. A rather small sandpiper. Adult in spring: above, dark brown, variegated on edges and tips of feathers with a little whitish or greyish and much deep rusty; below, white, blotched or spotted with grey, rusty and black in variable proportions without much pattern across breast and along flanks, throat paler. Legs dull yellowish or yellowish green. In autumn and winter almost identical with Atlantic Purple Sandpiper, which see.

*Distinctions.* A strictly maritime west coast species. In spring strongly reddish above, variously blotched on breast and with a more or less black abdominal patch. Much like the Red-backed Sandpiper, but a little larger and with a shorter bill. The red on the back is not so extensive and is confined to the feather borders, never barred across them, and the breast usually contains from traces of, to considerable, reddish.

Figure 285
Aleutian Purple Sandpiper; scale, ½.

In autumn or winter it may be distinguished from other similarly coloured grey and white waders, such as the Knot, Red-backed Sandpiper, Wandering Tattler, and Surf-bird by size—larger than the Red-backed, smaller than any of the others. From all except the Surf-bird it may be distinguished by its darker coloration, sharp, coarse spotting on lower breast and flanks, and the dark, almost black, centre to the feathers of the back. Besides having a darker back and being smaller, it is infallibly separated from the Surf-bird by having a dark instead of a white rump.

*Field Marks.* In spring, general suffused dark colour and short, yellowish legs. In autumn, it comes very late and winters on the rocky coast where it is likely to be confused only with the Wandering Tattler and the Surf-bird. It is smaller and darker coloured, especially across the breast, than the former and, unlike the latter, has a black instead of a white rump.

*Nesting.* On the ground amongst the rocks.

*Distribution.* Pacific regions of northern hemisphere. Breeds in the Aleutian and Pribilof Islands and migrates down the coasts. Winters along our coast.

*SUBSPECIES.* This species has hitherto been regarded as a western subspecies of *maritima* the Eastern Purple Sandpiper, but in the last edition of the Check-list it has been raised to a full species, a proceeding with which the present writer is in full accord. Two subspecies of this species are recognized: *Arquatella ptilocnemis couesi*, the Aleutian Sandpiper (la Maubèche aléoutienne), wintering on our coast; and *Arquatella ptilocnemis ptilocnemis*, the Pribilof Sandpiper (la Maubèche des îles Pribylov), a more heavily coloured bird that has not been recognized on Canadian shores.

The Western Purple Sandpiper and its races are birds of the rocky islet shores. It is a late autumn arrival and spends the winter on the sea-girt rocks of the outer Pacific coast in company with Black Turnstones and Surf-birds.

238. **Sharp-tailed Sandpiper.** LA MAUBÈCHE À QUEUE FINE. *Pisobia acuminata.* L, 8·50. A small sandpiper of same general size and coloration as the Buff-breasted, but with the ochres less extensive and solid. Back, dark brown with many feather edges of ochre and rusty. Below, white tinged with ruddy brown, strongest on breast where it is finely and brokenly streaked—not nearly as uniform or complete as in the Pectoral Sandpiper but more than in the Buff-breasted. Crown, strongly rufous, bordered by a light superciliary line. Tail pointed and composed of pointed feathers.

*Distinctions.* Most like the Pectoral or Buff-breasted Sandpipers, but with red crown and pointed tail. The breast is far more sparsely spotted and the breast-band more diffuse and inconspicuous than that of the Pectoral. Separated from the Buff-breasted by light superciliary line, red cap, more specklings on throat, and without the beautiful under-wing pattern of that species, back striped rather than with scale-like rings.

*Field Marks.* A little wader, similar to the Buff-breasted in colour, but of different habit, habitat, and outline. Has a reddish cap, a light line over the eye, and a white chin.

*Distribution.* Eastern parts of eastern hemisphere. Breeds on the Siberian coast and only occasionally wanders down to our shores. We have a few records from the vicinity of Vancouver Island and Queen Charlotte Islands. Not to be expected in the interior.

239. **Pectoral Sandpiper.** GRASS SNIPE. LA MAUBÈCHE À POITRINE CENDRÉE. *Pisobia malanotos.* L, 9. A small sandpiper with a distinct, plainly defined, buffy band, heavily and evenly streaked with fine, brown lines across breast and foreneck. Above—dark brown striped with many buff and whitish feather edges, rusty in autumn juveniles. White below.

Figure 286
Pectoral Sandpiper;
scale, ½.

*Distinctions.* A brown-backed sandpiper, with buffy breast-band sharply defined against white throat and underparts. Two other sandpipers—the White-rumped and Baird's—have similar breast-bands. In the White-rumped, the ground colour of the band is dull white or ashy rather than buff, the pencilling is sharper, and usually in greater contrast; it also has a white rump which is absent on the Pectoral. In Baird's, the breast-band is similarly buffy, but decidedly less pronounced, and sharply defined at its borders; the striping is obscure and very much blended and the back does not give a striped effect. The Pectoral, as a rule, is decidedly larger than either of the above, but there is considerable variation in size in the species. A bill of one inch or over will separate this species from the others.

*Field Marks.* A small sandpiper, with broad, dull breast-band, a striped back, rather rusty in autumn, and no other particular recognition marks. Usually found in grassy marshes.

*Distribution.* North and South America, breeding on the Arctic and Alaska coasts from the mouth of the Yukon to the Mackenzie, migrating throughout the whole of southern Canada.

The Pectoral Sandpiper like Wilson's Snipe is to be found in wet, grassy meadows or on mud flats, rarely on sandy beaches. In breeding season it develops a neck sac that can be inflated to an extraordinary extent, and it indulges in a remarkable flight song. Many of the waders have very interesting flight songs, but these are confined to the breeding season and the immediate vicinity of the nest and are seldom heard by the ordinary observer.

240. **White-rumped Sandpiper.** BONAPARTE'S SANDPIPER. LA MAUBÈCHE À CROUPION BLANC. *Pisobia fusicollis.* A small sandpiper. White below, brown above, variegated with feather edges of shades of buff, rusty, and white. In spring, breast and flanks sharply and clearly streaked with dark brown. Rump always white. In autumn, the breast streaking is often suffused with a vague breast-band of light ashy or even pale buffy.

*Distinctions.* Very much like an enlarged Least Sandpiper (Plate XXV B). May be mistaken, especially in autumn, for either the Pectoral or Baird's Sandpipers, but easily separable from them by the white rump. The Stilt Sandpiper also has a white rump, is of similar size, and in autumn of similar general coloration, but has a considerably longer bill (over 1·25, instead of under) with a slightly enlarged tip (*See* Figure 295), and long legs reaching beyond the tips of the closed wings.

Figure 287
White-rumped Sandpiper;
scale, ½.

*Field Marks.* A small sandpiper lacking strongly determinate coloration, with a short bill, about the length of the head, and a white rump.

*Distribution.* North and South America. Breeding on the central Arctic coast from the Mackenzie eastward, migrating through the interior and the east. More common in the eastern than the western prairies and so far not recorded from British Columbia.

Commonly seen with the Least and Semipalmated Sandpipers on muddy rather than sandy shores.

241. **Baird's Sandpiper.** LA MAUBÈCHE DE BAIRD. *Pisobia bairdi.* L, 7·40. A small sandpiper, somewhat similar to a large Least Sandpiper. Below, white; above, brown, variegated with feather edges of shades of buff, rusty, and white. A suffused band of pale buff across breast, softly streaked with darker.

*Distinctions.* The buff breast-band is suggestive of the Pectoral Sandpiper, but it is never so extensive nor so sharply defined and the striping is always soft and obscure. In some conditions of plumage it may look like the White-rumped Sandpiper, but the black instead of white rump will separate it easily.

*Field Marks.* In life, like a large Least or Semipalmated Sandpiper, but with a buffy breast suffusion and a scaly rather than striped appearance on the back. It commonly accompanies flocks of "peeps." Often in life like a Buff-breasted Sandpiper owing to white underparts being in shadow, but with black instead of dull yellow legs and with a whitish chin.

*Distribution.* North and South America. Breeding in western Arctics. Migrates along both coasts and through the interior.

Figure 288
Baird's Sandpiper; scale, ½.

PEEPS

"Peeps" is a colloquial, collective name applied to the smallest species of sandpipers. They do not form a systematic group but are similar enough in habit and general appearance to be popularly grouped together.

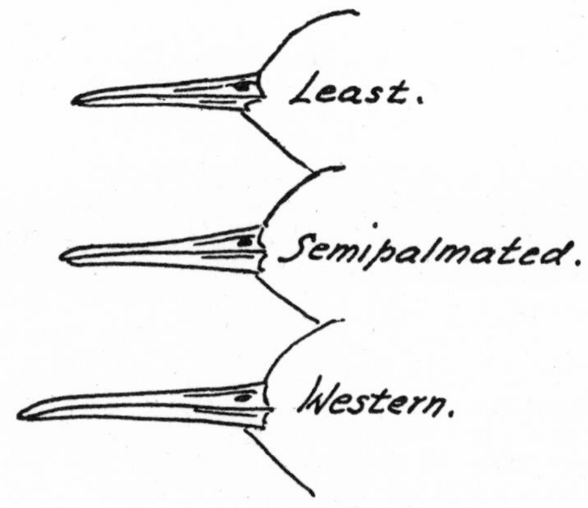


Figure 289
Characteristic bills of Peeps; natural size.

NOTE. These bill sizes are not by any means infallible. There is considerable individual variation and occasional Semipalmated, or even Western, Sandpipers may have bills smaller than some Leasts. In life it is claimed that the bills of the Least and Western are appreciably decurved, but that of the Semipalmated is straight or slightly upturned. It takes careful observation to note this, however.

They are minute shore birds, not larger than small sparrows. They come in immense flocks and cover the mud-flats and sand-bars with a dense, busy crowd, weaving complicated patterns of delicate footprints in the soft mud. They follow a retreating wave to garner the roughly tumbled insect life in the undertow, and glide back in calm haste, just ahead of the next inundation. They take advantage of every ebb and flow, and though not unduly hurried never overstay their opportunity, but judge each moment with exactness. Thus they work along a shoreline, examining its every inch. They are confiding, rather than brave, unconcerned where other species would be fearful. They fly suddenly in momentary panic with a chorus of fairy peepings, but the next moment forget their alarm, and return to the same spot immediately to continue rather than resume their interrupted microscopic searchings. By taking station close by the course along which they are working and remaining reasonably quiet, it is possible to have the whole, happy, busy, little company pass in close review. When they take flight, they start as if at a pre-arranged signal, with a shower of rippling little whistles, and dash off in a compact body, turning and wheeling as if moved by a single impulse. One instant they show a cloud of dark backs, and then, as they bank on another turn, every white underbody is simultaneously presented, and the flock flashes in the sun like a heliograph. After a few such turns they settle down again, and proceed immediately with the serious duty of cleaning up the beach as if not a moment should be lost.

Some of them remain with us almost into summer, and, in the autumn, they return long before most observers have any inkling that the migrations are under way. The first of June may see the last spring straggler, the first of July their autumn advance guard, and by August first their migrations are well under way. The species that associate together and are usually included as "peeps" are the Least, Semipalmated, and Western Sandpipers. They are often accompanied by Baird's, White-rumped, and others. Some of these species are very difficult to tell apart in life and, unless the observer has unlimited time and patience to examine critically the fine details of every flock he meets, many of them will be passed by as simply "peeps." In general, the Least is the darkest, the Western the reddest, and the Semipalmated the greyest, of the three.

242. **Least Sandpiper.** MUD PEEP. GREEN-LEGGED PEEP. LA MAUBÈCHE MINIME. *Pisobia minutilla.* L, 6. Plate XXV B. The smallest of our sandpipers.

*Distinctions.* Not easy to separate from the Semipalmated or the Western Sandpipers, but slightly smaller than either. The best distinction is the unwebbed toes (Figure 290, compare Figure 296). The legs are olive-green or ochre-yellow instead of dull black. In general, the Least is (excepting the Western Sandpiper, which is purely a west coast bird) the brownest, in some cases decidedly ruddy on the back. The breast-band often tends towards buffy and the stripes are rather diffused. The bill is slightly smaller and more slender than that of the Semipalmated and decidedly smaller than that of the Western (*See* Figure 289).

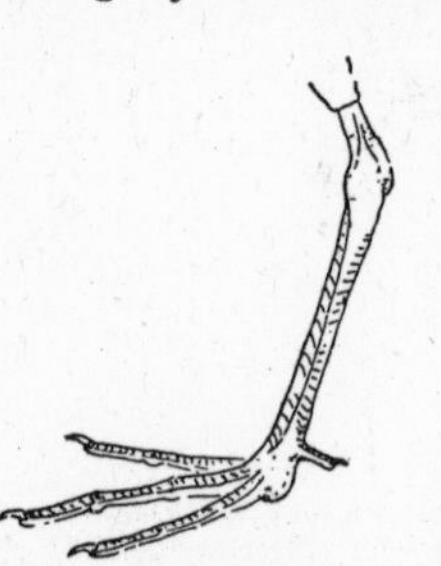

Figure 290
Foot of Least Sandpiper; natural size.

*Field Marks.* Very small size characterizes it as a peep. Averaging on the back darker and redder, ruddy rather than greyish; more decided breast-band with more diffuse striping than Semipalmated, darker and not quite as red as the Western. Careful observation under favourable circumstances will show dark olive-green legs.

*Distribution.* North and South America. Breeds across the continent south of the Barren Grounds. Migrates through the interior and along the coasts.

One of the most numerous of shore birds. Probably its diminutive size has protected it from the sportsman, though from its dense flocks numbers can be obtained with a single shot. It frequents sandy beaches and open mud-flats and is a tame and confiding bird. It associates largely with flocks of other species, though when disturbed separates from them to rejoin the company later.

244. **Curlew Sandpiper.** LE BÉCASSEAU COCORLI. *Erolia testacea.* L, 8. Small red-breasted sandpiper. Autumn birds greyish brown above and white below.

*Distinctions.* Resembles the Knot or Dowitcher in having red breast, but much smaller and of more slender build.

*Distribution.* Breeds in Arctic Siberia. Of only casual occurrence in eastern Canada. More records from the Atlantic coast than inland, though there is one from Lake Ontario. It has never been reported from the Canadian west coast.

Figure 291
Curlew Sandpiper; scale, ½.

An Old World form occasionally seen in the New World. Said to resemble the Red-back in habit, but too scarce in eastern Canada to be looked for as a regular visitor. Any record of this species should be founded on definite specimens and subjected to rigid scrutiny.

243. **Dunlin.** BLACK-HEART PLOVER. LE BÉCASSEAU CINCLE. *Pelidna alpina.* L, 8. A small sandpiper. Spring adult, back extending to crown predominantly red; very finely striped across breast, up neck, and on face, with ashy brown on white. Throat white. Large black area occupying abdomen. Bill slightly down-curved (Figure 292).

In autumn plumage soft, uniform, light ashy grey all above and suffusing across breast; remainder white. Autumn adults usually have a few of the red summer feathers on the back. There is a juvenile plumage with black and buffy back and a spotted breast of which only traces remain when the birds come to us in the autumn.

Figure 292
Red-backed Sandpiper; scale, ½.
Autumn Spring

*Distinctions.* In spring, the predominantly red back, and the black abdominal patch are absolutely distinctive. No other species has so much red on back. The Western Purple Sandpiper has a blended dark area on the breast instead of the abdomen that does not cut sharply against the white above as it does on this species. The grey autumn plumage resembles that of several other species of similar size, but of them only the White-rumped and Sanderling ever show the clear, patternless (except for a few black and red-margined intrusive feathers), grey back. The former has a white rump, the grey of the latter is almost white, and the hind toe is absent. The other evenly grey-backed autumn sandpipers—Knot, Wandering Tattler, and Surf-bird—are all so much larger that no mistake can be made. The moderately long (over 1¼ inches), slightly decurved bill is generally characteristic.

*Field Marks.* In spring, red back, and black abdominal patch contrasting sharply with nearly white breast. In autumn, small size, moderately long (longer than head) and slightly decurved bill, and patternless light grey coloration above.

*Distribution.* Eastern and western hemispheres. In America, across the Arctic, migrating down both coasts and through the interior. Common migrant in Manitoba, but authenticated records for Alberta and Saskatchewan are few. Not reported from interior of British Columbia, but common on the coast.

*SUBSPECIES.* The Red-backed Sandpiper or American Dunlin (le Bécasseau à dos roux) *Pelidna alpina sakhalina*, differs from the European race by its slightly larger size. It extends to the east Siberian coast.

This species frequents sand-bars, mud-flats, or tide-meadows. It is among the latest shore birds to arrive both in spring and autumn.

231. **Dowitcher.** RED-BREASTED SNIPE. ROBIN SNIPE. LE BÉCASSEAU ROUX. *Limnodromus griseus.* L, 10·50. Spring adult: throat, breast, and all underparts strongly brick-red. Back and upperparts, dark brown with feather edges of various shades of

Figure 293
Dowitcher; scale, ½.
Spring adult

reddish ochre. Tail and rump finely barred with black and white. Tail feathers tinged with reddish at tip and dark bars disappearing on lower back. Autumn plumage—dull grey on back, more or less interspersed with brown and ruddy ochre of summer plumage. Head, neck, breast, and flanks, lighter grey. Chin lighter than breast or face. Autumn adults often show the summer red-breasted plumage, but worn, faded, and interspersed with grey.

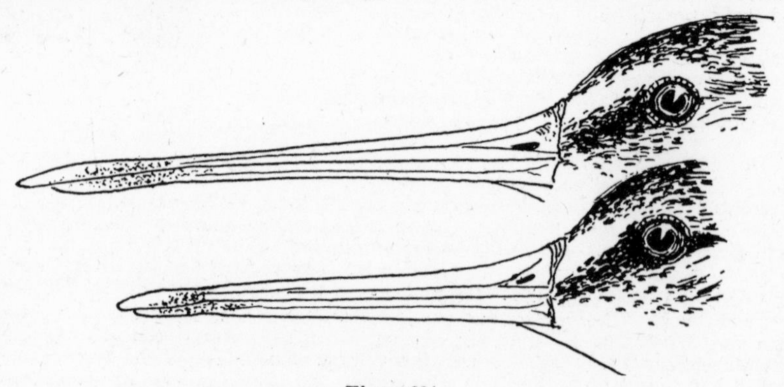

Figure 294
Bills of Long-billed and Short-billed Dowitchers; natural size.

*Distinctions.* Because of great length of bill (2·15-3·0) to be mistaken only for Wilson's Snipe. In spring, the red underparts make the Dowitcher unmistakable for that species, and in autumn the even grey breast, the lack of definite colour pattern on the back, and the pure white lower back barred with black on rump and tail are distinctive. In spring, the Knot has a similar red breast, but the bill is much shorter, scarcely over 1·50 (Compare Figure 294 with 283).

In the autumn the Wandering Tattler (to be met with only on the west coast) has a grey appearance similar to the Dowitcher at that season, but is a clearer ashy grey; the bill is much shorter and the rump and tail are the same colour as the back.

*Field Marks.* About the same size, general outline, and length of bill as Wilson's Snipe, but with white lower back. Generally found on bare mud-flats where Wilson's Snipe is seldom seen. Rarely seen in grassy meadows.

*Nesting.* On the ground.

*Distribution.* North and South America, breeding principally in the Arctic. Migrating along the coast and the interior, throughout Canada.

*SUBSPECIES.* The American Ornithologists' Union Check-list recognizes two subspecies: the Short-billed Dowitcher (le Bécasseau roux à bec court) *Limnodromus griseus griseus*, an Atlantic Coast race, and the Long-billed Dowitcher (le Bécasseau roux à long bec) *Limnodromus griseus scolopaceus*, a western one. These races are differentiated mostly by the length of the bill (Figure 294), but the eastern race is recognized in migration throughout the west. Specimens from the prairies to the Pacific coast show such a mixture of bill lengths that doubts are raised as to the existence of the two races. Birds breeding at the mouth of Yukon River, Alaska, are said to be of the Long-billed type. Colonies recently discovered nesting only some 60 miles northwest of Edmonton, Alberta, and on the west side of Hudson Bay are of the Short-billed group, but have recently been described as a third subspecies, the Interior Dowitcher (Le Bécasseau roux des prairies) *Limnodromus griseus hendersoni*.

233. **Stilt Sandpiper.** LA MAUBÈCHE À ÉCHASSES. *Micropalama himantopus*. L, 8·25. A small sandpiper. Spring adult with brown markings on a ground of dull white and cream; underparts with regular and narrow bars that change to fine obscure stripings on foreneck and minute spotting on throat. A vague rufous band across nape and continuing over eye, and another of same colour under eye and over ear (Figure 295). Rump, white, spotted with brown. Young autumn birds are entirely different, and so closely resemble several other species as to be difficult of separation by colour. Back, much like that of spring bird, brown with feather edges of ochre, cream, white, and rusty; incoming ashy grey winter plumage is likely to be intermixed and to predominate late in the season. Below, white, slightly tinged with tawny, which is most pronounced across breast with more or less striping. Head and neck a fine intermixture of ashy brown and dull white with little detail. The crown and a vague line through eye are dark and the superciliary line and throat light.

Figure 295
Stilt Sandpiper; scale, ½.
Autumn Spring
Above, broadened tip of bill.

*Distinctions.* The spring bird with its heavily brown-barred underparts is very distinctive. The autumn bird is much like the Pectoral, White-rumped, Baird's, or Red-backed Sandpipers, but from any of these it may be recognized by its long, yellow legs reaching nearly an inch or more beyond the tail, and the slight spatulate enlargement at the tip of the long bill, almost imperceptible, but very apparent to the touch (Figure 295). The rump may be almost pure white and bear a close resemblance to the White-rumped.

*Field Marks.* The regular and pronounced dark barring below is quite conspicuous in spring. When this detail cannot be seen, or in the autumn, the great length of leg furnishes the best field mark from all comparable waders, except the Lesser Yellow-legs which it may resemble in apparent size, length, and colour of legs, and white rump. It has a longer bill than any other sandpiper of similar size and in feeding may plunge its whole head and neck under water. It does not tip or nod.

*Nesting.* On the ground.

*Distribution.* Breeds in the western Arctic east to Hudson Bay, migrates mostly through the prairie interior. There are a few records for southern British Columbia.

246. **Semipalmated Sandpiper.** BLACK-LEGGED PEEP. LA PETITE MAUBÈCHE GRISE. *Ereunetes pusillus.* L, 6·30. Plate XXV B. Next to the smallest of our sandpipers, being only slightly larger than the Least (page 202).

*Distinctions.* Except on the Pacific coast, to be confused only with the Least Sandpiper. Compared with that species, slightly larger. The best distinction is the partial webbing of the toes that gives the name "Semipalmated" (Figure 296, compare with 290). Above, it is a greyer bird than the Least; the breast spotting is clearer and the white ground with less overwash. When overwash occurs it is greyish rather than buffy. Young birds may have slight buff breast-band, but the stripes are almost absent on it. The bill is slightly longer and thicker than the Least and the legs black instead of olive-green.

The Semipalmated is separated from the Western Sandpiper on the west coast with even greater difficulty than from the Least. The Semipalmated is smaller than the Western, but larger than the Least. The bill is considerably smaller (under rather than over 0·95 inch) (*See* Figure 289, page 201), the back rarely has an appreciable amount of red, and the breast spots in comparable plumages are not so sharp and clear cut. In high spring plumage the colour characters are plain, in autumn they are rather obscure; general size and size of bill make the best differentiation.

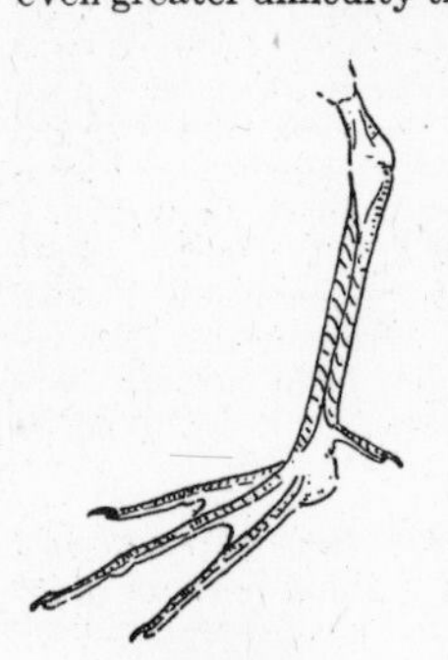

Figure 296
Foot of Semipalmated Sandpiper; natural size.

*Field Marks.* Away from the west coast, to be confused only with the Least Sandpiper. Larger size, greyer back, and, in spring, more sharply defined breast spotting. Legs black instead of olive-green. From Western by smaller size; in spring, by very much greyer back and less sharply defined breast spots; in autumn, size when possible to make direct comparison is the best criterion. One of the earliest of the migrant waders to arrive in the autumn.

*Distribution.* North and South America. Breeds on Arctic coast from Labrador to the mouth of the Yukon. Migrates through the interior and on both coasts. Common nearly everywhere in migration. Probably the commonest and most widely distributed of the Peeps.

247. **Western Sandpiper.** WESTERN PEEP. LA PETITE MAUBÈCHE GRISE DE L'OUEST. *Ereunetes mauri.* L, 6·50. Like the Semipalmated Sandpiper but larger, especially in the length of bill. In spring and in most young autumn birds, back strongly red, even redder than the Least, and with a well-defined reddish bar across nape.

*Distinctions.* Typical birds are easily recognized by their long bill (over 0·95 inch) (*See* Figure 289, page 201), large intermixture of red in black and across nape, and the heavy, sharp spotting of breast. Many specimens, however, are not so easily recognized and it is only by the aggregate of various characteristics that they can be determined.

*Field Marks.* The largest "peep," with bill longer than head, very red on back, and with sharply defined spotting on breast. Any one of these characters may be obscure or absent.

*Distribution.* North and South America. Breeds on northwest Alaskan coast. Of peculiar winter distribution. Occurs from California south and also on the Atlantic coast in migration as far north as New York, but as yet there are only a few casual records from the continental interior between and it is not known how they reach the extreme east from the far west coast.

262. **Buff-breasted Sandpiper.** LA MAUBÈCHE À POITRINE JAUNÂTRE. *Tryngites subruficollis.* L, 11·50. A small, buff-coloured sandpiper. A soft, light buff all below, strongest on breast. Above, from tail to crown, dark brown, nearly black, feathers heavily edged with light ochre. No conspicuous markings anywhere.

*Distinctions.* The only small sandpiper (about the size of Spotted) so evenly and extensively buff coloured. Further distinctions found on the underwing surface, which is mostly white but beautifully mottled and marbled with black (Figure 298), a character exhibited by no other shore bird.

PLATE XLI

A. Downy Woodpecker; scale, $\frac{1}{3}$

Male Female

B. Arctic Three-toed Woodpecker; scale, $\frac{1}{3}$

Female Male

Plate XLII

A. Eastern Kingbird; scale, $\frac{1}{4}$

B. Arkansas Kingbird; scale, $\frac{1}{3}$

*Field Marks.* As a rule an upland bird, but often seen with other waders on the shores. A round-headed, short-billed (bill shorter than head), buffy little wader, with dull yellow legs. Because of its upland habitat unlikely to be mistaken for anything except the Pectoral Sandpiper, but the buffy below is uniform and continuous over the underparts and not contrasted with the white throat and abdomen. On the beaches the species it is most likely to be confused with is Baird's Sandpiper; but it is more buffy, especially below, is without white throat, and has larger and rounder-appearing head.

*Distribution.* North and South America. Breeding on the Arctic coast, west of Hudson Bay. Migrates in limited numbers through the Prairie and Eastern Provinces of Canada. Occasional records from the coast of British Columbia.

Figure 297
Buff-breasted Sandpiper; scale, ½.

This is one of the rarest of the generally distributed sandpipers. We have scattered records of it right across Canada from practically everywhere except the interior of British Columbia. There is some doubt as to whether it ever was very common in the west, but it has certainly become less numerous of late years and instead of occasional large flocks only singles or small companies are now reported.

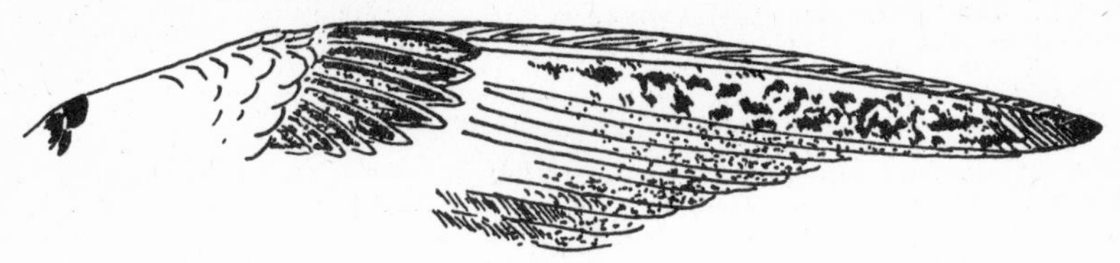

Figure 298
Underwing surface of Buff-breasted Sandpiper; natural size.

249. **Marbled Godwit.** LA BARGE MARBRÉE. *Limosa fedoa.* L, 18. Plate XXVI A. A very large, pink, buff, and brown wader with long, slightly up-turned bill.

*Distinctions.* In general appearance much like the curlews, but with slightly up-turned instead of decidedly down-turned bill. In colour, too unlike the Avocet, which also has an up-turned bill, ever to be confused with it. The only species it is likely to be confused with is its close relative, the Hudsonian Godwit. In spring, its breast is pinkish buff instead of chestnut-red. The wing quills are finely speckled or marbled with dark on pinkish buff (Figure 299), instead of being solidly dark, almost black. The tail and its upper coverts are barred with the pinkish buff and dark, instead of the tail being practically black and coverts white.

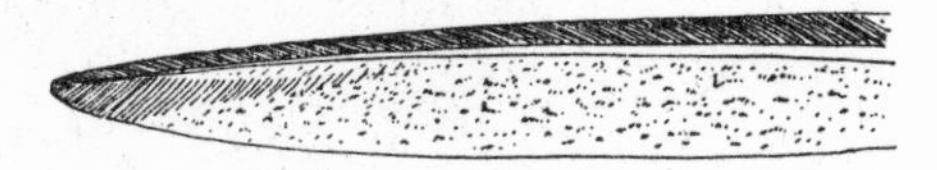

Figure 299
Marbled primary of Marbled Godwit; scale, ½.

In autumn, the Marbled Godwit is of the same general coloration as in spring, but slightly pinker and without the fine breast vermiculation. The autumn Hudsonian Godwits are almost pure white below with uniform shades of ashy elsewhere, though traces of the spring plumage often persist in the adults.

*Field Marks.* A large ochraceous and brown wader. Long, up-turned bill, yellow-orange at the base in spring, flesh-pink in autumn, separates it from the curlews; and general coloration and evenly coloured rump and tail of ochraceous barring from the black-tailed, white-rumped Hudsonian. Wings largely ochre instead of solid black.

*Distribution.* North America. In Canada, it breeds on the prairies. Rare in the interior of British Columbia, more common on the coast in migration.

A very conspicuous prairie bird. One cannot come within half a mile of its nest without both birds hurrying excitedly from afar, scolding and diving at the intruder. Their loud, exasperating "*eradica-radica-radica-radica*", varied with "*Your-crazy-crazy-crazy*", and confirmed by vociferous "*korect-korect*" sets all the prairie on the alert. The Godwit often becomes a decided nuisance to the ornithologist who is quietly stalking other and shyer species and finds his efforts fail through the senseless alarm of this meddler. However, it is only on such special occasions that we are aggrieved. At other times we feel only impatience at the heedless busy-bodies that rush into unnecessary danger and advertise what they should most artfully conceal. Too often this Godwit suffers from its lack of self control, for it offers a most tempting shot to the pot-hunter; an opportunity that is taken advantage of often enough to threaten the existence of the species.

250. **Bar-tailed Godwit.** LA BARGE À QUEUE BARRÉE. *Limosa laponica.* L, 15. Like the Hudsonian Godwit in general, but the uppertail-coverts decidedly streaked or barred with blackish, and axillars not solid black.

*Distinctions.* Large size and up-turned bill as a godwit. Mottled axillars and rump from the Hudsonian Godwit, and strongly marked blackish and white axillars and lack of general pinkish buff in body colour and under wings from the Marbled Godwit.

*Distribution.* Northern Europe and Asia to Alaska. There is a single record for near Vancouver in 1931.

*SUBSPECIES.* This is the Asian and Alaskan forms of the species, the Pacific Godwit (la Barge du Pacifique) *Limosa lapponica baueri.*

251. **Hudsonian Godwit.** LA BARGE HUDSONIENNE. *Limosa haemastica.* L, 15. In spring—upperparts, dark brown to crown, marked with more or less greyish or buffy and touches of rusty; underparts, brownish red, more or less barred with dark, and suffus-

**Figure 300**
Hudsonian Godwit; scale, ½.
**Spring adult**

ing up foreneck. Autumn—upperparts unmarked brownish grey; underparts, buffy white or dingy white, breast greyer.

*Distinctions.* Distinguished from the curlews by the slightly turned-up instead of distinctly turned-down bill; from the Marbled Godwit by the red underparts in spring, and at all seasons by the all-dark, white-shafted primaries without marbling (Compare with Figure 299) and white uppertail-coverts. This species shows almost endless variation between the above plumages, but suggestions of the spring coloration are usually recognizable in all except young birds.

*Field Marks.* Large size, straight or slightly turned-up bill, and white coverts at base of black tail, will separate this from either the curlews or the Marbled Godwit, which are the only species that are likely to be confused with it.

*Distribution.* North and South America. Breeds in the north from Mackenzie Valley eastward to Hudson Bay. Migrates through the prairies and the east, south to Patagonia.

The Hudsonian Godwit is a fine bird on the verge of extinction. As frequently happens, it seemed to disappear suddenly and before its growing scarcity was realized. It is doubtful whether shooting in this country was altogether responsible for this condition. When a species is greatly reduced in numbers by any cause, an otherwise comparatively unimportant adverse influence may suffice to snuff it out unexpectedly. Protection is ineffective when delayed so long that the breeding stock is too greatly reduced for recovery. This godwit disappeared before serious effects of western settlement could have occurred, and we can console ourselves with the reflection that its disappearance was probably due mostly to conditions on the Argentine pampas and in its winter quarters.

260. **Ruff** (*female*, **Reeve**). LE CHEVALIER COMBATTANT. *Philomachus pugnax.* L, 12·5. A rather large sandpiper. Male in breeding condition exceedingly variable in coloration, in fact it is said that no two ruffs are ever exactly alike in colour. With extraordinary feather ruff or frontal shield on neck and breast. This shield may be either black, white, or red, nearly immaculate or heavily barred with any of these colours. The female, called Reeve, is dull, dark sandy without any striking colours.

Figure 301

Reeve and Ruff; scale, ½.

*Distinctions.* The male in spring plumage is unmistakable. In other plumages, and the female, of general soft, earthy coloration, with breast evenly clouded or margined with faint, broad, scale-like crescents without indication of striping. In this plumage to be identified in Canada with great care. About the size of a knot, or larger, with unusually long, pale yellow legs with feet extending well beyond the tail tip.

*Distribution.* Eastern hemisphere. Of only accidental occurrence in Canada. There are individual records for Nova Scotia, New Brunswick, and southern Ontario.

248. **Sanderling.** LE SANDERLING. *Crocethia alba.* L, 8. In spring—upperparts, including crown, dark brown, variegated with much light rusty ochre, or white, or both. Below, white. Throat, neck, and upper breast overwashed with variable amounts of reddish ochre spotted with brown. The details of these colourings are exceedingly variable. The back may show enough of the various colours to make it either generally greyish, ochraceous, or rusty, and the usually coloured and spotted throat may be nearly immaculate white. The autumn bird is similar without much buffy or any reddish or ochraceous tint, it is pure white below and in front, and often predominantly grey to light ashy above.

*Distinctions.* From traces to strong washes of rusty on neck and around head in the spring, and the general whiteness in autumn. The Sanderling may be told from all other sandpipers by having three toes instead of four (Figure 303).

Figure 302
Sanderling; scale, ½.
Spring

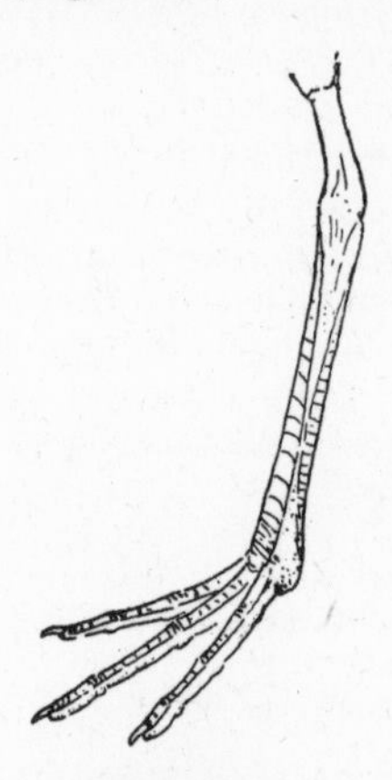

Figure 303
Foot of Sanderling;
natural size.

*Field Marks.* Rufous suffusion about the head in some spring birds, general contrasting black and white appearance on the wing. The line of white along the bases of flight feathers is probably the best field mark common to all plumages. The pure white breast in autumn is also characteristic.

*Distribution.* Breeds on the islands of the Arctic west to Alaska. A common migrant on sandy shores throughout Canada except interior of British Columbia where it is rather rare.

FAMILY—RECURVIROSTRIDAE. AVOCETS AND STILTS

*General Description.* Among the largest of the shore birds and recognizable by their strikingly contrasted colours and great length of leg and bill. The single species that occurs in Canada, the avocet, is so well characterized and so easily recognized from the specific description that nothing more need be said here.

The Black-necked Stilt *Himantopus mexicanus* may have occurred occasionally in Manitoba, but the records are too uncertain for unquestionable acceptance. It is almost as large as the Avocet, but even longer in the legs. It is pure black and white, the black including all the back and extending up the back of the neck over the crown. The bill is very long, fine, and straight (Figure 304). It should be looked for near the alkaline pools along the southern borders of the Prairie Provinces.

Figure 304
Black-necked Stilt;
scale, ⅓.

225. **American Avocet.** L'AVOCETTE D'AMÉRIQUE. *Recurvirostra americana.* L, 16·50. A very large and striking shore bird. Head, neck, and breast, warm vinaceous-pink, lightening to white about eyes, base of bill, and at base of hindneck, blending into white on abdomen and flanks. Closed wings and centre of back nearly black, separated by broad line of white. Rump and tail white. Wing coverts, outer edge of tertiaries, and inner secondaries, broadly edged with white, making white bar on wing in flight. Legs very long, and pale plumbeous blue. Bill long, very slender, and turned up (Figure 305). All plumages are practically the same.

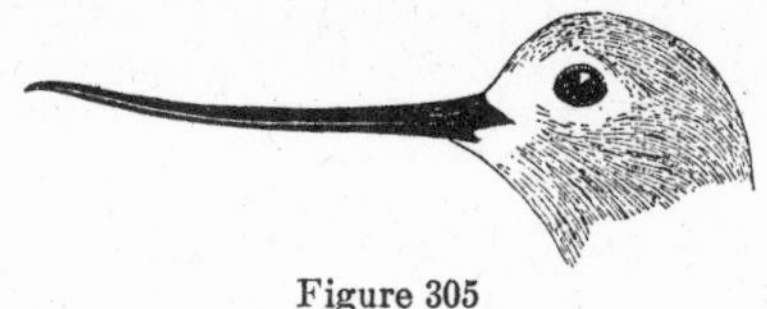

Figure 305
Avocet; scale, ⅓.

*Distinctions.* With size, striking coloration, and long, delicate, recurved bill, the Avocet cannot be mistaken for any other bird.

*Field Marks.* Recognizable by size and remarkable coloration at almost any distance.

*Nesting.* On the ground, near alkali sloughs.

*Distribution.* Central North America. Breeding on the prairies from the western Manitoba boundary to the mountains, more common in the southern parts and the United States. Occasional records for western Manitoba, and two records from southern British Columbia.

This showy and wonderfully graceful bird is characteristic of the alkaline lakes and pools of the arid prairies. Seen with its delicately blended pink and white coloration, accented by black, on a snowy, alkali-encrusted shore, against deep blue water, it makes a sight that lingers long in the memory. It is not an uncommon bird in certain localities, but how long it will remain so is a matter of some concern to all lovers of the beautiful. Large and showy birds do not thrive in close proximity to settled communities and the scale is turning daily a little more against it, together with the Long-billed Curlew, the Marbled Godwit, and the Willet. Their nests are being trampled by cattle, seeking the moisture of the shrinking pools, their habitat being broken up into wheat fields, and the lakes and pools that are essential to their existence are being drained or are drying up. These are unavoidable circumstances and we would not prevent them altogether, even if we could, for they are but the necessary concomitants of the making of productive acres. However, even under the fullest development of the country there will still remain waste land to harbour a certain number of these attractive waders, but when they have also to contend with even a small amount of unnecessary disturbance or thoughtless poaching the result is easily foreseen. Today, it is only in the lonelier localities that Avocets remain in appreciable numbers and these places are becoming progressively fewer and more restricted. Under the Migratory Birds Convention Act, a constant close season has been declared on these and similar birds, but unless its terms are fully supported in spirit as well as letter and by public conscience as well as law enforcement, the prairies will soon lose some of their brightest and most interesting features.

There is one particular circumstance in the Avocet's favour. By nature and preference it inhabits those alkaline areas that are of least agricultural value. That this is but a partial and not complete protection is shown by its appreciable but steady decline in numbers throughout the last decade. England regrets the loss of her Avocets; it is to be hoped that Canada will profit by her experience.

### FAMILY—PHALAROPODIDAE. PHALAROPES. SEA SNIPES

*General Description.* Small birds between 7·75 and 8·75 inches long, wader-like in form, but with plumage dense and gull-like. This, combined with their toes, bordered with web-lobes or edgings, and flattened tarsi (Figures 306 and 308), makes them comparatively easy to recognize.

*Distinctions.* Small waders characterized as above. Cannot be mistaken for any other birds.

*Field Marks.* Size, and the habit of commonly swimming and feeding in deep water. These are the only shore birds that habitually swim.

*Nesting.* On the ground, nest lined with a few mosses or grasses.

*Distribution.* Northern and western America. One species breeds in the Prairie Provinces, the other two along the Arctic coasts and adjoining islands.

The phalaropes constitute a small, anomalous family of shore birds whose true affinities are hardly well understood or settled. They swim with ease and are often found in the open water, even out at sea, where they are as much at home as any pelagic species.

Anomalous in structure and systematic relationships, they are equally so in habits. The female instead of the male is the bright-coloured member of the family circle, and she takes the initiative in courting rites; makes the first advance towards her shy and modestly coloured prospective mate; and upon fulfilling her duties of egg deposition, leaves the cares of incubation and family-raising largely to him.

*Economic Status.* Inhabit water or waste shores and are of little or no economic importance.

222. **Red Phalarope.** GREY-PHALAROPE. WHALE-BIRD. LE PHALAROPE ROUX. *Phalaropus fulicarius.* L, 8·12. Adult female (Figure 306a): all below, including breast, foreneck, and sides of neck, brownish red; white cheeks; black cap; back striped with black and light ochre. Adult male similar, but crown streaked and with less white on face. In winter, an altogether differently coloured bird (Figure 306b). Adult: mostly white, with slate-blue mantle; head white, with poorly defined dark spot about eye, and stripe down nape. Juvenile: like winter plumage of adult, but vague dusky breast-band, and all coloured parts more or less mixed and striped with black and ochre.

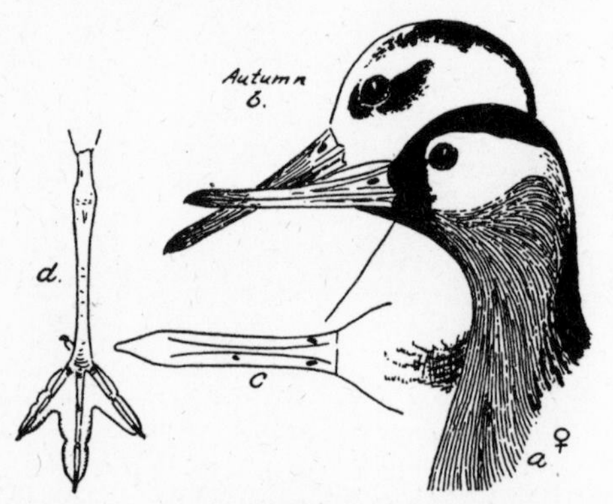


Figure 306

Red Phalarope; natural size.

*a*, summer female; *b*, juvenile and winter; *c*, bill, from above; *d*, foot.

*Distinctions.* A phalarope with solid red underbody in spring. In autumn a white one with more or less slate-blue on back. In any plumage specifically recognizable by its broad bill (Figure 306c) and as a phalarope by its scalloped-webbed toes (Figure 306d). The inner secondaries are largely white.

*Field Marks.* Swimming habits and whirligig action on the water, as a phalarope. Red underparts in spring, large amount of slate-blue on back, and large white area of secondaries. It has a short, heavy bill for a phalarope.

*Distribution.* Northern and southern hemispheres. In America breeds along the whole Arctic coast and the Arctic islands. Migrates down both coasts of the continent, but rare inland. Isolated records from northern Saskatchewan, southern Alberta, and the interior of the eastern provinces.

Though a common bird in the far north, the Red Phalarope as it goes south is seldom detected on our western waters. It is the most maritime of the phalaropes and probably, when it migrates, strikes out to sea, rarely coming in to our shores.

224. **Wilson's Phalarope.** GRUNTER. LE PHALAROPE DE WILSON. *Steganopus tricolor.* L, 8·75. Plate XXVI B. Adults as shown on plate. Young birds similar to the spring male but paler and striped with reddish ochre above. Winter adults are plain greyish above and white below, with no pronounced dark on head. Many birds begin to assume this dress before they leave Canada in the autumn.

*Distinctions.* About the same size as the Red Phalarope, but with a much longer awl-shaped bill. Considerably larger than the Northern and with longer bill. Toes scarcely webbed but margined with a narrow border, not scalloped as in those species (Figure 308, compare with 306d).

*Field Marks.* Swimming habit and whirligig action as a phalarope. Because of interior range, likely to be confused with Northern Phalarope only. Much larger size and characteristic coloration in spring. In autumn, size is probably the best means of separation.

*Nesting.* On the grass in damp places near sloughs.

*Distribution.* The prairie regions, southward. Nesting wherever regularly found in Canada. Only two records for British Columbia.

Figure 307
Wilson's Phalarope; about natural size.
Male Female

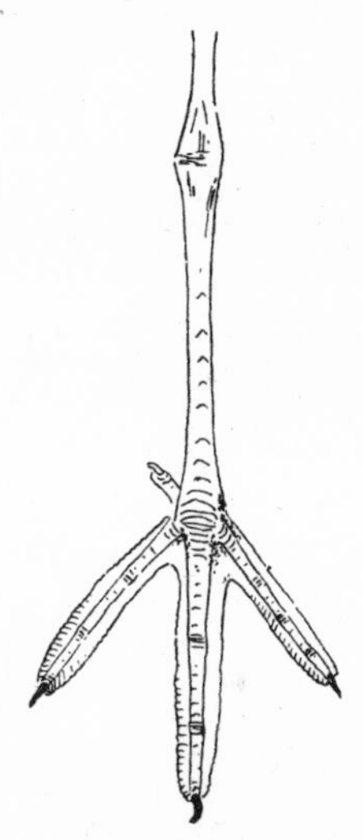

Figure 308
Foot of Wilson's Phalarope; natural size.

One of the commonest as well as one of the loveliest of the inhabitants of the prairie sloughs. It loves the little sunny mud-bottomed pools of shallow water in the meadow. While the males, in grass-shaded nests, are performing the duties of incubation, the females, in little friendly parties, disport themselves with exquisite grace on nearby open water. They swim about like blown thistle-down, their white bodies riding high breaking up the smooth surface into innumerable interlacing lines of silvery ripples. They pause here and there and whirl about in little circles as the black water-beetles do, stirring up the mud with their delicate little feet and bringing to the surface a harvest of tid-bits which they seize with quick passes of their rapier-like bill. Anon they disperse to repeat the pretty performance a little farther on. A flock of phalaropes so feeding forms the brightest, most graceful scene imaginable. It is calumny to call their low monosyllabic voice a "grunt", yet it is the origin of one of their local names.

223. **Northern Phalarope.** LE PHALAROPE À PETIT BEC. *Lobipes lobatus.* L, 7·75. Adult female (Figure 309c): above, very dark grey, almost black, including head and face, and extending almost across the breast. Below and a sharply defined throat patch, white. Sides of neck, brick-red and a line of reddish ochre down back over each wing. Male (Figure 309b): similar, but colours less pure and pattern less definite. Autumn birds (Figure 309a) largely white. Adult: back, striped grey and white. Juvenile: sooty and ochre. Both—with white throat and face and dark cap, and bar through eye black.

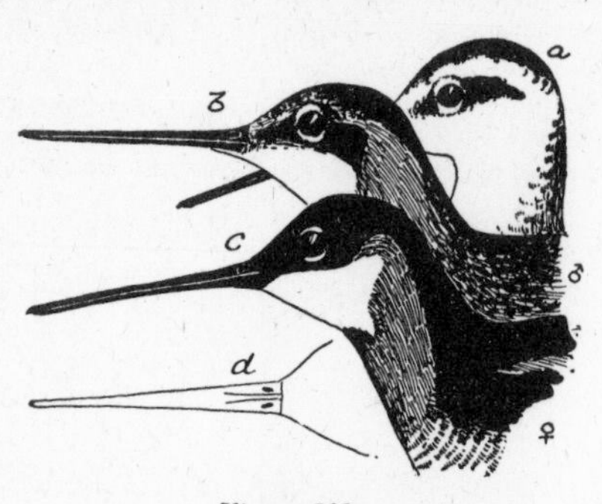


Figure 309
Northern Phalarope; natural size.
*a*, winter; *b*, summer male; *c*, summer female; *d*, bill, from above.

*Distinctions.* Colours as above are quite distinctive. The smallest of the phalaropes. Bill fine and awl-like (Figure 309d), similar to that of Wilson's, but shorter, and quite different from the broad bill of the Red Phalarope. Toes with scalloped half-webs, like the Red (*See* Figure 306d), not a narrow, even border, with slight webs, as in Wilson's (Compare Figure 308).

*Field Marks.* Swimming habits and whirligig action as a phalarope. Small size. Distinguished from the Red Phalarope in spring by white throat and underparts and in autumn by dark line through eye and white superciliary line. When the colours are not very evident, probably difficult to separate in life from Wilson's except by smaller size.

*Distribution.* Northern and southern hemispheres. In America, breeds on the Arctic mainland and islands across the continent. Migrates down both seacoasts and through the prairie interior. Common in the interior of British Columbia. Less so through Ontario and interior Quebec. Not quite such a maritime bird as the Red Phalarope, but more so than Wilson's.

## Suborder—Lari. Long-Winged Swimmers

*General Description.* The Long-winged Swimmers are sea birds, with four toes and two webs, and with the closed wings projecting beyond the tail, if the excessively lengthened middle tail feather of some Jaegers and the equally elongated outer swallow-tails of some Terns are disregarded.

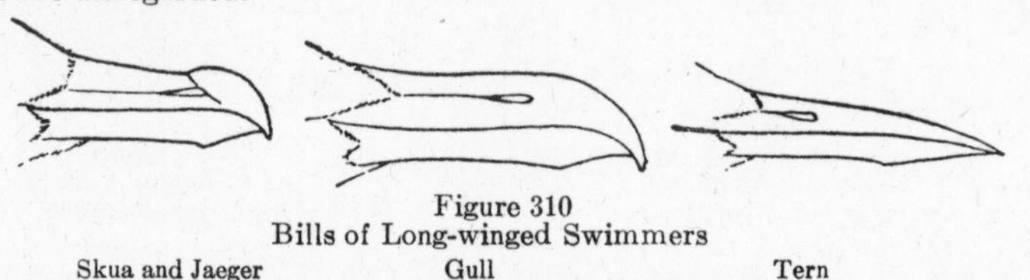

Figure 310
Bills of Long-winged Swimmers
Skua and Jaeger Gull Tern

*Distinctions.* Can be recognized as an Order by their long wings and bill characters (Figure 310). They are separated from the Tube-nosed Swimmers by the position of the nostrils which are in the sides of the bill and not in a tube on top (*See* Figures 83 to 88, pages 46 to 49, for comparison), and from the Cormorants by the presence of nostrils and the completely feathered faces and throats (*See* Figures 94 to 97, pages 56 to 58).

*Field Marks.* No field marks can be given covering the order except length of wing and mode of flight.

*Nesting.* Usually breed on the ground or on cliff ledges, but there is little uniformity in their nesting habits.

*Distribution.* Some species are more or less common over all the waterways of Canada.

The Long-winged Swimmers are wonderful fliers, being both tireless and agile on the wing. In habit they are fishers, scavengers, or pirates. There are only two families of the order in Canada; the Jaegers *Stercorariidae* and the gulls *Laridae*, the latter including the closely allied terns or "Sea Swallows."

Plate XLIII

A. Eastern Phoebe; scale, $\frac{1}{3}$

B. Say's Phoebe; scale, $\frac{1}{3}$

PLATE XLIV

A. Western Wood Peewee; scale, $\frac{1}{4}$

B. Horned Lark; scale, $\frac{1}{3}$

Desert Horned Lark    Arctic Horned Lark

All birds of this order are protected by the Migratory Birds Convention Act and none of them may be killed legally in any part of the United States or Canada without special permission.

*Economic Status.* Being sea birds, the damage they do ordinarily is slight and some of them are actively beneficial to man.

### FAMILY—STERCORARIIDAE. SKUAS AND JAEGERS

*General Description.* The skuas and jaegers are predaceous sea birds and as such have strongly hooked bills. The feet, webbed like gulls, are armed with small but sharp, strongly curved, raptorial claws. The skuas occur only in a single dark coloration, but the jaegers (except perhaps the Long-tailed) are dichromatic and show two distinct colour phases with various though less common intermediate stages between. The dark phase is almost evenly dark brown like the skua, but usually faintly lightening on the face and showing a suggestion of dark cap. The light phase has white or light underparts, often more or less crossbarred with dark, especially on flanks, throat, and cheeks (Figure 311), the latter as a rule with a golden tinge, and showing a distinct black cap. Young birds are usually in the dark phase and more or less completely barred with dark, or feather-edged with light. The species of this family are so similar to each other in coloration that the above is descriptive of all of them and they are almost inseparable by colour characters.

Figure 311
Jaeger, light phase; scale, ⅓.

*Distinctions.* The bills are diagnostic (Figure 311), there being a distinct nail at the tip forming a well-marked hook, plainly separable from the softer cere that occupies most of the upper mandible. This characteristic easily distinguishes them from the gulls, whereas the presence of nostril openings at base of the hook and two instead of three webs distinguishes them from the cormorants which have bills similar in general outline (*See* Figures 94-97, pages 56-58). That the nostrils are not in tubes and are at the forward end of the cere instead of at the base of it, differentiates them from the shearwaters and petrels (Figures 83-88, pages 46-49) that also have hooked bills.

Figure 312
Wing of Jaeger, showing white at base of primaries; scale, about ¼.

*Field Marks.* Jaegers and skuas are sooty dark above and light or white below. In some all the body is evenly sooty in colour. Except the Long-tailed Jaeger all have a conspicuous light band (Figure 312) on the under-wing surface across the base of the primaries. They are very hawk-like in flight. Skuas are too rare with us ever to be recorded on sight evidence. The long central tail feathers (Figures 313-315) of the adult jaegers make good recognition marks. This characteristic tail is so conspicuous as to have suggested to sailors the colloquial names of "Mason" (referring to the trowel-like tail), "Bos'n" (from the tail like a marlin-spike, the special tool of a boatswain), or just "Marlin-spike."

*Nesting.* On the ground.

The occurrence of the two colour phases, as well as every possible intermediate plumage, makes the identification of some of the jaegers a difficult matter. Skuas and jaegers are pirates of the air; they pursue successful fishing birds and force them to drop the fish they have caught. Eggs and young birds in the nest are never safe from them.

Three jaegers occur in Canada and two skuas—the latter very rare.

*Economic Status.* The jaegers are not very numerous and except in far away, wild localities, where numbers give them local importance, they have no economic influence.

36. **Pomarine Jaeger.** BOS'N (BOATSWAIN) BIRD. LE LABBE POMARIN. *Stercorarius pomarinus.* L, 22 (tail 9·25 maximum). Projection of centre tail feathers beyond outer ones 4·25 inches. Occurs in two phases and intermediate stages. In the dark phase, the general colour is dark brown, slightly lighter below and on cheeks, with a black cap. In light phase, the underparts, breast, neck, and face are white; cheeks mostly, and throat in some cases, tinged with golden; the cap is black (Figure 311) and the rest of body dark brown. Dark barring may occur on flanks, breast, and underparts. Hardly distinguishable by colour from the two next jaegers.

*Distinctions.* The largest of the three jaegers. (Disregarding the long projecting tail feathers, 17·75 in length.) A jaeger with a wing over 13½ inches probably belongs to this species. The elongated tail feathers of the adult are wide, instead of pointed, and twisted at the tip so that the ends stand in a vertical plane instead of lying horizontally (Figure 313).

Figure 313
Tail of Pomarine Jaeger; scale, about ⅓.

*Field Marks.* For recognition as a jaeger see *Field Marks* under Family, page 215. The trailing, broad, twisted tail feathers are probably the best specific field marks.

*Nesting.* On the ground, on the moors and tundras of the north.

*Distribution.* Breeds on the islands and mainland of the Arctic, across the continent. Recorded from Great Slave and Athabaska Lakes, but not elsewhere in the interior, except one record from Saskatchewan and one from Ontario. Much less common on the British Columbian than on the east coast.

37. **Parasitic Jaeger.** ARCTIC OR RICHARDSON'S SKUA. LE LABBE PARASITE. *Stercorarius parasiticus.* L, 17 (tail 8·25 maximum). (Projection of centre tail feathers 3·25.) In coloration hardly distinguishable from the other two jaegers (*See* preceding species for general description). Occurs in both phases there described and in various intermediate stages.

*Distinctions.* Decidedly smaller than the Pomarine, slightly larger than Long-tailed Jaegers. Length, disregarding elongated tail feathers, 13·75 instead of the 17·75 of the former or 13 of the latter. A jaeger with a wing under 13 inches is probably either this or the next species. The elongated tail feathers of the adult are pointed and narrow instead of wide and twisted as in the Pomarine and only 3·25 inches projection beyond the rest, instead of 8 inches as in the Long-tailed (Compare Figure 314 with 313 and 315). Immatures and birds with the centre tail feathers in moult are difficult to separate from the Long-tailed. The best distinction seems to be in the colour of the shafts of the primary feathers. In this species the shafts of the three first primaries (counting from outside) are white, the remainder darkening progressively as they succeed each other on the wing. In the Long-tailed there is an abrupt darkening of colour of the shafts with the third primary. This distinction is not infallible and occasional juvenile specimens are very difficult of determination.

Figure 314
Tail of Parasitic Jaeger; scale, about ⅓.

*Field Marks.* For recognition marks as a jaeger *See* Family *Field Marks*, page 215. The small projection of middle tail feathers and their not being broad and twisted probably make the best specific field marks.

*Nesting.* On the ground, on the moors and tundras of the north.

*Distribution.* Breeds in the Arctic across the continent. More common in migration on the sea-board than in the interior, but may occur anywhere in Canada. This is the jaeger that is probably most likely to be met with in the Prairie Provinces and the commonest in migration on either coast.

Juveniles have often been recorded as the Long-tailed and considerable caution should be used in identifying them.

38. **Long-tailed Jaeger.** MARLINE-SPIKE. BUFFON'S SKUA. LE LABBE À LONGUE QUEUE. *Stercorarius longicaudus.* L, 21 (tail 13·25. Maximum projection of centre feathers 8). In coloration hardly distinguishable from the two preceding jaegers. (*See* Pomarine Jaeger for general description.) Only the light phase certainly known to occur.

Figure 315
Tail of Long-tailed Jaeger; scale, about $\frac{1}{5}$.

*Distinctions.* Decidedly smaller than the Pomarine, slightly smaller than the Parasitic. Length, disregarding greatly elongated tail feathers, 13 instead of 17·75 and 13·75 of the two former. A jaeger with wing under 12 inches is probably this species. The very long tail feathers of the adult are narrow and attenuated instead of being broad and twisted as in the Pomarine, and project 8 inches beyond the rest of the tail instead of 3·25 as in the parasitic (Compare Figure 315 with 313 and 314). Immatures and birds with the centre tail feathers in moult are difficult to distinguish from the Parasitic. The best distinction seems to be in the colour of the shafts of the primary feathers. In this species the first two feather shafts (counting from the outside) are white, the remainder darken suddenly instead of gradually and progressively as on the parasitic. This distinction may not be infallible and occasional juvenile specimens may occur that are very difficult of determination. A seemingly reliable character based on the length of certain wingbones has lately been worked out for this species. A jaeger able to fly with an ulna (in "forearm" of wing) 3·8 inches or under should be a Long-tailed.

*Field Marks.* For recognition as jaegers *See* Family *Field Marks,* page 215. The excessive projection of middle tail feathers and their being fine and attenuated instead of broad and twisted probably make the best specific field marks.

*Nesting.* On the ground, on the moors and tundras of the north.

*Distribution.* Breeds in the arctics of Europe, Asia, and America. Probably less common out of the far north than either of the other two.

Many old records of this species have proved to be Parasitics and the species should be identified with care.

35. **Great Skua.** LE GRAND LABBE. *Catharacta skua.* L, 22. Larger and more robust than the jaegers, all dark brown with little variation.

*Distinctions.* This is the skua of the Atlantic coast as the Chilean Skua is of the Pacific. Like a dark phased jaeger but without the elongated tail feathers and considerably larger and more robust, especially in the bill, which is about 2 inches long.

*Distribution.* The north Atlantic. Accidental on the American coast but perhaps more regular on the Grand Banks and Davis Strait. A few records for Nova Scotia.

35·1. **Chilean Skua.** LE LABBE DU CHILI. *Catharacta chilensis.* L, 20-22. A large, dark brown, jaeger-like bird with a rounded tail. With or without scattered lanceolate feathers of a dull golden hue down the back of the neck and upper shoulders. A conspicuous white bar at base of primaries (Figure 312).

*Distinctions.* As above.

*Field Marks.* Would probably be seen in life as a large, nearly black bird with round tail and conspicuous white spot at base of primaries. Disregarding the elongated tail feathers of the jaegers, the skua is considerably larger than any of them.

*Distribution.* Both shores of South America, wandering north in the Pacific occasionally. Breeds in the Fuegian Archipelago.

*Nesting.* Probably similar to the other members of the family.

A skua taken off southern Vancouver Island in 1917 was originally identified as the Great Skua *Catharacta skua,* but has recently been assigned to this species. This is the only record of this bird in Canada. The skuas are typically birds of the Antarctic where they occupy the same place in the natural economy as do our birds of prey. Too rare on our coast to be recorded except by specimens authoritatively identified.

## FAMILY—LARIDAE. GULLS AND TERNS

*General Description.* The gulls and terns are Long-winged Swimmers, easily differentiated from the jaegers by the shape and construction of the bill (Figure 316), which shows a single continuous surface without distinct parts or joints. The colours of the adult are usually pure white, with white or pearl-grey to black mantles, often with black wing tips, hood, cape, or cheek spots.

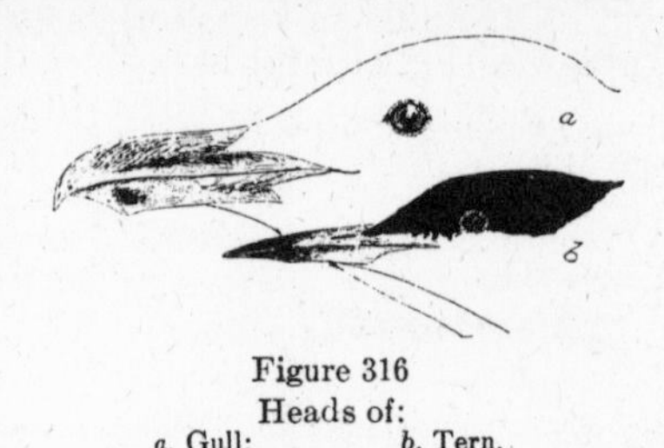


Figure 316
Heads of:
*a*, Gull; *b*, Tern.

*Distinctions.* Bill with continuous surface and sharp projecting angle on lower mandible is sufficient to diagnose the family in all plumages. Colours are quite characteristic, though some species during juvenility are uniformly dark, approaching the dark phases of the jaegers.

*Field Marks.* Coloration and flight characteristics are the best field marks.

*Nesting.* Gulls generally build on ground, on rocky ledges or flat shores, in sandy, grassy, or marshy places; rarely in trees.

*Distribution.* Gulls and terns are distributed over all the world, usually near large bodies of water, but sometimes occurring far inland; for instance, in our prairie regions.

### Subfamily—Larinae. Gulls

*General Description.* With the family description in mind the gulls can be confused only with the terns (*See* page 234).

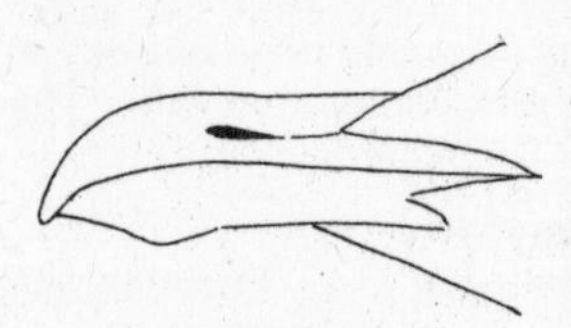

Figure 317
Typical bill outline of gull; (Glaucous-winged); scale, ½.

*Distinctions.* May be distinguished from the jaegers by the bill and coloration characters. (*See* previous family description, page 215); from the terns, by their more robust build and mode of flight. Bills especially are heavier and stronger (Figure 317). As a rule, tails are square. Distinctly forked in only one species, Sabine's Gull, *See* page 234. Though as much masters of flight as the tern they have less agility and perform fewer aerial gymnastics. Young gulls are often quite brownish and dark, in marked contrast with the adult. Young terns are usually light in coloration.

There are two principal distinctly characteristic types of adult coloration amongst our Canadian gulls: the Herring Gull type, large or medium-sized gulls, white with bluish mantle, and the Bonaparte's Gull type, similar but smaller, with black hood over whole head and neck. Species that do not fall into either of these categories are the Ivory Gull, entirely pure white, and Heermann's Gull, generally grey, lighter below, and with a nearly white head.

*Field Marks.* Large birds of heavier flight than the terns. Square tails, surface feeding habits (gulls rarely diving from the wing), and the horizontal carriage of the bill when flying are the best guides by which to distinguish the gulls from the closely allied terns.

*Nesting.* On rocky shores or cliffs near the water in various localities, depending upon the species and locality.

*Distribution.* Almost cosmopolitan in range and few countries are without representatives of the subfamily. In Canada about twenty-five species are known to occur.

Though gulls are essentially sea birds they are at times found at considerable distances from large bodies of water and flocks often follow the prairie ploughman to search for insects in the newly turned furrows. They feed from the surface of the water, seldom diving, or glean from the shores, beaches, or fields.

*Economic Status.* Gulls eat any form of animal matter, fish, crustaceans, molluscs, insects, offal, and—when opportunity offers—young birds and mice.

The amount of fish they consume is relatively unimportant, as it is usually only very abundant small species occurring in great schools that attract their attention. They are not patient fishers like Herons, content to stalk their prey and take one fish at a time, but want them in abundance so that they can gulp them in quantities. They search low tidal shores for crabs and other shell-fish, showing considerable ingenuity in breaking the hard shells and extracting the contents, in many cases carrying them into the air and dropping them on the hard ground and rocks to shatter them. The food supply from these sources is economically insignificant. Gulls annually dispose of vast quantities of garbage and offal in the harbours and waterways and hence are beneficial scavengers. On the British Columbia coast they frequent the salmon rivers and gorge themselves on the spent and dying salmon. (The western salmon, unlike those of the east, after completing their mission of procreation die by thousands in the streams.) Undoubtedly at times some species destroy salmon eggs, but, as most of these are laid at the heads of streams rather than at the mouths where the greatest number of gulls congregate, their opportunity for serious damage is not great, except under exceptional circumstances or on short streams where the spawning grounds are within easy reach of the coast. Another charge against them is their egg-stealing proclivities when in the vicinity of rookeries of other species such as murres and cormorants, nor do they confine themselves to eggs alone, helpless unguarded young birds being equally welcome to them. It is apparent that when gulls attack economically valuable species, objection may be taken to too great numbers of them, but their normal activities in this direction can as a rule be disregarded.

Gulls also frequent agricultural land for insect food. Indeed, some species are characteristic of the broad inland prairies. At times gulls have been instrumental in stopping small mammal and grasshopper plagues and the Mormons of Utah have erected a monument to gulls that appeared at an opportune moment and destroyed the crickets that were ravaging the fields and producing famine. Gulls must be considered, therefore, as beneficial on the whole, and should be protected, although they do sometimes destroy eggs, young birds, and fish, and occasionally thieve from the fishermen.

42. **Glaucous Gull.** BURGOMASTER. LE GOÉLAND BOURGMESTRE. *Larus hyperboreus.* L, 28. One of the largest of the gulls. Of Herring Gull type of coloration, but mantle very pale and wing tips white (Figure 318). In the adult the mantle is only tinged with grey and younger specimens are nearly white, being only clouded with brownish or brownish cream. Birds of the year are slightly barred with ashy brown.

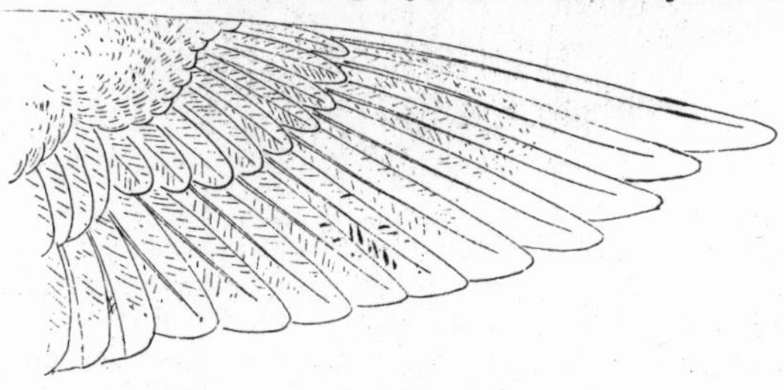

Figure 318
Wing of Glaucous Gull; scale, about ⅓.
Iceland Gull the same but smaller.

*Distinctions.* Large size, general whiteness, and brown to flesh-coloured legs.

*Field Marks.* Size, general coloration, and lack of black wing tips.

*Distribution.* The northern coasts from Newfoundland to Bering Sea. Common on the east coast in winter. A regular but rare winter visitor to British Columbia waters. Only a straggler inland. There are occasional records for the lower Great Lakes, western Alberta, and one from Lake Okanagan, British Columbia.

*Nesting.* On the ground, nest of seaweed or vegetable fragments.

*SUBSPECIES.* It has been proposed to separate the Glaucous Gull of the west coast from that of the east coast under the name Point Barrow Gull *Larus hyperboreus barrovianus,* on the basis of slightly smaller size. The form has not yet been recognized by the American Ornithologists' Union, but it may be the basis of the occasional reports of the Iceland Gull on the west coast of the continent.

43. **Iceland Gull.** LE GOÉLAND À AILES BLANCHES. *Larus leucopterus.* L, 24. The Iceland Gull is of about the same size as the Herring Gull, but with very light grey or white mantle and white wing tips—a smaller edition of the Glaucous (*See* Figure 318).

*Distinctions.* Size, and white instead of black wing tips.

*Field Marks.* Size, wing tips, and general whiteness of coloration.

*Nesting.* On ground.

*Distribution.* Breeds in the Arctic regions of Greenland and western Europe. Visits our Atlantic coast in winter only, rarely straggling inland as far as Lake Ontario.

*Economic Status.* As it is only a winter visitor on our seacoasts and accidental on the Great Lakes, it has little if any economic importance.

44. **Glaucous-winged Gull.** LE GOÉLAND À AILES GLAUQUES. *Larus glaucescens.* L, 25. Plate XXVII A. A Herring Gull with grey instead of black wing tips. It is to be noted that the bird in the coloured plate shows the autumn or winter plumage with the crown and neck clouded with ashy.

*Distinctions.* The soft grey patterned wing tips are always distinctive of this species (Figure 319). Some juveniles and faded adults have practically white primaries and in this condition could easily be mistaken for Glaucous Gulls were the mantle lighter. Younger birds are difficult to distinguish from similar ages of Herring Gulls. In comparable plumages this species is consistently lighter in colour and the back is of finer and less decided pattern. The tail and wing tip of the Herring Gull of the year are nearly black, but those of similar Glaucous-winged are decidedly mouse colour. In birds of this species assuming the adult blue mantle, the blue blends imperceptibly into the adjoining drab patches instead of forming piebald blotches.

Figure 319

Glaucus-winged Gull; scale, $\frac{1}{3}$.

It may best be known from other similar gulls of the coast by size and the details given under those species. *See* Ring-billed and California Gulls.

*Field Marks.* Large size and grey wing tips or grey mantle and faded white wing tips. No characteristics can be given by which juveniles may be certainly recognized.

*Nesting.* On the ground or rock ledges; nest scanty, of seaweed or waste vegetable matter.

*Distribution.* Coast of north Pacific and Bering Sea. Breeds from Washington northward.

This is the common summer gull of the west coast. It throngs the harbours and waterways, from whence, during the salmon run, a few wander up rivers. Not otherwise known far inland and not recorded from the prairies. Much that has been said of the Herring Gull applies to this species.

45. **Kumlein's Gull.** LE GOÉLAND DE KUMLIEN. *Larus kumleini.* L, 24. A grey mantled gull like the Herring, but with a very restricted grey pattern on the primary tips (Figure 320), like the Glaucous-winged Gull but the wing pattern much reduced.

Figure 320
Kumlein's Gull; scale, ⅕.

*Distinctions.* The adult with its characteristic restricted grey pattern on the wing tips is easily identified. There is, however, much variation in this pattern. It may be unusually deep and extensive so as to almost suggest the *thayeri* form of the Herring Gull or even the Glaucous-winged. On the other hand it may be reduced to almost the vanishing point and resemble the wing of the Iceland Gull. The mantle is usually perceptibly lighter grey than any form of the Herring Gull and much darker than that of the Iceland. It is distinctly an east coast bird and supposed west coast examples that have hitherto been reported are open to doubt. The juvenile has never been definitely identified.

*Distribution.* The eastern Arctics, breeding on southern Baffin Island and occurring on our Atlantic coasts in winter.

In the last Check-list of North American Birds this species has been relegated to the hypothetical list as a probable hybrid between Thayer's and the Iceland Gulls. Recent investigations, however, have demonstrated that it breeds in pure colonies and not in association with either of the above birds, therefore its status as a good species can hardly be doubted.

46. **Nelson's Gull.** LE GOÉLAND DE NELSON. *Larus nelsoni.* L, 24 or over. Practically the same as Kumlein's Gull but larger.

*Distribution.* Little is known of this species. It has been identified from St. Michaels, Alaska, and Cornwallis Island in the high Arctics, and individuals have been accredited to Lower California and the Hawaiian and Vancouver Islands. It should be identified with very great caution.

47. **Great Black-backed Gull.** SADDLE-BACK. COFFIN CARRIER. LE GOÉLAND ANGLAIS (le Goéland à manteau noir). *Larus marinus.* L, 29. A very large gull, the adult with a distinctive black mantle. Restricted to the eastern side of the continent.

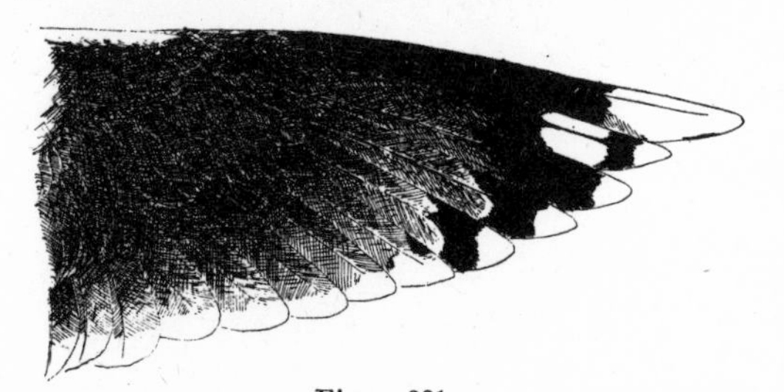

Figure 321
Wing of Great Black-backed Gull; scale, ⅕.

*Distinctions.* Large size and black back are characteristic of the adult. Juveniles are brown instead of ashy or white as in the Glaucous Gull, more striped on back and less evenly coloured than the Herring Gull.

*Field Marks.* Large size and black back are good field marks for the adult. Size is the only describable distinction for juveniles in life.

*Nesting.* On ground, nest of seaweed or vegetable fragments.

*Distribution.* Eastern Canada, breeds on the Atlantic coast from Nova Scotia northward along the Labrador coast. Owing to advancing settlement nesting localities have at present been reduced to the more isolated situations. Is a more or less regular but rather sparse winter visitor upon Lake Ontario, but rarely wanders farther inland along the Great Lakes.

*Economic Status.* With similar feeding habits to those of the other gulls, the superior size, strength, and numbers of the Black-backed Gull increase its powers for good or harm. The species is certainly not to be trusted in the vicinity of unprotected nests of other species, or even young birds, as both eggs and young are eagerly devoured when opportunity offers. To offset this, however, the opportunity to become an important pest is small except in a few localities, as on the Labrador coast where the Black-back breeds abundantly in close proximity to great numbers of eiders and other sea birds. The damage it does on the Labrador coast, however, is small compared with the more serious and wanton waste of some of the fishermen.

49. **Western Gull.** LE GOÉLAND DE L'OUEST. *Larus occidentalis.* L, 24. Like the Herring Gull, but with a very dark mantle, lead-colour rather than light slaty or pearl grey.

*Distinctions.* Dark, lead-coloured mantle, primaries black to base with only subapical white mirror or single outer feather (Figure 322). Juvenile birds seem almost identical with Herring Gulls of similar ages, but the browns are of a blacker and bluer shade.

*Field Marks.* Dark mantle, when adult, with large amount of black with very little or no white to wing tips. The adult Herring and California Gulls, which are most likely to be mistaken for the Western Gull, have only the primary tips black.

*Nesting.* On ledges, crannies, grassy hillsides, and similar localities by the sea. Nest of grasses, etc.

*Distribution.* Western, from Washington to lower California. Occasionally wandering north to Vancouver Island.

*SUBSPECIES.* The form accredited to Canada is the North-western Gull (le Goéland du Nord-Ouest) *Larus occidentalis occidentalis.*

Figure 322
Wing of Western Gull; scale, $\frac{1}{3}$.

Most of the references in literature to this species on the British Columbia coast refer to the Herring Gull. On investigation it has been found to be very rare, though perhaps of regular occurrence after the breeding season. More information is desired concerning this species in Canada. At present we have only two localities absolutely substantiated, Comox and Clayoquot on Vancouver Island.

51. **Herring Gull.** LE GOÉLAND ARGENTÉ. *Larus argentatus.* L, 24. Plate XXVII B.

*Distinctions.* Probably the commonest and most generally distributed gull in eastern and interior Canada. Several other gulls so closely resemble this species, except for size and slight colour details, that considerable care must be used in identification. In autumn and winter, adult has head and neck flecked with ashy brown. Similar to Glaucous-winged Gull shown on Plate XXVII A, except wing tip black instead of grey.

PLATE XLV

A. Violet-green Swallow; scale, $\frac{1}{3}$

B. Tree Swallow; scale, $\frac{1}{3}$

Juvenile Adult

Plate XLVI

A. Bank Swallow; scale, $\frac{1}{3}$

B. Barn Swallow; scale, $\frac{1}{3}$

Juvenile Adult

Typical adults with pearly grey back and black wing tips are likely to be confused in the east with the Black-backed and the Kittiwake (on the coast) and the Ring-billed; in the central provinces with the Ring-billed and the California; and on the west coast with the Ring-billed, the California, the Short-billed, the Glaucous-winged, and the Western Gulls.

From the Ring-billed distinguished by being larger, having flesh-coloured (pink) instead of yellowish or greenish legs and feet, and a red spot on the lower mandible instead of a black band around the bill. Note, however, that in birds coming into maturity the remains of the black bill of juvenility often resemble the ring of the Ring-billed (*See* Figures 324 and 328).

From the Black-backed by smaller size and grey instead of black mantle.

From the kittiwake in being larger, the legs and feet flesh coloured instead of black, and the red spot on the lower mandible.

From the California in having flesh-coloured legs and feet instead of pale greenish or yellowish and there being no black fleck in the red spot of the lower mandible (Figure 326).

From the Short-billed in being larger, legs and feet flesh-colour instead of yellowish, and the red bill spot.

From the Glaucous-winged by black, instead of grey, wing tips.

From the Western by having a lighter coloured mantle, pearl grey instead of dark lead, and black on wing tips less extensive (Figure 323, compare with 322).

The juvenile gulls are more difficult to distinguish and it will sometimes take the nicest discrimination to do so. The Herring Gull of the year is the darkest and most evenly sooty of any of the young gulls it is likely to be confused with. The Black-backed is noticeably larger and the dark colouring of the back is more broken and less even. The juvenile Kittiwake is entirely different, being largely white on back with prominent dark shoulder streak and a sharply defined dark terminal tail band. The Western resembles the Herring Gull closely in colour, but is of a bluer cast, and is less even in tone. The Glaucous-winged is appreciably lighter, the darkest shade being mouse-coloured instead of nearly black. The California is considerably lighter, with more white mixed in above and below. The Ring-billed is still lighter, being more white than dark below, shows indications of the pearly mantle even during the first autumn, and has a broad, suffused, dark terminal band instead of an all-dark tail. Between the dark, juvenile Herring Gull

Figure 323
Wing of typical Herring Gull; scale, $\frac{1}{5}$.

with brown legs and bill and nearly black tail and wings and the light-coloured adult with flesh-coloured legs, red-spotted yellow bill, and black wing tips there is every gradation and it is only by careful attention to details that some of them can be separated. There is great individual and sex variation in size, and care must be taken in comparing this character that due allowance is made for these sources of confusion. The following schedule of characters of the Herring Gull may assist in the separation of these birds. Compare with similar schedule under other species. Large gull about 24 inches.

Evenly very dark; tail evenly dark; bill dark with flesh-coloured base, feet brownish or flesh (Figure 324a)........First autumn

Light; slightly clouded with dark; tail clouded near end; bill yellowish, with partial or complete ring; feet flesh (Figure 324b)..........................................Immature

Light; tail white; bill yellow with red spot; feet flesh. Eyelids and gape yellow or purplish pink........................Adult

*Field Marks.* Size and general colour. Smaller than the Black-backed and mantle grey instead of black. Distinguished from the Kittiwake by larger size, presence of white, apical mirrors on primary tips; round instead of squarish, or slightly forked tail, and flesh-coloured instead of black legs and feet. Similar to the Glaucous-winged and larger than

76916—15½

the California or Ring-billed. The bill and feet colorations are often seen plainly enough for diagnosis. The very dark coloration of the juvenile of the year makes it easily distinguishable from the California or the Ring-billed and the lack of a sharply defined tail band distinguishes it from any plumage of the latter and the juvenile Kittiwake.

*Nesting.* On the ground, on rocky ledges or the flat tops of isolated rocks, in nests of seaweed or vegetable matter.

*Distribution.* Across northern parts of Old and New Worlds, generally breeding north of our southern areas. On the upper Great Lakes and on the east coast. Common on almost all the larger bodies of water, fresh or salt, at various seasons. Numbers of non-breeding birds summer far south of their nesting grounds. Common in winter on the west coast and occasionally so in summer, but we know of no regular breeding grounds in the immediate vicinity of the Pacific coast. In the central provinces the species breeds probably from the Arctics south to the edges of the prairies, though along the latter line the distribution is not well defined, for, in many cases, it has been confused in breeding season with the California Gull.

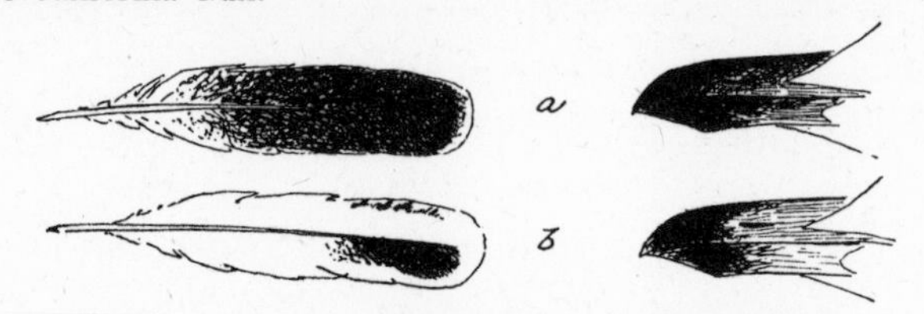


Figure 324
Tail feathers and bills of Herring Gull at various ages:
*a*, first year; *b*, approaching maturity.

*SUBSPECIES.* The American form, the American Herring Gull (le Goéland argenté d'Amérique) *Larus argentatus smithsonianus* has been separated from the Herring Gull of the Old World and is generally recognized as a distinct subspecies.

A form, Thayer's Gull (le Goéland de Thayer) *Larus argentatus thayeri*, characterized by paler and more restricted black in wing tips (Figure 325), has been described from the eastern Arctics. It has been traced across the northern coast and down the Pacific shores of British Columbia where it occurs with more normally coloured types. The breeding distribution of these two forms requires further investigation.

Figure 325
Wing of typical Thayer's Gull; scale, $\frac{1}{5}$.

The Herring Gull is the large gull of the interior and is common on the coast. It is a great wanderer and is often seen on the smallest of our lakes, even at a considerable distance from its nesting grounds. The gulls that remain south of their normal nesting grounds through the summer are immatures or non-breeding birds. In winter the species remains upon the larger waters until they are frozen over and often throughout the entire season, beating over the open water or perched on the floating ice. The gulls haunt harbours and congregate in large numbers about sewer outlets for the floating offal. They have also learned that ships are abundant providers of toothsome scraps. Fishing stations have great attractions for them and there is almost certain to be a large flock in attendance about the cleaning tables on the shore. At the seashore, shell-fish are eagerly sought for at low tide and the gulls have learned the trick of carrying their hard-shelled prey into the air and dropping it upon the rocks, after which they descend and extract the savoury morsels from the broken case. In rough weather they congregate about foamy breakers off stormy points for the food that is brought to the surface. Occasionally they follow the immense schools of small fish that periodically visit our shores, and take toll of the inexhaustible supply.

*Economic Status.* It will be seen from the above summary of the Herring Gulls' food habits that as scavengers they are important and should be protected.

53. **California Gull.** LE GOÉLAND DE CALIFORNIE. *Larus californicus.* L, 20-23. Like a small Herring Gull, but with light yellow, greenish yellow, or pale glaucous-green legs and feet, and a dark as well as a red spot near the end of the lower mandible (Figure 326).

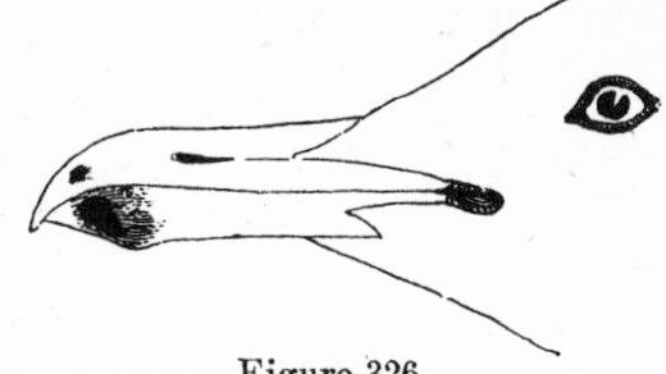

Figure 326
Bill of California Gull;
scale, ½.

*Distinctions.* Central and Western. In size between the Herring and the Ring-billed Gulls, but with sex and individual variation specimens may overlap either of these species in this character.

Distinguished from the Herring Gull in having a dark spot in the red of the lower mandible, red eyelids and gape, and having yellowish or greenish yellow instead of flesh-coloured legs.

The Ring-billed is without red on the bill tips and has a large dark spot on both mandibles, making a more or less complete ring about the bill (*See* Figure 328), and its feet are generally more strongly yellow.

The Short-billed Gull is the only other species with which the California Gull is likely to be confused. It is considerably smaller and has a plain greenish yellow bill without either red or dark marks. The legs are greenish in colour, never yellow. Both Ring-billed and Short-billed may have red eyelids and gape like the California.

These birds are easily separated in maturity by the above characteristics. In juvenility the difficulties are greater. The following schedule may assist:

Medium-sized gull, L, 20-23.

Quite dark; tail evenly dark; bill dark, with flesh-coloured base; feet brownish or flesh-coloured.....................First autumn

Light, speckled, or clouded; tail clouded towards end (Figure 327); bill yellowish with more or less dark ring; feet flesh or light greenish.......................................Immature

Light; tail white; bill yellowish with red and black spot; feet light greenish or yellowish, eyelids and gape red..........Adult

Figure 327
Details of California Gull:
Wing of adult, tail of sub-adult just before reaching maturity; scale, ⅓.

The juveniles are never as dark as first year Herring Gulls, but are darker than Ring-billed or Short-billed of similar ages. They never have a decided or clear-cut subterminal (Compare Figures 327 and 329) tail band as do the Ring-billed or the Short-billed, though the dark of immaturity lingers irregularly on the tail tip after the remainder has become pure white. Probably, in certain plumages, size of carefully sexed birds is the only means of separating them.

*Field Marks.* Size, smaller than a Herring Gull and larger than the Ring-billed, is generally suggestive. The red and black spot on the bill of the adult when seen is determinative. Yellowish or greenish, legs distinguish it from the Herring Gull and the red on the bill from the Ring-billed.

In juvenility it is never as dark as the Herring Gull in the first year. Eye-sight records of some plumages are unreliable.

*Nesting.* On the ground, on low, flat islands, as a rule marshy, or near the water.

*Distribution.* Western North America. Breeding in the interior in the Prairie Provinces (Saskatchewan and Alberta), north to the Arctic circle. Migrating to the Pacific coast of British Columbia southward. Winters south of our boundary.

Many of the records of the Herring Gull breeding in the prairie lakes apply to this species. Owing to the similarity of the two birds their occurrences have not been well delimited. This is probably the common large gull breeding south of the Canadian National Railway tracks in Saskatchewan and Alberta. Its occurrence in Manitoba has yet to be recorded.

54. **Ring-billed Gull.** LE GOÉLAND CRIARD OU LA MAUVE CRIARDE. *Larus delawarensis.* L, 19·75. Similar to the Herring and California Gulls, but slightly smaller, and having a black ring about the bill near the tip (Figure 328) and with yellow legs and feet.

*Distinctions.* East, central, and west. Smaller size, lack of red and the presence of dark ring on bill, and yellow legs, differentiate the Ring-bill from the Herring Gull.

From the California Gull, smaller size, in duly sexed specimens, and lack of red on the bill.

From the Short-billed Gull, larger size and presence of dark ring on bill.

In juvenility, distinctions are finer. The following schedule of characters may assist:

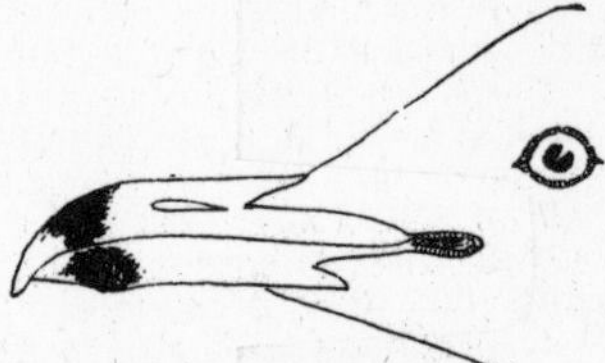

Figure 328
Bill of Ring-billed Gull; scale, $\frac{1}{2}$.

Figure 329
Details of Ring-billed Gull:
Wing of adult, tail of juvenile; scale, $\frac{1}{5}$.

Medium-sized gull, L, 19·75.

Comparatively light, much spotted; tail mottled, with extensive subterminal band; bill dark, with flesh-coloured base, feet dark or flesh-coloured.................................First autumn

Light; tail white with conspicuous band; bill yellowish with more or less ring; feet yellowish or flesh-coloured (Figure 329).................................................Immature

Light; tail white; bill yellow or greenish yellow with dark ring; feet yellow; eyelids and gapes red.........................Adult

The Ring-billed Gull in first year is the lightest coloured of the larger gulls, even at this time showing indications of the blue mantle on the back. Underparts nearly pure white, peppered with sparse, fine, dark bands. This and the sharp terminal tail bar will distinguish it from the Herring Gull and usually from the California. Size and general spottiness of the younger birds are probably the best criteria for separation from the Short-billed.

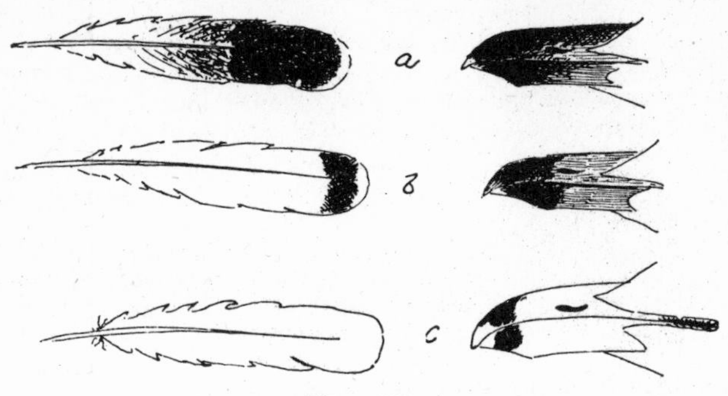


Figure 330
Age characters of Ring-billed Gull:
a, first year; b, approaching maturity; c, adult.

*Field Marks.* Size, decidedly smaller than the Herring Gull and slightly smaller than the California, larger than the Short-billed. The ring on the end of the bill is distinctive. Differentiated from the Herring Gull also by yellow instead of flesh-coloured legs.

In juvenility, the whitest of the young of the larger gulls. Decidedly lighter than the dark Herring Gull of the first year and with a tail bar that is never present in that species. More spotty than similarly juvenile California or Short-billed Gulls. Eye-sight records in juvenility are not very reliable in localities where the two latter species may be expected.

*Nesting.* On the ground, on rocky, stony, or marshy shores.

*Distribution.* Across the continent, breeding over most of eastern and central Canada north to Great Slave Lake. No records of breeding in British Columbia, but probably does so in the northern interior. Common on the coast in migration. Competes in numbers with the Herring Gull on the Great Lakes.

This is probably the commonest of the large gulls throughout the interior, and the one most often seen on or about the lakes and sloughs of the prairie region.

55. **Short-billed Gull or American Mew Gull.** LE GOÉLAND CENDRÉ. *Larus canus.* L, 17·50. Similar in coloration to the Herring Gull, but the smallest of this type of coloration.

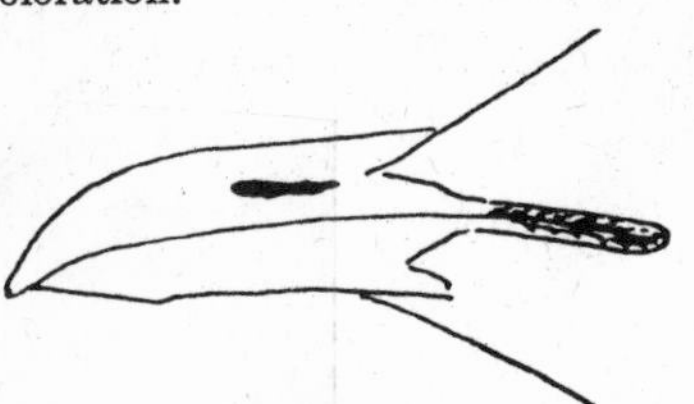

Figure 331
Bill of Short-billed Gull;
scale, natural size.

Figure 332
Wing of Short-billed Gull.

*Distinctions.* West coast and northwest interior. Its clear yellow bill without dark or red spot or ring (Figure 331), is distinctive from all others except the Kittiwake. Its feet and legs are yellowish or yellowish green, similar to its two larger relatives. Likely to be confused only with the Ring-billed or perhaps the California. When juvenile it may at times be difficult to distinguish from either of these. The following schedule may assist:

Small gull, L, 17·50.

Evenly dark; tail evenly dark; bill dark, flesh-coloured at base; feet brownish or flesh-coloured............................First autumn

Light, clouded and speckled; tail white with subterminal bar; bill dark or dark greenish; feet light greenish.............Immature

Light; tail white; bill yellow; feet yellowish green; eyelids brown, gape red..........................................Adult

*Field Marks.* The smallest of the common gulls of Herring Gull type of coloration. Bill without dark or red spot or ring. Field separation of juveniles except by size is somewhat unreliable.

*Nesting.* On the ground on stony, rocky, or marshy shores of freshwater lakes.

*Distribution.* Western North America. Breeding in northern Alberta and Saskatchewan, north throughout the Mackenzie and Yukon basins and the interior of Alaska. Migrates to the Pacific coast, wintering from the south half of Vancouver Island southward. Not recorded from the southern parts of the Prairie Provinces.

*SUBSPECIES.* This is the American representative of the Old World Mew Gull *Larus canus* and has been proposed as a subspecies, the Short-billed Gull (Le Goéland à petit bec) *Larus canus brachyrhynchus.*

The migration route of this species is most interesting, being one that is followed by several other species. Breeding in the centre of the great northern land mass of Mackenzie region, it migrates to the west coast, crossing the mountains in the north and not regularly coming south into settled country en route, though occasionally seen on the interior lakes of British Columbia.

### Little Black-headed Gulls

There is a group of rather small gulls in America readily distinguished from the other members of the genus *Larus* by having in spring and summer plumage a complete black head and cape. In winter the black head is lost or represented only by more or less veiled or softened dark spots or suffusions, principally on ears and nape.

58. **Laughing Gull.** LA MOUETTE OU MAUVE RIEUSE. *Larus atricilla.* L, 16·5. A small, white-bodied, grey-mantled gull with a black hood like Bonaparte's Gull but distinctly larger and with a noticeably darker mantle.

*Distinctions.* Only occurring on the east coast, it requires particular separation only from Bonaparte's Gull. Size, wing over 11 inches, will usually be diagnostic. In the adult the mantle is distinctly darker (about as in Franklin's Gull) and the wing tips are solid

Figure 333

Field marks of:

*a*, Franklin's Gull; *b*, Laughing Gull; *c*, Bonaparte's Gull.

black instead of containing much white. The juvenile is decidedly darker than the young Bonaparte's. It gives the general effect of a brownish bird just whitening on the abdomen, whereas Bonaparte's is a generally pure white bird lightly clouded above, with a white face and conspicuous ear spots instead of a generally brownish grey face. The solidly dark wings (Figure 334) are equally characteristic in the young plumages.

*Distribution.* Temperate and tropical coasts of North America. There are a few records for our east coast.

Figure 334
Wing of Laughing Gull; scale, ¼.

59. **Franklin's Gull.** PRAIRIE PIGEON. LA MOUETTE OU MAUVE DE FRANKLIN. *Larus pipixcan.* L, 14. Plate XXVIII A.

Practically identical with Bonaparte's Gull, from which it differs only in detail.

*Distinctions.* Central Provinces. To be seriously confused only with Bonaparte's Gull, but may be distinguished by its slightly darker mantle and the small amount of white on the wings (wrists and most of the primaries being slate grey instead of pure white) (Figure 335, compare with Figure 336). The bill and feet vary, with age and season, from black to maroon. In Bonaparte's Gull the bill is always black and the feet vary from flesh-coloured to coral-red. In both species the rosy suffusion of the underparts is evanescent and not always present in specimens, as it quickly fades to white after death and exposure to light. The juvenile can best be distinguished by the wing pattern in which the primaries are solid black in the bird of the year instead of with large white areas.

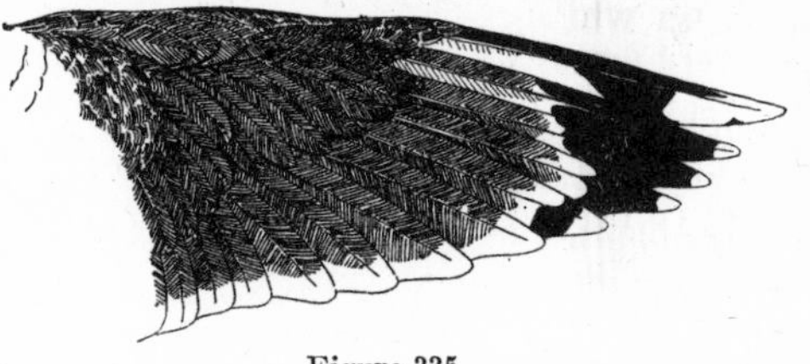

Figure 335
Wing of Franklin's Gull; scale, ¼.

*Field Marks.* The blackness of the wings without prominent white wrists makes the best field marks for all plumages. The black or deep maroon legs and the dull red bill also assist in recognition (Figure 333a). Either Franklin's or Bonaparte's Gull may be known from the terns which they may resemble in life by the decided wing pattern instead of the even pale greyness of those species.

*Nesting.* Nest of dead rushes and debris in wet marshes adjoining prairie lakes and sloughs.

*Distribution.* The interior, from Manitoba to Alberta. Not known to breed north of the prairie sections and not recorded from British Columbia.

This is a characteristic gull of the prairies. Nesting in large colonies in the marshy sloughs and lakes, these gulls appear in clouds of thousands of individuals and follow the heavy gang ploughs in flocks that almost hide the driver and team from view.

They settle on the freshly turned black earth, packing into their eager crops the grubs, worms, and larvæ that are scurrying to new shelter after the upheaval. One surface quickly exhausted, they rise to air again, beat over their companions still busily at work, whirl once or twice about the ploughman so closely that he might cut them down with his whip, and settle on freshly turned clods again, to repeat the operation over and over. Thus it goes from daylight to dark and the destruction carried into the insect ranks on these fields preparing for cultivation is enormous and well appreciated by the husbandman. Later in the season when the green, half-grown grain waves in the wind, there is a constant procession from the breeding sloughs out over the farmland. Beating across the soft green fields, a flock of a hundred or more will pause, hover a moment, and then drop into them, sinking from sight—one, a few, or many at a time, in a little spot that makes the onlooker wonder that so many can find shelter and concealment in so small a space; but the sea of grain closes over them so that no sign is visible of the eager activity below. Presently a black wing is raised, a white body flashes in the sun; others follow, and for a moment there is a white outboiling that presently resolves itself into the flock, wing-borne, to again circle away over the many-acred field and repeat the performance. At times a number of such aggregations can be seen at once over a single field. The attraction is generally grasshoppers and the number of these insects that a few hundred gulls can devour on a long summer day, and day by day throughout the season, is an important factor in insect control.

Again, in the evening, they may mount the upper air over or near lake shores and, high up, gleaming like jewels in the last rays of the setting sun while the ground below perhaps is lost in blue evening shadows, they weave intricate aerial patterns in pursuit of the "lake flies" that blow in smoke-like clouds about them.

In the autumn they often unite with flocks of Bonaparte's Gull, forming incredible numbers, and drive up and down over the harvest fields, rising on whistling wings to pass over obstructions and again descending to barely a man's height from the ground as they gather the insects from the air. What species forms their special pursuit at this time has not been definitely ascertained, but undoubtedly the great majority of their tiny prey are better placed in the crops of hordes of gulls than peaceably permitted to prepare for next season's crops.

*Economic Status.* On the whole, the western farmer probably has no more efficient friend than this little gull of tireless wing, and the indignation of the community should be experienced by those who disturb their nesting or interfere with their security. In many localities, a swamp where these gulls breed is worth far more as insect insurance to the surrounding community than if it were drained and its small acreage brought under cultivation. A few hundred acres are an inappreciable addition to the sum total of productive land and may at times be bought at too high a price. Consideration should be given to this factor sometimes before the last bits of reclamation are undertaken.

**60. Bonaparte's Gull.** LA MOUETTE OU MAUVE DE BONAPARTE. *Larus philadelphia.* L, 14. Plate XXVIII A.

Figure 336
Wing of Bonaparte's Gull; scale, ¼.

*Distinctions.* East, central, and west. Likely to be confused only with Franklin's Gull and with it only in the Prairie Provinces. It can be distinguished from that species by its slightly lighter mantle and large amount of white on the wings (wrists and most of the primaries pure white instead of slate grey) (Figure 336, compare with Figure 335). The bill is black in all ages instead of maroon and the feet vary with age and season from flesh-coloured to coral-red instead of from black to dull maroon. In both species the rosy suffusion of the underparts is evanescent and not always present, quickly fading to white after death and

A. Cliff Swallow; scale, $\frac{1}{3}$

Adult Juvenile

B. Purple Martin; scale, $\frac{1}{3}$

Male Female

PLATE XLVIII

A. Canada Jay; scale, $\frac{1}{3}$
(Eastern form)

B. Blue Jay; scale, $\frac{1}{3}$

exposure to light. The juvenile can best be distinguished by the wing pattern, in which the primaries contain large white areas and the wrist is almost all white.

*Field Marks.* The whiteness of the wings, and prominent white wrists make the best field mark for all plumages. The coral legs and black bill also assist in recognition (Figure 333c). Either this or Franklin's Gull can be distinguished from the terns, which they may resemble in life, by the decided wing pattern instead of the pale, even greyness of those species.

*Nesting.* Singly or in small, scattered associations in trees, a wide departure from custom in this class of birds usually (?) near small inland lakes or muskeg ponds.

*Distribution.* Across the continent during migration. Nests have been reported in the far northwest, the interior of Alaska, central Alberta, and the west side of Hudson Bay. In migration common throughout all parts of southern Canada.

*Economic Status.* Much that has been said of Franklin's Gull might be repeated here as it often joins flocks of that species and has very similar habits, though it does not spend as much time in cultivated sections.

57. **Heermann's Gull.** WHITE HEADED GULL. LE GOÉLAND DE HEERMANN. *Larus heermanni.* L, 17·50-20. A distinctively coloured gull. Adult in summer: grey, darker to plumbeous above, lighter to ashy below, with black wings and tail, and white head usually slightly speckled when seen in our waters. Bill, bright red. Adults in autumn: heads heavily marked or speckled with brown, the head above darker than neck; chin and throat white. Juveniles are uniform dark brown, chin in some cases whitish.

Figure 337
Heermann's Gull; scale, ½.
Winter plumage.

*Distinctions.* West coast. Well characterized as above.

*Field Marks.* A grey gull with light or white head, red bill, and black feet.

*Nesting.* On the ground amidst rocks and stones on level spots of lonely rocks and islets.

*Distribution.* Breeding along the shores of Lower California, migrating in autumn northward to Vancouver Island, but rarely winters there.

A bird of anomalous habits and the only species of gull breeding in the northern hemisphere and migrating northward as far as Canada in winter. A few, probably sub-adult are to be seen on the Vancouver Island shores in summer.

39. **Ivory Gull.** LA MOUETTE OU MAUVE BLANCHE. *Pagophila alba.* L, 16-19. Entirely pure white when adult. Juvenile with slight grey clouding in front of eyes, and sparse, sharply defined, dark feather edges and flecks on the larger feathers (Figure 338).

*Distinctions.* The only absolutely pure white gull with black legs. Young Glaucous and Iceland Gulls are not only larger birds, but, though nearly white, are always slightly clouded with brownish ash, and with legs brown horn colour to flesh-pink.

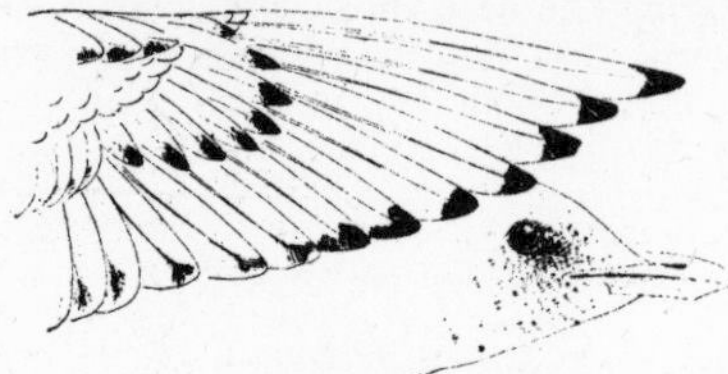

Figure 338
Ivory Gull; scale of wing, $\frac{1}{5}$.
Juvenile

*Field Marks.* Too rare to be recorded on sight.

*Distribution.* The Arctic seas, more common on the east than the west coast. In winter south to the coasts of the Maritime Provinces. Three specimens have been taken in Manitoba, near the big lakes, and other individuals in Cassiar and Okanagan Districts of British Columbia.

Too rare except in the far north to be further mentioned.

40. **Kittiwake.** LA MOUETTE OU MAUVE À TROIS DOIGTS. *Rissa tridactyla.* L, 16. A medium-sized gull of the same general coloration as the Herring Gull (*See* page 222).

*Distinctions.* Both coasts. May always be known by the almost total absence, or rudimentary condition of the hind toe. The tail is also slightly forked, the outer feathers being a quarter to half an inch longer than the centre ones (Figure 339). Of Herring Gull type of coloration but even smaller than the Ring-billed which are the only species in the east from which it will need particular distinction. About the same size and general appearance as the Short-billed of the west coast. Wing tips black without the white sub-apical spots common to those species. Dark brown or black legs and feet and evenly yellow bill will distinguish it from any other gull with which it might be confused.

Figure 339
Wing, foot, and tail of Kittiwake.

The juvenile kittiwake, unlike juveniles of most other gulls, is not brownish or clouded anywhere with any shade of ash. The white below is always pure and the mantle clear slaty. There is a dark aural spot, a heavy band of dark about the base of the hindneck, and another along the greater wing-coverts, making a bar across the base of the flight shafts (Figure 340). The tail has a subterminal bar.

Figure 340
Kittiwake; scale, $\frac{1}{3}$.
Juvenile

*Field Marks.* The smallest of the Herring Gull type of coloration. The lack of white spot on wing tip, and dark legs are probably the best field marks. The tail is slightly forked when closed, and when fully spread is squarer than in other comparable species (Figure 339).

The species is rare except on eastern coast and should be identified elsewhere with caution.

*Nesting.* On shelves and ledges on perpendicular sea-cliffs.

*Distribution.* A strictly maritime species, not found in the interior. Inhabits both seacoasts, more common east than west. Breeding south in the east to the Gulf of St. Lawrence, in the west to Alaska Peninsula and only a casual migrant to British Columbia. Occasionally recorded from Queen Charlotte Islands and southern Vancouver Island.

*SUBSPECIES.* The Eastern representative of this species is the Atlantic Kittiwake (la Mouette ou Mauve à trois doigts de l'Atlantique)*Rissa tridactyla tridactyla.* The west coast form of the Kittiwake is the Pacific Kittiwake (la Mouette ou Mauve à trois doigts du Pacifique) *Rissa tridactyla pollicaris*, separated from the eastern type form by slightly more distinctly formed hind toe, and claw, slightly less amount of black on primary tips, and rather larger size, and longer, more tapering bill. The distinctions, however, are slight and based on averages rather than individuals.

41. **Red-legged Kittiwake.** LA MOUETTE OU MAUVE À PATTES ROUGES. *Rissa brevirostris.* L, 15. A kittiwake with darker mantle and coral-red legs, inhabiting the Alaskan coast of Bering Sea, but which has not yet been recorded on the British Columbia coast. One record from Fortymile, Yukon Territory.

61. **Ross's Gull.** ROSS'S ROSY GULL. WEDGE-TAILED GULL. LA MOUETTE OU MAUVE ROSÉE. *Rhodostethia rosea.* L, 14 (Projection of centre tail feather, 1). A pale-mantled gull with white head and fine black collar line. Tail wedge-shaped, graduated from long centre feather (Figure 341).

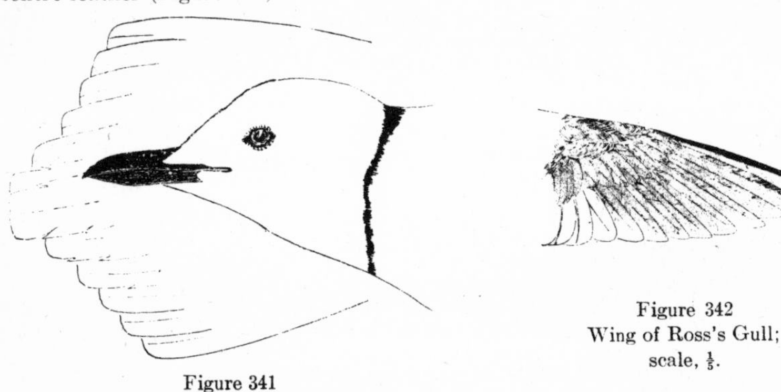

Figure 342
Wing of Ross's Gull;
scale, 1/5.

Figure 341
Ross's Gull; scale, about 1/2.

*Distinctions.* The Arctics. The above description of adult is unlike any other bird it is likely to be compared with. The juvenile resembles, in general, parallel plumages of the black-headed gulls. The secondaries and secondary coverts of Ross's Gull are largely white (Figure 342), showing even more white than Sabine's Gull, and the tail is wedge-shaped instead of forked (Figure 341, compare with 343).

*Field Marks.* A small white-headed gull with large amount of white in wings (Figure 342) and a wedge-shaped tail.

*Nesting.* On the ground, near tundra lakes and ponds.

*Distribution.* The high Arctic regions, nearly circumpolar. Reported to breed in northeastern Asia and Greenland, but not reported as doing so north of American continent.

This species is one of the very rarest of the gulls and has not been recorded south of Norton Sound, Alaska. Within Canadian limits we have only a few scattered records from the Arctic Islands. It is not to be expected elsewhere in Canada.

62. **Sabine's Gull.** LA MOUETTE OU MAUVE DE SABINE. *Xema sabini.* L, 13·50. Similar to Franklin's or Bonaparte's Gull, especially the latter, but smaller and with wings largely black, a dark slate-grey hood bordered basally by a black line making a narrow ring around the upper neck, cutting sharply against a white lower neck (Figure 343).

*Distinctions.* The Arctics. Like a small Franklin's Gull, but with a grey, black-bordered hood instead of a black one. Black legs and feet and black bill tipped with yellow. Tail forked, outer feathers about 1¼ inches longer than middle ones (Figure 343).

Juvenile darker and more evenly sooty above than either Franklin's or Bonaparte's Gulls. Tail forked. In all plumages the wings seem characteristic, the primaries and wrist are almost solid black, the secondaries very largely solid white.

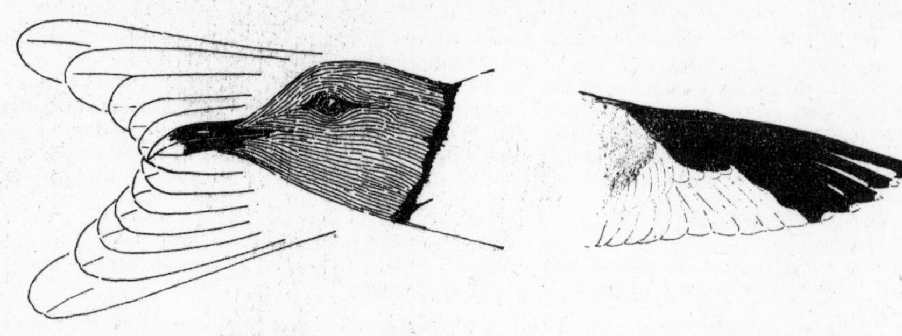

Figure 343
Specific details of Sabine's Gull; scale, ½.

Figure 344
Wing of Sabine's Gull.

*Field Marks.* Should be an easy bird to recognize in life, a small dark-hooded gull with forked tail, intensely black primaries and wrist contrasted with a great white area of secondaries (Figure 344). It is, however, too rare, except in the far north, to be accepted as a record on field observations alone.

*Nesting.* Usually on the moss of the boggy edges of tundra pools.

*Distribution.* The Arctic regions, only occasionally wandering down into southern sections. We have stray records for northern Manitoba, northern Saskatchewan, and southern British Columbia.

One of the most delicately beautiful of the gulls, but too rare to receive more than passing mention.

### Subfamily—Sterninae. Terns

*General Description.* The terns, or Sea Swallows as they are sometimes called, are smaller, lighter, and of more graceful build and habit than the gulls.

*Distinctions.* The bill—lighter, and more slender than that of the gulls (*See* Figure 316, page 218)—and the forked tail are characteristic of the terns and will usually separate them without difficulty. All Canadian species have a more or less forked tail and all but one (the Black Tern) in summer adult plumage have a sharply defined black cap. The forking of the tails of young birds, though beginning to show early in their development, does not reach its maximum until after they leave for the winter; hence, through the summer and autumn, many individuals will be seen with much smaller forks than the given measurements indicate.

*Field Marks.* The greater lightness of action on the wing and constant and rapid aerial evolution; the fact that terns constantly dive from the wing, and the habit of commonly turning the bill straight down towards the water instead of carrying it on a line with the body, are characteristic. The forked tails and black caps are also good recognition marks for adults.

*Nesting.* Whereas gulls seem to prefer rocky shores upon which to breed, the terns, except Forster's and the Black, favour sandy beaches or bare rock surfaces, laying their eggs in a smooth circle of pebbles without other nest preparation.

*Distribution.* As a subfamily, terns are more southerly in distribution than gulls, though at least one species, the Arctic Tern, has been found as far north as land occurs. All our species migrate, none remaining in Canada during the winter.

One has only to watch a flock of terns feeding to recognize the appropriateness of the popular term Sea Swallow. Their active grace and dainty, pearl-like colours are a joy to the nature lover. Terns are, on the whole, less maritime in their habits than gulls and are not so often seen far from land. They haunt harbours, shores, and beaches, and live largely upon small fish caught near the surface by quick, sudden dives from the wing, but they are not scavengers. In these dives the birds plunge in head first with a splash of white spray in which for a moment they disappear, but they never go far under water.

63. **Gull-billed Tern.** LA STERNE HANSEL. *Geochelidon nilotica.* L, 14. About the same size and coloration as the Common Tern, but with a heavier and more gull-like black bill (Figure 345).

Figure 345
Gull-billed Tern; scale, ½.

*Distinctions.* East coast. Characteristic tern-like coloration but moderately forked tail. Comparatively stout, gull-like bill and large legs and feet. Tarsus well over instead of under 1 inch. Hind toe well developed and half the length of the inner one instead of nearer a third as long.

*Distribution.* Nearly cosmopolitan on warm temperate waters. There is one old record for the southern New Brunswick coast.

69. **Forster's Tern.** LA STERNE DE FORSTER. *Sterna forsteri.* L, 15 (Forking of tail 4·1).[1] Plate XXVIII B.

*Distinctions.* Central provinces. Forster's Tern so nearly resembles both the Common and Arctic Terns as to require close attention to small details to differentiate it from them. The most determinative characteristic by which it may be separated from any other species is the coloration of the long outer tail feathers, which are shaded with dark on the inner instead of the outer web (Figure 346). The underparts are also pure white instead of being delicately shaded with pearly grey. In juvenility and autumn or winter plumages, the face markings are quite characteristic. In Forster's Tern the dark face patch is sharply defined and does not overspread the nape to meet its fellow from the other side (Compare with Figure 347). In juvenile and winter plumages the bill is largely or completely black.

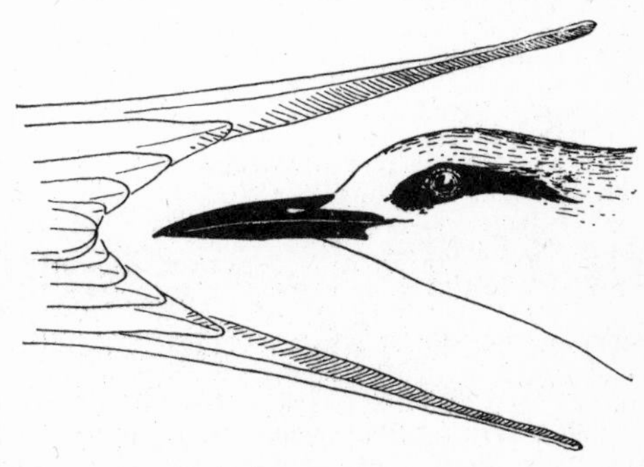

Figure 346
Specific details of Forster's Tern; tail and head of juvenile or winter plumage; scale, ½.

*Field Marks.* In mixed flocks of Common and Forster's Terns the latter can sometimes be distinguished by the superior silvery whiteness of the underparts. The juvenile and autumn plumages are separable by the face mark being confined to the cheeks and not spreading across the back of the neck to make a dark nape band. The best criterion of the species in any plumage, however, is its call-note which is very different from that of the Common. Instead of a sharp *"Tearrrr"* it is a wooden and lower pitched *"Churrrr."* When this difference is once heard and marked it affords the most reliable field guide that can be given.

*Nesting.* On slight elevations in grassy marshes, in nests built of waste vegetation.

[1] This measurement shows the difference in length between the middle and outer tail feathers. A great part of the total length of these birds is in the greatly elongated outer tail feathers and these do not reach their maximum in juvenile birds. Hence this figure is given to correct the oftentimes greatly misleading nature of the usual length measurement.

*Distribution.* A bird of the prairie interior, probably nesting in any suitable place wherever found in Canada. Not yet reported from British Columbia, although there are records from the State of Washington. There are old records for southern Ontario, but not from farther east.

These terns frequent marshes rather than beaches and do not seem to gather in such large flocks on the big lakes as do the Common Tern, to which they are otherwise very similar in habit. Though common throughout the eastern prairie sections they are more local and less generally distributed than the Common Tern.

70. **Common Tern.** WILSON'S TERN. LA STERNE COMMUNE. *Sterna hirundo.* L, 15 (Forking of tail 3·1). Plate XXIX A.

*Distinctions.* East, central, and west. The Common Tern resembles both the Arctic and Forster's Terns so nearly as to require close attention to small details to separate it from them. The certain characteristic by which it can be separated from Forster's, but not the Arctic, is the coloration of the long outer tail feathers, which are shaded with dark on the outer instead of the inner web (Figure 347). The underparts in the adult are also delicately shaded with pearly grey, averaging appreciably lighter than the Arctic but slightly darker than Forster's. This distinction does not always hold with juvenile birds. In young or autumn plumages, the face markings are quite distinct from those of Forster's, but not from the Arctic. In the Common Tern, the dark face patch suffuses across the nape of the neck to meet its fellow from the opposite side, making a continuous nape band (Compare with Figure 346). In juvenility the bill is largely flesh coloured and black and in the autumn adult much of the redness is lost. From the Arctic Tern distinction is rather more difficult. The grey below does not average quite as deep, but this characteristic is not common to all individuals. The forward third of bill of the adult Common Tern is black, but the bill of the Arctic is red to the tip. The only distinction from that species that holds in all plumages is that of the feet and legs. Those of the Arctic Tern are particularly small, the tarsus being not more than 0·65 inch in length; that of the Common Tern is not less than 0·8 inch.

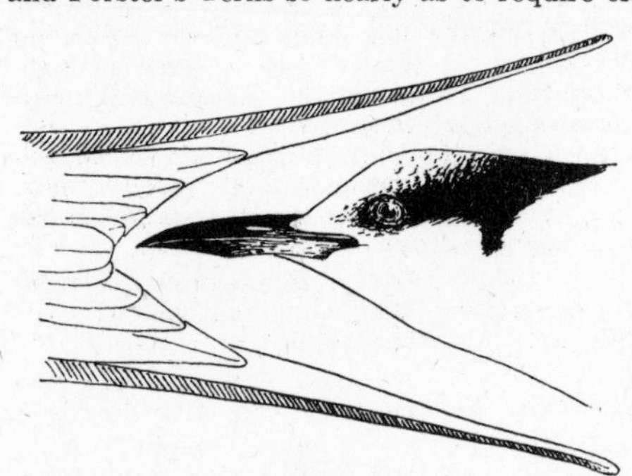

Figure 347
Specific details of Common Tern; tail and head of juvenile or winter plumage; scale, ½.

*Field Marks.* In mixed flocks of Common and Forster's Terns the Common can sometimes be distinguished by the slightly greyish clouding of the white underparts. In autumn and juvenility it can be separated from Forster's by the face mark spreading over the back of the head. The best field distinction between the two species, however, is the call-note which is very different from that of Forster's, which is a sharp *"Tearrrr"* instead of a duller and more woodeny-sounding *"Churrrr."* From the Arctic Tern differentiation is more difficult. The black-tipped instead of all red bill may be made out under favourable circumstances. When on the ground the Common Tern stands up higher on its legs than the Arctic Tern. The latter hugs the ground with its body as it walks, and has a mouse-like glide. The Common Tern is likely to be confused with Forster's only in the interior, and with the Arctic only in the high north and on the two coasts.

*Nesting.* On sandy or gravelly bars. Eggs laid directly on the ground.

*Distribution.* Across the continent, breeding north to southern Labrador, James Bay, and Great Slave Lake. This is the most abundant tern throughout most of southern Canada.

Common, especially in the interior about sandy shores, scarcer on rocky ones. The Common Tern may be seen on most of our larger bodies of water, salt or fresh, throughout the summer. Its wonderful lightness of wing, and graceful circlings—one instant hovering on rapidly beating wings, stationary in the air, as it searches for some tid-bit below, and the next dropping like a plummet with a sparkling splash—are constant delights to a seeker of the beautiful. Its shrill cry, harsh in itself, blends harmoniously with the soft surge of the surf and remains in keeping with marine surroundings.

*Economic Status.* Though fairly numerous in suitable localities this species is too small to be seriously destructive. Late banding activities have given some interesting information on the migrational wanderings of this species. Birds banded at the west on the Massachusetts coast have been taken in the West Indies, the Guianas, the mouth of the Amazon, and even across the broad oceans at the mouth of the River Niger, West Africa.

71. **Arctic Tern.** LA STERNE ARCTIQUE. *Sterna paradisaea.* L, 15·50 (Forking of tail 4·50). Closely resembling the Common and Forster's Terns (*See* Plates XXVIII B and XXIX A) in size and colour.

*Distinctions.* The Arctic Tern has a little deeper greyish suffusion over breast and underparts than the Common Tern. Bill is red to tip, and feet and legs are very small and weak. It is not likely to be confused with Forster's on account of difference in range. In its colour characteristics it resembles the Common Tern very closely.

*Field Marks.* An all red bill, and little short legs that make it look when standing as if crouching directly on the ground, and when walking it moves with a mouse-like glide.

*Distribution.* The Arctic regions, south in the interior to the big lakes of Mackenzie region, southern Alaska, and Nova Scotia. It has been taken along the west coast as far as the Canadian line, but rarely in British Columbia waters. We have records from the northern interior of that province, but none from anywhere east of the mountains. It is particularly a maritime species, rarely seen inland or on fresh water.

The remarks made under the Common Tern will apply to this species. It is remarkable that it has not been observed more often in our southern latitudes, for the species makes one of the longest migrations known. Summering north as far as land occurs, it winters as far south as the Antarctic continent. How it journeys there from the northwest coast without being noted more often en route is one of the interesting problems of American ornithology. Recent migration studies have produced interesting results. Birds banded on the Labrador coast have been taken on the coast of France and south as far as Natal, South Africa, on the Indian Ocean.

72. **Roseate Tern.** LA STERNE ROSÉE. *Sterna dougalli.* L, about 14·5. **Like the** Common and Arctic Terns but with a black bill.

Figure 348
Roseate Tern; scale, ½.

*Distinctions.* Like the Common and Arctic Terns but with a very long black bill (1·5 or over). Pure white or rosy underparts and excessively long white streamers to tail (Figure 348).

*Distribution.* Temperate and tropical seas of both hemispheres. In North America breeding up the Atlantic coast to southern Nova Scotia.

75. **Sooty Tern.** LA STERNE FULIGINEUSE. *Sterna fuscata.* L, 16·5. A little larger than the Common Tern but with a solid black mantle.

*Distinctions.* Solid black mantle and white underparts and forehead. The juvenile has a generally dark appearance but is considerably larger than the Black Tern.

*Distribution.* Tropical and sub-tropical seas. The Canadian status rests on a single specimen taken in Nova Scotia.

Figure 349
Sooty Tern; scale, ½.

74. **Least Tern.** LA PETITE STERNE. *Sterna antillarum.* L, about 9. Like a very diminutive Common Tern.

*Distinctions.* Evident tern-like form and extremely diminutive size make this species unmistakable.

*Distribution.* Tropical and southern temperate America. Canadian status based on a few old records, for Nova Scotia and southern Ontario, some probably incorrect and none beyond dispute.

67. **Sandwich Tern.** LA STERNE DE MER CAUGEK. *Thalasseus sandvicensis.* L, about 15 (Forking of tail about 2·25). About same general coloration as the Common and Arctic Terns but paler of mantle, larger of body, and with black, yellow-tipped bill.

*Distinctions.* A distinctly heavier bird than the Common Tern, but not measuring as long by reason of shorter development of tail. The black bill with yellow tip is distinctive of most plumages.

*Distribution.* Europe and North and South America north to Virginia. In Canada there seems to be a fairly well substantiated old record for southern Ontario.

*SUBSPECIES.* Represented in America by Cabot's Tern (la Sterne de Cabot) *Thalasseus sandvicensis acuflavides.*

64. **Caspian Tern.** LA STERNE CASPIENNE. *Hydroprogne caspia.* L, 21 (Forking of tail 1·50). The largest of our Canadian terns. In colour very similar to the Common Tern (*See* page 236 and Plate XXIX A).

*Distinctions.* Large size of this tern is characteristic. The Caspian Tern is as large as some of the smaller gulls; but its bill, though comparatively heavy for a tern, is too graceful and tapering to be gull-like.

*Field Marks.* Rather distinctively marked in life. In size, it is more likely to be compared with a Ring-billed Gull than a tern, but its big red bill, black cap, slightly forked tail, and general tern-like coloration are plain. The slow beat of its long wings is different from the more quickly moving small tern and its voice is raucous; a single hoarse monosyllable that may be rendered *"Casp"* is characteristic.

*Nesting.* On sandy beaches, or rocky or gravelly islands.

*Distribution.* A nearly cosmopolitan species. Found in the Old as well as the New World. Occurs rather irregularly all over Canada, but its known nesting stations are few and scattered over the continent from Great Slave Lake to Labrador.

*SUBSPECIES.* The American Caspian Tern (la Sterne caspienne d'Amérique) has been lately separated from that of the Old World under the name of *Hydroprogne caspia imperator.*

We have breeding records for this species on the Gulf of St. Lawrence, Lakes Ontario, Huron, Michigan, Winnipeg, and Great Slave Lake, and occasional sight records down through the Prairie Provinces and southern British Columbia.

PLATE XLIX

A. Steller's Jay; scale, $\frac{1}{4}$
(Black-headed Jay)

B. Magpie; scale, $\frac{1}{5}$

Plate L

A. American Crow; scale, $\frac{1}{5}$

B. Clarke's Nutcracker; scale, $\frac{1}{3}$

*Economic Status.* Though probably a fish feeder and the largest of its subfamily the Caspian Tern is too scarce and its food is too small to have any appreciable economic influence.

A particularly beautiful and interesting bird. Its wide range, scattered breeding stations, and growing scarcity suggest that the numbers we see today are the remnants of a once much more numerous and generally distributed race and that if we are to have it with us in the future special care should be taken to guard its local nesting communities from molestation.

77. **Black Tern.** LA STERNE NOIRE. *Chlidonias nigra.* L, 10 (Forking of tail 0·8). The smallest of our common terns, dark slate-grey, deepening to dull black on head, neck, and underparts.

*Distinctions.* The above description is sufficient to separate summer adults. Winter and immature birds have a dirty white face, throat, neck ring, and underparts, and the grey above is suffused with more or less brown. It is, however, always considerably darker than corresponding plumages of other species. This fact, and the small size of the bird, should be sufficient to differentiate it at all times. Immature plumages retained throughout the following summer have been the basis of occasional records for the White-winged Black Tern, which has been removed from the Canadian list.

Figure 350
Black Tern; scale, ½.
Winter Spring

*Field Marks.* Size and coloration make this species easy to recognize in life.

*Nesting.* On slight elevations such as old muskrat houses or floating debris in wet marshes, nest of vegetable matter.

*Distribution.* The American Black Tern is a bird of the interior, breeding from the Great Lakes region westward, north as far as Great Slave Lake in the interior, and in southern British Columbia.

*SUBSPECIES.* The Black Tern occurs in both Europe and America in allied subspecific forms of which the European is the type. The American Black Tern (la Sterne noire d'Amérique) *C.n. surinamensis* is the subspecies with which we are concerned.

This is a bird characteristic of the inland marshes, only rarely seen on the larger bodies of water. In southern Ontario and throughout the interior prairies no extensive expanse of watery marsh is without it. Its general habits are much like those of the other terns. It is less common in British Columbia than east of the mountains.

*Economic Status.* The insect content of this bird's food is probably larger than that of the other terns. In the south it is known to consume the larvæ of the cotton-boll weevil and it follows the ploughman of the west for the grubs turned up. Therefore, we may venture to state that it is probably actively beneficial. At any rate the fish it takes, if any, are mud-inhabiting forms of small economic importance.

### FAMILY—RYNCHOPIDAE. SKIMMERS

The skimmers are a small family strongly characterized by having the lower mandible projecting far beyond the upper. We have but one species of only casual occurrence in Canada.

Figure 351
Bill of Skimmer; scale, ½.

80. **Black Skimmer.** LE BEC-EN-CISEAUX NOIR. *Rynchops nigra.* L, 18. Large, black and white birds of the east coast, with long mandibles, flattened and deepened like paper knives and the lower mandible extending far beyond the upper one (Figure 351).

*Distinctions.* Strongly characterized as above.

*Distribution.* Tropical and south temperate parts of the American coast. Occurs casually as far north as Nova Scotia.

## SUBORDER—ALCAE. SEA-DIVERS

*General Description.* The Sea-divers are birds fitted for sub-aquatic pursuits. The hip-joint is set far back on the body and the leg mechanism is better fitted for swimming than for walking. The toes are completely (Figure 352) webbed, but lack the hind toe. The wings are small in comparison with the size of the body. The bill is straight and usually tapered, moderately long (Figures 355 to 361); but occasionally flattened and deepened, as in the cases of the auks and puffins (Figures 353, 354, and 367 to 371); in the latter group this specialization reaches its highest development in the order.

Figure 352
Typical foot of Sea-diver.

*Distinctions.* Toes, three, entirely webbed.

*Field Marks.* Small wings and tail; and straight, narrow bills—not duck-like. The divers bear a superficial resemblance to ducks, but where ducks would fly they dive.

*Nesting.* In the immediate vicinity of water on reedy shores or rocky ledges, or crevices and holes in the ground.

In consequence of the peculiar leg construction, an unusually upright carriage of body is necessitated when on land, and the birds walk with difficulty. Indeed some species are almost helpless on the ground and are unable to rise into the air except from the water, off steeply rising ground, or against a strong head wind. They swim and dive with ease, and, though their wings are small in proportion to the size of the body, when once on the wing they fly with rapid beats, swiftly and strongly, in straight lines or long curves without evolution or manœuvring.

*Economic Status.* The diving birds feed almost entirely upon aquatic life, usually captured by diving and pursuit under water. Economically, they are of slight importance.

### Subfamily—Plautinae. Great Auks

As there is but a single well-characterized species in this subfamily, and that one is now extinct, see following species for description.

33. **Great Auk.** GARE-FOWL. LE GRAND PINGOUIN. *Plautus impennis.* L, 30. The Great Auk was the largest of the American divers. Its wings were so reduced in size that though they made excellent swimming organs they were useless for flight. As the species is now extinct no further description is necessary.

This bird had become so well adapted to an aquatic life that flying was no longer necessary and consequently its wings became reduced to mere swimming flippers like those of the penguins of the Antarctic, and flight was impossible. Though as well able to live at sea as any fish or marine animal, land was as necessary to it for reproduction as to any other bird. Even then, if it had inhabited the very extremes of the Arctic regions for nesting purposes it would probably have survived; but lonely outlying rocks and islets about the British Isles and, on our side of the ocean, south to Newfoundland, were its nesting places and immediately in the course of the fleets of hardy fishermen who early in our history flocked to our shores. To them, these then countless thousands of large sea birds inhabiting islets in the immediate vicinity of their fishing grounds, so helpless on land that they could be killed in unlimited numbers with sticks and clubs, were irresistible. They took full advantage of their opportunities and the story passes current that to save labour, gang planks were placed ashore from the boats and the unresisting birds were driven aboard in droves to be clubbed to death on deck. Of course no numbers could long resist such destruction and today the Great Auk is an interesting memory represented by only individual specimens and fragments in a few favoured museums.

Figure 353
Great Auk; scale, about $\frac{1}{8}$.

## FAMILY—ALCINAE. AUKS AND MURRES

*General Description.* This family is composed of strictly maritime species of rare or only accidental occurrence on fresh water. Though most at home in the water, the birds stand upright on land and walk about with considerably more ease than do the grebes or loons. Their bills are usually straight and tapered.

*Distinctions.* The obvious diver-like form, combined with webbed feet and no hind toes (Figure 352), is diagnostic.

*Field Marks.* General resemblance to ducks, but with short necks, and pointed bills.

*Nesting.* Usually breed in large colonies, many of mixed species, on rocky islets or inaccessible sea-washed cliffs. Build no nest, but lay their eggs directly on the ground. Eggs are unusually large for the size of the bird and markedly pyriform, a shape that causes them to roll in circles rather than in straight lines and lessens the danger of their falling from the bare, rocky, nesting ledges.

*Distribution.* Along the seacoasts to the Arctic, rarely occurring on fresh water.

This family frequents the open sea, coming ashore only to breed. The birds differ from the other divers in habitually using their wings under water as in flying. In primitive Indian and fishing communities Sea-divers and their eggs have in the past been much used for food. In certain localities, they may still be a most important food supply for tribes who have little other source of fresh meat and who have depended upon them from time immemorial. It is not suggested that they are legitimate food supply for white men, who are expected to provide themselves with other supplies beforehand. These birds are protected under the Migratory Birds Convention Act and cannot legally be killed anywhere or at any season in United States or Canada, except for personal consumption by certain Eskimos and Indians. There is no systematic difference between murres and guillemots; the names are practically interchangeable and it is only usage that determines which name to apply to various species.

*Economic Status.* Eating nothing but the smaller sizes of fish and crustaceans taken at sea, where the supplies are more than ample, there is little harm that these species can do. A new and modern enemy of these birds is the oil-burning ship. These have been in the habit of filling their fuel tanks with water as the oil is burned. On approaching harbour, or before refuelling, this water is discharged into the sea and with it large amounts of oily waste and sludge, which float on the surface and thoroughly permeate the plumage of any birds swimming in it, quickly causing their death. A comparatively small amount of oil will cover a vast extent of sea and at times thousands of sea birds have been killed in this way. Steps have been taken to prevent this pollution of the sea, and the danger to birds is being controlled. However, unavoidable loss of oil by such accidents as wrecks, and occasional violations of the law, will destroy numbers of birds every year.

Figure 354
Razor-billed Auk; scale, ⅓.

32. **Razor-billed Auk.** TINKER. LE GODE (Le Pingouin commun). *Alca torda.* L, 16·50. The Razor-billed Auk is, except for bill, of the same general appearance as the next two species.

*Distinctions.* Bill is considerably deepened and flattened (though not nearly as much so as in the puffin); it is thus easily distinguished from the murre, especially in summer when a white line connects the eye and the base of the culmen and the bill is crossed by a white band near the tip. Bill of the winter juvenile is less characteristic but may still be distinguished from that of the murres.

*Field Marks.* Deepened bill and, when swimming, cocked-up tail make good field marks.

*Nesting.* Similar to that of the two succeeding species but rather less gregarious.

*Distribution.* Frequents our Atlantic coasts north to the Arctic.

30. **Common Murre.** LA MARMETTE COMMUNE OU LE GUILLEMOT COMMUN. *Uria aalge.* L, 16. The Common Murre in summer is white below, with head and neck dark seal-brown, and back and wings black. On the Atlantic occurs a sporadic form with a narrow white ring about the eye and a line back therefrom. This was at one time thought to be a distinct species and given the name *ringvia* (*See* Figure 357, right). In winter the throat is light (Figure 355) veiled with more or less greyish, and the brown is replaced with black almost unicolour with the back.

Figure 355
Common Murre; scale, ⅓.
Winter

*Distinctions.* On the Atlantic coast easily separated from the Razor-billed Auk by its tapering, sharply pointed bill (Compare Figure 355 with 354). The Thick-billed Guillemot, however, causes more difficulty. In summer the adult murre lacks the pale blue streak at the gape of the bill, and the bill is slightly longer and more slender (Compare Figures 355 and 358). In winter this species has a dash of black back from the eye and across the cheek (Figure 355, compare with 358). On the Pacific coast the Rhinoceros Auklet is the Canadian species that most closely resembles it, but is much smaller, has a short bill, usually with a horn (Figure 365, page 247), and an evenly dark greyish throat.

*Field Marks.* Large size and general black and white coloration as a murre. Swimming, the sharp bill and tail carried low instead of slightly cocked-up will separate from the Razor-bill. From the Thick-billed Guillemot, the squarer line between the white breast and black throat and the absence of light streak along the bill gape are the best field marks in summer. In winter the white patch back from the eye may sometimes be seen. From the Rhinoceros Auklet, larger size and longer bill.

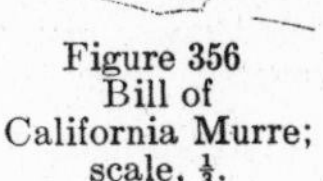

Figure 356
Bill of
California Murre;
scale, ⅓.

*Nesting.* In large colonies amongst rocks and in crevices of bold sea faces.

*Distribution.* Coasts and islands of north Atlantic and north Pacific. In America from southern Nova Scotia north along the Labrador and locally from California northward to Alaska.

*SUBSPECIES.* The Murre of the east coast is the Atlantic Murre (la Marmette ou le Guillemot de l'Atlantique) *Uria aalge aalge;* of the west coast the California Murre (la Marmette ou le Guillemot du Pacifique) *Uria aalge californica,* distinguished by a more salient angle at base of lower mandible (Figure 355, compare with 356).

The numbers of murres that find breeding room on some sea-cliffs is astonishing. At the edge of the rocky shelves they gather as closely as they can stand, like files of soldiers, bearing strong resemblance to the lines of penguins that we see in pictures from the Antarctic.

Figure 357
Field marks of Murres:
Left, Thick-billed Guillemot; Centre, Common Murre; Right, *ringvia* form of Common Murre.

31. **Thick-billed Murre.** BRÜNNICH'S MURRE. LA MARMETTE OU LE GUILLEMOT DU NORD. *Uria lomvia.* L, 16·50. This murre is almost exactly similar to the preceding species.

*Distinctions.* Like the Common Murre, but the bill is somewhat larger and noticeably heavier (Figure 358, compare with 355). In summer the base of the upper mandible at the gape is light bluish, the head and crown are perceptibly darker than the throat instead of being similar in colour, and the white breast invades the black foreneck in an acuter angle (Figure 357). In winter the black of the crown comes down over the eyes and ears without a break, leaving no white dash back from over the eyes (Compare Figures 358 and 355).

Figure 358
Thick-billed Guillemot;
scale, ½.
Winter

*Field Marks.* Stubbier, heavier bill and coloration of the head and neck will under exceptional visual conditions separate this bird in life from the Common Murre. Sharp and tapering instead of blunt and deep bill, and tail not turned up in swimming, should serve to distinguish it from the Razor-billed Auk (*See* previous species)

*Distribution.* More northern than the Common Murre. Breeding from the Gulf of St. Lawrence into the high Arctics in the east and Bering Sea in the west.

*SUBSPECIES.* Eastern and western birds are represented by two subspecies. The eastern form is Brünnich's Murre (la Marmette ou le Guillemot de Brünnich) *Uria lomvia lomvia*, the western is Pallas' Murre (la Marmette ou le Guillemot de Pallas) *Uria lomvia arra.* The latter has never been identified in Canadian waters but may be expected on the British Columbia coast occasionally in winter.

Brünnich's Murre is the only member of this family that is found on the Great Lakes. The birds have at irregular times come in hundreds on Lake Ontario, Lake Erie, and tributary waters in late autumn and early winter, all in a starving condition, and none seem to survive or return to their sea homes. These occurrences are as yet inexplicable.

Figure 359
Dovekie; scale, ⅓.
Winter
Summer

34. **Dovekie.** SEA DOVE. LE MERGULE NAIN (Petit bonhomme). *Alle alle.* L, 8. The Dovekie is a diminutive diver, the smallest of its family in eastern Canada. When in our waters it is generally black above and white on throat, cheek, and below.

*Distinctions.* Its size is enough to separate it from any other diver in eastern Canada, though on the west coast there is a species comparable with it in size.

*Field Marks.* Size and extremely rapid wing beats make the best field marks.

*Nesting.* On cliff ledges in the far north.

*Distribution.* In summer in the far north in the eastern Arctic, in winter along the Atlantic seacoasts.

On our eastern coastal shores and harbours this little bird should be looked for only in the winter. It flies with a very rapid wing motion.

27. **Black Guillemot.** PIGEON. SEA PIGEON. LE GUILLEMOT NOIR. *Cepphus grylle.* L, 13. In summer the Black Guillemot is a small, coal black diver with large white wing patches and red feet (Figure 360, right). In winter the underparts are white and the feathers above are black but broadly tipped with white. The wings remain as in summer (Figure 360, left).

Figure 360
Black Guillemot; scale, ⅐.
Winter Summer

*Distinctions.* In summer the species cannot be mistaken for any other. In winter, the size and wing coloration are almost equally distinctive.

*Field Marks.* The characters above make easily recognizable field marks.

*Nesting.* In cavities in the rocks or in openings in the rough talus at the foot of sea cliffs.

*Distribution.* The Black Guillemot is common along our Atlantic coast but is rarely if ever seen inland.

*SUBSPECIES.* There are two subspecies of the Black Guillemot in Canada, the Common Black Guillemot (le Guillemot noir commun) *Cepphus grylle grylle*, and Mandt's Guillemot (le Guillemot noir de Mandt) *Cepphus grylle mandti*, a northern race inhabiting Arctic regions and distinguished by having all the wing coverts white to the base instead of with a concealed dark wing bar.

The Black Guillemot is one of the commonest inhabitants of our eastern seacoast and is known to nearly all who visit there. It is less gregarious than the other members of the family and usually nests alone and not in rookeries, though sometimes numbers are drawn together in localities by a community of interest.

29. **Pigeon Guillemot.** LE GUILLEMOT DU PACIFIQUE. *Cepphus columba.* L, 13·50. In summer (Figure 361, left) solid greenish black with conspicuous white wing patch and bright red feet and legs. Juveniles (Figure 361, right) and winter birds: underparts white, above mostly black, but the white feathers are tipped with black and the black ones broadly edged with white, the wings being as in summer.

Figure 361
Pigeon Guillemot; scale, $\frac{1}{7}$.
Summer Winter

*Distinctions.* Just like the Black Guillemot except the white wing patch divided by a black bar and is a Pacific instead of an Atlantic species.

*Field Marks.* Summer adult: an all black bird with white wing patches and bright red feet. Too large for a murrelet and too small for a murre.

*Nesting.* In crevices of the cliffs and under rocks on steep shores.

*Distribution.* Coasts of Bering Sea and the Pacific Ocean south to California.

One of the commonest inhabitants of our western seacoasts and familiar to all who frequent them. It is less gregarious than many of its relatives and nests alone rather than in rookeries, though sometimes common interest attracts numbers to limited localities.

This is the western representative of the Black Guillemot of the Atlantic, *Cepphus grylle,* from which it differs only in having the white wing-spot divided by a black bar.

23. **Marbled Murrelet.** LA PETITE ALQUE MARBRÉ. *Brachyramphus marmoratus.* L, 9·50. Plate XXIX B. Adult in summer: all wood-brown with reddish feather edgings on back and mottled softly with white on forward and under surfaces. Juveniles and in winter: blackish above, deeper on crown, and white below to chin.

*Distinctions.* Similar in size and, in winter, in colour, to the Ancient Murrelet, but with longer and more slender bill. Winter birds otherwise differ from that species in having white chin and lores; back slightly bluish on feather edges instead of solidly so, and a broad white line on the back over the folded wing.

*Field Marks.* In the summer adult, its small size and general blackness. Also the perky way in which it carries its bill and tail cocked up when sitting on the water. In winter plumage, when Ancient Murrelets are about, probably the small amount of black on the head and the less sharply defined pattern are the best distinctions.

*Nesting.* In burrows in the ground.

*Distribution.* The Pacific coast of Alaska to the State of Washington, wintering to southern California.

All summer the Strait of Georgia, especially along the edges of the kelp beds, may often be sprinkled with these little sea-birds. They scatter over the smooth surface in fine weather, generally in pairs, floating high and lightly, with bill and tail cocked up at a perky angle, and converse in low, soft whistles. On being approached by a boat, they seem indifferent at first, but gradually grow uneasy and circle with increasing confusion. Just as their panic seems to culminate, and they are apparently in doubt where next to turn, they bethink themselves of the safe green depths, and, with a forward spring, a partial opening of the wings, and a little splash, they dive with an unexpected suddenness which suggests that a new and entirely unlooked for discovery in the tactics of escape has just been made.

Though common in full summer plumage throughout the summer along the whole British Columbia coast and suspected to nest nearby, its breeding is still more or less of a mystery. It is yet doubtful where the great number that haunt the coast breed, but it is probable that their nests will be found eventually at considerable elevations some distance inland from the adjoining sea.

21. **Ancient Murrelet.** LA PETITE ALQUE À TÊTE GRISE. *Synthliboramphus antiquus.* L, 9·50. Adult in summer: slaty blue above; white below; head, hindneck, face, and sharply defined throat patch pure black (Figure 362b). A few small, white, lanceolate feathers forming stripe back from over eye and scattered through black at base of hindneck. Juvenile plumage similar (Figure 362a) but black restricted, the throat and side of neck being conspicuously snowy white. None of the little white feathering in the black.

Figure 362
Ancient Murrelet; scale, ⅓.
*a*, Juveniles and winter; *b*, Summer.

*Distinctions.* The sharply defined black and white coloration of the head and foreparts. Winter juveniles are quite similar to winter Marbled Murrelets (*See* Plate XXIX B) in size and general coloration, but the back is pure, even slate-grey without white stripes over the wings and the black of the face includes all in front of the eye, without the loral spot, and extends in light smokiness across the chin. The bill is also much shorter and proportionally deeper.

*Field Marks.* In the case of the adult the intense black head contrasted with the pure white foreparts should be very conspicuous in life.

*Nesting.* In burrows in the ground.

*Distribution.* Breeds on the Pacific coast of Alaska south to Queen Charlotte Islands and migrates down to southern California.

This little murrelet breeds on Forrester Island across Dixon Entrance from the Queen Charlottes, but has not yet been known to nest within our borders, although it frequents our waters in winter.

16. **Cassin's Auklet.** LA PETITE ALQUE DE CASSIN. *Ptychoramphus aleuticus.* L, 8·75. The smallest of the divers commonly occurring on the Pacific coast of Canada. The only other diver that is smaller is the Least Auklet which so far has not been detected in our waters. Above, black, greying on back, deepest on crown, lightening across face and throat to ashy grey (Figure 363) and blending into white underparts. Small white spots over and below the eye. Juveniles are similar but brownish instead of blackish and without the loral spot.

Figure 363
Cassin's Auklet; scale, ½.

*Distinctions.* Small size, light ashy or brownish grey throat, and small white spot over and below the eye.

*Field Marks.* Small size and dull, obscure coloration.

*Nesting.* Burrows in the ground and in some cases in niches and crevices in the rocks. Often in large communities.

*Distribution.* Breeding from Lower California to the Aleutian Islands. North of California very local in distribution. The only ascertained nesting record known in British Columbia is at the north end of Queen Charlotte Islands.

Gambel's Chickadee; scale, $\frac{1}{3}$

A. Black-capped Chickadee; scale, $\frac{1}{3}$

B. Chestnut-backed Chickadee; scale, $\frac{1}{3}$

Plate LII

A. White-breasted Nuthatch; scale, $\frac{2}{5}$

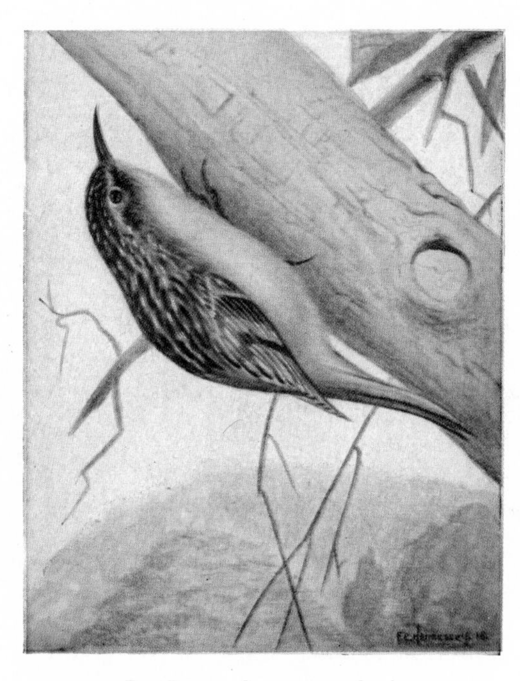

B. Brown Creeper; scale, $\frac{1}{2}$

This little diver should be noted more often than it has been along our coast, especially on the outer shore of Vancouver Island where breeding colonies will probably be found.

17. **Paroquet Auklet.** LA PETITE ALQUE PERROQUET. *Cyclorrhynchus psittacula.* L, 9·75. Adults: head, neck, and back dull brownish; all below white. Bill small, bright red, and with cutting edges peculiarly upturned. A narrow spray of fine white plumes extending backward from under the eye (Figure 364). Juvenile and winter plumage: with white invading the dark foreneck and without facial plumes.

*Distinctions.* Small size, little red bill, and facial plumes.

*Field Marks.* Small size, dark head, neck, and back, with white underparts, and little red bill should be distinctive in suitable circumstances.

Figure 364
Paroquet Auklet; scale, ½.

*Nesting.* Under stones or in clefts in the rocks.

*Distribution.* Northern Pacific and Bering Sea coasts of Alaska. This bird has been noted at Forrester Island, across Dixon Entrance from Queen Charlotte Islands, and also in the Strait of Juan de Fuca and must eventually be taken along the intervening coast, though up to the present it has not been so recorded.

15. **Rhinoceros Auklet.** LA PETITE ALQUE À BEC CORNU. *Cerorhinca monocerata.* L, 14·50. One of the larger members of the subfamily. Dark, smoky brown, slightly lightening on foreneck, breast, and flanks and pure or dirty white below. In breeding plumage, there are remarkable sparse sprays or tufts of white, plume-like feathers extending from above the eye and the angle of the mouth back and downward (Figure 365). The name "Rhinoceros" is obtained from the single upstanding process at the base of the culmen, nearly half an inch high and half as wide. In winter, the plumes and horn are usually shed, the horn being indicated then and in juveniles only by a small, soft knob (Figure 366).

Figure 365
Rhinoceros Auklet; scale, ½.

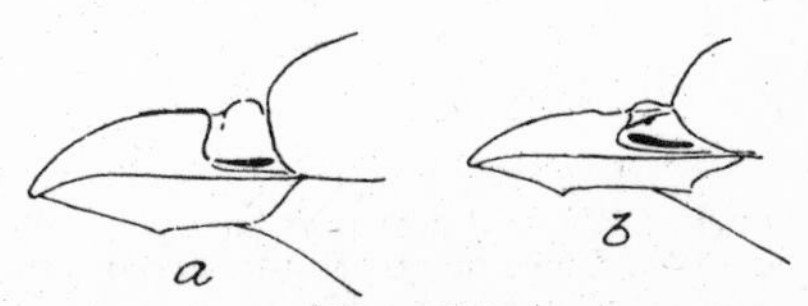


Figure 366
Bills of Rhinoceros Auklet; scale, ½.
*a*, Adult in winter;
*b*, Juvenile.

*Distinctions.* Size, general smoky-brown coloration with light underbody, and the rhinoceros horn or knob at base of upper mandible.

*Field Marks.* Probably in life to be confused only with the puffins or the murres. When seen, the horn or face tufts should be determinative. Has not the big, highly coloured bill of the puffins. Larger than the auklets and murrelets, smaller than the murres and more stubby in build, especially about the head. Of different colour from the guillemots. No bright colour anywhere.

*Nesting.* In burrows in the ground, usually in steeply sloping banks facing the sea.

*Distribution.* Coast and islands of the north Pacific. Breeding from Sitka south to Washington.

We have few actual breeding records for the species in British Columbia. There are colonies, however, about the south end of Vancouver Island and elsewhere in the lonelier spots along the coast between Vancouver Island and the Alaska boundary.

**Subfamily—Fraterculinae. Puffins**

The puffins are stockily built sea-birds and like the others of the family strictly confined to salt water. Their striking peculiarity is a highly coloured and tremendously exaggerated bill. This is triangular in profile, nearly as deep as long, flattened, and knife-like in section. In winter, puffins shed most of the brilliant plates that form their extraordinary bill and consequently at that season it is much reduced in size and coloration. However, immediately after the nesting season, puffins go out to sea, where they scatter and are seldom seen in that condition.

13. **Atlantic Puffin.** SEA PARROT. PAROQUET. LE MACAREUX DE L'ATLANTIQUE. *Fratercula artica.* L, 13. The puffin is a grotesque little diver, black above, white below, and with a grey face. It is notable for its absurdly deepened and flattened bill, nearly as high as long and highly coloured with reds and yellows (Figure 367). In winter most of this bill is shed (Figure 368).

*Distinctions.* East coast. Bill is always distinctive.

*Field Marks.* Bill can be recognized in life nearly as far as the bird can be seen.

Figure 367
Atlantic Puffin; scale, ½.

Figure 368
Atlantic Puffin; scale, ½.
Adult in winter.

*Nesting.* Breeds in the crannies and cracks of rocky cliffs or burrows in the soil on lonely islets. Along the Canadian Labrador coast there are several "Paroquet" islands, so-called from the great numbers of these birds breeding on them. However, the depredations of fishermen have sadly reduced their numbers and unless protective steps are taken they may shortly be exterminated.

*Distribution.* Puffins are distributed over the seacoast on both sides of the Atlantic from Canada and England northward far into the Arctic zone.

A sight of this bird is sufficient for recognition of the appropriateness of the names Sea Parrot or Paroquet. Unlike other divers it stands up on its toes and is quite agile afoot.

14. **Horned Puffin.** LE MACAREUX CORNU. *Fratercula corniculata.* L, 14·50. A slightly smaller puffin than the Tufted, but with a similarly flattened and deepened bill. The whole face is pure white (Figure 369), as is the underbody, and there are no crests.

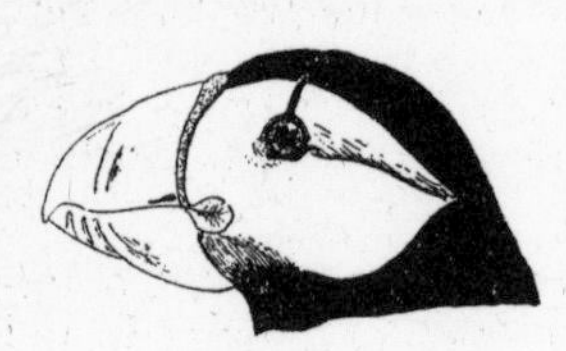

Figure 369
Horned Puffin; scale, ⅓.

*Distinctions.* West coast. The black neck and throat and white underbody in contrast with the all-black body of the preceding species, the only bird likely to be confused with it, are unmistakable. It gets its name of "Horned" from the peculiar excrescent growth from the eyelids, one process of which projects upward nearly half an inch like a rather flaccid, erectile horn.

*Field Marks.* Puffins in summer are always recognizable by their big, showy bills. The white instead of almost black underparts should be distinctive from the next species.

*Nesting.* In crevices in sea-cliffs or in burrows in the ground.

*Distribution.* Coast and islands of Bering Sea south just to Canadian territory. We have no substantiated breeding records in Canada.

Figure 370
Horned Puffin in winter; scale, $\frac{1}{3}$.
Adult Juvenile

This puffin probably migrates in winter seaward rather than south along the coast and we have no record of it for southern British Columbia. It should be looked for along the outer coast of Vancouver Island.

12. **Tufted Puffin.** LE MACAREUX HUPPÉ. *Lunda cirrhata.* L, 15·50. A very dark brown bird, almost black on back and crown, with white face, and in full plumage with long, sweeping, plume-like crests of straw yellow, springing from behind and over the eye, falling almost to the shoulders. The bill is nearly 2 inches high at base and $2\frac{1}{2}$ long, and coloured bright red (Figure 371). An altogether extraordinary looking bird.

Figure 371
Tufted Puffin; scale, $\frac{1}{3}$.

*Distinctions.* West coast. Enormous red bill, dark underbody, and long, sweeping, straw-coloured crests. Young Tufted Puffins, before the large bill has developed, are very like young Rhinoceros Auklets, but lack the horn on top of bill (*See* Figure 366) which is rudimentary even at that age in those birds.

*Field Marks.* The striking, coloured bill is conspicuous in the puffins in life. The distinctive character of this species is probably the dark underbody, instead of white as in the last species, and the conspicuous, light-coloured crests.

*Nesting.* In cracks and crannies of rocks, or in burrows in the ground. Cliffs or steep banks preferred.

*Distribution.* The Pacific coast of North America, breeding from California to Bering Sea.

The known breeding grounds in Canada of these striking and interesting birds are about the south end of Vancouver Island, the Triangle, and Queen Charlotte Islands. Others no doubt exist.

## Order—Columbiformes. Pigeons and Doves

This order, of world-wide distribution, is variously divided by different authors. According to the system of classification of the American Ornithologists' Union all our American species are included in the one family, *Columbidae.* They are the most typically pigeon-like in form and, therefore, may be called the True Pigeons.

### FAMILY—COLUMBIDAE. TRUE PIGEONS AND DOVES

Pigeons and doves may in a general way be said to resemble in outline and actions our familiar domestic stock. Characters are more easily felt than described. Systematically, they may be recognized by their bills. These are hard and horny at the tip, which is very slightly enlarged. The basal half is furnished with a soft, slightly swollen membrane in which the nostrils open (Figure 372). The legs and feet are weak, fitted only for walking over small level areas or for simple perching. Our common domestic

Figure 372
Bill of Pigeon.

Pigeons, descended from the Rock Dove of Europe, show the most distinctive characteristics of the family. There are no recognizable or taxonomic differences between the so-called pigeons and doves.

312. **Band-tailed Pigeon.** LE PIGEON À QUEUE BARRÉE. *Columba fasciata.* L, 16. Plate XXX A. The largest of our pigeons, resembling in general outline and build the common domestic inhabitants of our dovecots.

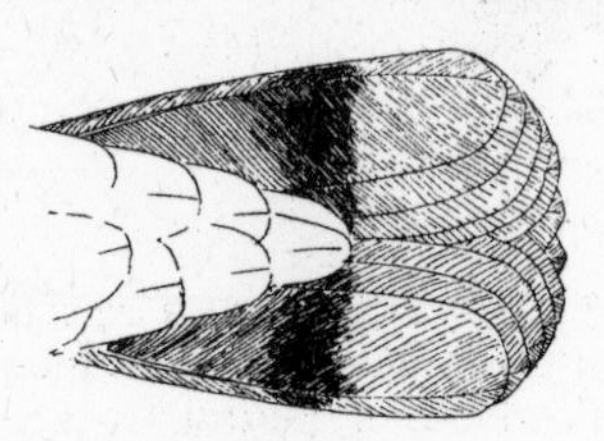

Figure 373
Tail of Band-tailed Pigeon (under side); scale, ⅓.

*Distinctions.* Easily separated from the Mourning Dove and Passenger Pigeon by its large size, bluish colour, and broad, rounded (Figure 373), instead of long, pointed, tail. From the White-winged Dove, which has a similarly shaped tail, by its greatly superior size, bluish to purple general colour, and the lack of white patch on wings.

*Field Marks.* Evident dove appearance, round tail, large size, and general blue coloration. Separated from the domestic dove by its habitat and readiness to alight in trees.

*Nesting.* Platform of sticks in dense shrubbery.

*Distribution.* In Canada, west of the Coast Range north at least to Bella Coola; west in the United States to central Colorado and south to Central America.

*SUBSPECIES.* All birds except those of Lower California are referred to the type form, the Northern Band-tailed Pigeon (le Pigeon à queue barrée du Nord) *Columba fasciata fasciata.*

The Band-tailed is the common pigeon of the west coast. Its large size makes it a rather valuable table bird, but it has not been hunted much nor seriously reduced in numbers in Canada. In the United States it has been pursued in winter to such an extent as to seriously deplete its numbers and arouse some anxiety regarding its future. Since adequate protective measures have been established, it seems to be recovering satisfactorily.

In the spring the species forms vast flocks that move irregularly about, and considerable more or less justified complaint against them comes from farmers whose newly sowed crops they have settled upon. It does not seem that they commonly take other than surface grain, and drilling it in should normally afford ample protection against damage to small grain. They are especially partial to peas and are said to pull up the sprouting seeds. The flocks so engaged are described as being numerous enough to turn the colour of the fields they alight upon from brown to blue. As they are large birds, each one intent on filling a capacious crop, their power for damage is not small. In the autumn they alight on the stooked grain and may take a considerable toll of it. It is fortunate that the birds are very irregular and local in their habits. One field may suffer one season, whereas others, apparently equally attractive, are untouched. The next season appreciable flocks may be totally absent from the neighbourhood and appear in an unexpected quarter. In British Columbia, at least, there is at present no fear for the survival of the species and when it becomes too numerous its numbers can be easily reduced. They are exceedingly wary and with us seem well able to take care of themselves.

Periodically old-time eastern pigeon-hunters note this western species and exultantly proclaim the rediscovery of the Passenger Pigeon that dropped from sight so suddenly as to suggest change in range rather than extermination. Unfortunately no such explanation can be accepted and the merest comparison of the long, slender, rosy-breasted Passenger Pigeon with this heavy, round-tailed, purplish bird shows the error of the supposition.

316. **Mourning Dove.** CAROLINA DOVE. LA TOURTERELLE TRISTE. *Zenaidura macroura.* L, 11·85. Plate XXX B. A small pigeon with a pointed tail much like the Passenger Pigeon in colour and outline, but smaller and duller in colour.

*Distinctions.* The Mourning Dove occurs over nearly all the southern parts of Canada. It is easily separated from the Band-tailed Pigeon of the west coast by its smaller size, fawn coloration, and long, pointed tail (Figure 374). It is often mistaken for the extinct

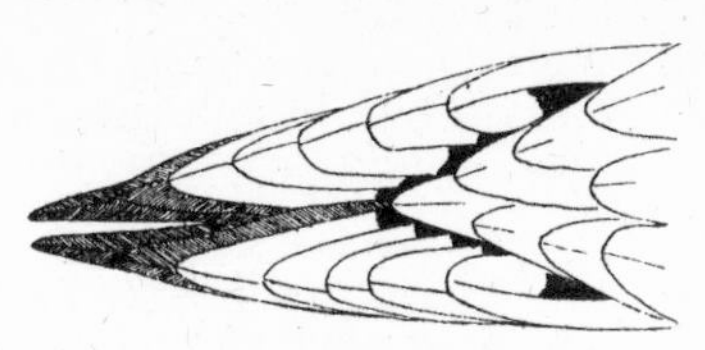

Figure 374
Tail of Mourning Dove (under side);
scale, ⅓.

Passenger Pigeon, but is considerably smaller than that bird—wing under 6 inches instead of over 8. It is similar in colour to females and juveniles of that species, but quite distinct from adult males. The breast is light purplish pink instead of distinctly red, the head is pale fawn colour with but little bluish cast, the back is olive-fawn, and there is in all but the most immature plumages a small black spot on the side of the neck below the ear. Four middle tail feathers are dark to the tip (Compare Figure 374 with 375).

The White-winged Dove has occurred on Vancouver Island and is a bird of similar size and colour. It has a round tail, however, and a large white patch on the wings that this species never has.

*Nesting.* A loose nest of sticks in brushy thickets, occasionally on the ground. Nests alone and not in communities.

*Distribution.* North America, from southern Canada to Panama and the West Indies.

*SUBSPECIES.* The type form of the species inhabits the West Indies and some of the adjoining mainland. The subspecies of eastern North America is the Eastern Mourning Dove (la Tourterelle triste de l'Est) *Zenaidura macroura carolinensis.* Throughout most of the west the Western Mourning Dove (la Tourterelle triste de l'Ouest) *Zenaidura macroura marginella* occurs. It is paler and greyer in colour and slightly larger in size than the eastern bird, but the difference is slight, and one of averages rather than individual specimens. This form extends east in Canada to include Manitoba. A dark, heavily coloured form, the Dusky Mourning Dove *Zenaidura macroura caurina,* has lately been officially recognized from the coast of Oregon and may occur on the southern British Columbia coast.

Though the Passenger Pigeon has disappeared entirely, the smaller Mourning Dove still exists and probably has greatly increased with the clearing of the country. The general food habits of the two birds were much alike except in the proportion of the various food elements. The Mourning Dove eats mast readily, but mast formed the principal food of the pigeon which was, therefore, more of a woodland bird. The Mourning Dove is of more solitary habits and rarely goes in flocks of any size. It nests entirely alone. This may be a large factor in its continued existence where its larger and originally more numerous relative has failed. Disease could not spread through the ranks so thoroughly and any other calamity that might affect individuals or small bodies would not involve the species as a whole. In many sections the Mourning Dove is regarded as a game-bird, but such status is not recognized by law anywhere in Canada. Numbers are killed, however, incidental to other sport, in spite of legal protection, and the life of the species is not an undisturbed one. It is, however, a strong and thriving race and is in little immediate danger.

Its long-drawn mournful note of "*Oh-woe-woe-woe*" is well known and has given the name to the species. It has a peculiar quality like that produced by blowing softly into the neck of an empty bottle.

*Economic Status.* Though feeding largely upon mast (acorns, beechnuts, and other soft-shelled tree-fruit) it eats grain readily and a considerable amount of insect food and weed-seed. Most of the grain it takes is waste. Seed properly planted and covered is absolutely safe from it for it never scratches. No serious unpreventable harm can be proved against it and the good it does is positive.

315. **Passenger Pigeon.** WILD PIGEON. LE PIGEON VOYAGEUR (La Tourte). *Ectopistes migratorius.* L, 16·29. Plate XXX B. Larger than the Mourning Dove, but smaller than the Band-tailed, though measuring more through its long, tapering tail (Figure 375). Much like the Mourning Dove in colour and outline, but more richly coloured.

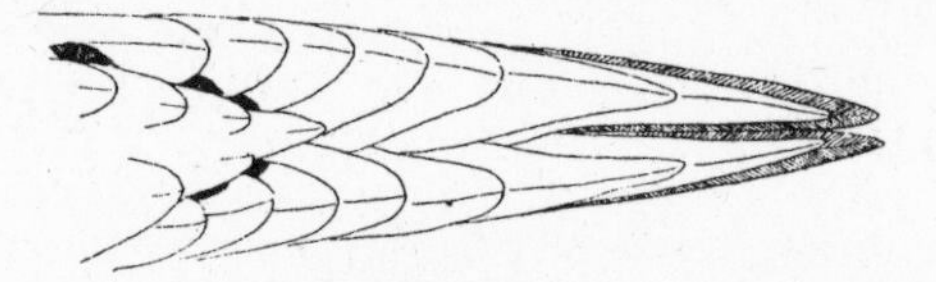

Figure 375
Tail of Passenger Pigeon (under side); scale, $\frac{1}{3}$.

*Distinctions.* The Passenger Pigeon was never more than a straggler west of the mountains, but as the Mourning Dove has been so often mistaken for it the following distinctions should be noted. It was considerably larger than the Mourning Dove—wing 8 inches or over instead of 6 inches or under. Females and juveniles similar to the Mourning Dove in colour, but the adult male had a decidedly red throat and breast, was slate-blue on head and back, and never had the small black spot below the ear that is characteristic of the Mourning Dove. Only two middle tail feathers were dark to the tip instead of four (Compare Figure 375 with 374).

*Field Marks.* The species being extinct, field marks are unnecessary.

*Nesting.* In rough nest of sticks in trees, in large communities.

*Distribution.* Bred formerly in the wooded sections of Canada east of the mountains, from Mackenzie Valley to the east coast and southward. Wintered in the southern states. Once common in Manitoba, but last recorded in 1898. Records for the southern parts of the other Prairie Provinces are few and unsatisfactory. The species is now extinct, the last bird having died in captivity in 1914.

The immense flocks of Passenger Pigeons that once darkened the air were one of the wonders of America. The descriptions of their number, if they were not circumstantial and well vouched for by men of undoubted veracity, would sound like wild stretches of the imagination; flocks, so dense that haphazard shots into them would bring down numbers, travelled rapidly with a front miles in width and so long that it took hours to pass a given point. Audubon estimates one such flock as containing over a billion birds, basing his figures upon the density and area of the congregation and not by mere guess. They bred in dense rookeries where their weight often broke the branches from forest trees. Trees containing their nests were cut down and though each nest contained only one squab there were so many that the pigs were turned in to feed upon them. Later, the netting of pigeons was the occupation of professional fowlers who shipped their proceeds by the car-load to the centres of population. Of course, not even the immense numbers of the Passenger Pigeons could stand such attacks without diminution. To suggest a halt in the proceedings at that time, however, aroused nothing but ridicule, their numbers being held to be inexhaustible, but today the species is extinct and the single survivor, a captive bird, died in Cincinnati a short time ago. The last great rookery was near Petoskey, Mich. In the autumn of 1878 the birds left on their usual migration, but failed to return in commercial numbers the following spring. For a few years afterwards occasional small flocks were seen and isolated rookeries were reported, but as the fowlers investigated each case it became apparent that the netting of pigeons as an occupation was a thing of the past. Thereafter, the birds became fewer and fewer each year until they disappeared altogether. There are occasional rumours even yet of flocks occurring in out-of-the-way places, in the western mountains, in Mexico, or South America, and elsewhere, but in each case investigation has proved that the reports are based on other species or on misinformation. For several years a large reward was offered for news of a single nesting pair. Of course, the author of the reward was flooded with reports, but not a single case stood examination, the reward was never earned, and was finally withdrawn. In the east, the Mourning Dove was the usual basis of report, in the west the Band-tailed Pigeon. Even yet rumours and circumstantial accounts of Passenger Pigeons still extant appear from time to time, vouched for by those who remember the bird in their childhood, but there is little doubt that the species is extinct.

319. **White-winged Dove.** LA TOURTERELLE À AILES BLANCHES. *Melopelia asiatica.* L, 12. Similar to the Mourning Dove in size and general coloration, but with a round tail and much white on the wings.

*Distinctions.* A Mourning Dove with a round tail white-tipped except for the centre feathers, and a pronounced white patch on the wings including secondaries and their coverts.

*Field Marks.* A Mourning Dove with above characters.

*Distribution.* Southeastern California east to Texas and southward. Also Florida and some of the West Indies. Casual visitor northward on the coast and single records for the state of Washington and southern Vancouver Island.

*SUBSPECIES.* The western form *Melopelia asiatica mearnsi* is the only one to be expected in western Canada.

To be identified only by unmistakable evidence or actual specimen.

## Order—Cuculiformes. Cuckoos

*General Description.* Birds with weak feet and yoke toes (two toes directed forward and two backward). The bills are rather long, gently curved, and sharply pointed (Figure 376). The plumage is soft and thin, lacking in cohesion, and has the soft, silky feeling associated with many tropical species. The tail is long, soft, and graduated.

*Distinctions.* May be distinguished from the woodpeckers, which also have yoke toes, by the difference in the bills and tails. In the woodpeckers, the bills are straight, stout, the tip chisel-pointed, and the tail rather short, very stiff, and bristle-like at the tip (Figure 391a, page 277).

The cuckoos are largely tropical in distribution. The two Canadian cuckoos are outliers from the main body of species in warmer latitudes. They are possessed of a tropical grace and air that are out of keeping with northern climes. This is exhibited in their lithe, sinuous carriage; full, round, deep throat; long, graceful tail; and thin but soft and silky plumage. They haunt hot and humid jungles of shrubbery, and flit across the open spaces with a silent undulating flight that seems in harmony with their exotic nature. English literature is rich in references to the cuckoos, but little that is so said is applicable to the Canadian cuckoo. The latter is not an early-arriving species and comes in spring with a quietness that hides its presence for some time after arrival. Its notes, too, are entirely different from those with which European writers have made us familiar. The calls of our birds are less musical but have a charm of their own and a wildness and unusual quality in keeping with their natures. The two Canadian species are very much alike in their calls; a loud, startling "*Kaow-kaow-kaow*" is the most characteristic and one that, on the still summer air. can be heard for a quarter of a mile or more. Again they have a "*Kuck-kuck-kuck*" note, like a big clock beating seconds, that has not the range of the above but has considerable carrying power. None of these notes has any resemblance to those of the European Cuckoo which are so familiarly rendered by the common cuckoo clock. In regard to their parental duties, our birds show considerable more realization of responsibility than the European. They are slightly parasitic in their habits, that is, they occasionally drop their eggs in the nests of other birds and shelve upon them the cares of raising their young, but the practice is not common and is perhaps only accidental. It may suggest the origin of the parasitic habit in other species. The old English word "cuckold" refers to and is based upon this habit of the European bird.

*Economic Status.* Cuckoos are almost entirely insectivorous, but occasionally take small amounts of wild fruit. The great value lies in the fact that they show special fondness for certain insects that other species rarely touch. Hairy caterpillars which, on account of their bristly coatings, are safe from more fastidious birds, are regularly eaten by cuckoos. The interior of a cuckoo's stomach will be found lined with a coating of spiny caterpillar bristles set in the walls and projecting from them like fur.

Only one family *Cuculidae* is represented in Canada.

387. **Yellow-billed Cuckoo.** LE COUCOU À BEC JAUNE. *Coccyzus americanus.* L, 12·20. Plate XXXI A. Olive-fawn above; all white below; long tail, with outer feathers black tipped with white. Curved bill, the lower mandible largely yellow.

*Distinctions.* To be mistaken only for the Black-billed Cuckoo, but of very limited and local occurrence in Canada. It is distinguished, however, by the yellow lower mandible; a cinnamon suffusion on the wings, conspicuous in flight; tail feathers, except centre ones, mostly black, and with large, white tips (Figure 376).

Figure 376
Specific details of Yellow-billed Cuckoo; head and foot, scale, ½; tail, scale, ⅓.

*Field Marks.* The long, flexible outline in flight, and general colour, make this species recognizable as a cuckoo. The yellow bill, cinnamon wing patches, and tail largely black with conspicuous white tips, are best specific field marks. In Canada, only likely to be seen in southern Ontario and southwestern British Columbia.

*Nesting.* A loose structure of sticks, not far from the ground, in thickets.

*Distribution.* Temperate North America, north to just across our border. Common in southern Ontario, absent from the Prairie Provinces, scarce in southern British Columbia, west of the Coast Range.

*SUBSPECIES.* Two subspecies are recognized. The Eastern Yellow-billed Cuckoo (le Coucou à bec jaune de l'Est) *coccyzus americanus americanus* occurs west to Minnesota, and may some day straggle north into southeastern Manitoba. The California Cuckoo (le Coucou à bec jaune de l'Ouest) *coccyzus americanus occidentalis* is the western form from Lower California, northward. In the south it extends east to Colorado, but in the north it is confined to the coast districts, and only enters Canada in southern Vancouver Island, and the adjoining mainland west of the Coast Range.

PLATE LIII

A. Dipper; scale, $\frac{1}{3}$

B. House Wren; scale, $\frac{1}{2}$

Plate LIV

A. Bewick's Wren; scale, $\frac{1}{3}$
(Seattle Wren)

B. Catbird; scale, $\frac{1}{3}$

388. **Black-billed Cuckoo.** LE COUCOU À BEC NOIR. *Coccyzus erythrophthalmus.* L, 11·85. Plate XXXI A. Olive-fawn above, all white below, long tail, outer feathers only slightly tipped with white. A slightly curved black bill (Figure 377).

Figure 377
Specific details of Black-billed Cuckoo;
scale, ½.

*Distinctions.* To be mistaken only for the Yellow-billed Cuckoo, but not occurring in British Columbia. It is distinguished from that species by all-black bill, practically an evenly coloured wing, black on tail only in faint subterminal bar, and the white tail-tips reduced to thumb marks.

*Field Marks.* The long, flexible outline in flight and general colour make this species recognizable as a cuckoo. The black bill, lack of conspicuous cinnamon patches on wing in flight, and tail the same colour as the back, and with only small white tips, are the best specific field marks. The presence of cuckoos in the neighbourhood will always be known by their characteristic notes, especially a slow, measured "*kuck-kuck-kuck,*" etc., and the bird is more often heard than seen.

*Nesting.* A loose structure of sticks near the ground, in thickets.

*Distribution.* Eastern North America. In Canada, westward, occasional in the southern parts of Manitoba and Saskatchewan, and sections of Alberta. Slightly more northern in its range than the Yellow-billed.

## Order—Strigiformes. Nocturnal Birds of Prey. Owls

The owls are easily recognized. The cere hidden in the feathers of the face, and the striking facial disk or feather rings about the eyes (Figures 378 and 380) are distinctive to the most casual observer. They are mostly nocturnal, but a few species habitually hunt by day and some others do so occasionally. Even the nocturnal owls, however, see quite well by day. They may be momentarily dazed when brought suddenly from dark to bright light, and some species repose such confidence in immobility to escape detection by day as to allow themselves to be almost caught in the hand, but when finally they take flight they thread the tangled mazes of the tree tops and brush so unerringly that little doubt of their visual powers remains.

The feathers are a most interesting feature in owls. They are peculiarly soft and cling together in a way that keeps the air from passing through the small interstices and ensures the silent flight characteristic of the suborder. An owl can pass so closely as to fan the face with its wing and yet be inaudible.

Two families are represented in Canada: *Tytonidae* the Barn Owls, represented by one species which is an accidental visitor from the south; and *Strigidae* the Typical Owls.

### FAMILY—TYTONIDAE. BARN OWLS

The barn owls, sometimes called the monkey-faced owls from the heart-shaped character of the united facial disks, are represented in Canada by only one species and that species is rare. The middle claw is pectinated, having comb-like teeth on its inner edge (Figure 379b) and the inner toe is as long as the middle instead of being slightly shorter as in the typical owls.

365. **American Barn Owl.** MONKEY-FACED OWL. L'EFFRAIE. *Tyto alba.* L, 18· General ground colour a reddish ochre, lighter below, facial disk dull white with an outer edging of darker ochre, to brown. Back, to top of head, frosted over with ash-grey with numerous small eye-spots outlined in black. Underparts, throat, and around face, sprinkled with scattered round, dark spots.

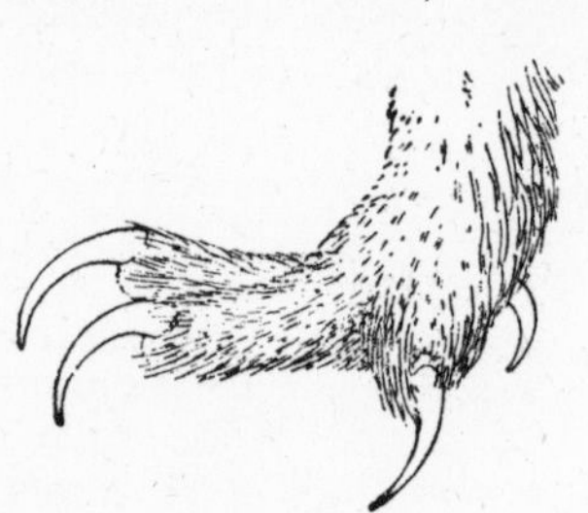

Figure 378
Barn Owl; scale, about ⅓.

*Distinctions.* The strongly outlined, heart-shaped facial disk and black eyes, without horns or ear tufts (Figure 378), soft yellow coloration with a suggestion of pink, and the tarsi, almost bare of feathers (Figure 379b) are distinctive.

*Nesting.* In towers, steeples, or holes in barns, banks, or trees.

*Distribution.* Nearly cosmopolitan in the warmer regions. In America, occurring across the continent, northward only casually across the Canadian boundary. There are single records for the species in Ontario, Manitoba, and southern British Columbia.

*SUBSPECIES.* The American bird is now regarded as a geographical race, of a nearly world-wide species, under the name of American Barn Owl (l'Effraie d'Amérique) *Tyto alba pratincola.*

This is the American representative of the ruin-haunting European owl so familiar in song and story. It is a wonderfully efficient mouser and a most valuable bird, but is rare in Canada.

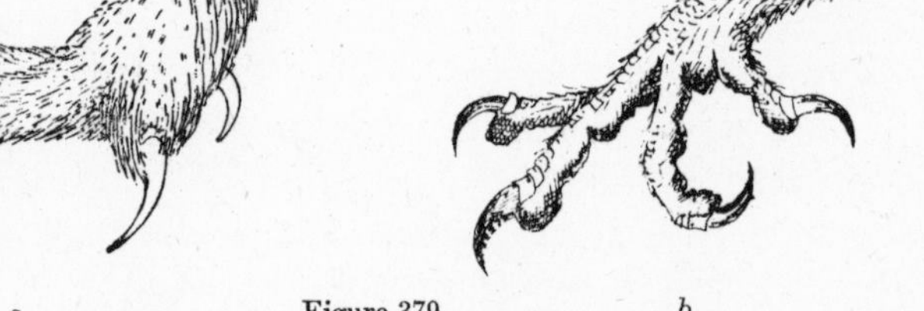

*a* Figure 379 *b*
*a*, well feathered foot of Horned Owl. *b*, Scantily feathered foot of Barn Owl.

### FAMILY—STRIGIDAE. TYPICAL OWLS

The typical owls were formerly generalized under the term "Horned" or "Eared" owls from the tufts of feathers projecting from the forehead of many, but not all, species. It includes all the Canadian owls except the Barn Owl previously mentioned. With the exception of the small Burrowing and the still more minute Pygmy Owls, all species mentioned here have the feet heavily feathered to at least the base of the toes (Figure 379a). In these exceptions, the feathering of the feet is bristle-like and rudimentary (Similar to Figure 379b).

373. **American Screech Owl.** LE PETIT-DUC D'AMÉRIQUE. *Otus asio.* L, 9·40. Plate XXXI B. A small, eared owl. The eastern race occurs in two well-marked colour phases, irrespective of age, sex, or season. One is rich brown and white, with much fine pattern, giving a grey effect, the other has the brown replaced by bright rufous, almost brick-red. The western races, however, are practically single phased, resembling the grey plumage of the eastern race, but of a ruddier brown.

*Distinctions.* With one very rare exception, the Flammulated Screech Owl, the only horned owl with wing under 7 inches. Easily known from that species by having yellow, instead of black, eyes.

*Field Marks.* Size, and the distinct horns, are the best field marks. Its call, a long quaver, is very distinctive.

*Nesting.* In hollow trees.

*Distribution.* Nearly all of temperate North America north to southern Canada. Scarce, or not occurring in Saskatchewan and Alberta.

*SUBSPECIES.* The Screech Owl is divided into a number of geographical races. Eastern birds are the Eastern Screech Owl (le Petit-duc de l'Est) *Otus asio naevius.* Manitoba specimens and probably those specimens from Saskatchewan are noticeably paler and can be referred to Aiken's Screech Owl (le Petit-duc d'Aiken) *Otus asio aikeni.* Both these forms have good strong red and grey phases. In southern British Columbia we have MacFarlane's Screech Owl (le Petit-duc de McFarlane) *Otus asio macfarlanei* in the interior, and Kennicott's Screech Owl (le Petit-duc de Kennicott) *Otus asio kennicotti* west of the Coast Range. These are both single phased, of the grey type, or if two phases can be recognized, the red colour is much subdued and not nearly as brilliant as in the Eastern race. The browns are always warmer and redder than the Eastern form, and, the coast birds especially, are of darker general colour.

Although called "Screech" owl, the notes of this bird certainly are not screeches. They may be heard at night coming from a distant copse, melodious and soothing, with a tinge of melancholy, and contain nothing harsh or grating. The commoner call is a long, soft, tremolo whistle. An imitation will bring the original author close up to see what rash stranger Screech Owl invades its chosen haunts, and it challenges with answering whistles and chuckles. When undisturbed by intruders, the notes include an infinite number of low croons and gurgling tones. Occasionally Screech Owls can be induced to nest or rest in boxes, and every day, as evening approaches, the alert round head with feather-ringed, yellow eyes framed in the opening and awaiting the coming dusk is a pretty sight. Though generally inoffensive, Screech Owls sometimes show surprising courage in defence of their fledgling family. At night the parent bird will boldly attack, sweeping down at the head of the intruder with a startling, hollow-sounding "*who-who*" and snapping bill. This is usually little more than a demonstration, however, and, just before striking, it wheels up into the darkness again to gather momentum for a return. Such attacks, although sometimes disconcerting, are far from dangerous, and more a source of amusement and admiration than alarm.

*Economic Status.* The official finding on the food of the Screech Owl is warrant for its protection. Of 212 stomachs examined, 1 contained poultry; 38, other birds; 91, mice; 11, other mammals; 2, lizards; 4, frogs and toads; 1, fish; 100, insects; 5, spiders; 9, crawfish; 7, miscellaneous; 22, scorpions; and 2, earthworms. The poultry item must be regarded as an accidental occurrence, as the bird represented, a pigeon, would be exceedingly large prey for this owl.

The loss of the small birds it takes under natural conditions may be regarded with equanimity. Unless individuals depopulate our bird-houses and garden preserves, little can be said against the species.

374. **Flammulated Screech Owl.** LE PETIT-DUC NAIN. *Otus flammeolus.* L, 6·50. Like a small, grey Screech Owl, but with dark, instead of yellow, eyes.

*Distinctions.* Like a very small, light grey Screech Owl, but with dark eyes, and toes naked to their base.

*Field Marks.* Too rare to be recorded on eyesight observation, but very small size, ear tufts, and dark eyes will serve to distinguish this species.

*Nesting.* Similar to the Screech Owl.

*Distribution.* Too few specimens of this species have been recorded to base a detailed distribution upon them. It has occurred irregularly from British Columbia to Guatemala, and east to Colorado.

We know hardly anything of its habits, but presume they are similar to those of the Screech Owl. One found dead on the lake shore at Penticton, British Columbia, is the only Canadian record.

375. **Great Horned Owl.** CAT OWL. LE GRAND-DUC D'AMÉRIQUE. *Bubo virginianus.* L, 22. Plate XXXII A. A large owl, over 15 inches, with prominent horns. It may vary from a dark bird with much black only touched with white here and there, and strong ochre tints showing through from the undercoat, to largely or nearly entirely white, with much, or little, fine, sharp black vermiculation, and a buff to cream undercoat.

*Distinctions.* The only owl over 15 inches in length with prominent horns. The finely vermiculated pattern, and buffy under plumage, differentiate it from the broadly barred or spotted, and hornless Snowy Owl, with which the whitest specimens of Great Horned might possibly be confused.

*Field Marks.* Large size and prominent horns or ear tufts.

*Distribution.* The greater part of North and South America. In Canada, across the continent, north to the tree limit.

*SUBSPECIES.* An extremely variable species. In Canada four or five subspecies are recognized. The Horned Owl of the east, except in Labrador and an indefinite part of Ungava Peninsula, is the type form, the Eastern Horned Owl (le Grand-duc de l'Est) *Bubo virginianus virginianus.* Its distinctive character is its general redness. In Labrador is a dark, sooty form, the Labrador Horned Owl (le Grand-duc du Labrador) *Bubo virginianus heterocnemis.* The Prairie Provinces and indefinitely northward are inhabited by a very pale form, the Arctic Horned Owl (le Grand-duc arctique) *Bubo virginianus subarcticus,* occasionally almost immaculately white. Most of British Columbia and the Yukon has a dark race the Northwestern Horned Owl (le Grand-duc du Nord-Ouest) *Bubo virginianus lagophonus* hardly distinguishable from *heterocnemis* of the Labrador, and on the southwest coast is a still blacker form the Dusky Horned Owl (le Grand-duc noirâtre) *Bubo virginianus saturatus.* As all these birds wander and move about considerably in winter, often lingering late in the season before returning to their proper nesting homes, they may turn up far from their natural habitats.

The Great Horned Owl is the evil genius of the woods. Winding silently through the shadowy foliage, through the dark forest, or along the steep mountain or coulée sides, it is monarch of all it surveys. In a natural state it fears no enemies save man, and all the lesser animals and birds cower at its soft, hushed flight. In minor affairs, however, it has not things always its own way. Often one will hear a great protracted outcry from the crows, and the black clans will be seen gathering to a common point where great excitement prevails. As likely as not, a Great Horned Owl will be found the centre of attraction. Some sharp-eyed crow has seen the sleepy bird hugged close against a tree trunk, awaiting the coming of the night. The alarm once given it is taken up by throat after throat, and soon all the corvine neighbourhood joins the mobbing. They surround him, screaming in his face and making dashing feints, at which he braces himself, and snaps a hollow sounding bill, but rarely has a chance of using his terrible talons against his agile and discreet tormentors. The owl cannot throw them off; it retreats from tree to tree, but, at the first movement, the black mob renews its screams, trails away after, and never loses sight of its quarry until the falling shades send all crows off to roost. Then the tables may be turned, and the occasional piles of glossy black feathers scattered about the ground show that revenge is especially sweet when it also furnishes a meal. It is difficult to say which, crow or owl, has the observer's sympathy, but perhaps the thought suggested is that "When knaves fall out, honest men prosper." Like other owls, the Great Horned

Owl answers and comes readily to an imitation of its deep "*Whoo-who-who*" challenge at night. Most owls can easily be called up by any one who is clever with his voice or whistles. Most of them are solitary by preference and impatient at poachers on their preserves. That this is the explanation of their coming to call and not sociability is proved by the fact that an imitation of the call of a large owl drives all the lesser ones to silent retirement, whereas the call of the small ones attracts the big ones almost as well as does that of their own species.

*Economic Status.* The economic status of this bird depends upon where it lives. In the deep woods away from settlement it is, of course, harmless to man and only the wild creatures it preys upon are affected by it. In settled districts it is to be guarded against in every possible way. Of 110 stomachs examined, 31 contained poultry or game-birds; 8, other birds; 13, mice; 65, other mammals; 1, a scorpion; 1, fish; and 10, insects. The evidence is, therefore, decidedly against this owl. There is no danger that over-restriction will result in its extermination since it is perfectly able to take care of itself and there are large sections of wilderness where the species can hold sway without molestation.

376. **Snowy Owl.** LE HIBOU BLANC (Le Harfang). *Nyctea nyctea.* L, 25. As large as the Great Horned Owl, but without horns, and pure white, usually with many, but sometimes only a few, sharp, dark bars on all parts of body except face. Occasional birds are almost immaculate.

*Distinctions.* A large, hornless owl, pure white, or white sharply barred with dark. Only possible of confusion with very white Horned Owls, but the round head, the body pattern broad and bold instead of fine and vermiculated, are distinctive.

*Field Marks.* A large, very white owl, with round head.

*Nesting.* On the ground of the tundra.

*Distribution.* Northern parts of northern hemisphere. In America, across the northern barren grounds, southward in winter.

Figure 380
Snowy Owl; scale, ⅓.

This is a winter visitor in the settled parts of Canada. It frequents frozen marshes and lake shores and is essentially a bird of the open. Usually the birds that come from the north are heavily marked juveniles, but occasionally flights occur in which the very white and almost unspotted adults are in the majority. Probably the juveniles are naturally greater wanderers than the adults, which migrate far from their home grounds only when driven out by a scarcity of food.

*Economic Status.* The food of the Snowy Owl consists largely of feathered game. Of 26 stomachs examined, 2 contained game-birds; 9, other birds; and 20, mice, rats, and rabbits. Were it not that this owl comes down into civilization after most of our birds have left it might do serious damage.

Though a big and powerful bird, feeding largely on ptarmigan and rabbits in its native north country, comparatively few complaints are substantiated against it when it comes south during migration. It does not often visit the farmyard, and normally its depredations on grouse do not seem serious.

377. **Hawk Owl.** LA CHOUETTE ÉPERVIÈRE. *Surnia ulula.* L, 15. Plate XXXII B. A medium-sized owl of hawk-like appearance and habits. Facial disk not as perfect as in most owls, and tail long.

*Distinctions.* The less flattened and less typically owl-like face, long tail, and sharp and regular barring below, are distinctive.

*Field Marks.* Diurnal habits, general coloration, and long tail are good field marks. In flight, except for its larger, more owl-like head, it has a strong resemblance to a goshawk. Any owl seen perched in a commanding position in full daylight is probably this species, though both the Long and the Short-eared Owls occasionally hunt by day.

*Nesting.* In evergreen trees or in holes in tree trunks.

*Distribution.* Northern parts of northern hemisphere. In Canada, in the northern wooded forests, across the continent and among the mountains at the higher elevations. Migrating in winter through most of southern Canada. More common near the mountains and in the foothills than out on the open prairie.

*SUBSPECIES.* The Hawk Owl of America is separated from that of the Old World as the American Hawk Owl (la Chouette épervière d'Amérique) *Surnia ulula caparoch.*

379. **Pygmy Owl.** LA CHOUETTE PYGMÉE. *Glaucidium gnoma.* L, 7. Plate XXXIII A. A very diminutive owl. Scarcely longer than many sparrows, though of heavier build. Coloured in wood browns and white.

*Distinctions.* Extremely small size, considerably smaller even than the Saw-whet. Sharply striped underparts; general wood-brown above, and a large, soft, black spot bordered with white on either side of the hindneck. Unmistakable for any other species.

*Field Marks.* Extremely small size for an owl. Wood-brown above, and white underparts sharply striped with dark. Much diurnal activity.

*Nesting.* In holes in trees.

*Distribution.* Western North America, mostly west of the Rockies. In Canada, practically confined to British Columbia; in the interior, north into Cariboo district, but west of the Coast Range, at least as far north as Wrangell, Alaska.

*SUBSPECIES.* The Pygmy Owl is divided into a number of subspecies of which three have been postulated for Canada. The California Pygmy Owl (la Chouette pygmée de Californie) *Glaucidium gnoma californicum* is the interior bird, the Coast Pygmy Owl (la Chouette pygmée côtière) *Glaudicium gnoma grinelli* that of the coast, and the Vancouver Pygmy Owl (la Chouette pygmée de Vancouver) *Glaucidium gnoma swarthi,* of Vancouver Island. *Californicum* has a slight greyish cast in the brown, whereas *swarthi* is darker and more reddish, has the white markings reduced, and more dark on the legs, *grinelli* in colour is about intermediate between them.

An extraordinary and interesting little owl. It is largely diurnal, and so small that one naturally expects it to have a gentle and unassertive disposition. This, however, may be far from being the case. If the reaction of the small woodland birds to its presence is any evidence, this little raptor, no larger than many of them, must be one of their worst enemies. Its friends would call it courageous and determined; its enemies, ferocious and bloodthirsty. Pause anywhere in its haunts, and whistle an imitation of its call—a half whistle, half spoken "*Cook-cook*" followed by hollow, woodeny, staccato whistles succeeding each other slowly at first, but with a gradually accelerated tempo, and every small bird within hearing will come to investigate. The nuthatches, hanging head downward, wave their heads like pendulums, and point their straight, upturned bills first to one side and then to the other, quanking as they do so. The chickadees "*dee-dee,*" their beady eyes twinkling with curiosity. Buzzing, squeaking, excited hummingbirds will hum angrily around. Sparrows, wrens, vireos, warblers, jays, and many others, hurry with anxious cheeps to the spot, from the deep tangles of the brush, the middle thicket of the branches overhead, or even the topmost tip of the giant yellow pines, and press in excited review about the alarum. With this call, bird study is made most easy in the difficult country of British Columbia, and no ornithologist there can afford not to learn it. If another Pygmy Owl hears the call, it comes immediately to challenge the intruder, sometimes two come together, find in each other the opponent they were seeking, and join in furious if elf-like combat. This is not direct evidence of the bird's food habits, but is a good indication, and suggests that it is only its exceedingly diminutive size that limits its power of destruction and excludes it from the short list of wholly obnoxious birds of prey.

*Economic Status.* The examination of six stomachs of southwestern birds showed insects and lizards in two of them, a white-footed mouse in another. Evidently, besides the bird-eating proclivities suggested by the preceding paragraph, it eats some insects, and is a mouser as would be expected.

378. **Burrowing Owl.** BILLY OWL. LA CHOUETTE À TERRIER. *Speotyto cunicularia.* L, 9·50. Plate XXXIII B. A small, round-headed, stumpy-bodied, long-legged owl, of light brown, or sandy, and white coloration, of rather indefinite pattern.

*Distinctions.* Small size, round head, bare toes, and legs only scantily feathered in front (much similar to Figure 379b), and pale, sandy coloration make this species unmistakable.

*Field Marks.* A small, sandy-coloured ground owl, inhabiting open prairie country; short stumpy body and long legs are easily recognizable in life.

*Nesting.* In holes made in the ground of the open prairie by gophers, badgers, or other animals.

*Distribution.* Western United States from southern Canada to Mexico, east in the south, to Florida and the islands of the Gulf of Mexico. In Canada, across the southern boundary, north to about the Canadian Pacific main line in the three Prairie Provinces, and the southern ends of the valleys in the interior of British Columbia. There are several records for Vancouver Island.

*SUBSPECIES.* The Canadian form is the Western Burrowing Owl (la Chouette à terrier de l'Ouest) *Speotyto cunicularia hypogaea* that inhabits most of the United States.

A very odd little owl, and the one around which has grown the myth of living in friendly harmony in the same burrow with prairie dogs and rattlesnakes. It can often be seen standing in the bright warm sun, a round bunch of feathers with long, un-owl-like legs, perched on the little mound of earth thrown up from its burrow, or on some small commanding elevation nearby. When disturbed it flies off with a musical little whistle or gradually disappears backwards down into the depths of the ground, the last thing seen in the darkness of the tunnel being the reflections from its bright, yellow eyes. About the burrow, vast numbers of weathering pellets may be seen. Examination shows that the majority of these are mouse and small rodent remains, but in British Columbia, where the Poor-will is common in Burrowing Owl country, its woody-brown mottled plumage is commonly intermixed with the mammal remains, showing that small birds are acceptable when opportunity for taking them presents itself, and also that those that haunt the night suffer from the creatures of darkness.

*Economic Status.* Of 32 stomachs examined in southern United States, 30 contained insects; 3, small mammals; and 3, lizards. That this is not a complete story, for Canada at least, is shown by the formerly mentioned regurgitated pellets about the nest-holes, but very little harm can be charged against the species, and there is much to its credit.

368. **Barred Owl.** LE CHAT-HUANT D'AMÉRIQUE. *Strix varia.* L, 20. Plate XXXIV A. A large, hornless, black-eyed owl, smaller than the Great Horned; coloured in brownish grey and white.

*Distinctions.* The only other round-headed owls this species resembles are the Spotted and the Cinereous. It is too far removed in range from the former to be confused with it. The smaller size, black instead of yellow eyes, and combination of sharply barred breast and striped underparts, will separate it easily from the Cinereous.

*Field Marks.* Size, absence of ear tufts, and general grey-brown colour with bars across breast.

*Nesting.* In hollow trees or in deserted nests of crows or hawks.

*Distribution.* Eastern North America. In Canada, west to, and including, southern Manitoba.

*SUBSPECIES.* Several subspecies of Barred Owl are recognized. The only one that occurs in Canada is the Northern Barred Owl (le Chat-huant du Nord) *Strix varia varia.*

Though apparently a fairly large bird the Barred Owl when stripped of its feathers is comparatively small. Added to this it is a bird of gentle nature and lacks the keen aggressiveness of some of its relatives. Its notes are loud, the weird hooting carrying far in the still, night air.

*Economic Status.* Though fowls have been known to roost repeatedly without harm in trees from which Barred Owls hooted every night, the latter are too often regarded as enemies and killed indiscriminately. Of 189 stomachs examined, 5 contained poultry or game; 13, other birds; 46, mice; 18, other mammals; 4, frogs; 1, a lizard; 2, fish; 14, insects; 2, spiders; and 9, crawfish. The fowls, only two cases, can be regarded as accidental, probably offal or carrion, as they were both taken in January, when ordinarily the fowl would be full grown and beyond the powers of this weak owl to kill. The status of this bird is most satisfactory.

369. **Spotted Owl.** LE CHAT-HUANT TACHETÉ. *Strix occidentalis.* L, 20. A large, round-headed, hornless owl, with black eyes, of same size and general appearance as the Barred, except that it is rich wood-brown instead of ashy brown and darker below; the light, dark-striped underparts of the Barred Owl being represented by dark feathers with large white spots along their sides, and showing the buffy ochre of the under-plumage. The general effect of the underparts suggests barring rather than striping.

Figure 381
Spotted Owl; scale, ⅓.

*Distinctions.* Most like the Barred Owl, but so separated from it in range as to make confusion very improbable. The only owl it is likely to be mistaken for is the much larger and yellow-eyed Cinereous.

*Field Marks.* The only large, round-headed owl likely to be met with in summer time in southwestern British Columbia. Much smaller and browner than the Cinereous.

*Nesting.* In caves and under heavy overhangs of rock.

*Distribution.* Western North America, north to the boundary. In Canada, occurring rarely only in extreme southwestern British Columbia.

*SUBSPECIES.* Two subspecies are recognized. The form to be expected in Canada is the Northern Spotted Owl (le Chat-huant tacheté du Nord) *Strix occidentalis caurina.*

This is a rare species anywhere, and has been taken in Canada on only a few occasions.

A. Brown Thrasher; scale, $\frac{1}{3}$

B. American Robin; scale, $\frac{1}{3}$

PLATE LVI

A. Varied Thrush; scale, $\frac{1}{3}$

B. Wood Thrush; scale, $\frac{1}{3}$

370. **Great Grey Owl.** LA CHOUETTE CENDRÉE. *Scotiaptex nebulosa* L, 27. Of much the same general grey tone as the Barred Owl, but considerably larger.

*Distinctions.* By measurement and in appearance the largest of our owls, but when stripped of its abundance of soft feathers a surprisingly small bird. Like the Barred Owl in general coloration and lack of horns; but with yellow instead of black eyes (Figure 382), and having the coloration of the breast and underparts diffused, and without a definite pattern of stripes and bars.

Figure 382
Cinereous Owl; scale, $\frac{1}{5}$.

*Field Marks.* Size, grey coloration, and lack of breast-bars.

*Nesting.* In trees.

*Distribution.* The forests of the north, across the continent.

*SUBSPECIES.* The Cinereous Owl occurs in the northern parts of both the New and Old Worlds, but is represented in each by distinct subspecies. The European form is the Lapp Owl *S. n. lapponica*, and the American is the Great Grey Owl (la Chouette cendrée d'Amérique), the type race.

This owl is only a winter visitor in the settled parts of Canada.

*Economic Status.* What economic influence this bird effects is a beneficial one. Data on its food are rather scarce. Of 9 stomachs examined, 1 contained a small bird; 7, mice; and 4, other mammals. It is evidently an efficient mouser.

366. **American Long-eared Owl.** BRUSH OWL. LE HIBOU À OREILLES LONGUES. *Asio wilsonianus.* L, 14·80. Plate XXXIV B. A medium-sized owl, similar in general coloration to the darker race of the Great Horned Owl, but much smaller and of more slender build.

*Distinctions.* Although the colouring is suggestive of a dark Great Horned Owl, the difference in size easily separates the two; besides this, the Long-eared Owl has none of the fine, sharp vermiculation, above or below, that is so characteristic of the other species. From the Short-eared Owl, which is about equal in size and build, it may be distinguished by the prominent horns or ear tufts that spring from the centre of the forehead, by its lack of decided, sharp striping, and the amount of grey, or black and white, that suffuses the body colour. The Long-eared Owl is softly striped below, but the stripes are somewhat crossbarred and there is much white overwash. The Short-eared Owl is sharply striped with brown on tawny and there is little if any crossbarring or white. It is decidedly a striped bird, the Long-eared is not.

*Field Marks.* The prominent horns standing up from the middle of the forehead, rusty-brown facial disks, and general greyness will differentiate this from the Short-eared Owl, the only species with which it is likely to be confused.

*Nesting.* In trees or bushes usually in the deserted nests of hawks or crows.

*Distribution.* Temperate North America. In Canada, across the continent, north to near the tree limit.

This is an owl of the brush land and coulées. In dryer parts of the Prairie Provinces there is scarcely a wooded coulée that has not its pair of Long-eared Owls, raising their brood in the nest once built by a crow or buteo. Brooding here or perched in the shadowy thicket, through the day, it sallies forth to the prairie level at night, carrying death and destruction into the ranks of the small nocturnal rodents. That it takes occasional feathered game on opportunity is evident from stomach examination, but the species cannot be an important economically harmful factor because of this. It is notable that although many coulées harbour a pair of this species, it is invariably absent from those occupied by its larger relative, the Great Horned Owl.

In the east evergreen or alder thickets on the edges of marshes or ash swamps are the preferred habitat of the species. During migration it is sometimes found in companies; resting by day in the dark recesses of wet woods.

*Economic Status.* Of 92 stomachs examined, 1 contained a game-bird (quail); 15, other birds; 84, mice; 5, other mammals; and 1, insects. From this record it is evident that the species is not seriously destructive. Its mousing proclivities are sufficient to give it a claim to protection and its small size and nocturnal habits prevent its interference with young poultry (at least those that are properly cared for at night).

367. **Short-eared Owl.** MARSH OWL. LE HIBOU À OREILLES COURTES. *Asio flammeus.* L, 15·50. A medium-sized owl. Much smaller than the Barred or Great Horned, but larger than the Screech or the Burrowing Owls. Similar in size and build to the Long-eared. In general, an ochraceous or buffy bird striped with brown; stripes sharply defined and narrower below; softly diffused and broader above. Small, inconspicuous ear tufts rise from centre of forehead (Figure 383).

Figure 383
Short-eared Owl; scale, ¼.

*Distinctions.* Likely to be confused only with the Long-eared Owl. The general light buff colour, and brown stripes without any pure white, are distinctive of this species. The ear tufts may be so poorly developed as to be almost absent. The body colour varies in individuals, and may be as light as rich cream, or deep enough to have a slight suggestion of rusty. Distinctly a striped bird.

*Field Marks.* Size, general buffy colour, and habitat.

*Nesting.* On the ground, in dry marshes.

*Distribution.* Nearly cosmopolitan. In Canada, in all suitable localities north to the Arctic Ocean.

This bird is a true marsh owl and is slightly more diurnal in its habits than many of its relatives. It is often seen in the dusk of the evening beating over the marshes in strong and hawk-like flight. As it lives in the marshes or along their brushy edges, a great number fall annually to the guns of thoughtless sportsmen after other game.

*Economic Status.* Of 97 stomachs examined, 11 contained small birds; 77, mice; 7, other mammals; and 7, insects. From this record and from the fact that the marsh edges, waste patches, and fence-rows which this species haunts are the reserves from which small rodent pests spread over cleanly cultivated land, it is evident that this is a most useful species and that killing it is removing one of the most efficient checks upon innumerable pests.

371. **Little Boreal Owl.** ARCTIC SAW-WHET OWL. LA PETITE CHOUETTE BORÉALE. *Cryptoglaux funerea.* L, 10. A small, hornless, brown and white owl. Rich blackish brown above, with semi-concealed, round, white spots; white below, vaguely striped. The colour pattern is soft and the design vague and diffused.

Figure 384
Richardson's Owl; scale, ⅓.

*Distinctions.* Slightly smaller than the Screech Owl, and hornless. Larger than the Saw-whet, which is the only species with which it is likely to be confused. Differs from that species in being a rich, warm, blackish brown, instead of rather reddish, greyish brown. The light facial disk is in sharp contrast with the surrounding dark ring, instead of blending softly into it. An owl of this type, with a wing over 5·5 inches, will be this species.

*Field Marks.* A small, round-headed owl, larger and richer brown in colour than the Saw-whet.

*Nesting.* In holes in trees.

*Distribution.* Northern parts of northern hemisphere. In Canada, across the continent in the northern coniferous forest, usually coming into southern sections only in winter.

*SUBSPECIES.* The American form of this species is separated from the European under the name of Richardson's Owl (la Chouette de Richardson) *Cryptoglaux funerea richardsoni.*

This is a very irregular and occasional winter migrant throughout most of our cultivated sections.

*Economic Status.* Though too rare to have any noticeable economic influence it must be regarded as a beneficial species. Of 9 stomachs examined, 1 contained a small bird; 7, mice; and 4, other mammals.

372. **Acadian Owl.** SAW-WHET OWL. LA CHOUETTE DES GRANGES. *Cryptoglaux acadica.* Excepting the Pygmy, the smallest of our owls. Above, almost solid chocolate-brown. Facial disk on crown and sides of head, bordered with many fine, short, white lines, extending back over crown (Figure 385a). Below, white, broadly and softly streaked with a slightly paler shade of the back colour; or—the same, but the white replaced by light rusty buff. A plumage of this owl, rarely seen, was long thought to be a distinct species, and was called Kirtland's Owl, but is now demonstrated to be only an evanescent juvenile plumage of the Saw-whet. This juvenile is solid brown above, redder than the adult, the brown extending across breast as a rufescent band. Below the breast-band, the abdomen is rusty-ochre, without stripes. The facial disks are almost black (Figure 385b), in striking contrast with the white above, and between the eyes.

Figure 385
Saw-whet Owls; scale, $\frac{1}{3}$.
*a*, adult *b*, juvenile

*Distinctions.* With small size, round, hornless head, and general coloration, likely to be confused only with Richardson's Owl. Differs from that species in being of a redder and greyer brown, especially the stripes below, and in the facial disk blending into the crown with but little contrast (Compare with Figure 384). An owl of this type, with wing between $5\frac{1}{2}$ and 4 inches, will be this species.

*Field Marks.* A small, round-headed owl, smaller, and of paler and more blended colour than the preceding.

*Nesting.* In holes in trees, sometimes natural cavities, at other times those made by woodpeckers or squirrels.

*Distribution.* Most of temperate North America. In Canada, in wooded sections, probably not north of latitude 60 degrees.

*SUBSPECIES.* Two subspecies of the Acadian Owl are recognized in Canada. The Eastern Saw-whet Owl (la Chouette des granges de l'Est) *Cryptoglaux acadica acadica* inhabits most of the Dominion. The Queen Charlotte Owl (la Chouette de Reine-Charlotte) *Cryptoglaux acadica brooksi* is at present known only in Queen Charlotte Islands. It is like the Acadian, but in adults the whites are replaced by rufous ochre. In the young the colours are all richer and darker than in the young of the Acadian. The difference between these two races is very striking and the absence of known intergrades suggests that *Cryptoglaux acadica brooksi* may be a distinct species. The Northwest Saw-whet *Cryptoglaux acadica scotaea*, heretofore ascribed to the Pacific coast of Canada, has lately been dropped as being identical with the Acadian Owl.

This diminutive owl haunts the dark tangle of cedar and tamarack swamps and similar localities, passing the day close to the trunk of a tree where its plumage blends indistinguishably with the bark. It has such great reliance in its protective coloration that it will allow close approach and can at times be almost taken in the hand. It takes its vernacular name from its call-notes, which are said to resemble the sound made by filing or whetting a saw.

*Economic Status.* Of 19 stomachs examined, 1 contained a sparrow; 17, mice; and 1, a moth. With this record the species deserves protection.

## Order—Caprimulgiformes. Goatsuckers

This is a widely distributed suborder. A description of the one family represented in North America will serve for the recognition of the native species.

### FAMILY—CAPRIMULGIDAE. GOATSUCKERS

*General Description.* The goatsuckers have flattened heads, very small bills, and enormous mouths, with gape extending to behind the eye (Figure 386). The feet are small and very weak and the middle claw pectinated or furnished with comb-like serrations as in the herons (Figure 387). The plumage is very soft in texture and coloured in wood-browns, neutral buffs, and greys.

*Distinctions.* The above characters should be sufficient to distinguish this family as they are not similar to those of any other Canadian birds.

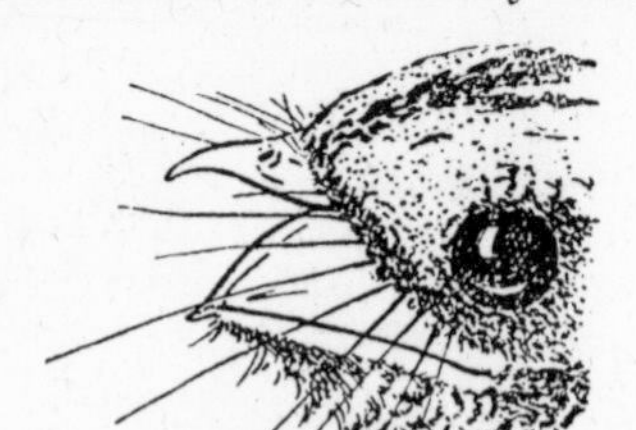

Figure 386
Bill and mouth of Whip-poor-will

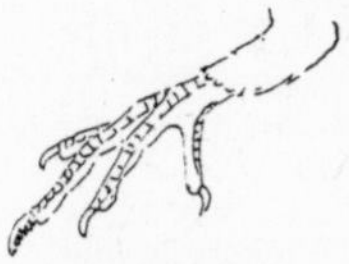

Figure 387
Foot of Whip-poor-will;
scale, about $\frac{2}{3}$.

The goatsuckers were given their name from an old but mistaken belief that they sucked the milk from the goats in the pastures over which they were seen to wheel and circle, and their immense mouths and pink throats gave support to the popular impression. As a fact the birds that frequented the pastures were hawking for flying insects that had been attracted by the animals. The birds of this family are nocturnal or crepuscular. They feed entirely upon insects caught on the wing and seldom come to ground except to nest or for repose. Their feet are too small and weak to clasp a branch securely and in perching they usually sit on large branches, lengthwise instead of—as do most birds—crosswise.

416. **Chuck-will's Widow.** L'ENGOULEVENT DE LA CAROLINE. *Antrostomus carolinensis.* L, 12. A large Whip-poor-will. *See* next species.

*Distinctions.* Size; it is a considerably larger bird than the whip-poor-will; the long bristles about the mouth with hair-like branches at their base instead of being clean and bare throughout their length.

*Distribution.* The southern states. Of accidental occurrence within our eastern borders.

The basis for the inclusion of this bird here is the taking of a specimen at Pelee Point on Lake Erie and another at Pictou, Nova Scotia. It is rare and is similar to the whip-poor-will in appearance, habits, and notes.

417. **Whip-poor-will.** LE BOIS-POURRI. *Antrostomus vociferus.* L, 9·75. Coloured in soft, indefinite patterns of wood-browns and grey with suggestions of rufous and ochre. There is little broad pattern in the colouring, but much fine detail. On the underparts there is only a faint suggestion of barring, and the coloration of the whole bird is like that of a great brown moth.

*Distinctions.* With its small bill, enormous gape, long mouth bristles (Figure 386), and soft, wood-brown coloration, possible of confusion only with the nighthawk. It is easily distinguished from that species by the following points: there is a white collar across the base of the throat, but the throat itself is dark; the last half of the tail feathers, except of the middle pair, is white in the male, and tipped with buffy in the female; the spread wing shows no white spot. Because of its eastern range, large size, and very much longer tail, not likely to be confused with the western Poor-will that resembles it closely in coloration and habit.

*Field Marks.* A wood-brown, long-winged, long-tailed bird, with no conspicuous white spot in the wing, that rises from the undergrowth with a loose, floppy flight, flies low, and soon alights again on the ground beyond. More often recognized by sound at night than by sight in the day. Its call at night, a soft whistle resembling the words *"Whip poor will"* repeated many times, is familiar to all frequenters of the eastern woodlands.

*Nesting.* Eggs laid directly on the ground or on dead leaves.

*Distribution.* Eastern North America. In Canada, west to and including the woods and bluffs of southern Manitoba. Has been taken as far west as Prince Rupert, Saskatchewan.

*SUBSPECIES.* The subspecies accredited to Canada is the Eastern Whip-poor-will (le Bois-pourri de l'Est) *Antrostomus vociferus vociferus.*

There is no other sound in the Canadian woods so poetically mournful as the reiterated call of the whip-poor-will. The translation of bird notes into words usually requires a stretch of the imagination, but this bird says *"Whip-poor-will, whip-poor-will"* with unusual distinctness. For a calling station it selects a perch on a fallen tree trunk, a bare branch, the roof of a building, or even a tent-pole. It returns to its various stations regularly on successive nights and seems to visit each in turn. Between periods of calling the bird hawks and wheels through the tree tops in large, interlacing circles, sometimes swooping towards the ground in a long, pendulum-like swing. In the daytime it seeks the ground in some quiet patch of underbrush where it passes the time at rest. When disturbed by an intruder it rises with a loose, poorly controlled flight that gives no indication of its wonderful command of the air at other times, flutters a short distance over the tangle, and drops again to earth.

The whip-poor-will is often regarded as identical with the nighthawk. This is a not unnatural mistake when they are not seen side by side, as they are quite similar enough to be confused.

*Economic Status.* The whip-poor-will feeds largely upon night-flying beetles, especially May beetles or June bugs.

418. **Poor-will.** L'ENGOULEVENT DE L'OUEST. *Antrostomus nuttalli.* L, 7·50. Above: a rich, dark, seal-brown, frosted over with a fine, complicated pattern of silver-grey. Below: the same colours, but the breast predominantly dark; the flanks and abdomen finely barred with silver-grey and predominantly light, the bars dying away on the breast. A triangular white patch occupies the throat. Tail rounded, under 3·50 inches, and the three outer feathers tipped with white thumb-marks.

*Distinctions.* Much like a small, short-tailed Whip-poor-will, but far removed from that species in range. Likely to be confused only with the Nighthawk, the only other goatsucker that is found in the same locality with it. Differs from that species in being smaller, having a shorter, round tail with outer feathers white tipped. The white throat patch does not reach the base of the bill, and there is no white spot in the outspread wing. The mouth is furnished with bristles, as in Figure 386.

*Field Marks.* A woody brown bird that is occasionally flushed just in front of the feet from the shade of a sage-brush or rock on the bare mountain benches, flops away over the open, and then drops suddenly. More often heard at night than seen by day. Its note, a soft, hollow-sounding, three-syllabled whistle resembling *"Cook -- Wid-ow,"* many times repeated. Sometimes the first word is omitted, and when very close to an agitated bird, a number of little clucks may be heard as it sails noiselessly about the intruder.

*Nesting.* Eggs deposited on the bare ground.

*Distribution.* Central and western North America. In Canada, only in the valleys of southern interior British Columbia.

*SUBSPECIES.* Of the three subspecies recognized in the Check-list only one, the **Nuttall's** Poor-will (l'Engoulevent de Nuttall) *Antrostomus nuttalli nuttalli,* is accredited to Canada.

This soft, moth-like, nocturnal frequenter of the lower mountain benches and sage-covered flats of the warm, arid valleys is the western representative of the eastern Whip-poor-will. Though it is a bird of the open rather than the forest, it is similar to the Whip-poor-will in general appearance and habit. The day is spent dozing in the sultry shade of some small bush or stone with its great eyes half shut, its mottled and frosted plumage blending into the background. In the cool of the evening it wakens, and all through the night, between sallies after insects, it reiterates its soft, far-carrying plaint from the small eminence of log, stump, or stone. The notes are much like those of the Whip-poor-will, but shorter. They are soothing and rich with mystery and probably to the majority of hearers their author remains unseen and unknown. An imitation of its call is not difficult, and will bring it close, and it can be lured for long distances along the trail by crafty repetition. The first word *"Cook"* should be spoken and whistled in a deep tone, followed by two short notes of similar pitch and timbre with a strong accent on the first—*"Cook - - - oo-oo."*

*Economic Status.* Undoubtedly similar to the Whip-poor-will, its food being night-flying moths, beetles, and other insects.

420. **Nighthawk.** MOSQUITO HAWK. BULL-BAT. NIGHT-JAR. LE MANGE-MARINGOUINS. *Chordeiles minor.* L, 10. Plate XXXV A. A long-winged, long-tailed bird with the big eyes, small bill, and the enormous gape of the goatsuckers (Figure 386), coloured in fine and rather indefinite pattern of rich, dark brown and frosty white and greys.

*Distinctions.* The size of, and very similar to, the Whip-poor-will, for which it is often mistaken. Easily distinguished from it by the following characters. The throat is white, instead of being dark with white collar, the long mouth bristles are lacking (Compare with Figure 386). The tail is slightly forked instead of round and has little white, except a narrow, broken subterminal bar. The underparts are distinctly barred and the wings have a prominent white spot at the base of the primaries. In the southern valleys of interior British Columbia to be confused only with the Poor-will, but much larger, the tail slightly forked and well over 3·50 inches long, with a white subterminal bar instead of small thumb-marks on tips. The chin and throat are white instead of dark. The barring below is more decided, and the white spot at the base of the primaries is very distinctive.

*Field Marks.* The Nighthawk often flies about in broad daylight, but the Whip-poor-will or the Poor-will never do so unless disturbed. A white spot on the wing shows very plainly in flight, resembling from a little distance the clear-cut hole made by a rifle ball. The wing action, and outline, as the bird flies about the upper air with long, irregular stroke, are very characteristic, and its often-repeated, harsh, squawk-like note and its sudden, perpendicular dive in the air accompanied by a hollow booming sound are very distinctive of the species.

*Nesting.* Eggs laid directly on the ground in a clear spot, often the bald top of a flat rock. Flat gravel roofs in our cities are admirably adapted to its purpose and much used.

*Distribution.* North and South America. In Canada, north to Yukon and Mackenzie.

*SUBSPECIES.* Of the four subspecies recognized in the Check-list, three are attributed to Canada. The Eastern Nighthawk (le Mange-maringouins de l'Est) *Chordeiles minor minor* extends over much the greater part of the Dominion. In extreme southern Alberta, and probably into adjacent Manitoba, and Saskatchewan, in the dry belt near the International border, is Sennett's Nighthawk (le Mange-maringouins de Sennett) *Chordeiles minor sennetti*, a pale, whitened form that ranges south to Nebraska. In southeastern British Columbia, south to northern California, is the Pacific Nighthawk (le Mange-maringouins du Pacifique) *Chordeiles minor hesperis*, a darker but rather poorly defined race.

Though called Nighthawk this bird has no relation to the *Raptores* in habit, structure, or outward appearance. Its large eyes directed slightly forward sometimes cause it to be mistaken by casual observers for an owl. These graceful aeronauts may be seen over almost any city or town as evening draws on, beating about on long, strong wings with slow, powerful, but rather erratically timed, beats. At intervals one will mount in steep spirals higher and higher, and then face earthwards and come down nearly perpendicularly like a falling stone. As it falls a hollow dull tremolo buzz is heard. Just before the observer thinks the bird must dash to the ground it recovers itself and glides off safely to repeat the operation.

Its notes are not musical in themselves, but, by association, they seem fitting to hot summer sunsets, with black steeples, and factory smoke-stacks silhouetted against glowing skies. Often the last thing seen at night is its long-winged, gracefully beating form high in the upper air, still illuminated by the ruddy afterglow that has deserted the lower world, while the harsh squawking comes down softened and harmonized by distance.

Through the day time, the nighthawk seeks such shade as may be available, but evidently coolness is not a necessity to it. The writer remembers one stifling day in the arid lands of southern Saskatchewan when the breeze made by the travelling car struck like a furnace blast instead of giving refreshment, yet for some distance along the prairie road every fence-post had a dozing Nighthawk upon it, absorbing in sleepy content the intense heat of the mid-day sun that was shrivelling the surrounding vegetation.

*Economic Status.* Of few birds can more good or less harm be told than of the Nighthawk. Its food, wholly of insects, is taken on the wing, high in the air where many of the insects are mating and at a time when their destruction does the most good. It is a surprisingly small bird when stripped of its thick coat of soft feathers, but requires a great amount of food. A list of the species taken by it includes great numbers of ants, June bugs, squash beetles, chinch bugs, leaf-hoppers, and other obnoxious species. The habit, common in some places, of using this bird as a live target for gunners when practising is inexcusable and those guilty of it should be rigorously prosecuted. It should be realized that every offence against the laws protecting insect-eating birds is something more than a technical offence against an impersonal state; it is a direct blow at the welfare of the whole community.

## Order—Micropodiiformes. Swifts and Hummingbirds

An order composed of two suborders, *Micropodii* the swifts and *Trochili* the hummingbirds. Superficially they are quite unlike and probably most easily recognized under their subordinate descriptions.

### SUBORDER—MICROPODII. SWIFTS

Mostly small birds in dull colours without much pattern or variegation. Usually, over-all colours of sooty or black. Bill very small with large gape. Feet weak and fleshy rather than scaled (Figure 388a and b). In general, resembling swallows, in detail more like the goatsuckers, but without the finely patterned plumages, and the feathers hard and compact rather than soft and full. The primaries very long, bowed, and extending when closed far beyond the tail (Figure 388d). It is a group of birds superficially resembling swallows, but structurally quite different from them, the similarity being brought about by common requirements and not by relationship (Compare Figures 388 and 400, page 298). The compactly, hard-feathered wings, the long, bowed primaries, short secondaries, and the peculiar wing action of the swifts are different from those of the swallows. The swallow beats the air with long, rythmical strokes, the swift buzzes through it like a beetle and then sails on stiff-set wings locked into an even bow (Figure 388e). The swallow glides up and down invisible ærial waves like a sailboat, the swift bores through them like a torpedo. The wing action of swifts has a peculiarity all its own and so rapid is the wing movement that it can hardly be analysed by the eye. Many who have studied the flight intensively have declared that the wings beat alternately instead of in unison. However, some recent slow motion pictures of the flying birds have demonstrated that this unconformity of wing action is an optical illusion and that, whatever other differences there may be, swifts fly in this particular like other birds. The shape and formation of the wing may give peculiar character to the flight of swifts. The flying surface is largely composed of the primaries, the secondaries give comparatively little of the supporting area. It is thus evident that the birds fly mostly with the wing tips which probably necessitates special technique and different action from that of most birds. The swifts are noted for the extraordinary development of the salivary glands that produce an abundant secretion with which the nest of sticks is cemented together and to its perpendicular support. It is the cement thus formed that comprises the edible bird's nests of Chinese epicures.

Swifts live entirely on insects caught on the wing. North American swifts are divided into two subfamilies.

**Subfamily—Chaeturinae. Spine-tailed Swifts**

Not all of this subfamily have spine-tails (Figure 388c). Amongst the species herein treated, the Black and the White-throated Swifts are without them. The tarsi and toes are never feathered, but are not as fleshy (Figure 388b) as they are in the next subfamily. Canadian species except one are solidly coloured.

422. **Black Swift.** BLACK CLOUD SWIFT. LE MARTINET NOIR. *Nephoecetes niger.* L, 6·75. The largest of our swifts. Very dark sooty, almost black, but faintly lightening about head and breast, and with greyish feather edges on forehead and crown. Below, the female may or may not be marked with white feather tips.

*Distinctions.* Large size (wing over 6 inches), black coloration, and tail not spine-tipped (Compare Figure 388c).

*Field Marks.* The peculiar, regular bow of the forward wing outline (Figure 388e), rapid, even, and continuous wing beat alternating with long, sweeping sails, general torpedo-like body outline, and dense, dark coloration will distinguish this as a swift. Its large size, only, will suggest its species.

*Nesting.* In inaccessible clefts and crannies in the face of high mountain cliffs.

*Distribution.* Western North America and the Indies, to South America. In Canada, only in the mountainous regions of British Columbia and adjoining Alberta, north at least to southern Alaska and Jasper Park.

*SUBSPECIES.* The type of the species inhabits the West Indies, the bird of continental North America is the Northern Black Swift (le Martinet noir du Nord) *Nephoecetes niger borealis.*

In the neighbourhood of the beetling mountains, at irregular intervals, one may see, high over head, mere specks in the vault, innumerable black forms darting about in intricate interweaving pattern. They work up the valley or down. For some minutes they may be in sight and then vanish for hours or days. Occasionally, in cloudy weather, they may come down low and then the details of the Black Swift can be made out. A mystery surrounds them and their comings and goings. Most swifts can be traced with ease to their nests in the inaccessible, narrow clefts high up on the cliff face, but, though the Black Swift is common in many localities and must certainly nest nearby in numbers, it guards its secret well, and few nests have ever been found, or their sites located with certainty.

PLATE LVII

A. Hermit Thrush; scale, $\frac{1}{3}$

B. Grey-cheeked Thrush; scale, $\frac{1}{3}$

Olive-backed Thrush; scale, $\frac{1}{3}$

Plate LVIII

A. Wilson's Thrush; scale, $\frac{1}{3}$

B. Red-breasted or Eastern Bluebird; scale, $\frac{1}{3}$

Female Male

423. **Chimney Swift.** CHIMNEY SWALLOW. LE RAMONEUR. *Chaetura pelagica.* L, 5·43. Plate XXXV B. A small Swift of even sooty-brown colour, only slightly lightening on the throat and breast.

*Distinctions.* The even sooty-brown colour, lightening on the throat and darkening towards the vent, and the tail feathers ending in a sharp spine (Figure 388c) are sufficient for recognition of the species in eastern Canada and the Prairie Provinces where it is the

Figure 388
Details of Chimney Swift.
*a*, head; *b*, foot; *c*, tail feather with spine; *d*, horned wing-tip; *e*, outline in flight; scale: *a-d*, natural size; *e*, ½.

only swift to be expected. It is very similar to the Vaux's Swift of British Columbia, which may occasionally occur in western Alberta, but which is considerably smaller and with rump evenly coloured dark like the back. The wing of the Chimney Swift is 5 inches or over.

*Field Marks.* The characteristic regular bow of the forward wing outline (Figure 388e), the rapid, even, and continuous beats alternating with long, sweeping sails, general torpedo-like body outline, and dense, dark coloration will distinguish this as a swift. In the eastern Prairie Provinces this is the only species to be expected. In western Alberta, the Chimney Swift in life can be distinguished from the Black and Vaux's Swift only by size. It is much smaller than the first and considerably larger than the second. Identification by this test, however, is very uncertain. High up in the air, with nothing to fix the distance or scale, size is difficult to estimate.

*Nesting.* Originally in hollow trees or in clefts in rock cliffs. In out of the way places this practice is still followed, but throughout the east such situations are almost entirely abandoned for the flues of unused chimneys, and occasionally the gable interiors of buildings.

*Distribution.* Eastern North America from the lower edge of the northern spruce forest southward. In Canada, west regularly to Manitoba and reported as far as central Alberta. The swifts of Alberta should be closely scrutinized, and carefully identified.

This is an interesting species, swallow-like in outward appearance and food-hunting habits yet structurally distinct from the swallows. It is an odd example of parallel development of widely separated characters induced by similarity of requirement. Its habits have entirely changed since the advent of the white man and, forsaking hollow trees, it is now practically dependent upon chimneys for sites in which to build its nest. The winter home of the Chimney Swift is unknown. The mystery, however, should not be exaggerated, as there are numbers of swifts in the western hemisphere looking very like this one and the bird has probably been overlooked in its winter quarters or confused with closely allied forms. The swift spends much time on the wing and seldom comes to rest except in a chimney or hollow tree. In the autumn, before migration, great numbers gather together and at evening seek the shelter of some ample chimney where they pass the night. They may be seen just before dusk flying about in complicated patterns near the chosen chimney, and as the sun sets, circling, until, as they throw the wings straight up over the back and drop fluttering into the stack, one rapidly following another, they appear to pour in like a miniature maelstrom. The birds cling to the perpendicular walls of the chimney by hundreds, in masses like lumps of soot. Occasionally one with insecure hold drops a few feet, loosening, as it does so, others below; there is a momentary flutter of wings and a small chorus of fine, sharp chippings until they find new holdings and settle for the night.

424. **Vaux's Swift.** LE MARTINET DE VAUX. *Chaetura vauxi.* L, 4·15. A small swift of even, sooty brown colour, lightening slightly on throat, breast, and rump. Like the Chimney Swift but smaller.

*Distinctions.* Its extremely small size (wing, 4·50 or under), faintly pale underparts. and the tail spines (Figure 388c) will separate it easily from the big Black Swift, the only species it is likely to be confused with in British Columbia. Its possible occurrence in western Alberta makes it necessary to differentiate it from the Chimney Swift; size is the best distinction, but the rump and uppertail-coverts are slightly lighter than the back, instead of being of the same colour.

*Field Marks.* The characteristic regular bow of the forward wing outline (Figure 388e), rapid, even, and continuous beats, alternating with a long, sweeping sail, and general torpedo-like body outline, with dense, dark coloration, will distinguish this as a swift. In the eastern Prairie Provinces this species is not to be expected. In British Columbia it is to be confused only with the Black Swift, which is a much larger bird, and the White-throated, which is very local and strongly marked with white. Near the mountains in Alberta it may be taken for the Chimney Swift, from which it can be separated only by its smaller size. Swifts in this locality should be very carefully identified.

*Nesting.* In communities in hollow cottonwoods, and similar trees, occasionally in buildings, water tanks, etc.

*Distribution.* Western North America. In Canada, interior valleys of southern British Columbia and on the coast as far north as southern Alaska.

This bird is somewhat local in British Columbia and its distribution is largely determined by the presence of suitable hollow trees. Though much like the eastern Chimney Swift, it has not followed the example of that species in using chimneys for nesting.

### Subfamily—Micropodinae. Typical Swifts

This subfamily is chiefly Old World in distribution and is represented in Canada by but one species of very rare or local occurrence. The tail is spineless. The feet are thick, fleshy, and more or less flattened. The single species here considered is easily recognized by its white throat and breast.

425. **White-throated Swift.** LE MARTINET À GORGE BLANCHE. *Aeronautes saxatalis.* L, 6·75. Nearly as large as the Black Swift, but with extensive white throat, breast, and line down abdomen, tips of secondaries, and a patch on each side of the rump.

*Distinctions.* The only Canadian swift with decided white patches.

*Field Marks.* The characteristic regular bow of the forward wing outline, rapid, even, and continuous wing beat, alternating with long, sweeping sail and general torpedo-like body outline will distinguish this as a swift. The white throat and breast, and the white spots on either side of the rump will identify it as this species. The Violet-green Swallow associates with it and has similar white spots beside the rump, but the flight action is that of a swallow instead of a swift.

*Nesting.* In inaccessible clefts and crannies high on the face of mountain cliffs.

*Distribution.* Western North America south to Lower California. In Canada, known to occur only in the southern Okanagan Valley of British Columbia.

Too rare and local in Canada to be of much general interest, but no Canadian ornithologist can visit their haunts without enthusing over them. Their wonderful and spectacular speed of wing and their unattainable communal nesting strongholds, around which they turn and wheel and swoop, so high as to make it uncertain even with field-glasses whether they are birds high up or flies lower down, pique the bird-lover who sees them day by day at their most private affairs and yet never gets familiar with them.

## SUBORDER—TROCHILI. HUMMINGBIRDS

These tiny birds, with brilliant, flower-like coloration, insect-like flight, and wonderfully varied form, are a typically American order. In a way, they occupy much the same position in the New World as the Sun Birds do in the Old World, but the similarity between the two is superficial and not one of relationship. Many species are highly specialized and exhibit some of the strangest forms in the bird world, including crests, ruffs, fans, and muffs, exaggerated tails, long plumes, and enormous sword-like and fine awl-shaped bills, but their most striking feature is the brilliant metallic colorations that gleam on various parts of the body. They feed largely upon the nectar of flowers. The tongue is very long and protrusive as in the woodpeckers, but with its sides curled over towards the middle to form a double tube frayed into a brush-like tip that makes a most efficient organ for sucking liquids. Numbers of small insects, however, are taken with the nectar and, judging from feeding experiments on captives, seem to be necessary to the bird's welfare. They are usually minute forms taken from the flowers from which the nectar is obtained.

Hummingbirds as a group are tropical and subtropical species and increase greatly in number to the south, though a few species range well to the north.

### FAMILY—TROCHILIDAE. HUMMINGBIRDS

There is only one family of hummingbirds in Canada, represented in the east by a single species, in the far west by three.

Very minute birds, 3·75 inches or less in length, with long, spine-shaped bill (Figure 389), and brilliant metallic colours.

428. **Ruby-throated Hummingbird.** L'OISEAU-MOUCHE À GORGE RUBIS. *Archilochus colubris.* L, 3·74. Plate XXXVI A. Male: rich, metallic, bronzy green above and on flanks. Below, dull white with throat patch of scintillating ruby-red. Female and juvenile alike, green above, with white throat slightly streaked with greyish or showing a few sparse spots of brilliant ruby.

Figure 389
Hummingbird; natural size.

*Distinctions.* To be mistaken in western Alberta only for the Rufous Hummingbird, Plate XXXVI B. The male with its brilliant green, instead of unmetallic brick-red, back is easily identified. Females and juveniles of the two species are more alike, but the green back in this species is always bright and complete; that of the Rufous is duller and has always considerable rufous suffusion on the flanks, below, and especially on the base of the tail.

*Field Marks.* Small size and buzzing, insect-like flight. Except in western Alberta, the only hummingbird to be expected east and in the Prairie Provinces. The green back and gleaming ruby throat in the male, and the green back of rufous suffusion in other plumages.

*Nesting.* In a beautiful structure, covered with bits of lichen cemented together with cobweb, saddled on the top of a branch.

*Distribution.* Eastern North America. In Canada, west to Alberta, probably to the foothills. The hummingbirds of Alberta have not been carefully identified.

Hummingbirds fly forwards, backwards, sideways, or remain perfectly stationary in the air with equal ease—another instance of parallel development—a bird flying like an insect yet in structure strictly bird-like. The wings vibrate with a rapidity that can be measured only by the tuning-fork method used with insects. This system of flight is fundamentally different in method from that of other birds and consequently the wings differ from the usual type. They are long, narrow, and non-flexible, and the keel of the sternum is immensely deepened to give support to the great muscles that move them. In proportion to its wing-spread a hummingbird has a breast keel nearly three times larger than that of a pigeon, a bird of average flight, or forty times larger than that of an albatross.

*Economic Status.* When it is remembered that some of the smallest insect pests are the most destructive, we can realize that possibly the economic importance of the hummingbird may be greater than suspected. Besides nectar, its food seems to be composed of small flies, gnats, minute bees, wasps, and other flower-haunting and pollen-eating forms. Apparently no harm can be charged against the species and it may do good out of all proportion to its size.

429. **Black-chinned Hummingbird.** L'OISEAU-MOUCHE À MENTON NOIR. *Archilochus alexandri.* L, 3·50. A small hummer. Male: metallic bronzy green above, dull whitish below. Throat and gorget black with purple-violet reflections on its lower edge. Female: similar, but with dull white throat.

*Distinctions.* The male, with its black throat and gorget not elongated or projecting at the sides, is very distinctive; but the female and young birds are quite like similar plumages of the other Canadian hummers. There is little geographical likelihood of confusion with the Ruby-throated. From the Rufous it may be easily separated by its lack of any rufous suffusion. From the Calliope by its larger size, solid dark throat in the male, and entire absence of rufous in the female.

*Field Marks.* The black throat and gorget are a certain recognizable field mark for the male, but it must be remembered that these jewel-like gorget colours in other species only flash out when viewed from particular angles, and from many directions they show as black. Females do not show ruddy on flanks and undertail as do the Rufous and Calliope Hummers.

*Nesting.* Nest a beautiful structure of vegetable down and cobwebs saddled on a branch.

*Distribution.* Western North America, from British Columbia to northern Mexico, east to Montana. In Canada, only on the coast and in the interior of southern British Columbia. Not so far noted on Vancouver Island. Most common in the interior valleys.

A rare and rather local little hummer.

433. **Rufous Hummingbird.** L'OISEAU-MOUCHE ROUX. *Selasphorus rufus.* L, 3·50. Plate XXXVI B. Male: all above bright, brick-red, not iridescent except for slight green reflections on crown. Red suffuses over underparts leaving band below gorget white. Throat and gorget fiery red. Female and juveniles: bronzy, iridescent green above, with base of tail rufous at sides; below, dull white washed with rufous on flanks and undertail-coverts. Usually irregular spots of flaming iridescence on throat.

*Distinctions.* The male with its red back and flaming gorget, elongated and projecting at the sides like a shield, is unmistakable. The large amount of rufous wash on the body will identify the female and young birds from the Black-chinned, but they may be difficult to separate from similar Calliope Hummingbirds even when in hand.

*Field Marks.* As above distinctions.

*Nesting.* Nest a beautiful structure of lichens and cobwebs saddled on a branch.

*Distribution.* Western North America from the southern Yukon boundary to New Mexico. In Canada, British Columbia and the adjacent foothills of Alberta. It is not known to extend east on the prairies.

This is the common hummingbird of British Columbia, and is seen in suitable localities everywhere. One of the problems of common bird life is what becomes of the male hummingbirds in the summer. In spring, and while the species are mating, the sexes are equally common, but as soon as nesting duties are seriously engaged in, the brilliant, jewel-throated male ceases his interest in proceedings and not only lets his more sober-coloured mate take the whole burden of family raising, but disappears from the scene entirely. That the gay Lothario follows the flower season up the mountain sides and, in the alpine meadows at higher altitudes, finds a prolonged, flower-producing spring, sounds reasonable, but so far lacks demonstration. At any rate, it fails to explain a similar disappearance of the male Ruby-throated that lives out on the flat lands far from such mountain summer resorts. The phenomenon being common to all the hummers requires an explanation that will fit them all. The author suspects that the males depart on their southward migration as early as July like some of the waders.

436. **Calliope Hummingbird.** L'OISEAU-MOUCHE DE CALLIOPE. *Stellula calliope.* L, 2·75. A small hummer Male: iridescent bronze-green above, dusky white below. Throat and gorget composed of elongated lanceolate feathers of metallic rose-violet. Female: similar but without violet gorget.

*Distinctions.* The male with gleaming violet gorget, elongated and projecting at the sides, is unmistakable. The female much like those of other species, but smaller and with less red overwash than the Rufous.

It is smaller and with a more rounded tail than the Ruby-throated, the only hummer that it is likely to be confused with in western Alberta. From the Black-chinned, it can be separated by its reddish flanks.

*Field Marks.* The male with its brilliant reddish violet gorget, like the half of a many-pointed star on a white ground, is easily recognized when it faces the observer. The female may be separated from the female Black-chinned by its rufous flanks, but it cannot be told in life with any certainty from the Rufous, except when in hand.

*Nesting.* Nest a beautiful structure of lichens and cobwebs on a branch.

*Distribution.* Western North America from British Columbia to New Mexico. In Canada, southern British Columbia, part of the Alberta foothills, and, on the coast, north to Wrangell, Alaska.

This little hummer is quite common in the interior valleys of southern British Columbia. In common with the other hummers it is attracted to the sweet oozing sap from sapsucker drillings in black birches, and about trees so tapped, the branches black with the sticky wetness, quite a cloud of mixed hummingbirds will often be found.

They are peppery, pugnacious little midgets, and never meet each other without a battle of elfin fury. They dash together squeaking in fine high tones almost above the limit of the ear to hear, tower into the air, exchange stroke and parry with their rapier-like bills, and then descend to opposite sides of the bush under examination only to meet and engage again shortly. None seems to be seriously damaged by the encounter, but they never learn to bear or forbear, and a sap-running tree is a centre of rapidly buzzing wings, thin, angry squeaks, and dashing forms mixing in constant fray, from which come flashes from gleaming throats of kaleidoscopic brilliancy. Were hummingbirds as large as their courage, their haunts would not be safe for anybody.

## Order—Coraciiformes. Kingfishers, Mot-mots, etc.

An order of which in North America we have but one family, *Alcedinidae* the kingfishers, and in Canada a single species.

### FAMILY—ALCEDINIDAE. KINGFISHERS

As there is only one species of the family in Canada, the description given under the species will serve for the family.

**390. Belted Kingfisher.** LE MARTIN-PÊCHEUR CEINTURÉ. *Megaceryle alcyon.* L, 13·02. Plate XXXVII A.

*Distinctions.* The great ragged crest and slaty blue back of the Belted Kingfisher cannot be very well confused with any other American bird. The weak feet, three toes in front, the two outer (Figure 390) joined for half their length, and the peculiar, clumsy grasping surfaces are diagnostic of the kingfishers.

Figure 390
Foot of Kingfisher; natural size.

*Field Marks.* The ragged crest and large head, general coloration, a habit of sitting motionless on a perch overhanging the water or diving into it with a splash, and its harsh, rattling cry make the kingfisher easily recognizable in life.

*Nesting.* Usually on the ground at end of a tunnel driven in the face of an exposed earth bank.

*Distribution.* All North America, breeding wherever found in Canada.

*SUBSPECIES.* The Belted Kingfisher is divided into two subspecies by present authorities. The Eastern Belted Kingfisher (le Martin-pêcheur de l'Est) *Megaceryle alcyon alcyon* ranges across most of the continent. The Western Belted Kingfisher (le Martin-pêcheur de l'Ouest) *Megaceryle alcyon caurina*, of the west coast, is described as having wings of a slightly different proportion, but the difference is slight, and it is not clear how far inland this form extends.

All frequenters of Canadian waters know the kingfisher. It sits motionless on a commanding perch over the water watching for the fish below. Suddenly it dashes off, hangs suspended a moment in the air, and then drops with a resounding splash into the water, rising a moment later with a luckless fish in its capacious bill, and is off around the bend of the stream. Within its daily range the kingfisher knows every perch and branch from which it can get a comprehensive view of its fishing grounds, and returns to them again and again. Streams are not its only habitat; it frequents lakes, ponds, and seashore. Kingfishers fish sometimes at considerable distances from their nests, as they are often seen in country where earth banks such as they require for nesting are few. However, they are adaptable and sometimes use the most unexpected substitutes, such as the earth clinging to the roots of an overturned tree, or the sides of a drainage ditch.

*Economic Status.* The Belted Kingfisher lives upon small fish, and whether or not this constitutes a grave economic offence is a question that cannot be answered offhand. The minnows caught by this bird along our larger streams, ponds, or lakes are certainly not of importance, but when kingfishers frequent small preserved trout streams they may possibly commit rather serious depredations. Their effect on the larger salmon waters is less clear. Ordinarily the fish they take are small perch, shiners, chub, and other minnows that frequent surface or shallow, warm water. The number of young game-fish that are taken cannot be great. On waters given to the culture of trout the question is different. The fish taken there are comparatively well grown and, even if the kingfishers are not very numerous, they cannot be looked upon with friendly eyes by the angler. However, the evil done by this species can easily be exaggerated.

## Order—Piciformes. Woodpeckers, Toucans, etc.

The world-wide order *Piciformes* is a rather heterogeneous division including numerous subdivisions, and there is little uniformity of opinion as to their exact relations. In Canada, there is only one family of the order —*Picidae,* the woodpeckers.

### FAMILY—PICIDAE. WOODPECKERS

*General Description.* The Woodpeckers are an easily recognized family. They have either three or four toes ending in well-hooked claws for clinging to the rough bark of trees, and, as in the cuckoos, two are directed forward. In one group, the Three-toed Woodpeckers, one of the hind toes is absent (Figure 391c). The bill is straight, stout, and chisel-shaped at the tip (Figure 391a). The tail is well developed; not remarkably long, but stout, and ending in stiff bristles that are commonly worn and frayed by pressure against rough bark (Figure 391b).

*Distinctions.* Feet, bill, and tail characters make reliable distinctions.

*Field Marks.* Tree-climbing habits; and flight by series of quick wing-strokes with slight pauses between, causing a waved course like a succession of festoons.

*Nesting.* In holes excavated in trees or stubs.

The woodpeckers are well known for their ability to cling to perpendicular or overhanging surfaces. The stout, chisel-shaped bill is admirably adapted to drilling into wood whence the larvæ of borers or other insects are extracted. The tongue is long and extensible, and in most species furnished with a sharp point, armed with minute barbs to assist in holding the impaled prey and withdrawing it from the wood (Figure

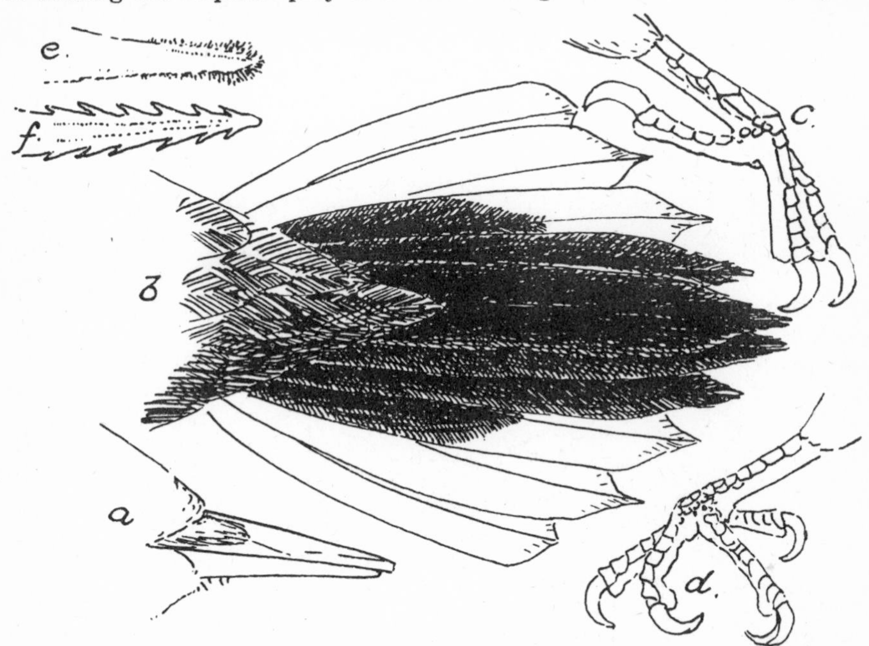


Figure 391

Characteristic details of Woodpeckers.

*a*, chisel-shaped bill. *b*, stiff tail of pointed feathers. *c*, three-toed foot. *d*, four-toed foot. *e*, tongue tip of sapsucker (greatly enlarged). *f*, tongue tip of typical woodpecker (greatly enlarged).

391f). The hyoid or tongue bones are so long that in the normal position of rest they wind over the base of the skull along the crown and in some species penetrate the nostrils beneath the bill-sheath and finally rest their ends near the tip of the bill. As a further aid, large salivary glands secrete a sticky fluid for the tongue, to which small insects stick and are caught as with birdlime. A few species, for example the sapsuckers, have the tip of the tongue frayed out into a sort of brush, that is evidently used in gathering up sap (Figure 391e).

*Economic Status.* Of the general usefulness of the woodpeckers, with the exception of the sapsuckers, there can be little doubt. They are almost entirely insectivorous. They pursue wood-boring grubs by drilling holes in even apparently healthy though really infested trees and are, therefore, beneficial, not harmful.

412. **Yellow-shafted Flicker.** YELLOW-HAMMER. HIGHHOLE. GOLDEN-WINGED WOODPECKER. LE PIVART DORÉ. *Colaptes auratus.* L, 12. Plate XXXVII B. Greyish fawn on back with broken bars of black; fawn face and throat fading to white below; light underparts and flanks, with many sharp, round, black spots; a black gorget across breast; crown slate-grey with red bar across nape. Male with black moustache mark from gape. Under-surface and shafts of flight and tail feathers in all plumages brilliant yellow; rump, white.

*Distinctions.* Unmistakable for any other species except the Red-shafted Flicker, which differs in having a grey instead of vinaceous throat and face, a red instead of black moustache mark, and the yellow of wings and tail replaced by pinkish red. These two species hybridize extensively and all sorts of mixtures of characters may be found. A tint of grey in throat or face, tinge of red in the under-wing or tail surface, or specks of red in the moustache, are indicative of mixed blood.

*Field Marks.* Size, general coloration with yellow under the wings visible in flight, and the white rump. Easily recognizable calls.

*Nesting.* In hole in dead tree or stub.

*Distribution.* Eastern North America from tree limit in the north to the Gulf coast. In Canada, west to the Rocky Mountains, and northwest to Alaska. In British Columbia, and adjacent Alberta, it intermixes and hybridizes freely with the Red-shafted Flicker.

*SUBSPECIES.* The Yellow-shafted Flicker now attributed to Canada is the Northern Flicker (le Pivart doré du Nord) *Colaptes auratus luteus*, that extends into the north-central United States.

The Flicker is perhaps the woodpecker most familiar to the general public. Its loud, characteristic notes of "*Flicker-flicker-flicker*," or long-drawn "*Piew-w-w-w*," are well known and easily recognizable sounds. It has a habit of clinging to some hollow-sounding tree trunk and rolling out a long, reverberating tattoo that can be heard for long distances. It sometimes uses a loose shingle or clapboard of a house or galvanized sheet as a drum or sounding board and delights itself with the increased efficiency of its efforts, often to the disturbance of others.

Though a somewhat aberrant woodpecker in habits, and less dependent on tree borers than many of the family, its summer range is strictly confined to localities where there is timber of sufficient size to be excavated for nesting holes. Consequently, in the great area of the bare prairies the species is only an occasional visitor, but every wooded coulée is frequented by it, and it has found that the telegraph poles strung across the open are most excellent artificial stubs, and its range has been considerably increased by the building of telegraph and telephone lines.

The Flicker is the carpenter of the bird world, and, without it, it is questionable where many cavity nesting species, which are unable to do their own excavating, would find quarters. Sparrow Hawks bluebirds, Tree Swallows, small owls, and many other species are almost rely dependent

A. Western Bluebird; scale, $\frac{1}{3}$

Male Female

B. Mountain Bluebird; scale, $\frac{1}{3}$

Male Female

PLATE LX

A. Townsend's Solitaire; scale, $\frac{1}{3}$

B. Ruby-crowned Kinglet; scale, $\frac{1}{3}$
Male Female

Golden-crowned Kinglet; scale, $\frac{1}{3}$
Female Male

on the Flicker for nest holes. The reproductive powers of the Flicker are phenomenal. When eggs were taken away as they were laid, it has been known to lay thirty or more eggs in a season.

The relation of this species to the Red-shafted Flicker is most interesting. It intermixes and crosses freely with that species and near the line of contact between them it is unusual to find pure-blooded birds of either species. That the two are distinct species and not subspecies is indicated by the nature of the intergrading specimens. The characters are not gradual blendings but mosaic mixtures. Thus the moustache mark is very seldom brown, which would be the result of blending between the black of the Yellow-shafted and the red of the Red-shafted, but it is pure black, pure red, black flecked with red, or vice versa. The same phenomenon is shown in the throat plumage, in which the feathers may be alternately grey and vinaceous, or one colour at the base and another at the tip; or even a difference between one barbule and thé next. The underwing and undertail surface may be orange, which is a blending between the yellow and red. This is not necessarily contrary to the rule of mosaic mixture in hybrids, because these two colour pigments in bird plumage are intimately related, chemically and physiologically, and may, perhaps, be regarded as one and the same substance in different concentration. The fact that in spite of the readiness with which these two species cross both species are not completely mongrelized, is suggestive that such hybrids have some handicap against indefinite persistence, and are continued only through constant fresh crosses of purer blood.

*Economic Status.* Ants constitute nearly half the food of the Flicker. The remainder of its insect food consists of both beneficial and harmful species, but the latter noticeably predominate. It takes some fruit, grain, and mast; but on the whole must be considered beneficial rather than harmful. Perhaps the most serious charge that can be made against the species is its scattering of the seeds of the poison oak and ivy and so aiding in the spread of these harmful plants.

413. **Red-shafted Flicker.** LE PIVART ROSÉ. *Colaptes cafer.* L, 12. Similar to the Yellow-shafted Flicker, but the face and throat slate grey, instead of fawn; red moustache mark, instead of black; normally with no red on nape, the lining of wings and tail pinkish red instead of bright yellow.

*Distinctions.* To be confused only with the Yellow-shafted Flicker, from which it differs as above.

*Field Marks.* Size, general coloration, with red under the wings visible in flight, and the white rump. As a flicker, by its easily recognizable calls.

*Nesting.* In holes in dead trees or stubs.

*Distribution.* Western North America from southern Alaska to Mexico. In Canada, southern and central British Columbia, intermixing and hybridizing with the Yellow-shafted over much of its range, and well into adjacent Alberta. Specimens with strong Red-shafted tendencies have been taken as far east as Manitoba.

*SUBSPECIES.* Owing to a late and interesting relocation of stations visited by Captain Cook, the navigator, it has lately been discovered that the specimen that first received the name of *cafer* came from Vancouver Island, and hence our British Columbia coast bird, the Northwestern Red-shafted Flicker (le Pivart rosé du Nord-Ouest), hitherto known as *Colaptes cafer saturatior*, is the type of the species and should be called *Colaptes cafer cafer*. It occupies the Pacific Coast region west of the Coast Range from Sitka to northern California. It is characterized by being generally darker coloured than the Common Red-shafted Flicker (le Pivart rosé commun) of the interior, *Colaptes cafer collaris.*

Everything said of the Yellow-shafted Flicker applies to this species.

405. **Pileated Woodpecker.** COCK-OF-THE-WOODS. LOGCOCK. (*Incorrectly,* Woodcock.) LE GRAND PIC. *Coephloeus pileatus.* L, 17. Plate XXXVIII A. A very large woodpecker, coloured in broad masses of black and white and with a conspicuous, pointed, brilliant red crest.

*Distinctions.* By far the largest woodpecker in Canada, it can be confused with no other Canadian species.

*Field Marks.* A woodpecker almost as large as a crow, with striking, pointed, red crest, and loud, characteristic cries.

*Nesting.* In holes excavated in dead trees and stubs.

*Distribution.* The northern forests across the continent, south along the mountains.

*SUBSPECIES.* Four subspecies of the Pileated Woodpecker (le Grand Pic du Nord) are recognized in the Check-list, two of which are accredited to Canada. The Northern Pileated Woodpecker *Coephloeus pileatus abieticola* is the form of eastern Canada, extending west. The Western Pileated Woodpecker (le Grand Pic de l'Ouest) *Coephloeus pileatus picinus* is accredited to the west coast mountains, and probably farther east. It is described as being slightly smaller and darker (browner), with the whites restricted. These distinctions are very slight, however, and are average rather than individual.

In the east, on account of the wanton destruction, this once much more widely distributed bird is to be found only in the quiet of the more northern woods. Even there, visitors and deer hunters could not resist the temptation of taking so spectacular a trophy home with them, and it was being rapidly reduced in number until the provisions of the Migratory Birds Convention Act extended practical protection over it. In the west, things have not gone so far, and, especially in the mountain and coast districts, it may still be seen in close proximity to civilization. It is a bird typical of the deep woods. It visits the rotten logs in the damp, shadowy undergrowth, and, with its powerful bill, tears and scatters them about in fragments for the grubs contained. These habits are the origin of the common vernacular names, Cock-of-the-Woods and Logcock, which have often been corrupted into Woodcock, a name already applied to an entirely different bird, and the source of much confusion and misunderstanding. Its principal value is that of a forest conserver, and it should be protected for economic as well as æsthetic reasons.

409. **Red-bellied Woodpecker.** LE PIC À VENTRE ROUX. *Centurus carolinus.* L, 9·50. Entire back and upperparts sharply and regularly barred with black and white. Whole back of neck to shoulder and, in the male, the top of head, bright red. All remainder and below ashy white with slight olive tinge. Abdomen slightly tinged with red.

*Distinctions.* The even barring of the whole back and the red colour of the crown and rear neck are easily distinguished (Figure 392).

*Distribution.* From the gulf coast to northern United States, occurring as a straggler to the north of the boundary in southern Ontario.

Figure 392
Red-bellied Woodpecker: scale, ⅓.
Male

This woodpecker is of rare and local occurrence in Canada. Its economic status is good, although it is fond of wild fruit and occasionally turns its attention to cultivated varieties.

406. **Red-headed Woodpecker.** LE PIC À TÊTE ROUGE. *Melanerpes erythrocephalus.* L, 9·75. Plate XXXVIII B. Solidly black above, with secondaries and rump pure white; head, neck all around, and upper breast bright crimson-red; below white. The juvenile has the red of head and neck replaced by dusky ash and the blacks and whites edged and obscured with the same.

*Distinctions.* The solid red head and the conspicuous black and white in large, unbroken masses, can be mistaken for no other species.

*Field Marks.* The red head and contrasting masses of black and white on the body, especially the large amount of white in the wings.

*Nesting.* In cavity excavated in dead tree or stub.

*Distribution.* Most of eastern and central North America, from southern Canada south to the Gulf of Mexico. In western Canada, southern Manitoba, and along the southern border as far west as Alberta.

*SUBSPECIES.* Birds from the western prairies are somewhat larger than eastern ones, and have been described as a separate subspecies, the Western Red-headed Woodpecker (le Pic à tête rouge de l'Ouest) *Melanerpes erythrocephalus erythropthalmus*, but the form has not, as yet, been recognized by the American Ornithologists' Union Committee. The author is unable to say which form is represented in Manitoba.

The Red-headed Woodpecker is really common in Canada only in southern Ontario where it is a familiar feature about orchards and wood lots. With its flaming red head and black and white banner-like body it is well known wherever it occurs. It has fewer of the regulation woodpecker habits than most of its family and has evolved some flycatcher-like traits in addition to its ancestral ones. Though some charges of fruit eating have been made against it, its total effect is good. Not numerous enough in the western or Prairie sections to be of much economic importance there. This is the woodpecker whose head Hiawatha, in Longfellow's poem, dipped in the blood of the Pearl Feather.

408. **Lewis's Woodpecker.** LE PIC DE LEWIS. *Asyndesmus lewisi.* L, 10·50. Plate XXXIX A. A solidly black-backed woodpecker. Abdomen an intimate mixture of rose and grey (mostly rose) with peculiar hairy effect; breast of similar texture, but grey, and continuing about neck in a narrow collar. Face and chin dull, dark crimson. Juvenile similar but without red face or grey collar, and the rose below duller.

*Distinctions.* The solid black back, grey collar and breast, and peculiar streaky rose underparts can be mistaken for no other bird likely to occur in Canada.

*Field Marks.* All black back and rose underparts, with characteristic flycatching habits.

*Nesting.* In holes excavated in trees and stubs.

*Distribution.* Western North America, from southern British Columbia south to New Mexico. In Canada, mostly west of the Rocky Mountains, but occasional as far east as Saskatchewan, and has been noted in Manitoba.

Lewis's Woodpecker is a conspicuous bird in southern British Columbia. Its habit of frequenting the tops of tall, isolated trees, and flying out from them, making short circles and returning, or passing back and forth between adjoining trees, well out in the open, would attract attention at once, even if the birds were not so noisy. The shiny black backs and rosy underparts enhance their ornamental value.

*Economic Status.* There are strong, and at least partly substantiated, complaints against them as fruit-eaters. When they confine their attention to wild varieties, no harm is done, but they take cultivated varieties, and may on occasion cause some loss where fruit-raising is an important industry. No complete study of their food habits has been made, but such evidence as we have indicates that the bird on the whole, and throughout the year, is largely insectivorous. It does not delve into wood for grubs as much as other woodpeckers do, but takes a considerable number of beetles, ants, and other hymenoptera, a few bugs, and some grasshoppers. Normally, about 15 per cent of the total food supply is fruit. Though undoubtedly too many fruit-eating birds in a fruit-growing district are a handicap, the species is never anything more than a local problem, and further investigation in field and laboratory is necessary to fix its definite economic status.

## Sapsuckers

The sapsuckers form a group of woodpeckers that are adapted for drinking sap rather than boring for grubs. In consequence the tongues are short and modified at the end into a sort of brush (Figure 391e), instead of into a sharp, barbed spear. The remarks made under heading of Yellow-bellied Sapsucker are largely true of the two other species dealt with here.

402. **Yellow-bellied Sapsucker.** LE PIC À VENTRE JAUNE. *Sphyrapicus varius.* L, 8·56. Plate XXXIX B. Variegated above with black and white without sharp contrast or very definite pattern; below, strongly tinged with yellow and a strong, black, crescentic gorget across the breast. Male with crimson crown and throat; female the same, or with dull white throat and, occasionally, with black cap. Juveniles lack the red crown and throat, and the black gorget, the whites are tinged with ochre and the breast is dull, dirty brown.

*Distinctions.* To be mistaken only for the Red-breasted Sapsucker of the west coast, which is similar in general coloration, but which has head, neck, and throat a solid crimson which is suggested even in juvenile birds.

*Field Marks.* The red cap and throat are conspicuous in life. When these are absent, the black gorget in the adult is usually distinctive. Otherwise, the indefinite black and white pattern, with a broad white bar on forward part of closed wing, make best field marks, but will not separate from the Red-breasted Sapsucker of the west coast. The rolling tattoo made by sapsuckers in drilling is distinctive from that of the other woodpeckers. It ends in four or five isolated taps with appreciable intervals between, instead of stopping abruptly in the middle of the roll.

*Nesting.* In holes excavated in dead trees and stubs.

*Distribution.* Northern North America, except Yukon, Alaska, and west of the Coast Range, from tree limits southward.

*SUBSPECIES.* The Eastern Yellow-bellied Sapsucker (le Pic à ventre jaune de l'Est) *Sphyrapicus varius varius* inhabits the wooded sections of the Dominion, west to the Rocky Mountains and into northern British Columbia. The Red-naped Sapsucker (le Pic à nuque rouge) *Sphyrapicus varius nuchalis* occupies British Columbia, except in the north, and on the coast, south to New Mexico, overlapping the range of *varius* in western Alberta. It differs from *varius* principally in having a red bar across the nape, separated from the red crown by a black line. The female has a red throat, which the female of *varius* rarely or never has.

*Economic Status.* This is the only Canadian genus of the family that seems to be questionable. The damage is done in quest of sap, by girdling the trunks and branches of orchard and other smooth-bark trees with rows of small squarish pits, regularly spaced in horizontal lines penetrating both outer and inner barks to the sap-wood beneath. Several trees may be so tapped and visited in turn as the sap exudes. Though it is primarily the sap that is sought, the insects attracted are also eaten, for though sap is a large item in the sapsucker's diet, insect food is also necessary.

Although the damage to trees so girdled is not nearly so great as might be expected, they are sometimes permanently injured and even killed. All are weakened and a lodgment prepared for fungoid growth and insects. Unless severely and repeatedly attacked, however, most trees survive and completely recover. Even forest growth suffers damage; timber trees are attacked and the consequent burr growths and wood stains in the manufactured lumber, marking the old, healed wounds made by the sapsucker, reduce the marketable value of the lumber products. The whole question of the damage done by sapsuckers has been exhaustively discussed in a United States Biological Survey Bulletin, No. 39, "Woodpeckers in Relation to Trees and Wood Products," by W. L. McAtee. Under the heading of defensive measures against sapsuckers the author advises a limited use of the gun or the use of poison where the species is doing appreciable harm. If the gun is used care should be taken that only sapsuckers are killed, and it must be remembered that with poison many small birds, especially hummingbirds, warblers, and other species that are often attracted in great numbers to the sweet, oozing sap, are likely to suffer also.

403. **Red-breasted Sapsucker.** LE PIC À POITRINE ROUGE. *Sphyrapicus ruber.* L, 8·50. Plate XL A. In general, similar to the Yellow-bellied Sapsucker, but with less fine white markings on back and wings, and with a bright crimson head, neck, and breast. Sexes alike. Juveniles similar to those of the Yellow-bellied, but darker and usually with suggestive suffusions of red on head and breast.

*Distinctions.* To be confused only with the Yellow-bellied Sapsucker, but confined to the vicinity of the west coast. Easily differentiated by extensive red head, neck, and breast, suggested even in juvenile birds.

*Field Marks.* Extensive red head, neck, and breast. The indefinite black and white coloration with broad white bar on forward part of closed wings will separate from all species but the Yellow-bellied Sapsucker.

*Nesting.* In holes excavated in dead or living trees or stubs.

*Distribution.* Western North America, mainly west of Coast and Cascade Ranges.

*SUBSPECIES.* This sapsucker has heretofore been regarded as a distinct species, but the 1931 Check-list has reduced it in rank to a subspecies of the Yellow-bellied Sapsucker under the name *Sphyrapicus varius ruber*, a conclusion with which the present writer finds it difficult to agree. The Red-breasted Sapsucker is divided into northern and southern races. The Northern *Sphyrapicus ruber ruber*, ranges from Skagway, Alaska, to northern California. In British Columbia mostly west of the Coast Range, but spreading into the interior near the northern extremity of its range.

The Red-breasted Sapsucker does not differ materially in habits or economical effect from the Yellow-bellied.

404. **Cut-throated Sapsucker.** WILLIAMSON'S SAPSUCKER. LE PIC À GORGE COUPÉE. *Sphyrapicus thyroideus.* L, 9·50. The male is a very distinctive bird. The species is notable for the extraordinary sexual difference in coloration. Male: solid black, except white rump, wing-covert patch, and two sharp lines on face; abdomen sharply defined lemon yellow, and a narrow, blood-red dash on the centre of the throat down from bill. Female: back, wings, and flanks regularly and sharply barred with narrow lines of black and white, having an appearance of being wound around with black and white worsted; black breast and throat patch, and yellow abdominal patch. Head mostly dull white or dirty brown. The black breast patch may be absent, and there may be indications of the red dash on the throat.

Figure 393
Williamson's Sapsucker; scale, ⅓.
Female Male

*Distinctions.* Unmistakable for any other species. The solidly black back, with contrasting white rump of the male, and the regular barring of the back of the female, are distinctive.

*Field Marks.* The general blackness of the male, with conspicuous white wing patch and rump, and the barred back and white rump of the female make good field marks. The female is strongly suggestive of a Flicker, especially in flight, when the white rump shows.

*Nesting.* In holes excavated in trees and stubs.

*Distribution.* The western mountain forests of North America, from southern British Columbia to New Mexico. Range very local and restricted in Canada. Recorded only from some of the higher tamarack forests near the southern boundary, from Okanagan Valley to the Alberta line.

Rare in Canada, and so confined to the wilder elevations as to have little economic influence.

393. **Hairy Woodpecker.** LE PIC CHEVELU. *Dryobates villosus.* L, 9·40. Plate XL B. A black and white woodpecker, the only other colour on it is in the two bright red nape spots on the male. Near the west coast, the whites may be slightly, to heavily, tinged with smoky brown. Juvenile males just from the nest show more or less red wash on crown, a character that is soon lost.

*Distinctions.* With its sharply contrasted black and white, or black and smoky white, most likely to be confused with its smaller relative, the Downy Woodpecker, which parallels it in all its plumages, and of which it is a larger edition. An additional difference is the outer tail feathers, which in the Hairy are solid white instead of being barred with black (Figure 391b, compare with Plate XLI A).

*Field Marks.* Black and white, or black and smoky white, coloration. Many white spots on wings. Separated from the Downy Woodpecker by larger size.

*Nesting.* In holes drilled in tree trunks.

*Distribution.* The wooded parts of North America. In Canada, wherever there is timber.

*SUBSPECIES.* Divided into a number of geographical races. The type form, *Dryobates villosus villosus,* is the eastern one extending into southern Manitoba, and perhaps into adjoining parts of the other Prairie Provinces. North of this is found the Northern Hairy (le Pic chevelu du Nord) *Dryobates villosus septentrionalis* which differs from *villosus* only in slightly larger size. It occupies the great north woodlands of the interior, south to northern British Columbia, and most of Alberta, Saskatchewan, and Manitoba. The Rocky Mountain Hairy Woodpecker (le Pic chevelu des Rocheuses) *Dryobates villosus monticola,* as its name suggests is the bird of the interior of southern British Columbia, extending southeastward to Colorado. It is of the size of *septentrionalis,* but with the white spotting of the wing-coverts reduced. Harris's Woodpecker (le Pic chevelu de Harris) *Dryobates villosus harrisi* is the Hairy Woodpecker of the Pacific coast, from Oregon north to Sitka. It is a very different looking bird from those before mentioned, having the whites of the breast decidedly tinged with smoky brown, and the spots of the wing-coverts almost absent. The Queen Charlotte Hairy Woodpecker (le Pic chevelu de Reine-Charlotte) *Dryobates villosus picoideus* occupies the islands of that name, and is a darker and still more smoky bird than *harrisi.* The Sitka Hairy Woodpecker (le Pic chevelu de Sitka) *Dryobates villosus sitkensis* is the bird of the southeastern Alaskan coast, and perhaps northwestern British Columbia. In coloration, it is between *harrisi* and *monticola.*

Some of these subspecies are founded on average characters, and there are many intergrades, as would be expected from the many geographical contacts between them. The extremes of the white and smoky-breasted types are very distinct.

The Hairy Woodpecker gets its name from the white feathers of the back, which fall over the black borders in a loose, disconnected way faintly suggestive of hair. It is one of the common woodpeckers and quite typical of the family in its habits. It is not as familiar about houses or orchards as the Downy Woodpecker, preferring the woods to orchards or shade trees.

*Economic Status.* Insects constitute 77 per cent of the food of this species; they are mostly beetles, but include ants, scales, and sawflies; 22 per cent is vegetable, almost entirely wild fruit.

394. **Downy Woodpecker.** LE PIC MINULE. *Dryobates pubescens.* L, 6·83. Plate XLI A. A very small, black and white woodpecker, the only other colour on it is in the small, bright red nape bar on the male. Hardly distinguishable in colour from the Hairy. In the far west, the whites may be lightly, to heavily, tinged with smoky brown. Like the Hairy Woodpecker juvenile males just from the nest show more or less red wash on crown, a character that is soon lost.

*Distinctions.* With its sharply contrasted black and white, or black and smoky white, to be confused only with its larger relative, the Hairy Woodpecker, which parallels it in all plumages. The principal difference, besides size, is in the outer tail feathers, which are barred with black instead of being solid white (compare with Figure 391b).

*Field Marks.* Black and white, or black and smoky white coloration. Many white spots on wings. Separated from the Hairy Woodpecker by smaller size.

*Nesting.* In holes drilled in trees.

*Distribution.* All wooded parts of North America, but not quite as northern in extreme range as the Hairy Woodpecker. In Canada, most of the wooded areas across the continent.

*SUBSPECIES.* Divided into a number of geographical races. Of these, the following are accredited to Canada. The Northern Downy Woodpecker (le Pic minule du Nord) *Dryobates pubescens medianus*, which occupies most of eastern North America, extends west throughout the Dakotas, and is probably the bird of the southern Prairie Provinces. The still more northern, or Nelson's, Downy Woodpecker (le Pic minule de Nelson) *Dryobates pubescens nelsoni* is very slightly larger, and with a whiter breast and less barring on outer tail feathers. It can be expected to blend into *medianus* in the Prairie Provinces, and extends northwestward through Mackenzie, northern British Columbia, Yukon, and the interior of Alaska. In southern British Columbia, east of the Coast Range, is Batchelder's Woodpecker (le Pic minule de Batchelder) *Dryobates pubescens leucurus*, of the size of *nelsoni*, but with little white on the wing-coverts, analogous to *monticola* in the Hairy Woodpecker. This race extends southward through the United States interior to New Mexico. On the coast, west of the Coast and Cascade Ranges, is Gairdner's Woodpecker (le Pic minule de Gairdner) *Dryobates pubescens gairdneri*, extending southward to northern California. It has the whites tinged with smoky similarly to *harrisi* of the Hairy Woodpeckers. On the Alaskan Coast, from Kenai Peninsula to northern British Columbia, is the Valdez Downy Woodpecker (le Pic minule de Valdez) *Dryobates pubescens glacialis*, in size intermediate between *nelsoni* and *medianus*, and with a slightly different distribution of white on the wings and coverts.

With the exception of the deeply coloured Gairdner's Woodpecker, these are all very slightly defined races, founded on more or less average characteristics, and naturally intergrade with each other along the lines of contact. Their boundaries have not been very well established in Canada.

The Downy Woodpecker shows an interesting case of parallel development with the Hairy, of which it is little more than a small replica. It breaks up into geographical races closely resembling those of that species. Thus we have the following analogous races, showing practically similar characters:

| | | |
|---|---|---|
| Eastern Hairy | Eastern Downy | Smaller |
| Northern Hairy | Northern Downy | Larger |
| Rocky Mountain Hairy | Batchelder's | Large and spots reduced |
| Harris's | Gairdner's | Smoky |

The Downy, over most of its range, is one of the commoner woodpeckers. It is more likely to come into the orchard and parks, and closer to the house, than is the Hairy. It is a valuable assistant to the husbandman, the orchardist, and the forester.

*Economic Status.* Being the most fearless of the woodpeckers and coming close about the fields and houses where it is most needed, it is an invaluable bird. Peering into every crack and crevice of shade and fruit trees and drilling for deeper-lying insects it well complements the work of the little chickadees and nuthatches. In fact, these three species often travel in company in the winter and there is little in the food line that is overlooked when the three species work together. The food of the Downy Woodpecker is similar to that of the Hairy Woodpecker, but, as would be expected from its smaller size and its more common presence in summer, includes more of the smaller insects. The various scale-insects make a larger item in its food and it takes more moth-caterpillars, including the tent caterpillar and those of the codling moth.

399. **White-headed Woodpecker.** LE PIC À TÊTE BLANCHE. *Dryobates albolarvatus.* L, 8·90. Male: all black, except for white head, foreneck, patch on wing, and a red bar across nape. Female similar, but without red bar.

Figure 394
White-headed Woodpecker; scale, ⅓. Male

*Distinction.* With above description, can be mistaken for no other species. The female Williamson's Sapsucker may have a whitish head, but her body, sharply barred with black and white, is quite different.

*Field Marks.* A black woodpecker, with white head and white wing patch.

*Nesting.* In a hole in a stub.

*Distribution.* In mountains from Washington to southern California. Occasional in southern British Columbia. Only three Canadian specimens known, from the Similkameen and Okanagan Valleys.

*SUBSPECIES.* The form to be expected in Canada is the northern or type race, *Dryobates albolarvatus albolarvatus.* Only an occasional wanderer across our far southwestern borders.

400. **Arctic Three-toed Woodpecker.** BLACK-BACKED WOODPECKER. LE PIC À DOS NOIR. *Picoides arcticus.* L, 9·50. Plate XLI B. A woodpecker with three, instead of four, toes (Figure 391c, page 277), and a solidly black back; male with a yellow crown cap.

*Distinctions.* With three, instead of four, toes, likely to be confused only with the next species. The back is solid black, however, instead of brokenly barred with white.

*Field Marks.* The yellow cap will identify the male as a Three-toed Woodpecker. This is the only woodpecker with white breast and throat and solidly black back.

*Distribution.* The northern coniferous forests across the continent, southward in the mountains.

401. **American Three-toed Woodpecker or Banded-backed Woodpecker.** LADDER-BACKED WOODPECKER. LE PIC À DOS BARRÉ. *Picoides tridactylus.* L, 8·75. A woodpecker with three, instead of four, toes (Figure 391c, page 277). Back, black with broken white bars, and male with yellow crown cap.

*Distinctions.* Except for the banded, instead of solid black, back, almost exactly similar to the Arctic Three-toed Woodpecker, which is the species most likely to be confused with it.

*Field Marks.* The yellow cap will identify the male as a Three-toed Woodpecker, and the barring of the back will indicate this species. Much like a Hairy Woodpecker, but back barred with white, instead of a longitudinal mass of that colour; flanks also heavily barred with black. The female Williamson's Sapsucker also has a barred back, but the barring is not confined to the centre of the back, and the crown is never black.

*Nesting.* In holes excavated in tree trunks, often living ones.

*Distribution.* The northern coniferous forests of North America, southward along the mountains to New Mexico.

*SUBSPECIES.* Several subspecies are accepted. Of these, two occur in Canada. The eastern American Three-toed Woodpecker (le Pic à dos barré de l'Est) extends west to Alberta where its place is taken by the Alaskan Three-toed Woodpecker (le Pic dos barré de l'Alaska) *Picoides tridactylus fasciatus*, characterized principally by more white on back.

The Three-toed Woodpeckers are typically north woods birds, and in summer come south only in the higher altitudes of the mountains. In the winter they may occur in migration in the foothills or southward in suitable localities.

PLATE LXI

A. Cedar Waxwing; scale, $\frac{1}{3}$

Bohemian Waxwing; scale, $\frac{1}{4}$

B. Common Shrike; scale, $\frac{1}{3}$

Plate LXII

A. Solitary Vireo; scale, $\frac{1}{3}$

B. Red-eyed Vireo; scale, $\frac{1}{2}$

## Order—Passeriformes. Perching Birds

The order *Passeriformes*, passerine or perching birds, is the largest and most important division of modern birds. The lower and more generalized types of birds have in the past been in the ascendant; but today the highly specialized *Passeres* are dominant; they constitute nearly if not quite half our present living forms and are put at the head of the classification by systematists. They are rather difficult to diagnose popularly, but they have a great number of characters common to themselves and not shared by other orders—the highly developed larynx, a singing organ, with complicated muscular control, for example. All are not notable singers, but all are equipped with song mechanism. Generally, a bird may be referred to this order by a process of elimination, as not belonging to any of the previous orders. The feet (Figure 395) are not webbed, the hind toe is nearly as long as the middle one, and the whole foot is well adapted for perching. The bill is hard and horny, without cere or soft base, and the nostril tubes do not communicate with each other as in some of the other orders. Two suborders are represented in Canada: *Tyranni*, the songless perchers; and *Passeres*, the song birds.

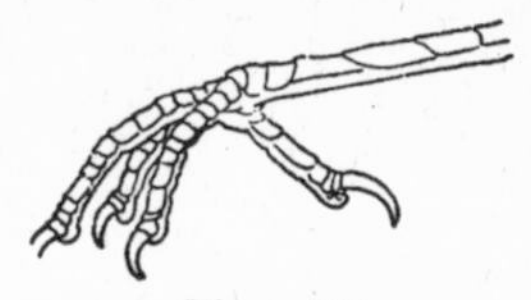

Figure 395
Foot of Percher.

### SUBORDER—TYRANNI. SONGLESS PERCHERS

This suborder is constituted upon a basis of anatomical structure. The name Songless Percher is not intended to indicate that the birds are silent, but that they are less tuneful than the *Passeres*, with a larynx less highly specialized. Only one family of this suborder occurs in Canada, the *Tyrannidae* or Tyrant Flycatcher.

#### FAMILY—TYRANNIDAE. TYRANT FLYCATCHERS

*General Description.* The Tyrant Flycatchers are most easily recognized among Canadian birds by their bills (Figure 396) which are comparatively long, somewhat flattened and broadened at the base, wider than high, and slightly hooked at the extreme tip.

All Canadian flycatchers except the spectacular Scissor-tailed, which is only a very rare visitor in this country, the strongly marked Kingbirds, and the Crested Flycatcher, are birds of dull olive coloration, only lightening or whitening on the breast, and without much colour variation.

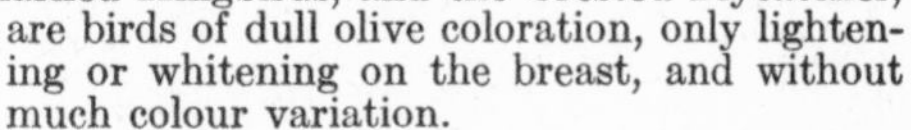

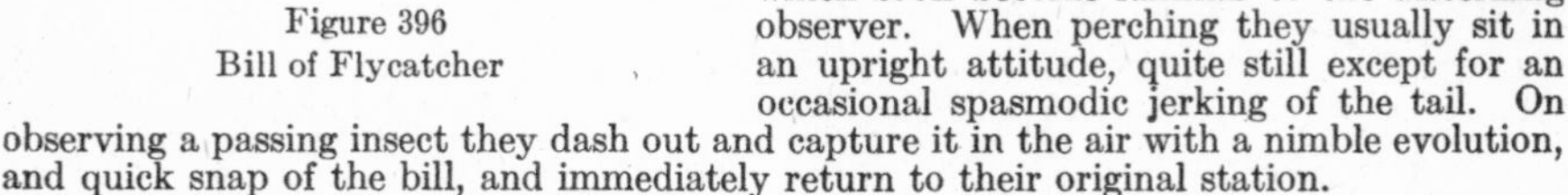

Figure 396
Bill of Flycatcher

*Field Marks.* Easily recognized in life by their characteristic habits and attitudes, which soon become familiar to the discerning observer. When perching they usually sit in an upright attitude, quite still except for an occasional spasmodic jerking of the tail. On observing a passing insect they dash out and capture it in the air with a nimble evolution, and quick snap of the bill, and immediately return to their original station.

The flycatchers are a most difficult family to identify specifically. A few of them are strongly characterized, but some of the commonest ones are so nearly alike as to puzzle the experienced ornithologist. In identifying flycatchers in life, attention should be paid to their voices. These and the type of habitat in which they are observed are good guides to differentiation in the case of the more puzzling species.

*Economic Status.* Their food consists almost entirely of insects, caught on the wing, for capturing of which the broad bill is well adapted. As they take most of their foód in the air near the ground they catch varieties of insects not taken by other birds. The species found in their stomachs include beetles, flies, wasps, crane-flies, ants, grasshoppers, tent-caterpillars, and moths. Indeed, nearly all the harmful species of insects are found in their crops and the group must be classed as highly beneficial birds.

444. **Eastern Kingbird.** BEE MARTIN. LE TRITRI. *Tyrannus tyrannus.* L, 8·51. Plate XLII A. A large, dark grey (almost black) and white flycatcher.

*Distinctions.* The black and white coloration, orange crown patch, showing in moments of excitement, and the black tail tipped with white, as if dipped in white paint, are unmistakable. Likely to be confused only with the Arkansas Kingbird, but blacker above, especially on head; white on throat, and white below instead of grey and sulphur-yellow.

*Field Marks.* A large black and white flycatcher, inhabiting the open spaces. The orange crown patch is rarely seen in life. The head and white-tipped tail appear to be dead black in strong contrast with the pure white front and underparts.

*Nesting.* Nest, a well-built structure of weed stalks, grasses, and waste vegetation, lined with plant-down, rootlets, and fine grasses, in bushes or trees. Nests commonly in orchards and shrubbery, near cultivated fields. It is partial to the vicinity of water.

*Distribution.* North and South America. Throughout southern Canada. Rare on Vancouver Island.

The kingbird is a familiar species, coming close around houses and orchards. The presence of a pair nesting nearby is one of the best preventives of the depredations of hawks or crows. None comes anywhere near the kingbird's home without being vigorously challenged. The kingbird flies at the intruders with an energy that is surprising in so small and weak a bird. It cannot do them any real harm, but it plagues them mightily and its outcries give wide notice of the affair. Owing to its small size and agility in the air, it can strike a large enemy from any quarter, and is practically safe from counter attacks from anything heavier and less agile.

It is amusing to see a great crow or hawk dodge its attack for a moment, and then make the best speed possible from the uncomfortable neighbourhood. After driving the intruder as far as it sees fit, and demonstrating its pre-eminence within its own territory, it comes back chattering with excited triumph and, with a flirt of tail, resumes its isolated outlook on some upstanding twig, as if to await the applause of its mate and the surrounding community. Withal, the kingbird is a charming fellow to have about. It may be something of a braggart and a swashbuckler, but with a grace and naturalness that disarm criticism. Certainly, the defence of hearth and home, especially when it assists in guarding the property of others, is not very reprehensible—even though unaccompanied by modesty.

*Economic Status.* The name kingbird is of obvious application, but the other term applied to it, "Bee Martin," naturally arouses suspicion as to its feeding habits. It is accused of catching honey bees, and most circumstantial accounts of its doing so are given credence. The record given below shows that the charge of taking bees is to some extent true, but it shows also that the bees caught are mainly drones that can well be spared. The old story of the kingbird opening its brilliant crest to decoy the bee within reach, under the impression that it is a flower, may be dismissed as groundless folk-lore, though it has received wide circulation and acceptation. Of 624 kingbirds' stomachs examined by the United States

Department of Agriculture in 1911, 22 contained a total of 61 bees—51 of which were drones, 8 workers, and 2 were indeterminate. The remainder of the food consists of other insects, including many noxious forms, and a little wild fruit and berries.

445. **Grey Kingbird.** LE TRITRI GRIS. *Tyrannus dominicensis.* L, 9. Like an Eastern Kingbird but lighter, ashy above rather than blackish, and underwing and tail-coverts faintly yellowish.

*Distinctions.* Somewhat intermediate in colour between Eastern and Arkansas Kingbirds, but nearer the former. Bill very thick and swollen and tail only lightening at tip instead of with sharply defined white band. Slightly yellow underwings and tail.

*Field Marks.* Too rare in Canada to be identified by sight.

*Distribution.* Southeastern United States, West Indies to northern South America. In Canada, one record for southern Vancouver Island.

An accidental straggler that may never occur again within our borders.

446. **Melancholy Kingbird.** LE TRITRI MÉLANCOLIQUE. *Tyrannus melancholicus.* L, about 8. Like the Arkansas Kingbird but with a more or less defined, darker cheek patch through eye and over ear, considerably larger bill, and slightly forked tail.

*Distinctions.* As above, culmen definitely longer instead of shorter than tarsus, and tail forked for about 0·5 inch.

*Distribution.* Southern Texas south to the Argentine. A single specimen in the Provincial Museum, Victoria, British Columbia, taken "some years ago" at Saanich, Vancouver Island, has recently been identified as this species.

*SUBSPECIES.* Of several races of this species, Couch's Kingbird (le Tritri de Couch) *T. m. couchi*, has long been known from the lower valley of the Rio Grande in Texas. Some species are notorious for wandering individually far from their natural habitat, but such has not been the reputation of this one and it was with considerable surprise that a Vancouver Island specimen was recognized. The occurrence is still more interesting, however, when it appears that it is not referable to the above race, but represents a subspecies not hitherto known north of Mexico—Lichtenstein's Kingbird (le Tritri de Lichenstein) *T. m. chloronotus*, whose normal range is western and southern Mexico south to the lower Amazon and Venezuela.

447. **Arkansas Kingbird.** WESTERN KINGBIRD. LE TRITRI DE L'OUEST. *Tyrannus verticalis.* L, 9. Plate XLII B. A large, pale-coloured kingbird, sulphur-yellow below.

*Distinctions.* With its light grey head, breast, and back, and bright yellow underparts, likely to be confused only with the Crested Flycatcher. Larger than that species; head and back greyish instead of olive, tail almost black instead of with bright rufous inner webs, and a concealed orange crown-spot.

*Field Marks.* In life, by habitat and action, likely to be confused only with the Eastern Kingbird; but the pale head and underparts, nearly white chin changing to grey on throat, yellow abdomen, and tail not tipped with white, but narrowly margined with it at the sides, make separation easy. In colour, superficially like the Crested Flycatcher, but inhabiting the open, instead of the forest tree tops, and with regular kingbird action. Voice entirely different, chattering like a kingbird and not "*whooping*" and "*whipping*" like the Crested.

*Nesting.* Nest a well constructed affair like the Eastern Kingbird's but more likely to contain bits of string, newspapers, or strips of rags. Nests close about the house and even in eaves-troughs, down spouts, and similar situations. Is probably a good tenant for bird boxes of proper type.

*Distribution.* Western North America. In Canada, north over the southern parts of all western provinces. Apparently a recent arrival in western Manitoba, and rare on Vancouver Island.

A very beautiful bird, similar in general habits and action to the Eastern Kingbird, but rather less aggressive, less likely to go out of its way to seek trouble, and rather more confiding in the human neighbourhood. It is not an abundant bird in the southern Prairie Provinces, but rather local, as it requires the presence of trees, and will probably increase with the growth of tree plantations. It is notable that nearly every station along the Canadian Pacific Railway where trees have been successfully planted has a pair of Arkansas Kingbirds in possession, and it seems almost to prefer the hubbub of such localities to quieter retreats.

443. **Scissor-tailed Flycatcher.** LE MOUCHEROLLE À QUEUE EN CISEAUX (l'Oiseau papillon). *Muscivora forficata.* L, 13 (about). (Tail, 9.) This flycatcher is an occasional wanderer from subtropical America within the borders of Canada. It is unmistakable—a light, ash-coloured bird about the size of a kingbird with darker wings, scarlet or orange cap, and the same colour under the wings, with a great tail 8 to 9 inches long, split to a depth of 6 inches or more, which, when the bird is at rest, opens and closes like a pair of scissors. Strangely enough two of our best authenticated records come from York Factory on Hudson Bay taken forty years apart, and the species has been seen in southern Manitoba. With this record before us, it is difficult to state positively what bird may or may not be found anywhere in Canada.

452. **Crested Flycatcher.** GREAT CRESTED FLYCATCHER. LE MOUCHEROLLE HUPPÉ. *Myiarchus crinitus.* L, 9·00. About the size of the Eastern Kingbird, but lighter in build. Even olive-brown above, turning to rufous on the inner webs of the tail. Throat and upper breast ash-grey. Underparts sulphur-yellow.

*Distinctions.* Likely to be confused only with the Arkansas Kingbird; like it in general coloration, but back to crown uniformly brown, and no orange crown-spot. Tail, browner than back and with inner webs strongly rufous.

*Field Marks.* A large, yellow-bellied flycatcher, inhabiting the upper branches in the woods. Unlike either of the kingbirds in habitat, action, or voice. Its loud, long-drawn cry "*Wheeeep*" and lower "*Whip-whip-whip*" are very characteristic, although something similar to some of the notes of the Olive-sided Flycatcher, which is a very different appearing and acting bird. The Crested rarely poses for long on isolated branch tips or dead tree tops, and is more often seen passing from branch to branch amidst the foliage, or from tree to tree.

*Nesting.* In holes abandoned by woodpeckers or in hollow trees and branches. It takes kindly to bird boxes in the garden. The bird shows a remarkable fondness for utilizing cast snake skins in nest building. Scarcely a nest of the species but contains one or more.

*Distribution.* Eastern North America. In Canada, including the wooded and bluffy parts of southern Manitoba.

A flycatcher of the woodland tree tops. Its loud insistent voice is constantly heard in the summer, but rarely at any distance from dense forest.

*Economic Status.* Beetles, locusts, ants, crickets, flies, and moths constitute the bulk of its food. It takes more parasitic wasps and beetles than most birds, but not enough to counterbalance the pests it destroys.

456. **Eastern Phoebe.** BRIDGE PEWEE. LE MOUCHEROLLE DES PONTS. *Sayornis phoebe.* L, 6·99. Plate XLIII A. One of the larger of the little green flycatchers, and much smaller than any of the preceding. All above, uniform, dull olive; dull white below, without any distinctive colour marks.

*Distinctions.* The small, greenish flycatchers are perhaps the most difficult of American birds to separate. Fortunately, each has a typical habitat and a characteristic note, which are both good guides to differentiation in the field. The Phoebe is, next to the Olive-sided, the largest of these small, dull-coloured flycatchers, and the most easily recognized. It is most likely to be confused with the two Wood Pewees, but its legs and feet are larger and stouter.

*Field Marks.* The head of the Phoebe is generally a little darker, and in stronger contrast with the body, than in other flycatchers. The sidewise sweep of tail and unbarrred wings are characteristic. The note, however, a quickly uttered "*Phoe-be*" with strong accent on the first syllable, is the best field mark. The Wood Pewee's note is long-drawn out and that of the Least is short and explosive. The habitat, about bridges and culverts, or in the vicinity of barns and buildings, is very suggestive of identity.

*Nesting.* A large structure of mud, moss, and grasses under bridges, or the overhangs of buildings or ledges of rock.

*Distribution.* Eastern North America. In Canada, west through the Prairie Provinces, northward in the woodlands.

No place suits the Phoebe so well for nesting as the flat timbers or projecting ledges of an old bridge over some little stream where the moist air abounds in insect food. In many parts of the country there is scarcely a bridge but has its pair of phoebes in the summer. However, the mud nests are not restricted to bridges but are plastered on the slightest projection under the eaves of an outbuilding or even under the family porch. It is a friendly, familiar bird and comes close to man wherever it finds a welcome. Unfortunately its large, untidy looking nests are occasionally the dwelling place of innumerable parasites, in other words, bird-lice. The usual course when they appear is to knock the nest down with a stick and apply boiling water. The application of common insect powder to the nest is better, for this will kill the parasites and help to retain about the house a confiding and attractive bird.

It is reassuring to know, however, that bird-lice will not remain on the human body, the temperature of which is not high enough for them.

457. **Say's Phoebe.** LE MOUCHEROLLE DE SAY. *Sayornis saya.* L, 7·50. Plate XLIII B. A large, phoebe-like bird; grey-brown, rather than olive-brown above, with head scarcely darkening. Greyish breast, and underparts suffused with rusty ochre.

*Distinctions.* An even grey-brown bird with abdomen washed with rusty ochre, fading away on dull grey throat. Can be mistaken for no other Canadian species.

*Field Marks.* A flycatcher, haunting barns, outbuildings, and cliffs. Even ashy brown in colour, similar in contour and poise to the Arkansas Kingbird, but much smaller and darker head; dark brick colour below instead of yellow.

*Nesting.* A large structure of moss, lined with vegetable fibre, fur, or feathers, on the sheltered beam of a building or in an horizontal cleft in a cliff.

*Distribution.* Western North America, from central Alaska and Mackenzie south to New Mexico. In Canada, east to southwestern Manitoba, where it seems to be a comparatively recent arrival.

Around farm buildings in the west, Say's Phoebe largely takes the place of the Eastern Phoebe in the east, but it also frequents the most arid and lonely spots. No coulée, bad lands, or mountain gorge is too dry or desolate to harbour a pair. About the tool-house of the farm, the freight sheds of a railway, or the heated exposures of rock-slide or cliff, it is equally at home.

463. **Yellow-bellied Flycatcher.** LE MOUCHEROLLE À VENTRE JAUNE. *Empidonax flaviventris.* L, 5·63. A small flycatcher, similar in pattern to the Wood Pewee (*See* Plate XLIV A), and the little green flycatchers, but the browns and olives of those species replaced by distinct olive-green and the whites by dull sulphur-yellow.

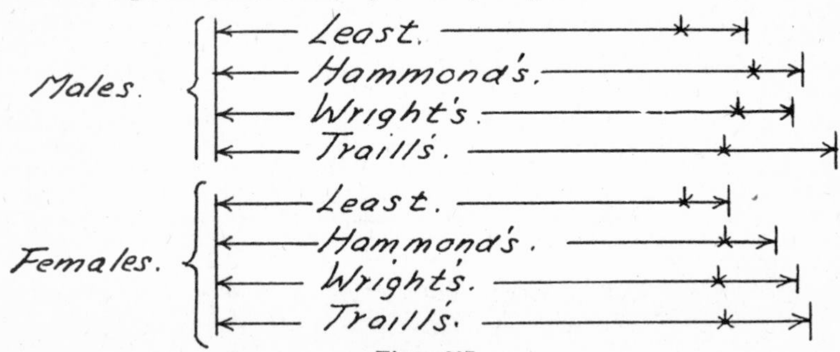


Figure 397
Maximum and minimum wing lengths of flycatchers most likely to be confused; laid off natural size.

*Distinctions.* This and the similar Western Flycatcher are the yellowest of all the small flycatchers. Other species in the autumn may show suggestions of yellow below, but never so clearly as in the least yellow individuals of these two. It resembles very closely the Western Flycatcher. In the Yellow-bellied Flycatcher, the olive and yellow are of a clearer and brighter tint and less ochreish than in the Western, and the first primary is longer instead of shorter than the sixth (Figure 398b).

*Field Marks.* A small, generally yellow flycatcher, most yellow below. The notes, "*Te-pee-a*"—three syllables with accent on the middle one, are distinctive. Its "*Pe-wick*" is something like the call of the Eastern Phoebe, but the first syllable is not accented. Probably not separable with certainty from the Western Flycatcher in life.

*Nesting.* On the ground, nest built of moss, lined with grasses.

*Distribution.* North and South America. In Canada, breeding in the coniferous forest, west to northern British Columbia. Rare on the prairies.

A woodland flycatcher that favours second growth and thickets bordering heavier timber.

*Economic Status.* Food habits very similar to those of the other small flycatchers. Its normal station on the edges of woods bordering cultivated land makes it of value to the agriculturist.

**465. Acadian Flycatcher.** LITTLE GREEN-CRESTED FLYCATCHER. LE MOUCHEROLLE VERT. *Empidonax virescens.* L, 5·63. A small flycatcher of about the same size as the Yellow-bellied, Traill's, and Least Flycatchers; smaller than the Wood Pewee; and much smaller than the Phoebes. In colour, like the Eastern Phoebe but distinctly olive-green above and more yellowish below. Wing-bars rather prominent.

*Distinctions.* This species agrees so closely in size and coloration with Traill's and the Least Flycatchers as to make identification most difficult. It is not so yellow in colour as the Yellow-bellied, there being no pure yellow on it anywhere, but it is the yellowest and greenest of the other small flycatchers. It is very rare in Canada and new records should be accepted only on the authority of experts.

*Distribution.* Eastern North America north to the borders of Canada only along the western end of Lake Erie.

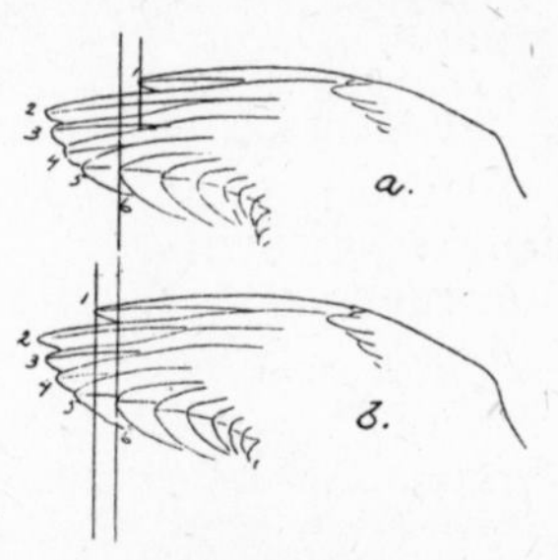


Figure 398
Wing formulæ of flycatchers most likely to be confused.
a, outer primary shorter than 6 — Wright's; Western.
b, outer primary longer than 6 — Yellow-bellied; Traill's; Least; Hammond's.

**466. Traill's Flycatcher.** LE MOUCHEROLLE DE TRAILL. *Empidonax trailli.* L, 6·09. A small flycatcher, slightly larger than other members of its genus (Figure 397) and very similar to them in colour. Coloration similar in general to that of the wood pewees, but bird is smaller.

*Distinctions.* Typical birds are olive or brownish olive on the back, and whiter below than other comparable species. There is a faint greyish breast-band, but the throat is distinctly white and the abdomen clear white, washed towards vent with clear, light sulphur. In general, it is the least muddy in coloration of these confusing flycatchers, but many individuals occur that are difficult to place. Its larger average size is a helpful character, but, as shown in the diagram (Figure 397), not conclusive, except in the largest individuals. It is best identified in the field.

*Field Marks.* A small flycatcher with whiter throat and underparts than its relatives A white eye-ring is usually distinct. In colour, most like the Least, but larger and with entirely different habitat and notes. It frequents willow and alder thickets, usually along streams; is quite shy, and flits from point to point ahead of the inquisitive observer, rarely allowing close approach, but alighting on commanding topmost twigs, from whence it utters a short staccato "*We're-here*" or "*Ezee-e-up*" with the accent on the last syllable in each case.

*Nesting.* In crotch of small growth near the ground; nest of coarse grasses, plant-down, and fibres, lined with grasses.

*Distribution.* North America to South America. In Canada, across the continent north to the coniferous forest.

*SUBSPECIES.* The races of Traill's Flycatcher have recently been revised. They now stand in the A.O.U. Check-list as: Alder Flycatcher (le Moucherolle des aulnes) ***Empidonax trailli trailli***, all the specific range except the far west; and the Little Flycatcher (le Moucherolle minule) ***Empidonax trailli brewsteri***, southwestern British Columbia and southward. The systematic change may be justified, but ornithologists will have to be on their guard against the confusion that will be consequent upon this change in application of a familiar vernacular name.

*Economic Status.* Similar to that of the other flycatchers. Its food is almost entirely insects, the species destroyed being mostly those frequenting waste land.

467. **Least Flycatcher.** CHEBEC. LE MOUCHEROLLE MINIME. *Empidonax minimus.* L, 5·41. The smallest of the little green flycatchers. General colour design of dusky olive and white like the Wood Pewee (Plate XLIV A), but very much smaller.

*Distinctions.* Almost identical in colour with Traill's. Best separated from other little flycatchers by size, wing 2·60 inches or under, though the diagram (Figure 397) shows that other species may come within this measurement. Distinguished from Wright's by having the outer primary longer than the sixth (Figure 398b).

*Field Marks.* A very small flycatcher of the usual dull olive coloration, with fairly conspicuous white eye-ring and throat. The greyish suffusion on underparts restricted. Best recognized by its characteristic call—a quick, explosive *"Chebec-,"* like a dry, hacking cough, sometimes repeated many times. Habitat—woodlands, instead of shrubbery wastes.

*Nesting.* In the crotch of a tree; nest of plant-down, fine wood fibres, rootlets, and long hairs.

*Distribution.* Northern and eastern United States to South America. West in Canada to Alberta, north into Mackenzie.

This is a bird of the orchard and the trees about the house, overgrown fence-lines, and other familiar localities where close proximity to cultivation makes its services of noteworthy benefit.

*Economic Status.* The food of the Least Flycatcher does not differ materially from that of the other members of the family, but the bird's familiarity and confidence bring it close to man where its useful qualities have the maximum effect.

468. **Hammond's Flycatcher.** LE MOUCHEROLLE DE HAMMOND. *Empidonax hammondi.* L, 5·60. The duskiest and, except the Least, the smallest of the little green flycatchers. General colour design of dusky olive and white, like the Wood Pewee, but much smaller.

*Distinctions.* Hammond's Flycatcher is almost identical in colour with Wright's and averages a little smaller in length than that species and a little larger than the Least, the comparative wing measurement can be seen in Figure 397. It is greyish olive rather than clear olive. The throat and breast are suffused with more dusky clouding than any other similar species, and the throat is never clear white. Best separated from the Least by its slightly larger size, wing 2·60 or over. From Wright's, with which it is most likely to be confused in British Columbia, by having the first primary longer than the sixth (Figure 398b). There is a yellowish phase of this species, and of Wright's also, in which the yellowness of the underparts approaches that of the Yellow-bellied or Western Flycatchers.

*Field Marks.* A very small, obscurely coloured flycatcher, with dingy, dull breast and throat. In the mountains, in summer, Hammond's Flycatcher is the *Empidonax* representative at 3,000 feet elevation, and above; Wright's and Traill's occupy the lower levels. In migration this distribution may not hold. The note is a brisk *"Sewick"* or *"Switch- -oo"* quite different from the hacking *"Chebec"* of the Least, or the longer *"We're-here"* of Traill's. It is difficult to separate from Wright's even by voice.

*Nesting.* Nest of fir twigs, grasses, and moss, lined with fine grasses and vegetable down, on horizontal limb at a considerable height.

*Distribution.* Western North America from southern Alaska to southern California. In Canada, east to the Rocky Mountains. It has been reported from Mackenzie River country and central Alberta, but its occurrence there is rather uncertain.

Much as this obscure little bird resembles the Least Flycatcher, it is still more like Wright's and the wing formula (Figure 398b) is the most certain distinction between them. In breeding season it is a bird of the higher elevations and not such a shade lover as the latter species. It will take the very closest observation and the collection of many specimens to establish the eastern boundaries of its range.

469. **Wright's Flycatcher.** LE MOUCHEROLLE DE WRIGHT. *Empidonax wrighti.* L, 6. A little longer than Hammond's Flycatcher, and shorter than Traill's. Of general colour design of dusky-olive and white, like the Wood Pewee, but smaller.

*Distinctions.* Almost identical in colour with Hammond's, but averaging a little longer with less greyish over throat and breast and approaching the Least in this character, but very variable. Best separated from the other similar little green flycatchers by the first primary being shorter than the sixth (Figure 398a), a character only shared by the Western Flycatcher. There is a yellowish phase of this species and Hammond's in which the underparts approach the yellowness of the Yellow-bellied and Western Flycatchers.

*Field Marks.* A very small, obscurely coloured flycatcher, difficult of separation from the Least and Hammond's. In the breeding season it is a bird of lower levels than the latter, inhabiting elevations below 3,000 feet. It is usually a shade lover, and most often seen in second-growth thickets and brush. It does not seem to have any very distinctive notes—a soft "*swit*" is the commonest, whilst others are reminiscent or so suggestive of calls of other species as to make identification by the notes uncertain.

*Nesting.* Nest of fibres, bark strips, etc., softly lined, in upright crotch, usually low down.

*Distribution.* Western North America from southern British Columbia to New Mexico. In Canada, southern British Columbia, east probably to western Saskatchewan. Its eastern range has not been very well defined.

Very closely resembling the Least Flycatcher and Hammond's and the wing formula (Figure 398) is probably the best distinction. It will take the closest observation and the collection of many specimens to define with accuracy the overlapping ranges of these species.

464. **Western Flycatcher.** LE MOUCHEROLLE OBSCUR. *Empidonax difficilis.* L, 5·60. A small flycatcher, similar to the Wood Pewees and the little green flycatchers in pattern, but the browns and olives of those species replaced by distinct ochraceous-olive and the whites by dull yellow tending towards ochre.

*Distinctions.* This and the Yellow-bellied Flycatcher are the yellowest of all the small flycatchers. Other species in the autumn may show suggestions of yellow below, but never so clearly as the least yellow individuals of these two. In the Western Flycatcher the olive and yellow are duller and more distinctly ochreish than in the Yellow-bellied, the inner edge of the wing at the wrist is brownish yellow, instead of sulphur-yellow, and the first primary is shorter than the sixth (Figure 398a).

*Field Marks.* A small, yellow flycatcher, most yellow below. The notes are like those of the Yellow-bellied, but more sibilant and softer. They may be syllabized as "*Tis-yip.*" It probably can not be separated from the Yellow-bellied Flycatcher in life with certainty.

*Nesting.* Low down, usually on the ground. Nest of moss lined with grasses.

*Distribution.* In Canada confined to the coast strip west of the Coast and Cascade Ranges in British Columbia.

461. **Eastern Wood Pewee.** LE PIOUI DE L'EST. *Myiochanes virens.* L, 6·50. A small, dull olive and whitish flycatcher, similar in general coloration and design to a number of allied species. Very like Plate XLIV A.

*Distinctions.* Separated from the Phoebe and other small flycatchers, except the Western, by short tarsi and long wings, the latter being decidedly longer than the tail. Differs from its close relative, the Richardson's Pewee, which is specifically distinct, by a more olive back, crown darker in more distinct contrast with the body; and in having the breast less suffused with brownish ash. These distinctions can only be determined by direct comparison of specimens, and even then are not always easy to see.

PLATE LXIII

A. Warbling Vireo; scale, $\frac{1}{2}$

B. Black and White Warbler; scale, $\frac{3}{5}$

Spring Autumn

PLATE LXIV

A. Orange-crowned Warbler; scale, $\frac{1}{3}$

B. Yellow Warbler; scale, $\frac{1}{2}$

Male Female

*Field Marks.* The pewees never flirt their tails as do the phoebes. The sides of the breast are slightly darker, giving a better defined and narrower light median line. Their best identification mark, however, is their call-note which is much like that of the Eastern Phoebe but drawn out into a long "*Pee-e-weee*" without appreciable accent but with a rising inflexion at the end. The female varies the call by dropping the last note, making it "*Pee-e-e-e.*"

Probably best separated from the Richardson's Pewee by this call, which is noticeably different from the note of that bird.

*Nesting.* A well made but slight structure of fine fibres and rootlets, covered with lichens and saddled on a branch.

*Distribution.* North and South America. In Canada, west at least to Manitoba.

The long-drawn, plaintive "*Pee-e-wee*" of this bird is a characteristic sound of the open woodlands in the spring, and after other birds have relapsed into midsummer silence its mournful note may still occasionally be heard.

*Economic Status.* The food of the Wood Pewee is similar to that of the other flycatchers, but modified, of course, by its woodland habitat. As it is not retiring, and frequents open groves and orchards freely, it is of direct benefit to the agriculturist.

462. **Richardson's Pewee.** LE PIOUI DE RICHARDSON. *Myiochanes richardsoni.* L, 6·50. Plate XLIV A. In colour and form like the Eastern Wood Pewee, but darker.

*Distinctions.* Separated from the Phoebes and other small flycatchers, except the Eastern Wood Pewee, by its short tarsi and long wings, the latter being decidedly longer than the tail. Differs from its close relative, the Eastern Wood Pewee, from which it is specifically distinct, by greyer (less olive) back, lighter crown in less distinct contrast with body, and in having the breast more suffused with brownish ash. The distinctions from this last species can only be made by direct comparison of specimens and then not always easily.

*Field Marks.* The pewees never flirt their tails as do the phoebes. Their best identification mark, however, is probably their call-note, which bears a casual resemblance to that of the Eastern Wood Pewee but is more abrupt and emphatic, and has been syllabized "*dear-me*" instead of a long drawn "*Pee-e-weee.*" Both pewees usually keep well up in the trees, and are seldom seen in the low brush where similar little flycatchers are often seen.

*Nesting.* A well-made but slight structure of fine fibres and rootlets, covered with lichens, lined with wool or hair, and saddled on a branch.

*Distribution.* Western North America. In Canada, from southern Manitoba westward to the coast. The ranges of this and the Eastern Wood Pewee have not been very well defined on the prairies, owing largely to the difficulty of separating the two birds and the lack of specimens.

*SUBSPECIES.* The race attributed to North America is the type one, the Western Wood Pewee (le Pioui de l'Ouest) *Myiochanes richardsoni richardsoni.*

Though so nearly like the Eastern Wood Pewee that even so keen an authority as Dr. Elliot Coues admits that it is "impracticable to pronounce upon a Pewee, in the closet, without knowing its locality" all are agreed from observation in life that the two are specifically distinct. Typical birds of the two species are noticeably distinct and groups of specimens *en masse* show convincing differences.

*Economic Status.* Probably very similar to that of the Eastern Wood Pewee.

459. **Olive-sided Flycatcher.** LE MOUCHEROLLE AUX CÔTÉS OLIVE. *Nuttallornis mesoleucus.* L, 7·39. The largest of the olive-green flycatchers. Much like the phoebe, but larger and the olive less clear (blacker), and with extensive masses of dark colour on either side of the chest, generally meeting in a narrow band across breast.

*Distinctions.* The conspicuous dark patches at the sides of the chest and along the flanks, and the dark undertail-coverts with white tips or broad inverted V marks near the tips will separate this species from the phoebe which it resembles. The head and face are not noticeably darker than the back. At the sides of the lower back occasionally displayed, though usually concealed by the closed wings, are patches of fine silk-like plumage of pure white or cream colour. These points will separate the Olive-sided from any of the other flycatchers.

*Field Marks.* In life, the Olive-sided Flycatcher looks more like an Eastern Kingbird with a dark coat partly closed over a white vest than a phoebe. When the white, silky feathers show over the wings just above the rump, as sometimes occurs, the species cannot be mistaken. The call-notes are distinctive, though something like those of the Crested Flycatcher. The most common is a loud, penetrating *"Quick- -three-beer"*; the Alder Flycatcher has a note that may be syllabized like the last two words, but it is low and sibilant and not loud and ringing.

*Nesting.* Nest of twigs and bark strips lined with moss and grasses on coniferous lands, usually very high up.

*Distribution.* North and South America. In Canada, across the continent, breeding in the northern evergreen forest.

This is typically a bird of the burnt ridges. Its favourite perch is on the tip-top of a gaunt dead pine in the open, surrounded by second-growth and brûlé, from whence its clear penetrating demand can be heard far and wide. In migration, its route probably follows the timber east and west and it is not often seen in the open prairie country.

## SUBORDER—PASSERES. SONG BIRDS

The suborder *Passeres* is a large division of birds, placed at the head of the list as exhibiting the highest development of the class *Aves*. It includes a great number of families and species. The characters differentiating the *Oscines* from the *Tyranni* are technical and anatomical and beyond the scope of a popular consideration of the subject. As might be gathered by the name the high development of the vocal organs and muscles attached is an important point in the classification. The members are more easily recognized from family descriptions than under this more general heading.

### FAMILY—ALAUDIDAE. LARKS

The larks comprise a large family of wide distribution. The systematic distinctions that characterize the family are rather technical, and as there is only one species native to Canada to consider, they will be described under the species following.

473. **Skylark.** L'ALOUETTE DES CHAMPS. *Alauda arvensis.* L, 7·75. Brown and white, much streaked above, white below with a breast-band of fine, sharp, brown stripes.

*Distinctions.* A brown, striped bird with very long hind toe-nail; long, fine bill like that of Horned Lark will distinguish from any longspurs that may show a comparable coloration. Much like a Horned Lark in general appearance, but note striped breast-band and absence of horns.

This is the famous skylark of Europe. It has been introduced in southern Vancouver Island and a few are to be seen occasionally about Victoria.

474. **Horned Lark.** SHORE LARK. L'ALOUETTE ORDINAIRE (Portolan). *Otocoris alpestris.* L, 7·75. Plate XLIV B. A ground bird, approximately of the size of a sparrow; greyish pink or light brownish above; white below with black gorget, face mark, and forehead; and white or pale yellow throat.

Figure 399
Horned Lark, showing long hind claw; natural size.

*Distinctions.* The long hind toenail (Figure 399b) is one of the distinctive marks of the true larks, but is shared by the titlark and the longspurs. The latter, however, are sparrows with typical conical bills, and very different from the larks. The yellow, creamy, or white throat, black gorget, and erect, horn-like black ear tufts are distinctive of the Horned Lark (Figure 399a).

*Field Marks.* Ground-frequenting habits, often in large flocks; extensive white below, erectile horns, and black gorget with white or pale yellow throat.

*Nesting.* On the ground in the open. Nest of grass in small, natural hollow. Often amid the snowdrifts of early spring.

*Distribution.* North America, Europe, and Asia. In Canada, all open country north to the Arctic Ocean and irregularly over the islands beyond.

*SUBSPECIES.* Few birds have been divided into as many, or as puzzling, subspecies as the Horned Lark. In Canada we have a northern and southern series of subspecies distributed across the continent, the northern ones being, in each case, slightly but consistently larger than their southern neighbours. Across the more southerly parts of Ontario and Quebec we have the Prairie Horned Lark (l'Alouette des prairies) *Otocoris alpestris praticola,* extending westward into Manitoba. This is a small, moderately pale bird; line over eye and forehead, white; throat, pale yellow, sometimes white. North of this subspecies is the type form, the Northern Horned Lark (l'Alouette du Nord) *Otocoris alpestris alpestris.* Slightly larger and more robust, all the colouring stronger, and the eyebrows, forehead, and cheeks distinctly yellow. This bird migrates irregularly through the southern parts of the eastern provinces, and occasionally through Manitoba. West of the range of the Prairie Horned Lark is the Desert Horned Lark (l'Alouette pâle) *Otocoris alpestris leucolaema,* of the same small size as the Prairie Horned Lark, but decidedly paler, the vinaceous of the upper parts is reduced to pinkish, and the brown back stripings are largely concealed with greyish. Throat, yellow or white. This form occupies most of our central prairies and southward. Some authorities divide *leucolaema* into two races, the northern of which enters Canada and is known as the Saskatchewan Horned Lark *Otocoris alpestris enthemia,* but it has not been accepted in the Check-list. North, along the central Arctic coast and extending eastward in the islands above, is Hoyt's Horned Lark (l'Alouette de Hoyt) *Otocoris alpestris hoyti.* It approximates the large Eastern Lark in size, but the forehead, eyebrow, and face are white. The throat may be pale yellow or white. In summer the body colours are bright and contrastive, with much strong ruddy. In migration season it is much like the Prairie Horned Lark, but larger. It migrates through the Prairie Provinces. In the lowlands of southern British Columbia the Dusky Horned Lark (l'Alouette noirâtre) *Otocoris alpestris merrilli* is a rather rare summer resident. It is a small dark form very similar to the Prairie Horned Lark, but usually with a yellowish eyebrow, and is far removed from that race geographically. At higher elevations through British Columbia and lower in Yukon and Alaska is the Arctic Horned Lark (l'Alouette arctique) *Otocoris alpestris articola.* It is another large race, paler than the Dusky, the Prairie, or Hoyt's, but darker than the Desert. The throat is always white. In size it agrees with Hoyt's and the Eastern Horned Larks. It migrates throughout the prairies, perhaps as far east as Manitoba. East of the Coast Range in southern British Columbia the Streaked Horned Lark (l'Alouette striée) *Otocoris alpestris strigata* may be found. It is the smallest of our Canadian Horned Larks, and the darkest and reddest in colour, with underparts usually showing faintly yellow below the black gorget.

The differences between some of these races is not very marked and even the expert must have an ample series of specimens for comparison before making decisive identification. The differences may not average more than half an inch in total length, even in characteristic birds of comparable age and sex. Intermediates are common and individual variation is considerable. In migration many wander far from their breeding homes and mix together, and, in some cases, late migrants do not leave southern stations before resident birds are rearing young. In the mountains, forms may be separated by no more than altitude and but a few miles of territory. All of these factors tend to make rules on identification and ranges of the forms of this species a difficult matter, and may require constant revision of opinion until much more work has been done and more complete series of specimens are available for examination and comparison.

The Horned Lark is a bird of the open, frequenting bare fields, beaches, or roadways. In the winter, the seeds of weeds projecting from the snow are its main food supply, and numbers frequent travelled roads for the partly digested grain dropped by the horses. Occasionally large winter flocks appear. It is in such migrant congregations that the rarer forms should be looked for.

### FAMILY—HIRUNDINIDAE. SWALLOWS

*General Description.* Mostly small birds, in Canada only one, the Purple Martin, is as large as a House Sparrow. Wings very long and pointed; feet small and weak, unsuited to walking; head flattened and bill very short, with deep, wide gape (Figure 400a and $a^1$).

*Distinctions.* In superficial characters and general proportions as here described, swallows resemble the goatsuckers and swifts, but are much smaller and entirely different in colour from the former and are not nocturnal. In the field, more likely to be confused with the swifts. The wings, with their looser and softer feathers, the nearly straight primaries, longer secondaries (Figure 400d and e), and the characteristic wing action are sufficient to show the great difference in the birds. The swift beats the air with rapid, regular strokes and then sails like a bullet; the swallow flies with long, rhythmic strokes, gliding up and down invisible aerial waves, instead of boring straight through them. The legs and feet of the swallow are more or less scaly, and not as fleshy as the swifts (Compare Figure 400 with 388, page 271).

A world-wide family, of aerial habits, seldom coming to the ground except for nesting material. Their feet are weak and suitable for alighting only on small twigs, telegraph wires, and similar perches. They take their

Figure 400
Characteristic details of Swallows.
head of Cliff Swallow. $a^1$, top view of bill. *b*, foot. *d*, wing tips. *e*, outline of Cliff Swallow in flight.
Scale: *a-d*, natural size; *e*, about ⅓.

food on the wing and can often be seen sweeping over ponds, slightly furrowing the still surface as they drink. They are skilful nestmakers and build a remarkable variety of forms, from bottle-necked structures of kneaded mud to holes tunnelled in earth banks.

*Economic Status.* Flying insects constitute almost the entire food of the swallows. Sailing high or low in the air as food results justify, the swallows attack many winged insects which are otherwise almost unmolested. Over grain fields and about barnyards where insect-eating birds are few the swallows congregate and give efficient assistance to the agriculturist. Their dirt is sometimes objectionable when they nest in numbers under the eaves of residences. It is well in such cases to provide suitable nesting sites for them elsewhere about the farm buildings where they can congregate without offence.

615. **Violet-green Swallow.** L'HIRONDELLE VERT-VIOLET. *Tachycineta thalassima.* L, 4·75. Plate XLV A. Solid white below from throat to undertail-coverts, and extending over face to include cheeks. Above: head to rump a rich velvety bottle green, washed with violet-bronze; rump and tail glossy, dark violet. Female similar but duller. Juvenile has the violet and green colours above replaced by ashy brown.

*Distinctions.* Adult birds, or those with any indication of the violet and green above, are unmistakable. Juveniles with their pure white underparts can be mistaken only for the Tree Swallow. Sometimes differentiation between them may be difficult without specimens for comparison. The Violet-green is distinctly smaller and the brown of the upperparts is generally greyer and less brownish.

*Field Marks.* With its black-appearing back and upperparts and pure white underparts, to be mistaken only for the Tree Swallow. It has two excellent marks for field distinction, however. The cheeks are clear white, giving a white face that is not apparent in the Tree Swallow, and in flight a sharp white spot shows on either side of the dark rump. The only other similar bird having such white rump-spots is the White-throated Swift, so far found in Canada only in the lower Okanagan Valley, a true swift and not a swallow. Note distinctions under family (page 269).

*Nesting.* Nest in crannies of high perpendicular cliffs, frequently in holes in trees and occasionally in bird-houses or about buildings. Nest of grasses with feathers when procurable.

*Distribution.* Western North America. In Canada, British Columbia north through central Yukon. Probably adjoining foothills in Alberta.

*SUBSPECIES.* The form of northern North America is the Northern Violet-green Swallow (l'Hirondelle vert-violet du Nord) *Tachycineta thalassina lepida.*

One of the loveliest of the swallows. Its distinctive violet and green colours can rarely be discerned in life and to the eye it flashes in the sun in contrastive black and white. It is seen to best advantage in the narrow, steep mountain valleys of the interior, skimming close to the lower ground or high up in the blue in flocks that weave in and out amongst themselves in complicated pattern. Their nests may be up a steep mountain face, so high that only a white spot on the rocks at the entrance to a community niche marks the spot, and from the ground below the birds can hardly be distinguished with the naked eye as they enter or leave; even powerful glasses may leave the observer in doubt as to whether the moving specks are swallows high up or flies lower down. The species will nest in boxes about the house when such cliffs are not immediately available.

614. **Tree Swallow.** WHITE-BELLIED SWALLOW. L'HIRONDELLE BICOLORE. *Iridoprocne bicolor.* L, 5·90. Plate XLV B. Pure white below, from throat to tail-coverts. Above, solid steely black. Juveniles have iridescent black replaced by sooty brown.

*Distinctions.* The adult uniform steely black above, and pure white below, is unmistakable in eastern Canada. Except from the Violet-green Swallow in British Columbia, juveniles can be distinguished by the purity of their white underparts and absence of any breast-band. A glance at the colours of the backs will separate adults from the Violet-green, but young birds may be difficult to recognize except by direct comparison with specimens. The Tree Swallow is a little larger, and the brown of the back is a little browner and less greyish.

*Field Marks.* A contrastive black and white swallow. Likely to be confused only with the Violet-green Swallow of British Columbia. It has two very distinct and easily recognizable field distinctions. The face and cheeks are black, not strikingly white, and in flight the rump shows solidly black, without white spots on either side that are characteristic of the Violet-green.

*Nesting.* In woodpecker's abandoned nest-holes or other cavities in dead stubs, preferably near or over water, or in nesting boxes. Lined with grasses and feathers.

*Distribution.* North America. In Canada north to near tree limits.

Though normally using Woodpecker's holes in dead stubs over the water the Tree Swallow is easily induced to nest in boxes in the garden. The beauty of its bright iridescence and the grace of its flight make ample payment for the work of preparation, even if its presence were not an important safeguard against insects in the garden. The continued existence of the species is threatened through the growing scarcity of natural nesting sites and an effort should be made to supply the nests artificially.

616. **Bank Swallow.** SAND MARTIN. L'HIRONDELLE DE RIVAGE. *Riparia riparia.* L, 5·20. Plate XLVI A. Above, dull brown; below, white with a sharp brown band across chest. Female like male. Juvenile similar, but the breast-band more diffuse.

*Distinctions.* Dull brown instead of iridescent back; white underparts with decided dark breast-band, extending in juvenility towards the abdomen. The complete breast-band will separate the Bank from the Tree or Violet-green Swallows that also have white underparts, and from the Rough-winged Swallows in which the white is less pure and the throat and breast are evenly suffused with ashy brown.

*Field Marks.* A white-bellied swallow with complete dark breast-band. A sturdily built bird. This character is most noticeable when flocks of mixed species are lined up on telegraph or other wires.

*Nesting.* Nearly everyone has seen how quickly the exposed sides of a sand or gravel pit excavation become pitted with the small nesting holes of these swallows. Too often the heedless small boy digs them out. Not only is this dangerous to the boy from the possibility of the bank caving, but it is a totally unnecessary disturbance of a very valuable species.

*Distribution.* Northern hemisphere. In Canada, across the Dominion, north to tree limits. Rarer on the west coast.

617. **American Rough-winged Swallow.** L'HIRONDELLE À AILES HÉRISSÉES. *Stelgidopteryx ruticollis.* L, 5·75. Dark brown and white like the Bank Swallow (*See* Plate XLVI A), but with breast and throat suffused with light ashy brown instead of crossed by a well-defined breast-band.

*Distinctions.* The uniform suffusion of light ashy brown on throat and breast will usually distinguish this bird from any other swallow likely to be compared with it. The surest test, however, is the roughness on the edge of the web of the outer primaries, composed of fine recurved hooks at the ends of the outer webs, barely visible to the naked eye, but in adults plainly perceptible to the touch as the finger is drawn along the edge towards the tip (Figure 401). Young birds do not always show this well, and various stages of the serration appear according to age and sex.

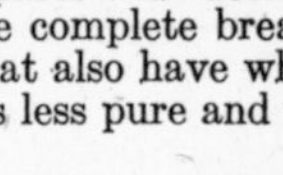

Figure 401
Showing hooks on outer edge of outer primary. Rough-winged Swallow; magnified.

*Field Marks.* Likely to be confused only with the Bank Swallow. The best recognition mark against that species is the even suffusion of light greyish brown over throat and breast instead of a white breast and throat with a more or less defined dark breast-band. In watching a flock of mixed Rough-winged and Bank Swallows, the former can usually be picked out by its slightly redder or rustier back, which seems sometimes more conspicuous in life than in the hand.

*Nesting.* Similar to the Bank Swallow, in holes in sand banks. Sometimes in sawdust piles of sawmills and occasionally in crevices in rock piles, cliffs, and masonry. More solitary than the Bank Swallow and does not nest in dense colonies.

*Distribution.* North America. In Canada, most of the southern parts across the Dominion. In the west, common in the wooded parts of southern Manitoba and southern British Columbia, but not so far detected in the provinces of Saskatchewan and Alberta.

The Rough-wings belong to a genus widely scattered over the world, characterized by the peculiar modification of the wing, the use or purpose of which is not at present known.

613. **Barn Swallow.** L'HIRONDELLE DES GRANGES. *Hirundo erythrogaster.* L, 6·95 (tail fork 1·75 deep). Plate XLVI B. Adult: with deeply forked tail. All steely black above. Below, reddish chestnut, deepest on upper breast and throat. Bar across forehead the same as throat. A somewhat broken and imperfect black bar separating throat and foreneck patch from the lighter underparts. Females: the same. Juveniles: similar, but lighter, and often with tail ungrown, less deeply forked, or almost square.

*Distinctions.* The deeply forked tail of the adult is a certain specific distinction. Likely to be confused only with the Cliff Swallow, but more reddish below, face black; dark, dull chestnut forehead-bar instead of cream one; rump black like the back.

*Field Marks.* The long "swallow-tail" is always diagnostic of this species. When this is not present, as in juvenile birds, the rufous cast to the underparts, white in the tail feathers, and solid black rump are good recognition marks.

*Nesting.* The nest is far from being the beautiful structure the Cliff Swallow builds. It is largely made of mud mixed with grasses, lined with grass and feathers, and set on a support such as a rafter or beam; but often the slightest projection will be utilized as a foundation upon which to build. Some farmers ensure the presence of the birds about the place and induce them to nest where they will be unobjectionable by furnishing small supports for their nests close under the eaves of their barns or inside where they will be sheltered but can do no damage.

*Distribution.* North America. In Canada, north to near tree limits.

This is the swallow commonly nesting in barns and outbuildings. It not only builds under the eaves, but enters the building and occupies the interior. Its long "swallow-tail" assists in making it perhaps the most graceful of all the Canadian swallows.

612. **Cliff Swallow.** EVE SWALLOW. MUD SWALLOW. L'HIRONDELLE À CROUPION JAUNE. *Petrochelidon albifrons.* L, 6·01. Plate XLVII A. Above, except rump, steely black; rump, light tan and a white or light cream-coloured bar across the forehead. Below, dull white; lower half of face and throat, rich chestnut, blending away in the breast and on flanks. A suffused iridescent black spot on foreneck and upper breast. Tail, slightly forked when closed, nearly square when open. Female and juveniles: similar to male, but colours of the latter are duller.

*Distinctions.* Much like the Barn Swallow (Plate XLVI B), but without long swallow-tails; pure or nearly pure white on abdomen; face, chestnut, and a nearly white forehead-bar. Rump, light tan instead of solid black like back.

*Field Marks.* The Cliff Swallow is a chunkily built bird; in flight, broader in proportion than any other swallow except the Purple Martin. In general colour effect much like the Barn Swallow, but with square tail (Figure 400e), instead of a deeply forked one, and a prominent light tan rump-spot. The less ruddy underparts and forehead-bar nearly white instead of dull red are also good distinctions. Cliff Swallows may always easily be picked out from flocks of mixed swallows by the tan rump-spot.

*Nesting.* A typical nest is built entirely of mud carried in little pellets in the bill and on the feet. The mud is mixed with saliva and plastered pellet by pellet on the wall under the eaves of some building or on cliff faces. The nest is first a shelf built out from the wall, then saucer-shaped and then cup-shaped, in any of which states it may be left as finished. In the best examples the sides are continued until the nest assumes the shape of a round flask with the neck drawn over and pointed outwards.

*Distribution.* North America. In Canada, across the Dominion north to the limit of trees near the Arctic coast.

*SUBSPECIES.* The only form to be found in Canada is the Northern Cliff Swallow (l'Hirondelle à crupion jaune du Nord) *Petrochelidon albifrons albifrons.*

76916—20

Most characteristically a cliff dweller as its name implies, but in many places it uses sides of barns and buildings for nesting sites. Along the steep canyon-like sides of many western rivers its mud nests may be seen in hundreds, covering many square yards of surface, so close together that their sides touch and are built together. It is interesting to note that, though sites are chosen apparently at random, and one occupied situation seems no more attractive than others adjoining, when the prevailing rains come, the nests, with their soluble walls, are invariably found to be on dry spots on the cliff face, in many cases the only dry spots in miles of rock front.

611. **Purple Martin.** L'HIRONDELLE POURPRÉE. *Progne subis.* L, 8. Plate XLVII B. About the size of the House Sparrow. Adult male, solid black, with steely blue and purple reflections. Female, dark, ashy brown above, lightening across breast, and dirty white below.

*Distinctions.* The largest of our swallows. Somewhat suggestive of the Black Swift, but black, highly iridescent, and a true swallow (Compare family details—Figure 400 with 388, page 271). The female is a big, brown swallow, much like a Rough-winged, but larger.

*Field Marks.* Size, colour, strong swallow flight, almost falcon-like in its directness, and voice make good field marks. Often seen about the business sections of the larger cities.

*Nesting.* Originally in holes and hollows in trees. Now, mostly in artificial bird-houses, cavities in the cornices of buildings, etc. They are sociable nesters and prefer to build in communities of their own kind.

*Distribution.* North and South America. In Canada, across the southern part of the Dominion, excepting the interior of British Columbia. They are common in eastern and central Manitoba, but are less numerous and rather local in Saskatchewan and Alberta and on the west coast.

*SUBSPECIES.* The Eastern Purple Martin (l'Hirondelle pourprée de l'Est) *Progne subis subis* is the only form of the species now known to occur in Canada, the western form *Progne subis hesperia* hitherto ascribed to our west coast is now regarded as restricted to southern California.

One of the most charming birds to have about. A well-occupied martin house in the garden adds a last homy touch to the homestead and is well worth striving for.

During the day the birds scatter over the country, returning at frequent intervals with food for their young. At evening all return to the house they occupy and retire within its shelter for the night. The young remain for a considerable time in the nest and, even after their first flight, old and young return to the nest at night. Martins are domestic and sociable birds and greet each other with welcoming gurgles and chatterings. Each is interested in the other's family affairs and there is a constant interchange of visits between neighbours. They rarely quarrel among themselves but show a united front to common enemies, especially the English Sparrow. A colony when established can hold its own against that pest very well indeed. A martin house should contain several rooms about 8 by 8 inches, weather and draft proof at all points except the door which should be about 2 inches in diameter and $1\frac{1}{2}$ inches from the floor. The house should stand 15 to 20 feet above the ground, out well in the open, and so arranged that it can be lowered for cleaning.[1]

[1] A pamphlet, "Bird Houses and Their Occupants," giving full particulars how to build Martin and bird-houses, may be obtained free of charge from the Dominion Parks Branch of the Department of the Interior, Ottawa, Ontario.

Plate LXV

A. Magnolia Warbler; scale, $\frac{1}{3}$

Male

Female

B. Myrtle Warbler; scale, $\frac{1}{3}$

Male Female

PLATE LXVI

A. Audubon's Warbler; scale, $\frac{1}{3}$

Autumn Spring

Female like that of Myrtle Warbler, *See* Plate LXV

B. Townsend's Warbler; scale, $\frac{1}{2}$

Male Female

Unfortunately, the treeless prairie is not an aboriginal home of the species and it is not as common as we should like west of Manitoba, nor has it there taken as kindly to nesting boxes as it has in the east. Wherever Martins occur they show the same appreciation of the hollow galvanized cornices of business buildings and without doubt a little coaxing would introduce them to the advantages of well-made bird-houses. Once established in such houses, the species would probably increase. It might take some time to accomplish this as the Purple Martin is greatly attached to its home locality, and, until forced to, does not usually seek new quarters.

*Economic Status.* The Martin like the other swallows is a bird with no bad habits, and with so many good ones that every effort should be made to aid its increase.

## FAMILY—CORVIDAE. JAYS AND CROWS

The crow family is very large and diverse, including many beautiful and highly coloured birds; indeed the famous Birds of Paradise are closely related to this family. The bill (Figure 402) is the most easily distinguished character. It is moderately long and stout with a well-arched culmen. At the base are tufts of dense, stiff, bristle-like feathers pressed close to it and covering the nostrils. The woodpeckers and the titmice have a suggestion of these nostril tufts, but the latter are all very small birds and the former have a straight culmen and the bill chisel shaped at the tip (*See* Figure 391a, page 277). They are not songsters in the ordinary sense of the term; their voices are hoarse and raucous, but the complexity of their vocal organs is very great and some of them can be taught to articulate words. They are amongst our most intelligent species and by some authors have been put at the head of the whole avian list.

### Subfamily—Garrulinae. Magpies and Jays

Medium-sized birds, many of them brilliantly coloured and with ornamental crests and flowing tails. They can be most easily recognized under their specific headings.

484. **Canada Jay.** WHISKEY JACK. MOOSE-BIRD. CAMP-ROBBER. MEAT-BIRD. LE GEAI DU CANADA. *Perisoreus canadensis.* L, 13. Plate XLVIII A. About the size of a robin; soft, plumbeous ash; head, throat, and breast white, with dark cap over rear crown and nape.

*Distinctions.* Size of robin. Body a soft neutral grey colour, without pattern, and a very loose, fluffy plumage. A dark cap and white forehead, face, and throat. The juvenile has an evenly dark, almost black, head and neck.

*Field Marks.* Size: in adult, uniform grey coloration, and white forehead and face, with dark cap or nape. Juveniles have an almost black head and face, gradually greying above and below towards tail.

*Nesting.* A deep nest of twigs and fibres, thickly lined with fur or feathers, in dense coniferous trees. Eggs deposited very early. In northern Manitoba, eggs have been recorded in January, with official thermometer registering 50 degrees below zero.

*Distribution.* The northern coniferous forest of North America. In Canada, across the continent, coming south along the mountains.

*SUBSPECIES.* The race that inhabits the greater part of Canada is the Eastern Canada Jay (le Geai de l'Est du Canada) *Perisoreus canadensis canadensis.* In the mountains, south from central British Columbia, except near the coast, is the Rocky Mountain Jay (le Geai des Rocheuses) *Perisoreus canadensis capitalis,* characterized by slightly lighter general coloration and the extension of the white forehead on the crown, reducing the dark cap to little more than a nape bar. On Vancouver Island and the adjoining coast is the Grey Streaked Jay (le Geai strié gris) given in the Check-list as *Perisoreus obscurus griseus,* and accredited full specific distinction, but, as intergrades can be demonstrated, in the opinion of the writer, worthy of only subspecific status. It is characterized by slightly brownish coloration and in having the feathers of the back distinctly white-shafted. In Alaska and perhaps adjacent parts of the Yukon the Alaska Jay (le Geai de l'Alaska) *Perisoreus canadensis fumifrons* has been recognized.

If the other jays are clownish, one scarcely knows how to characterize the Canada Jay. It has all the family characteristics in an exaggerated form, but seems to lack the keen appreciation of its own humour that the others possess. Its entire lack of self consciousness or pose is notable, and it does the most impudent things with an air of the most matter of fact innocence. No sooner is the camper's fire lighted than the Whiskey Jack is on hand for any good thing that may come its way. Almost before the echo of the rifle has died on the hills, he is in at the death to share in the offal of the game. Food on the camp table, bacon in the frying pan, or even soap by the wash dish are never safe from it, and if any little thing is missing in camp, its absence can well be blamed on the Whiskey Jack. The tent has to be tightly closed against its sharp eyes and inquisitive bill. Yet it does little real harm, its confiding presence is always welcomed, and its petty pilferings usually laughed at. Few wild things have as many human friends in the woods as this bird. It probably has the usual Jay fondness for eggs and young birds, but it does not flaunt its vices in our faces, and when man is present, devotes all its attention to salvaging waste scraps from camp. Though always present about camp, its total numbers are never large, and its population seems to consist of single families evenly scattered over the wildest country. A peculiar thing about it is that, whereas other jays increase rapidly under cultivated conditions, the Canada Jay shrinks from civilization. Lonely places are its favourite haunts, and as soon as the temporary camp becomes a permanent settlement, it deserts the neighbourhood and retires to more secluded localities, or possibly suffers the fate resultant on too great confidence, for often civilized man is more intolerant of wild life than are more primitive hunters and trappers.

*Economic Status.* No definite study has been made of the food of this species. Its habits, when under observation, show it to be omnivorous; probably its food is much similar to that of the other jays, but its habitat removes it from close contact with man, and its comparatively small numbers make its effects economically unimportant.

477. **Blue Jay.** LE GEAI BLEU. *Cyanocitta cristata.* L, 11·74. Plate XLVIII B. A bird about the size of a robin, sky blue on back, wings, and tail; a conspicuous, pointed blue crest. Nearly white below; and a black necklace draped around neck and over the upper breast (Figure 402).

*Distinctions.* Large size, general sky-blue colour, and prominent, upstanding crest. Not likely to be confused with any other species, except Steller's Jay, which is very different, being much darker all over, with a black head, and deep blue back and underparts.

*Field Marks.* Distinctions as above, and characteristic cries and calls, the most common of which is a loud, "*Jay - - jay - - jay,*" another resembles the squeak of a rusty hinge, but the bird is a mimic, and acquires many strange notes.

Figure 402
Blue Jay; scale, about ½.

*Nesting.* Nest of twigs and rootlets in trees.

*Distribution.* Eastern North America, from the northern coniferous forest south to the Gulf of Mexico. In Canada, west to the foothills.

*SUBSPECIES.* The Blue Jay that occupies most of the continent, except Florida, the type form, *Cyanocitta cristata cristata.*

The jays are all much alike in their nature. They are clowns, intelligent, alert, inquisitive, mischievous, and noisy. Much said of the magpie applies, in a measure proportionate to its size, to both the Blue and Steller's Jays. The gay coat of the Blue Jay, and its knowing airs, disarm criticism.

*Economic Status.* Economically the Blue Jay occupies a doubtful place; in food habits it is omnivorous, eating in turn, insects, fruit, acorns, grain, eggs, or young birds. Undoubtedly acorns, in their season, form its staple food. It is a bird that may have to be discouraged where other more useful birds are nesting.

478. **Steller's Jay.** LE GEAI DE STELLER. *Cyanocitta stelleri.* L, 12·50. Plate XLIX A. Somewhat larger than a robin. Back, wings, and tail dark blue, gradually turning to black on head. Conspicuous, pointed crest.

*Distinctions.* Large size, general dark blue colour, black head, and prominent, up standing crest. Not to be confused with any other species except, perhaps, the Blue Jay, but quite different, being dark blue, instead of sky-blue with white abdomen.

*Field Marks.* Distinctions as above, and loud, characteristic voice. Steller's Jay, Clarke's Nutcracker, and the magpie all have an extended vocabulary with much in common. The most usual call of this species is a harsh "*Shaack-shaack-shaack*" or "*Chack-ah, chack-ah, chack-ah,*" quite different from the clear "*Jay-jay-jay*" of the Blue Jay.

*Nesting.* A bulky mass of twigs lined with mud and rootlets, usually in evergreen thickets.

*Distribution.* Western North America from Alaska to Central America. In Canada east to the edge of the plains. Occasionally in Saskatchewan.

*SUBSPECIES.* Steller's Jay is divided into a number of subspecies, the following of which occur in Canada. The typical form *Cyanocitta stelleri stelleri* is the bird of Vancouver Island and coast from Cook Inlet, Alaska, to Oregon. The Queen Charlotte Jay (le Geai de Reine-Charlotte) *Cyanocitta stelleri carlottae* is confined to Queen Charlotte Islands. The blues are darker, and the black is deeper and more extensive. The Black-headed Jay (le Geai à tête noire) *Cyanocitta stelleri annectens* is the bird of the interior. It is most like the typical form, but on an average has more decided whitish blue streaking on the forehead, and usually has a silvery grey spot over the eye. These characters are not constant, however, some coast birds having considerable forehead streaking, and many interior ones having no spot over the eye.

A true jay in all its habits, ways, and actions. All said of the Blue Jay will apply to this species, but it being more numerous in its natural habitat must be considered more seriously.

475. **Magpie.** LA PIE. *Pica pica.* L, 15·20 (Tail 10). Plate XLIX B. A large appearing, very long-tailed bird, spectacularly coloured in black and white.

*Distinctions.* With large size, long, sweeping tail, and intense black and white contrasts, mistakable for no other Canadian bird.

*Field Marks.* Showing distinctions as above.

*Nesting.* An enormous mass of sticks in lower branches of trees or bushes, with nest in centre, entrance and exit in opposite sides.

*Distribution.* Europe, northern Asia, and western North America. In America, west of the Great Lakes from middle Yukon to New Mexico. In Canada, common on the southern prairies, in the bluffy country adjacent, and in southern British Columbia, except the coast district. Occurs erratically north and eastward. Apparently extending its range in these directions.

*SUBSPECIES.* The American Magpie (la Pie d'Amérique) *Pica pica hudsonia* differs from the Old World form only slightly in plumage characters, but very much in voice.

One of the most spectacular, beautiful, and interesting of western birds, but a considerable pest for all that. It is most often seen retreating up the coulée, chattering as it glides from bush to bush, its broad showy colour surfaces in brilliant contrast with the dark green background. At other times a small flock or family party will be seen passing noisily along the tops of the hills, from brush clump to brush clump. Again, they steal silently into camp or about the farm buildings intent on any mischief that may present itself, but flee away in consternation when disturbed, and talk the matter over in loud raucous voices in the nearest safe shrubbery. The Magpie cannot remain hidden or silent long, except when up to mischief. For purposes of brigandage and rapine it can contain itself admirably, but just long enough to accomplish its schemes. In all, the Magpie is a bird amply able to take care of itself, and such a handsome, knowing, and resourceful fellow that he almost disarms justice. From all accounts the Magpie is extending its range both northward in Alberta and eastward into Manitoba. Stray records of the species have been made east into Ontario, and north into the Mackenzie country. Wherever it goes it is the same unscrupulous roisterer, perfectly confident in its ability to take care of itself, though surrounded by enemies, its hand against everybody and every hand against it. But when it does lose the game, and finds its wits fatally outmatched, it is a bad loser and has no shame in showing its terror and calling loudly on the whole world to witness the unprecedented outrage.

*Economic Status.* Next to the crow, and possibly before it, the Magpie is the most persistent nest robber in the bird world. No eggs or young birds are safe from it, and where it is numerous it is one of the important determining factors in limiting the increase of the smaller birds. It even enters poultry yards and hencoops, timing its visit nicely when the owners' eyes are turned elsewhere, and chicks and eggs are its prey. Occasionally it attacks horses and cattle, even to their death, perching on the foolishly unresisting animals' backs and enlarging saddle galls, fresh brand marks, or other open sores to serious proportions. The animals, for some unaccountable reason, seem to make no objection, and even appear to enjoy the sensation of being pecked to death. A few Magpies may be a picturesque accompaniment of the landscape, but even those can only be enjoyed at a price, and certainly any great number of them in a neighbourhood are to be discouraged by the use of gun and trap.

### Subfamily—Corvinae. Ravens and Crows

The crows and ravens, large, all black birds, are too well known to require much description. One nutcracker is the only other species of the subfamily in Canada. It is a strikingly marked black and grey bird of the western mountain sections, in habit and actions between the crows and jays.

486. **Raven.** LE GRAND CORBEAU. *Corvus corax.* L, 22. An entirely black bird, like a crow (Plate L A), but decidedly larger.

*Distinctions.* Like a very large Crow, with wing over 15·5 inches long. The most obvious distinction, other than size, is the long-pointed, lanceolate feathers on the throat, each lying separate, one on the other, and not softly blended as in the crow (Figure 403).

*Field Marks.* Next to size, which is always an uncertain guide in open spaces, the voice is the most certain distinction. The Raven croaks instead of caws. The voice is hoarse and rattling, with a wooden quality. Young Crows sometimes have raven-like notes, but usually the voices of the two species are perfectly distinctive. The flight of the Raven is more dignified and impressive than that of the Crow, slower in beat, and with more sailing. It is sometimes very playful in the air, and executes many aerial manœuvres.

*Nesting.* Large nest of sticks, usually on cliff ledges; sometimes in trees.

*Distribution.* Europe, northern and central Asia, and North America. In Canada, across the continent. It has disappeared or is now disappearing from most of the settled parts.

*SUBSPECIES.* We have two recognized subspecies of Raven in Canada, the Northern American Raven (le Grand Corbeau de l'Amérique du Nord) *Corvus corax principalis,* that extends north over the Arctic islands. It differs from a more southern form in the interior of the continent by slightly larger size and heavier build.

In southeastern British Columbia the Western American Raven (le Grand Corbeau de l'Amérique occidentale) *Corvus corax sinuatus* has been recognized.

Figure 403
Raven, showing lanceolate feathers on throat;
scale, $\frac{1}{3}$.

The Raven is traditionally a bird of ill-omen. Sombre of colour, dismal in voice, solitary and wild of habit, it fills in the far north the place of the vulture in the south. The Raven holds aloof from the haunts of men. As civilization has advanced into the primeval vastnesses, the Raven, unlike its close relative the Crow, has retired and is still today what it was in the beginning, a bird of the wilderness. Knowing only the physical requirements and food habits of the two species, one would naturally think that the Raven could thrive as well under civilization as the Crow. It is omnivorous and can adjust itself to almost any food supply. It is hardy and can live under severer conditions and climate than its congener, yet for some unexplained reason the Crow increases and the Raven disappears when settlement advances.

*Economic Status.* The Raven eats both animal and vegetable food, but has a strong partiality for the former. It seeks the offal from the hunter's dressed game, or the game itself if it be available. It lurks about the outskirts of rookeries and makes dashes for eggs and young. By the sea it searches the shores at low water for crabs, other sea life, and anything edible that may be washed up. Avoiding cultivation as it does it has little direct economic influence.

**488. American Crow.** LA CORNEILLE D'AMÉRIQUE. *Corvus brachyrhynchos.* L, 17. Plate L A. A large, all black bird, too familiar to need much description.

*Distinctions.* A large bird, jet black all over, with considerable metallic iridescence. To be confused only with the Raven, but smaller, and the throat feathers blend together in a smooth, even mass, instead of standing out one from the other in sharp-pointed lanceolate individuality (Compare with Figure 403).

*Field Marks.* Large size, solid black coloration, distinctive wing action, and familiar voice.

*Nesting.* Nest of sticks in trees.

*Distribution.* All temperate North America.

*SUBSPECIES.* The Eastern Crow (la Corneille de l'Est d'Amérique) *Corvus brachyrhynchos brachyrhynchos* is the east Canadian form, extending westward into Manitoba. From here to the coast district of British Columbia it is replaced by the Western Crow (la Corneille de l'Ouest d'Amérique) *Corvus brachyrhynchos hesperis*, which is identical in colour with it, but averages slightly smaller. The difference in size is not great and many specimens cannot be referred to their expected appropriate geographical race by any test. On the coast is the Northwestern Crow (la Corneille du Nord-Ouest) *Corvus brachyrhynchos caurinus*, hitherto commonly regarded as a separate species, but lately officially reduced to subspecific status. Its only outward distinction is its much smaller size. A male with wing under 12 inches, or a female with wing 11 inches or under, should be of this race.

Although the Raven retreats before the advance of civilization, the Crow increases. It is omnivorous, feeding readily on anything from carrion to sprouting corn. It is an open-country bird and probably arrived in eastern Canada about the time of the first white man's clearing of the forest. In the west, where prairies and open spaces were the original condition of the country, it probably has always occurred, but it has increased enormously with cultivation. Over the colder sections of its range it is a migrant, though locally many birds may be induced by the abundant food supply furnished by slaughter houses and garbage dumps to winter far north of their accustomed range. Probably its great increase in numbers in western Canada is due as much to the present greater winter food supply in its southern stations as to summer conditions within our borders. Food in summer on our prairies was probably always sufficient for many more Crows than originally occupied them, but their numbers were controlled by the scantiness of the winter supply. Nowadays, with much of the great southern interior under cultivation, undoubtedly many more can find support through the winter and return in the spring. As far as the Crow is concerned, the primitive "balance of nature" has been profoundly and irrevocably changed in its favour, and it has increased abnormally. A policy of non-interference, as is advocated by many nature lovers, would, of course, eventually permit of a new balance being established, but it would not be the original one and under it the Crow would be more secure than under primitive conditions. It is for us to consider whether such a consummation is desirable.

*Economic Status.* The economic status of the Crow is a much argued question. Sentimental enthusiasts and some cautious agricultural investigators regard it as a valuable species. Others, perhaps equally prejudiced in the opposite direction, refuse to admit any good in the black robber. The actual fact probably lies within these extremes. In 1895 a study of the "American Crow in Relation to Agriculture," by W. B. Barrows and E. A. Swarz, was published as Bulletin No. 6 of the United States Department of Agriculture. It was a brochure of nearly one hundred pages, based on almost a thousand stomach examinations and on testimonies from all over North America. Again in 1918 the subject was rediscussed in "The Crow in Its Relation to Man," by E. R. Kalmbach, Bulletin No. 621 of the same Department. The new findings were based on 2,118 stomachs, much new field work, and the replies from some 3,000 letters of inquiry. The results of the two investigations do not differ materially, but the latter author gives a very guarded approval of the Crow. The insect food throughout the year is given as 18·97 per cent of the whole, grasshoppers and May beetles being prominently represented, especially during certain months. Carrion and animal matter, 9·15 per cent; grain, mostly Indian corn, 51·12 per cent; fruit, mostly wild, 17·70 per cent; and weed seed and rubbish. 3·06 per cent. In the east, the Crow is condemned mostly as a grain eater; in the west, complaints of this nature are few and in any event Indian corn is not an important crop there. It is notable that much of the "other grain" is taken in early spring months when it is obviously waste. On the other hand, from May until the end of August, the Crow makes a striking record as an insect consumer. During these months, insects average 36 per cent of its food, of which, during August and September, grasshoppers constitute 19 per cent, and in May, May beetles over 10 per cent of the total. Nineteen per cent of the food of so large and common a species as the crow is an important economic item. When it is noted that these figures are for the average of North America and mostly where grasshoppers are but incidental and not unduly numerous, it is evident that the benefit that may be derived from the species is well worth considering. Undoubtedly, the Crow's worst enemies will admit that, where grasshoppers occur in pestilential numbers, the Crow subsists upon them almost entirely. The writer has seen the ground under Crow stations covered with the ejected pellets composed entirely of the horny, undigestible parts of grasshoppers. No less convincing an observer than Mr. Norman Criddle of Aweme, Manitoba, studying the grasshopper pest for the Entomological Branch of the Dominion Government, cites cases where land protected by numerous Crows escaped serious damage, but adjoining localities, where they had been lately systematically shot, were devastated by grasshoppers. Based on stomach examinations, usually the most reliable evidence on the subject, and from a purely agricultural standpoint, it seems that a very good case can be made for the Crow in the Canadian west. It does not seriously affect grain and does good duty in controlling some of the worst insect pests the farmer has to contend with. But there is another side to the story, and one that stomach examination does not usually show.

As an egg eater and a young bird destroyer, the Crow is probably the very worst enemy of some of our largest and most useful wild birds. Throughout the spring and early summer, before grasshoppers are out in number, the Crow in the west makes its worst showing, and one that in the eyes of many cancels all the good it may do at other times. In the itemized tables given by Mr. Kalmbach, animal matter other than insects and carrion constituted over 10 per cent of its food for May, June, and July. In this, however, no account can be taken of the enormous number of eggs consumed during this time, as they seldom leave any record in the crop or stomach for subsequent recognition. Field observations show that Crows destroy an astonishingly large proportion of the eggs of water-fowl and upland game. Probably in many cases of the first layings of these birds scarcely one out of four is brought to hatching. Later broods, when the cover is better grown, fare better, but even they suffer severely and in any event several weeks are lost of the precious summer in which to mature and harden the young generation in preparation for the hardships of migration and winter. It is nothing uncommon to see newly hatched broods of ducks as late as the end of August, the results of several interruptions to breeding. Of course, all the nest destruction cannot be blamed on Crows. Coyotes, dogs, cats, the trampling cattle, and other factors are also to a greater or less degree responsible. But taking such evidence as the culprit leaves behind, it is only too evident that the Crow is the cause of the larger proportion of loss. A dozen nests may be found occupied one day and destroyed the next, with suggestions or evidence of Crows about them. A duck or Prairie Chicken flushed from the nest in sight of the ever vigilant marauder puts him at interested attention immediately, and if watched he will be seen to investigate the promising spot as soon as the intruder has left. Crows also profit by disturbances in large nesting coummnities, such as of gulls or terns, that cause the owners to leave their premises temporarily unguarded; later examination generally shows the clean sweep they make on the opportunity. During the nesting season they hunt indefatigably for eggs and seem to favour them above all other food and the thoroughness with which they search all possible grounds only raises wonder that any are left to hatch. However good the Crow may be as an insect destroyer, it is doubtful if it can, in this direction, replace the birds that it supplants. It will certainly take a number of Crows to replace the work of a covey of Prairie Chicken that one Crow has destroyed, and when the great number of other birds so lost are taken into consideration, it is very questionable how far, if at all, the evidence is in its favour. In the case cited by Mr. Criddle, it may be held that the Crows had already eliminated the majority of other grasshopper destroyers before they were themselves killed off. Such things as these cannot fail to impress the unprejudiced observer, and when he marks the dearth of bird life in situations that seem most favourable, but where Crows and Magpies are numerous, he cannot help but add reservations to his acceptance of official findings that do not take them into consideration.

Altogether, in the opinion of the writer, the Crow is pretty nearly as black as he is painted. The fact that Mr. Kalmbach rather withholds judgment, and gives modified approval when the most adverse factors are unrepresented in his evidence, suggests that, when all things are considered, the Crow will be placed in the category of the undesirable. Certainly there is no call to protect the Crow. It is wary, intelligent, adaptive, and well able to survive even if every man's hand is turned against it. The most strenuous efforts practicable will never imperil the species. As for active methods of control, probably the least satisfactory and most expensive one is the bounty system. From a purely agricultural point of view, the status of the Crow in the west is doubtful. At the best, it is mildly beneficial, at the worst, but neutral. The Crow question becomes, therefore, one for the sportsman rather than the farmer. The policy of public bounties and taxing the general public for the benefit of a particular class is a questionable one. Could it be regarded as a permanent investment, if the species would stay reduced when once brought to a normal number, it might be differently viewed and the expense justified as for the general good. But the relief is only temporary and unless continued year after year as a running expense is of no permanent benefit. It behooves the sportsman to protect his own sport and to take the burden of controlling one of the worst game destroyers.

491. **Clarke's Nutcracker.** CLARKE'S CROW. LE CASSE-NOIX DE CLARKE. *Nucifraga columbiana.* L, 12·50. Plate L B. A heavily built jay-like bird without crest, uniformly smoky grey body, slightly whitening to face, with black wings and centre tail feathers. Extensive white tips to secondaries and white outertail feathers and undertail-coverts.

*Distinctions.* The shrikes are the only species this bird resembles in colour, but the Nutcracker is much larger and has no black bar through eye (Compare with Plate LXI B).

*Field Marks.* A large grey bird, with black wings and much white in tail. Of jay-like habits, and very noisy and talkative.

A. Black-throated Green Warbler; scale, ½
Male Female

B. Blackburnian Warbler; scale, ½
Female Male

Plate LXVIII

A. Oven-bird; scale, $\frac{1}{2}$

B. Macgillivray's Warbler; scale, $\frac{1}{3}$

Female Male

*Nesting.* Nest a large structure of sticks in the lower branches of conifers on the mountain sides.

*Distribution.* Western North America. In Canada, throughout the mountain regions from Alaska through British Columbia, south mostly east of the Coast Range. East, casually as far as Saskatchewan.

Clarke's Nutcracker, named after the junior leader of the Lewis and Clarke expedition that first brought the species to the attention of science, is one of the most interesting birds of the mountains. It comes into camp almost as freely as its relative, the Canada Jay or Whiskey Jack, and like it in some localities is called "Camp Robber." It is a very noisy and talkative bird, with many queer antics. One of the best places to study this species is in the Banff National Park. Here almost any morning in summer its harsh voice is one of the first sounds that steals in through the bedroom windows and by following the sound, one may soon come upon a small party performing their peculiar gymnastics and loudly discussing neighbourhood topics in the evergreens near at hand.

FAMILY—PARIDAE. TITMICE

The titmice are birds of wide distribution in the northern hemisphere and are as familiar to European residents as to us. They are small birds with rather short but comparatively strongly arched bills (Figure 404). Their plumage characters are usually easily recognized.

735. **Black-capped Chickadee.** CHICKADEE. LA MÉSANGE À TÊTE NOIRE. *Penthestes atricapillus.* L, 5·25. Plate LI A. A diminutive bird. Back, olive grey, with intensely black crown spreading over face to eyes and down back of neck; below white with sandy suffusion on flanks; a full black throat in sharp contrast with pure white cheeks.

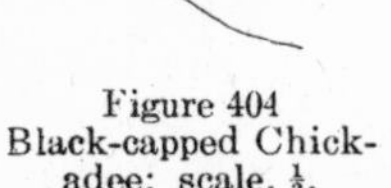

Figure 404
Black-capped Chickadee; scale, ½.

*Distinctions.* Easily recognized as a titmouse or chickadee. The intensely black crown and throat will separate from the Brown-headed; the lack of white eyebrow stripe from the Mountain; and the lack of rufous from the Chestnut-backed Chickadees.

*Field Marks.* Their shape, a round bundle of feathers with long tail and no appreciable neck, and the contrastive face marks make them easily recognizable. Except in British Columbia not likely to require separation from anything but the Brown-headed Chickadee. The intensely black instead of brown head and throat marks, and its clearly uttered "*Chick-adee-dee,*" instead of a flatter and hoarser "*Chick-adaa-daa,*" make separation comparatively easy.

*Nesting.* In old stumps, holes in trees, etc. Nest of moss, grasses, feathers, and plant-down.

*Distribution.* North America. In Canada, across the Dominion north to near the tree limit.

*SUBSPECIES.* Three subspecies are recognized in Canada. The Eastern Chickadee (la Mésange à tête noire de l'Est) *Penthestes atricapillus atricapillus* occurs westward to or near the Manitoba line. The Long-tailed Chickadee (la Mésange à longue queue) *Penthestes atricapillus septentrionalis* continues from there to the east side of the Coast Range in British Columbia. It averages a slightly longer tail and some very fine colour differences, none of which is constant enough for recognition without a large series for comparison and which are too slight for popular observation. The Oregon Chickadee (la Mésange de l'Orégon) *Penthestes atricapillus occidentalis* is the chickadee of the southern British Columbia coast. It is a rather more decidedly marked race, shorter in wing and tail than either of the above, and with slightly darker, more olive, less ochraceous, back.

Through the coldest, most blustery, or the wettest and rawest of days, if a Chickadee is to be found, it will be "chickadeeing" as cheerfully as in the brightest weather. A discouraged Chickadee is yet to be seen by the writer. In the autumn and winter when birds are scarce one should listen to its cheery "*Chica-chicka-dee-de,*" for it usually leads a little company of congenial spirits cruising through the woods, and its notes seem to form a rallying cry that keeps them together. Thus in the autumn the Chickadee is often the centre of a little host of mixed species of warblers, vireos, kinglets, nuthatches, and an occasional Downy Woodpecker or a Brown Creeper. After the migrant members have left for the winter, the remaining, hardier ones keep casual company until spring when nesting duties scatter them for the season. As spring approaches, the Chickadees remember a new song consisting of two whistled notes, high and clear. The first is prolonged, and the second about two tones lower. It has been translated as "*Spring's here.*"

*Economic Status.* Few birds are more useful to mankind than the Chickadee. Though small, it is constantly at work, and being with us all winter its good work is continued throughout the year. All insects are very small in their early stages and the little bird that devours a whole cluster of eggs at a gulp may benefit agriculture as greatly as a larger one that makes a meal from one or two large caterpillars or adult insects but scorns the minute ones. The prying habits of the Chickadee and its companions the nuthatch, creeper, etc., and their close examination of the small crevices where many insects hide or hibernate, render their services of great value to the husbandman, especially in winter, when insect enemies are scarce, and the total taken throughout the year by these allied species must be very great. These active little birds demand comparatively large quantities of food to resist the intense cold, and the smallness of their prey necessitates the consumption of innumerable individuals.

The Chickadee's food is 68 per cent insect and 32 per cent vegetable. The former comprises eggs, larvæ, chrysalids, and small insects, largely weevils, and includes some of the worst orchard and crop pests. The vegetable matter is largely small seeds and wild fruit. No charges of damage to cultivated varieties have been advanced. Chickadees can easily be induced to come about the home grounds in winter and with a little coaxing become tame enough even to alight on the person and feed from the hand. A lump of suet fastened to a tree trunk is a never failing attraction to them and ensures their constant visits.

738. **Gambel's Chickadee.** MOUNTAIN CHICKADEE. LA MÉSANGE DE GAMBEL. *Penthestes gambeli.* L, 5. Plate LI A. Almost exactly like the Black-capped Chickadee but greyer, with less sandy wash on flanks or back, and with a white eyebrow-line.

*Distinctions.* Likely to be confused only with the Black-capped Chickadee, but see distinctions above.

*Field Marks.* Like a Black-capped Chickadee with a white line over the eye.

*Nesting.* In an old woodpecker-hole or natural cavity in stub; nest usually lined with rabbit fur.

*Distribution.* Mountains of western North America. In Canada, the western mountains, except the coastal slope, north to northern British Columbia.

*SUBSPECIES.* The Canadian representative of the species is given by some authors as the Short-tailed Mountain Chickadee (la Mésange de Gambel à queue courte) *Penthestes gambeli abbreviatus,* though the A.O.U. Check-list refers it to Grinnell's Chickadee (la Mésange de Grinnell) *Penthestes gambeli grinnelli.*

So nearly like the Black-capped Chicadee as scarcely to require special mention. It frequents somewhat higher altitudes in summer and at that season the two species are rarely seen together.

739. **Siberian Chickadee.** ALASKA CHICKADEE. LA MÉSANGE DE SIBÉRIE. *Penthestes cinctus.* L, 5·50. A rather large chickadee, like the Brown-headed, but distinctly different in colour; a greyer brown and the cheeks clear and sharply white, almost meeting across the back of the neck.

*Distinctions and Field Marks.* As above.

*Distribution.* Eastern Siberia and Alaska. In Canada, only recorded from near the Arctic coast on Anderson River and the mouth of the Mackenzie.

*SUBSPECIES.* The Alaska Chickadee (la Mésange de l'Alaska) *Penthestes cinctus Alascensis* is the only American form.

This species is to be expected only in the high western sub-arctics and is not likely to be observed elsewhere.

740. **Brown-headed Chickadee.** LA MÉSANGE À TÊTE BRUNE. *Penthestes hudsonicus.* L, 5·12. Similar to the Black-capped Chickadee; but duller and darker in general tone; cap greyish brown of nearly the same colour as the back; throat patch present but veiled; flanks rufous tinted.

*Distinctions.* The brownish cap and back and general duller and less contrasted coloration.

*Field Marks.* A very dark chickadee with coloration diffused and pattern lacking distinctness. Its characteristic *"Chick-a-da"* note is hoarse, but otherwise similar to that of the common chickadee.

*Nesting.* In holes in trees and stubs in nest of moss and felted fur.

*Distribution.* Northern North America. In Canada, across the Dominion, in the heavy northern spruce forest, except the west coast region.

*SUBSPECIES.* Three subspecies of Brown-headed Chickadee are generally recognized. The Hudsonian Chickadee (la Mésange hudsonienne) *Penthestes hudsonicus hudsonicus,* the northern evergreen forests from Ontario to northern Alaska. The Acadian Chickadee (la Mésange d'Acadie) *Penthestes hudsonicus littoralis,* Quebec and the Maritime Provinces; the Columbian Chickadee (la Mésange de Colombie) *Penthestes hudsonicus columbianus,* southern Alaska, British Columbia, and Alberta. The distinctions between these races are slight and the limits of these ranges have not been well worked out.

The Brown-headed Chickadee is so similar in habits to the Black-capped that description would be little more than repetition.

741. **Chestnut-backed Chickadee.** LA MÉSANGE À DOS MARRON. *Penthestes rufescens.* L, 4·75. Plate LI B. A chickadee with dark brown crown and throat, and bright white cheeks. Back and flanks coloured with strong reddish chestnut. Below white.

*Distinctions.* Our only chickadee with back and flanks strongly reddish.

*Field Marks.* A chickadee with strong red flanks and back. Face mark a comparatively narrow but contrastive white stripe extending well over shoulders.

*Nesting.* In holes in stubs, lined with rabbit fur, feathers, and other soft material.

*Distribution.* Pacific Coast region of North America. In Canada, British Columbia, mostly west of the Coast Range but locally in the interior southern sections.

*SUBSPECIES.* The form referred to Canada is the northern type race *Penthestes rufescens rufescens.*

A bird characteristic of the heavily wooded west coast. There, in the upper branches of the giant firs, the birds may be seen flitting about in true chickadee fashion, but often so high that it is difficult to separate them from kinglets. When they come closer their ruddy coloration is quite evident. They have the confiding ways and gentle inquisitiveness of the Black-capped Chickadee and are much like them in habit and action.

731. **Tufted Titmouse.** LA MÉSANGE HUPPÉ D'AMÉRIQUE. *Baeolophus bicolor.* L, 6. The largest of our titmice without the characteristic chickadee colouring. All above, an almost even stone-grey,; white below slightly washed on flanks with rufous. A distinct almost blue jay-like crest.

*Distinctions.* The plain grey and unmarked coloration with striking crest are unmistakable distinctions and field marks. Its common note, a loud clear *Peetle-peetle—peetle,* is most characteristic but is very like one of the phrases of the Orchard Oriole.

*Nesting.* In old woodpecker's holes, stumps, etc., in nest of leaves, moss, strips of bark, feathers, etc.

*Distribution.* Southern and eastern United States north to and just touching Canadian boundaries in the lower Great Lakes region.

Figure 405
Tufted Titmouse; about natural size.

The only Canadian records for the Tufted Titmouse are two noted on Point Pelee in southern Ontario in the western Lake Erie country. It is rather common on the Michigan side of Detroit River and even on Grosse Isle in midstream and should eventually be found on the Canadian side of the river, though as yet we have no record of its occurrence there.

743. **Little Bush Tit.** LA PETITE MÉSANGE DES BUISSONS. *Psaltriparus minimus.* L, 4. Like a very small kinglet in size, and perhaps the most inconspicuously coloured bird that we have. Dark brownish grey on back changing to warm sepia brown on crown; below, white, tinged with brownish on flanks. No definite markings anywhere.

*Distinctions.* With small size likely to be mistaken only for a female Ruby-crowned Kinglet, but without any trace of green, suggestion of wing-bar, or light eye circle. Tail distinctly long and bill very short and stubby.

*Field Marks.* Probably in life the Bush Tit looks like a diminutive kinglet with a long tail, greyish instead of greenish, and without wing-bars, light eye circle, or eyebrow stripe.

*Nesting.* A beautifully woven pouch with entrance hole in the side, suspended from a branch.

*Distribution.* Pacific coast of North America. In Canada known only from a few specimens near Vancouver, British Columbia.

## FAMILY—SITTIDAE. NUTHATCHES

The nuthatches are small, woodpecker-like birds in general habit, but their toes are of the usual Passerine type with three toes in front and one behind instead of the characteristic two and two of the woodpeckers. The bills are somewhat like those of the woodpecker in outline, but without their chisel-shaped point and are set on a slightly up-tilted angle with the head, giving a turned-up or retroussé appearance (Figure 406, compare with Figure 391, page 277). The colours of our species are characteristic. The name nuthatch is derived from their habit of wedging nuts and other hard food into crevices and "hatching" or hacking them until an entrance is made. Though capable of considerable excavating in wood or bark they do not use their powers to delve deeply into trees, but as a rule content themselves with flaking off the loose bark scales and searching the open cavities and seams.

727. **White-breasted Nuthatch.** BIG QUANK. LA SITTELLE À POITRINE BLANCHE. *Sitta carolinensis.* L, 6·07. Plate LII A. Above, slate-blue with shiny black crown, hindneck, and upper shoulders. Female: duller. Below, white, including all of face, with chestnut about vent and on undertail-coverts. Juveniles: with flanks and lower abdomen also slightly washed with chestnut.

*Distinctions.* With creeping habits and general coloration, to be mistaken only for the Red-breasted Nuthatch, but larger, and the breast and most of the underparts pure white instead of heavily washed with rufous. The sides of the face are pure white (Figure 406), instead of with a black line through eye and a prominent white eyebrow-line (Figure 407). The Pygmy Nuthatch is much smaller, and has a brownish crown blending into a dark eye stripe (*See* Figure 408).

Figure 406
White-breasted Nuthatch; about natural size.

*Field Marks.* Creeping habits, and even, blue-grey back are characteristic of the nuthatches. The white underparts and the solid white face separate the White-breasted from the other species.

*Nesting.* In a hole in a tree, usually a natural cavity, in nest of leaves, feathers, etc.

*Distribution.* Temperate North America. In Canada, across the southern part of the Dominion, rare or absent on the prairies.

*SUBSPECIES.* Two subspecies are recognized in Canada. The Eastern White-breasted Nuthatch (la Sittelle à poitrine blanche de l'Est) *Sitta carolinensis carolinensis* extends throughout the east, westward to Manitoba and probably through the northern forested areas to the mountains. The Slender-billed Nuthatch (la Sittelle à bec fin) *Sitta carolinensis aculeata* occupies southern British Columbia. The grey on the back is slightly darker, or duller in tone, and the bill averages slightly longer in proportion to its width. The Rocky Mountain Nuthatch (la Sittelle des Rocheuses) *Sitta carolinensis nelsoni* has probably been attributed to southern British Columbia in error.

The climbing and trunk-creeping of the nuthatches is a wonderful accomplishment. They travel upwards or downwards, forwards or backwards, or even along the underside of branches like flies on the ceiling, with apparently equal ease. Though industrious little workers they enjoy life in their own quiet way, being neither so absorbed in their never-ending task of keeping the tree trunks free from insects as their friend and oft-time companion, the Brown Creeper, nor so light-hearted and mercurial as the irrepressible chickadees. They take time occasionally to court, play, chase each other merrily about, and to sing a little spring song, to show that they are not overcome by their responsibilities. Their usual note is a hoarse "*Quank-quank*" and they are often found with small groups of chickadees and creepers; they do their share in holding the little company together with their frequent conversational remarks.

*Economic Status.* One of the most useful birds. Although it pays much attention to forest trees it often comes to orchard and shade trees and as a member of the above-mentioned company, which examines with microscopic eyes every part of the winter tree trunks for insects, it consumes great quantities of pests in adult, egg, or larval stages.

728. **Red-breasted Nuthatch.** LITTLE QUANK. LA SITTELLE À POITRINE ROUSSE. *Sitta canadensis.* L, 4·62. A smaller nuthatch than the White-breasted. Above, slaty blue with shiny black crown and hindneck, duller on females. Below, all rusty ochre. Cheeks white, a sharp black line through eye expanding on upper shoulders, and a conspicuous white eyebrow streak (Figure 407). Juveniles with the rusty ochre below reduced.

*Distinctions.* Small size, general ruddy colour beneath, the black bar through eye, and a conspicuous white eyebrow streak.

*Field Marks.* As above.

*Nesting.* In hole in tree or stump, nest of grasses or moss.

*Distribution.* North America. In Canada, across the Dominion north to Great Slave Lake.

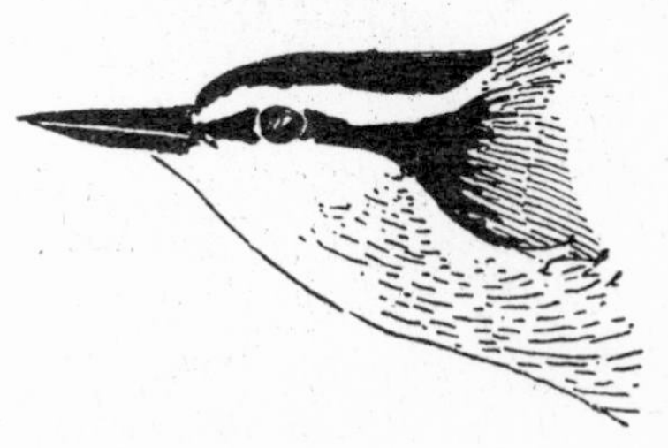

Figure 407
Red-breasted Nuthatch; natural size.

A slightly more active bird than the preceding, and more inclined to forage about the extreme tips of branches and to cling there upside down very much like crossbills. This is the commoner nuthatch in the prairie sections.

730. **Pygmy Nuthatch.** LA SITTELLE PYGMÉE. *Sitta pygmaea.* L, 4. The smallest of our nuthatches. Above, slaty blue changing to greyish brown or olive-grey on crown. Sometimes a dull white cloud on nape. Below, creamy white, clouded with light grey on flanks. Cheeks white, and a dark bar through eye, blending into crown without any eyebrow streak between (Figure 408).

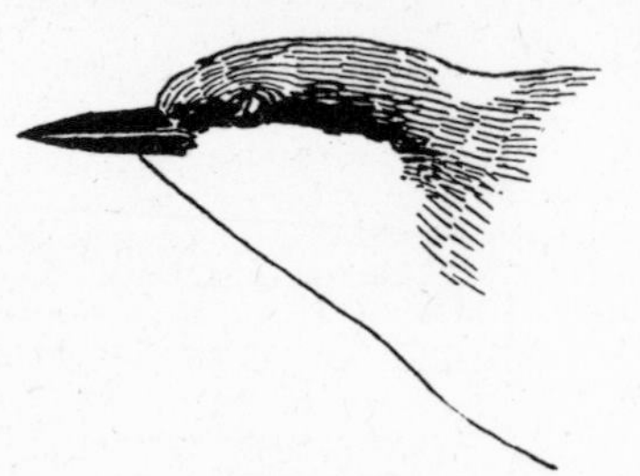

Figure 408
Pygmy Nuthatch; natural size.

*Distinctions.* Small size, almost clear white below, and greyish brown or slightly olive crown continuous with dark eye-bar.

*Field Marks.* As above.

*Nesting.* In crevices in bark or holes in stubs, lined with wool, feathers, and other soft materials.

*Distribution.* Western United States and Mexico. In Canada, the southern interior valleys of British Columbia, confined to the region of yellow pine *Pinus ponderosa.*

*SUBSPECIES.* The Canadian form of the species is the Black-eared Nuthatch (la Sittelle à oreilles noires) *Sitta pygmea melanotis.*

A very characteristic bird of its habitat. As agile and lively as the Red-breasted Nuthatch and, going in flocks, when too high or distant to show details, they may be taken for crossbills or Pine Siskins. The notes are only faint chippings, quite unlike the horse "quanking" that is so characteristic of the other nuthatches.

## FAMILY—CERTHIIDAE. CREEPERS

The name of the only Canadian creeper, the Brown Creeper, describes the bird very well. It is a small brown bird that creeps or climbs woodpecker-fashion on the trunks and larger branches of forest trees. It is smaller than any Canadian woodpecker and the bill is comparatively long, light, delicately tapered, and sickle-shaped (Figure 410), adapted for extracting small insects and insects' eggs from narrow cavities, but not for chiselling in even the softest wood or bark to reach them. The tail is rather long and stiff (Figure 409) and the claws are quite long and much curved.

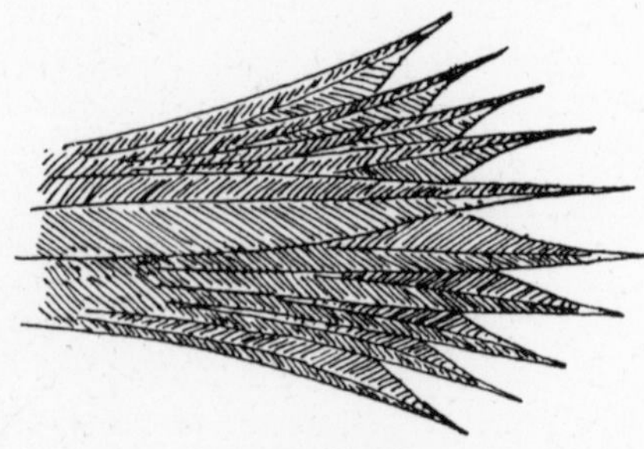

Figure 409
Tail of Brown Creeper; natural size.

Figure 410
Brown Creeper; about natural size.

726. **Brown Creeper.** LE GRIMPEREAU BRUN. *Certhia familiaris.* L, 5·66. Plate LII B. A small, wood-brown bird, white below and evenly striped with white above. A long, curved, delicately pointed bill (Figure 410), and a long, stiff tail of pointed feathers (Figure 409).

*Field Marks.* Our only small brown bird with pronounced tree-creeping habits.

*Nesting.* Behind the loose bark of trees in nest of twigs, strips of bark, bits of dead wood, moss, etc.

*Distribution.* Greater part of northern hemisphere. In Canada, across the Dominion except on the treeless prairies.

*SUBSPECIES.* Four subspecies of Brown Creeper are accredited to Canada. The Eastern Brown Creeper (le Grimpereau brun de l'Est) *Certhia familiaris americana* extends as far west as Manitoba. It is not known whether it, or any Brown Creeper, extends north of the prairies or to the mountains. The Rocky Mountain Brown Creeper (le Grimpereau brun des Rocheuses) *Certhia familiaris montana* should occupy from central Alaska through central British Columbia and to Alberta and along the mountains. It is a pale greyish bird. The California Creeper (le Grimpereau brun de la Californie) *Certhia familiaris occidentalis* is brown and tawny and should occur on the British Columbia coast. The Sierra Creeper (le Grimpereau brun des sierras) *Certhia familiaris zelotes* is even browner and should range over the interior of southern British Columbia. The distinctions of these races are rather fine for popular recognition.

Pressed tightly to the trunk of forest trees the Brown Creeper may be seen spiralling up the perpendicular trunk and industriously gleaning from every crack and crevice in the bark. Reaching the section where the branches begin to grow smaller and the bark smooth it drops down to the base of an adjoining tree and works upward again, never hurrying, never pausing, filling its stomach with small beetles, larvæ, and insect eggs. The skill with which this bird can cling to smooth surfaces is remarkable. The writer once saw a Brown Creeper climb the polished corner of a black walnut bookcase with as little concern as if it had been the roughest-barked oak in the woods.

*Economic Status.* The Brown Creeper is purely insect-eating in its habits and its constant microscopic attention to every little crevice in the rough bark must account for innumerable insect pests. Most of its work is done in the woods, but as the bird frequently appears in the orchard and on shade and ornamental trees about the town and house the species has a powerfully beneficial influence.

## FAMILY—CINCLIDAE. DIPPERS OR WATER-OUZELS

A small but remarkable group in which warbler and thrush-like characters are blended with, and modified by, singular aquatic habits. As only one species is here under consideration the specific description will be sufficient for recognition.

701. **American Dipper.** AMERICAN WATER-OUZEL. LE CINCLE D'AMÉRIQUE. *Cinclus mexicanus.* L, 6·50. Plate LIII A. A little smaller than the robin, but with short, stubby tail, solid dull, dark grey all over, faintly browning on head in adult and slightly lightening below in juvenility. No pattern or defined detail anywhere.

*Distinctions.* Solid grey all over without other defined marking, and short stubby tail not extending back to tips of outstretched toes. Can be mistaken for no other Canadian species.

*Field Marks.* About the size of a large sparrow or small robin; slaty coloration; water-frequenting habits about mountain streams; diving, flying, and walking under water; dipping or bobbing habit when on land.

*Nesting.* In the rocks, near water or behind waterfalls. Nest of moss lined with fine grasses, arched over, with entrance in the side.

*Distribution.* Mountains of western North America. In Canada, British Columbia and adjacent Alberta foothills, north to Yukon River.

A very characteristic bird of the mountain streams. It dives or walks into the swiftly running water, disappears and reappears like a witch. Its nest is usually behind a waterfall and it dashes to or from it, through the falling veil, as indifferently as though a cataract were nothing. It is a winter as well as a summer resident and is as much at home on the slippery snowy margins and ice-draped rocks as on soft summer moss.

*Economic Status.* Unfortunately the dipper has had laid against it well-substantiated charges of devouring large numbers of salmon eggs and small fry. As normally scattered, a pair here and another there throughout the summer, the damage done is probably slight, but when numbers congregate about restricted open waters in the winter time, especially in the neighbourhood of fish hatcheries, they are factors to be considered. Doubtless local conditions must govern our attitude towards it. In the lonely mountain streams it is a rare attraction to the landscape, and should receive every protection; where it is economically objectionable it may be well to reduce the superabundance. A few dippers in their proper place add an air of wildness to the locality, but many in the wrong place may have an unpleasant effect.

### FAMILY—TROGLODYTIDAE. WRENS

The wrens are small brown birds living close to the ground. Though diminutive in size they are very energetic and except when brooding or asleep are rarely still. They may be recognized by their small size, brown coloration, small stubby tail often thrown up over the back, and their restless habits, winding in and out amongst the densest brush piles more like mice than birds. The wrens are a large family well distributed over the world, but better represented in species in the New than in the Old World. Their habitat varies from watery swamps to arid canyons and from open thickets to deep, dense woods. The family name *Troglodytidae*, cave-dwellers, is derived from their habit of nesting in holes.

721. **House Wren.** LE RAILLEUR OU TROGLODYTE DOMESTIQUE (Improprement Roitelet). *Troglodytes aëdon.* L, 5. Plate LIII B. A slightly ashy brown wren, finely but softly vermiculated with dark brown on back and barred across tail and wings. Below creamy white, slightly browning across the breast and flanks and softly barred on the latter.

*Distinctions.* An ashy brown wren creamy below, but without any strongly characterized markings. By habitat most likely to be confused with Bewick's Wren of the southern British Columbia coast: It is a greyer brown with fine vermiculations on back and the whiteness of the underparts is strongest on the abdomen instead of on the throat. No eyebrow stripe as in Bewick's or the Long-billed Marsh Wrens. No back striping as in the Short-billed and not strongly coloured below as is the Winter Wren.

*Field Marks.* An ashy brown wren slightly vermiculated on back and flanks and creamy white below, clearest on abdomen. No facial marks or striping anywhere.

*Nesting.* In a hole in a tree, bird-box, or similar places, in a nest of twigs, lined with grasses, feathers, etc. The House Wren will occupy any kind of bird-house that is suitably placed. The English Sparrow can be kept away by making the entrance hole small; a one-inch auger hole is sufficient for a wren and will bar the sparrows entirely.

*Distribution.* United States and southern Canada. In Canada, across the Dominion as far north as the heavy spruce forest region.

*SUBSPECIES.* The Eastern House Wren (le Railleur ou Troglodyte domestique de l'Est) *Troglodytes aëdon aëdon* extends westward to or near the Manitoba line. The Western House Wren (le Railleur ou Troglodyte domestique de l'Ouest) *Troglodytes aëdon parkmani,* slightly paler and greyer, with the back a little more distinctly barred, occupies the country farther west. The distinctions are fine, however, and the division between the ranges is not well marked.

A. Maryland Yellow-throat; scale, $\frac{1}{3}$

Male Female

B. Wilson's Warbler; scale, $\frac{1}{3}$

(Pileolated Warbler)

Plate LXX

A. American Redstart; scale, $\frac{1}{2}$

Male

Female

B. English Sparrow; scale, $\frac{1}{3}$

Male Female

The House Wren is a busybody; it has the business of everybody else to attend to as well as an enormous amount of its own, and it raises infinite protest. Its energy is irrepressible; no crack or crevice in the fence escapes its fine, investigative bill, and scarcely a leaf stalk in the garden but is carefully examined above and below for such insects as it may yield. It bustles hither and thither scolding and ejaculating until unable to suppress its mere happiness, and in spite of the heavy responsibility of ruling the garden, it flits to an elevated perch and fairly boils over with a rolling, spluttering song that seems to gush out of its little throat more quickly than it can articulate the notes. It is an indefatigable singer. During the height of its song season it can be depended on for a song a minute throughout the busy hours. As if this were not enough to work off its superabundant energy, the House Wren fills with sticks every possible cavity or nesting site it does not occupy. This not only satisfies its exaggerated nest-building instinct, but, the method in its madness, it effectually prevents other birds from building within its declared preserves. It is intolerant of bird neighbours of either its own or other species and herein is shown a darker side to its character. Not able to oppose other species directly, it sometimes resorts to questionable practices to preserve the inviolability of its territory and steals into the nests of other birds in their absence and punctures their eggs. This may be largely the habit of some individuals rather than a general specific one, but it is common enough to deserve notice. House Wrens are delightful birds to have about the house, but if other species are desired or present, the busy little mischief-maker must be closely watched and in extreme cases eliminated.

722. **Winter Wren.** LE RAILLEUR OU TROGLODYTE DES FORÊTS. *Nannus hiemalis.* L, 4·05. A small wren of very dark, even coloration. Below, rich wood-brown only partly lightening, and sometimes faintly greying. Back faintly, and flanks and abdomen heavily, vermiculated or finely crossbarred.

*Distinctions.* General wood-brown, especially the rich full colour below and the heavy barring on flanks and abdomen.

*Field Marks.* A small, darkly coloured, brown wren; commonly found in deep woods.

*Nesting.* Under logs or roots in deep woods. Nest of moss, lined with wool and fine materials.

*Distribution.* North America. In Canada, across the Dominion except the prairie sections, north to Lake Athabaska and northern British Columbia.

*SUBSPECIES.* Two subspecies have been recognized in Canada. The Eastern Winter Wren (le Railleur ou Troglodyte des forêts de l'Est) *Nannus hiemalis hiemalis* occurs west to the mountains. The Western Winter Wren (le Railleur ou Troglodyte des forêts de l'Ouest) *Nannus hiemalis pacificus* is the bird of British Columbia. It is darker, richer, and warmer brown, and with little or no greying on breast. Several other subspecies are found in Alaska, but as yet have not been detected in Canada even in migration.

A bird whose vocal powers have hardly been appreciated at their true worth. It is perhaps the finest songster of the northern woods. Its song, strangely disconnected yet continuous, composed of jerkily jumbled trills and staccato notes, dies down as though about to cease, only to revive and continue with full vigour several seconds longer. The length of a complete typical song is between eight and ten seconds and is thus one of the longest performances of any of our birds. It is shy and retiring, and inhabiting the densest and deepest woods is seldom heard in full song by the ordinary observer and still more rarely seen by him.

76916—21½

719. **Bewick's Wren.** LE RAILLEUR OU TROGLODYTE DE BEWICK. *Thryomanes bewicki.* L, 5·60. Plate LIV A. A little larger than a House Wren. Even, warm, chocolate brown above, throat and breast white, clearest on throat; shaded with greyish and brownish on flanks.

*Distinctions.* With size, brown coloration, and habit likely to be confused only with the House Wren. The back is warm dark brown instead of ashy brown and is without barring or vermiculation except on tail and wing quills. The white is clear on throat instead of being tinged with brownish. No barring on flanks.

*Field Marks.* A medium-sized dark brown wren without barring or vermiculation on body. A very distinct white eyebrow streak. Haunts the vicinity of buildings and tangled thickets much like the House Wren.

*Nesting.* In holes or crannies in stumps, buildings, or bird-boxes. Like the House Wren it sometimes occupies the most absurd nesting quarters. Nest of dried grasses and leaves, rarely of twigs; lined with wool, hair, or feathers.

*Distribution.* United States and Mexico. In Canada, occasional in extreme southern Ontario, and common in southern British Columbia west of the Coast Range.

*SUBSPECIES.* Two forms have been recognized in Canada. An eastern one, the Eastern Bewick's Wren (le Railleur ou Troglodyte de Bewick de l'Est) *Thryomanes bewicki bewicki* of the eastern United States, straggling occasionally into southern Ontario along Lake Erie; and the Seattle Wren (le Railleur ou Troglodyte de Seattle) *Thryomanes bewicki calophonus* of the west coast from extrême west coast of southern British Columbia southward.

Very rare in eastern Canada but one of the notable songsters of our southwestern coast. It has the intimate, confiding attitude of the House Wren when in contact with civilization, but has a finer, more liquid voice. Altogether a very delightful bird to have around and as far as present reports go it does not seem to develop intolerance towards other species nesting in the vicinity.

718. **Carolina Wren.** LE RAILLEUR OU TROGLODYTE DE LA CAROLINE. *Thryothorus ludovicianus.* L, 5·50. The largest of our wrens and the reddest, the back approximating the red of the Brown Thrasher, of a lighter yet distinctly warm tint below.

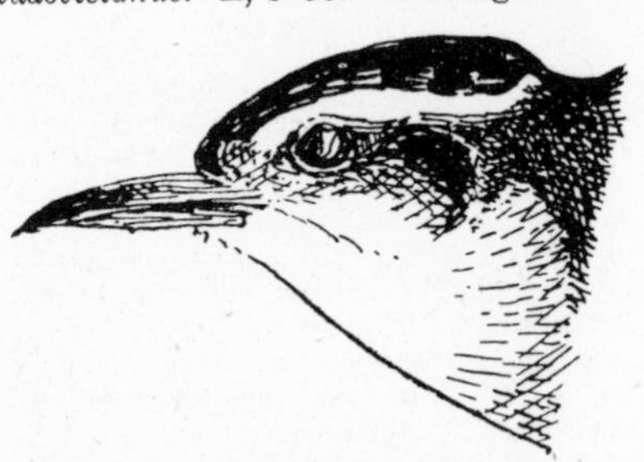

Figure 411
Carolina Wren; natural size.

*Distinctions.* Size, comparative redness of back, and the distinct light eyebrow-line are distinctive of this species.

*Field Marks.* The above distinctions make the best field marks. The Long-billed Marsh Wren has a similar eyebrow-line but size, general colour, and habitat will prevent confusion with it.

*Nesting.* In holes in trees or stumps or in nooks and crevices about buildings, in bulky nest of grasses, feathers, leaves, etc., lined with finer grasses, long hairs, etc.

*Distribution.* Eastern United States north intermittently into Canada in the western Lake Erie section. For a number of years the species was quite common on Pelee Point and on Pelee Island, but since 1913 it seems to have become rarer. Of irregular appearance in the southern peninsula of Ontario along Lake Erie. A winter as well as a summer resident, it appears, persists for a few years, and then vanishes again. All species seem constantly endeavouring to extend their ranges along the boundary of their normal habitats. They take advantage of a favourable cycle of years to extend, only to retract when the conditions in their natural swing turn unfavourable to them. Other species that show this cyclic fluctuation in Canada are the Cardinal, the Grasshopper Sparrow, the Dickcissel, Yellow-breasted Chat, and the Mockingbird.

*SUBSPECIES.* Of the three subspecies of Carolina Wren only one, the Northern Carolina Wren (le Railleur ou Troglodyte de la Caroline du Nord), the typical race, is to be expected in Canada.

The Carolina Wren is one of the finest singers of the family. The song is not continuous or long but it has a peculiar flute-like, liquid quality and is of striking beauty. The species is rare in Canada and its song is heard either regularly or occasionally in only a few localities.

*Economic Status.* Too rare in Canada to have any perceptible economic influence.

725. **Long-billed Marsh Wren.** LE RAILLEUR OU TROGLODYTE DES MARAIS. *Telmatodytes palustris.* L, 5·2. A richly coloured wren with dark brown, or almost black, mantle falling from hindneck over shoulders which are streaked with white; all remainder above brownish red; creamy white below, with flanks washed with light brown.

*Distinctions.* A wren with a streaked back and a uniformly coloured crown.

*Field Marks.* A wren inhabiting wet cat-tail or tule marsh, streaked on back, plain on crown, and with a decided eyebrow-line (Figure 412).

Figure 412
Long-billed Marsh Wren; natural size.

*Nesting.* Near the top of the reeds or rushes in wide, wet marshes; nest, a ball of dead cat-tail leaves, grass, or reeds. Unlike many other marsh-haunters this species is not attracted by marshes of small size. A swampy pool a few yards across attracts the Red-wing and perhaps a rail or two, but the Long-billed Marsh Wren demands a considerable area. An interesting trait of many of the wrens and well developed in this species is the habit of building numerous sham nests near the one really occupied. The use made of these nests is not known, but as many as eight or nine nests that can be reasonably attributed to the efforts of one pair may at times be found.

*Distribution.* United States and southern Canada. Across the Dominion.

*SUBSPECIES.* Four subspecies of this species are recognizable in Canada. The Eastern Marsh Wren (le Railleur ou Troglodyte des marais de l'Est) *Telmatodytes palustris palustris* extends west to the Great Lakes. The bird of Manitoba and west to the mountains is the Prairie Marsh Wren (le Railleur ou Troglodyte des marais des Prairies) *Telmatodytes palustris dissaëptus*, a lighter-coloured bird, especially on the back, where the dark cape is less continuous and the light browns tend toward ochre. The Western Marsh Wren (le Railleur ou Troglodyte des marais de l'Ouest) *Telmatodytes palustris plesius* inhabits the interior of British Columbia; it is like the prairie bird, but the breast is dirty greyish instead of white or washed with clear tawny. On the coast we have the Tule Marsh Wren (le Railleur ou Troglodyte des marais à joncs) *Telmatodytes palustris paludicola*, a generally much darker bird than any of the above. An Alberta Marsh Wren (le Railleur ou Troglodyte des marais de l'Alberta) *Telmatodytes palustris laingi* has been proposed in Saskatchewan and Alberta.

Wide, watery tule swamps or quaking bogs grown with cat-tails and reeds are the places to expect the Long-billed Marsh Wren. Here in the reedy tangle just above the water it climbs and creeps about, scolding occasionally but usually keeping well from sight. At a safe distance from the intruder it mounts a tall, solitary stalk to reconnoitre and then launches itself into the air some 10 or 15 feet and gurgles out a rippling, melodious little song as it gently sinks on fluttering wings to another station. This bubbling song of the Marsh Wren is one of the pleasantest characteristics of the marsh lands.

724. **Short-billed Marsh Wren.** LE RAILLEUR OU TROGLODYTE DES PRÉS. *Cistothorus stellaris.* L, 4. A very small wren; light below and decidedly streaked in wood-browns above and on crown.

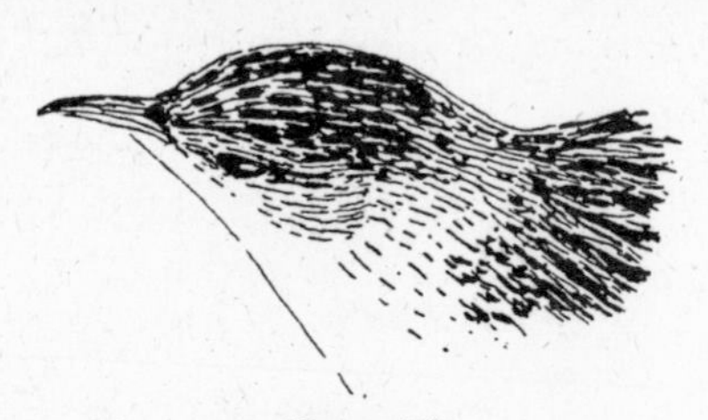

Figure 413
Short-billed Marsh Wren; natural size.

*Distinctions.* A small wren, sharply streaked above to crown (Figure 413).

*Field Marks.* A small wren with streaked back and crown, inhabiting dry marsh and grass.

*Nesting.* In dry marshes, amidst the grass. Nest a globular structure of green grasses, placed low down near the ground. Many false nests are built in the grass tops in the vicinity of the one occupied.

*Distribution.* Eastern North America. In Canada, the southern parts of the Dominion west to central Saskatchewan.

The Short-billed Marsh Wren is local and irregular in its distribution; it may be present one year in a locality and absent the next, and little is really known of its distribution in Canada. It frequents damp, grassy marshes rather than wet swamps and is usually found in little colonies. It is shy and difficult to find in its regular haunts, and its voice is entirely different from that of the Long-billed Marsh Wren with which it may occasionally be confused.

717. **Cañon Wren.** LE RAILLEUR OU TROGLODYTE DES CAÑONS. *Catherpes mexicanus.* L, 6. A rather large wren with very long, slender bill (Figure 414). Above, bright reddish brown changing to cinnamon on tail and greying on crown, finely speckled with minute black and white spots except on tail which is sharply barred with dark brown. Brown, extending below over abdomen, speckled or finely vermiculated with black; throat and breast white.

Figure 414
Bill of Cañon Wren; natural size.

*Distinctions.* The long, slender bill, warm, speckled, ruddy brown back, and white throat are diagnostic characters.

*Field Marks.* By habitat likely to be confused only with the Rock Wren, but of warm ruddy brown colour with conspicuous white throat instead of general dull dry-earthy hue. Its song, consisting chiefly of a regularly descending scale of clear, individual, whistled notes, is very distinctive.

*Nesting.* Like the Rock Wren in crevices of rocks and cliffs.

*Distribution.* Arid parts of United States and Mexico. In Canada known only in the southern Okanagan Valley of British Columbia.

*SUBSPECIES.* The form to be expected in Canada is the Northern Cañon Wren (le Railleur ou Troglodyte des cañons du Nord) *Catherpes mexicanus conspersus.*

The Cañon Wren is an unsurpassed rock-creeper. So high up the rocky canyon walls as hardly to be recognizable as a bird it creeps and runs across the rocky surfaces, indifferent as to whether they are horizontal, perpendicular, or overhanging. Occasionally it disappears into some cranny and remains in secret seclusion. At intervals it emerges and perching on the tip of some outstanding spur, only its white throat showing over the edge, it drops its clear staccato notes in rapid but unhurried succession. They bound and rebound from the rocky masses, echoing and re-echoing, and momentarily fill the valley with their liquid tones.

**715. Rock Wren.** LE RAILLEUR OU TROGLODYTE DES ROCHERS. *Salpinctes obsoletus.* L, 5·75. A large wren. Above, evenly greyish brown, greyer on head and approaching cinnamon on lower back and rump; dull whitish below; faintly streaked with brownish on breast.

*Distinctions.* Easily separated from any other wren by its general even, pale greyish or dry-earthy coloration variegated above by barely perceptible black and white arrow-head spots and suggestions of vermiculation. The tail broadly terminated with white or whitish, with sharply contrasting subterminal suffusion of brownish black (Figure 415) is very characteristic.

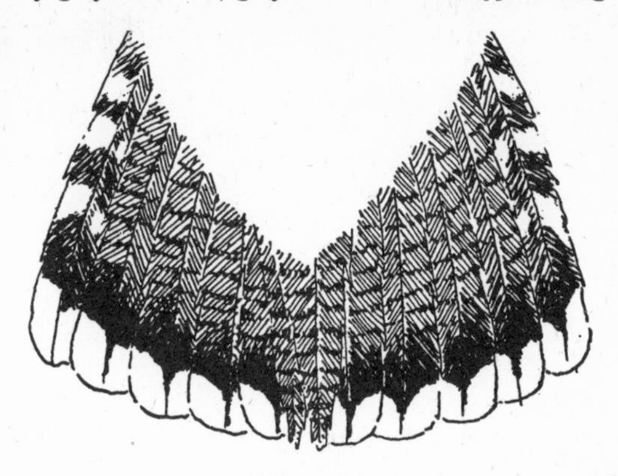

Figure 415
Tail of Rock Wren; natural size.

*Field Marks.* A large, dry-earth coloured wren inhabiting the most arid canyon faces and bad lands. Its song, far carrying and clear, quite unlike the bubbling confusion of the House or other familiar wrens, attracts attention immediately. It approaches to, and retreats before, the puzzled observer in the most baffling manner. Once a few of the infinite variety of their notes are learned, many unfamiliar, clear, or pearly notes will be attributed to this species.

*Nesting.* In crannies in rocks and cliffs, nest of sticks, grasses, wool, hair, and other soft materials. A peculiarity is that each nest entrance is approached by a little path paved with pebbles.

*Distribution.* Western North America. In Canada, the bad lands and rocky defiles of southern Saskatchewan, Alberta, and British Columbia.

*SUBSPECIES.* The form accredited to Canada is the "Common" or type race (le Railleur ou Troglodyte commun des rochers) *Salpinctes obsoletus obsoletus.*

The Rock Wren is the very spirit of the mysterious bad lands. Where canyon walls or coulée sides are broken, steep, and bare, where the mercury stands near the top of the tube, and not a drop of water can be found, the Rock Wren is at home. Stealing in and out of crevices, exploring cracks in the hot cliffs to their deepest extremity, the busy little midget never rests. Its voice can be heard here, there, and everywhere and when we attempt to steal closer it is gone to mock us from the next neighbouring canyon buttress.

### FAMILY—MIMIDAE. MOCKERS AND THRASHERS

The imitative faculty of the Mockingbird that has given the family its name is well developed in Canadian representatives. The family is peculiarly American and like many of the subdivisions of the order *Passeres* is difficult to diagnose in non-technical language. The birds are rather large. The Catbird is of even shades of stone-grey and the Brown Thrasher bright rufous brown above with heavily spotted whitish or creamy underparts and an unusually long full tail. They are both good mockers and diversify their song with imitations of all the common sounds around them, including the songs of other birds, and are capable of effects that are rarely equalled by the most famous songsters of either the New or Old World.

**703. Mockingbird.** LE GRAND MOQUEUR. *Mimus polyglottos.* L, 10·50. A large Catbird in appearance without black cap or red under the tail; almost white below and with large amounts of white in wing and tail (Figure 416).

Figure 416
Mockingbird; scale, ¼.

*Distinctions.* The above characters will separate the Mockingbird from the Catbird. It closely resembles the shrikes in coloration, but is without the conspicuous black patch across the eyes (*See* Plate LIV B).

*Field Marks.* General greyness and white patches on wing and tail with absence of black face mask.

*Nesting.* In thickets of coarse twigs and weed stalks in nests lined with rootlets and shreds of cotton.

*Distribution.* Southern United States north into Canada at the western end of Lake Erie. This is the only locality where the species has obtained what approaches an established foothold in Canada. A few pairs have been known to summer there for the last decade. Lately stray individuals have been seen in southern Manitoba, Saskatchewan, Alberta, and in southwestern British Columbia. Whether they will form permanent settlement there is yet to be seen (*See* remarks under Carolina Wren, page 320).

*SUBSPECIES.* The Mockingbird is divided into two forms. *Mimus polyglottos polyglottos*, the Eastern Mockingbird (le Grand Moqueur de l'Est), is the one occurring in the east. The Western Mockingbird (le Grand Moqueur de l'Ouest) *Mimus polyglottos leucopterus* is probably the one that has wandered to southern British Columbia. The subspecific identity of the prairie occurrences is doubtful.

The species is rare in Canada. It is very similar to the Catbird and most of what is said of that species applies with even greater force to the Mockingbird, for it is in many ways only a glorified Catbird and is probably the finest native singer in America.

**704. Catbird.** LE MERLE-CHAT. *Dumetella carolinensis.* L, 8·94. Plate LIV B. Evenly slate-grey all over except for a black cap and chestnut undertail-coverts.

*Distinctions.* Not likely to be mistaken for any other species. In spite of uniform greyness like the dipper an entirely different looking and acting bird—long and slender, with long tail and black cap. A brush-haunter with no particularly aquatic habits.

*Field Marks.* Even grey colour with black cap and sprightly habits. Its characteristic call, a cat-like "*Meouw,*" has given the bird its name. Another common note is like "*Ma-ry*" many times repeated and has suggested the homely name of Mary-bird. Its song is very fluent and easily distinguished from the similar one of the Brown Thrasher by its consisting of single phrases.

*Nesting.* In thickets or densely foliaged shrubs, nest of twigs, grasses, and leaves lined with rootlets.

*Distribution.* Most of temperate North America. In Canada, across the southern part of the Dominion west to the coast in southern British Columbia.

Though the acknowledged vocal inferior of the Mockingbird, the Catbird at its best rises to a high position as a songster, but there is much individual variation and while one bird may be of prima-donna rank, an excellent singer, the next may be quite ordinary in voice and performance. Much depends on the sounds it hears, as it is a mocker by disposition and inclination, and it takes the agonizing squeak of an ungreased wagon wheel or a rusty barn-door hinge as a model as readily as more agreeable sounds. But even with such parenthetic interpolations occasionally introduced the song of the Catbird is a remarkably fine performance when listened to with an understanding ear. Those to whom it has become endeared by association might not trade it for a more consistently perfect performance. A good Catbird song needs no excuse or apology. Its common plaintive inquiry for "*Ma-ry*" may become slightly exasperating when reiterated too close to the house. Its usual call-note like the mew of a cat, which it utters in the brush while curiously investigating the human intruder, is well known to most country frequenters, and seems to have aroused some slight illogical prejudice against it in the minds of its less experienced hearers.

It is a brush frequenter, and like many other species haunting such habitats from whence close observations can be made with a minimum of danger, its curiosity is well developed. It sits on some tall spray rising above the general tangle, its tail depressed and body held low to the perch, and pours forth its medley of song. Phrase follows phrase in rapid succession and snatches of all the bird songs of the neighbourhood appear intermixed with occasional harsher notes which are given with as much care and finish as the more melodious ones. When an intruder is detected approaching, the outpour stops with a sudden squeak, the tail flies up, and the bird comes to attention. After a moment's observation it drops to a lower level where, with safe tangle close at hand, it saucily investigates the approaching intruder, and, with expressive tail, wig-wags the results of its observations, presumably to a hiding mate. Finally it plunges into the tangle where, confident of security, it peers out at the disturber of its privacy through the many small openings between crisscrossed branches. Gradually it works closer and closer for a better view, hopping from perch to perch, alert, mewing and uttering low asides to the world in general and perhaps its mate in particular. Its remarks may be humorous and even sarcastic but never become caustic, and though the general bearing is saucy it never degenerates into impudence. When left to its own devices and at ease, the Catbird often hunches up and fluffs its feathers in a shady retreat within hearing distance of its incubating mate and carries on a long, low-toned monologue, every tone soft and throaty and altogether delicious. What it says then is impossible to translate and probably is none of our business.

*Economic Status.* The Catbird lives largely upon fruit in season, of which perhaps a third may be regarded as cultivated, but many insects are also taken. The fruits are small, soft varieties and it is very seldom, if ever, that perceptible damage is done.

705. **Brown Thrasher.** LA GRIVE ROUSSE. *Toxostoma rufum.* L, 11·42. Plate LV A. A large, reddish brown bird with long, sweeping tail. Uniform reddish above, creamy white below sharply striped with dark brown on breast and along flanks.

*Distinctions.* The Brown Thrasher with its red-brown back and sharply streaked breast has the general outward appearance of a thrush, but its large size, ruddiness of the brown, straw-coloured eye, and long tail are distinctive.

*Field Marks.* The bright red-brown back, sharply striped breast, long tail, and general carriage and habits.

*Nesting.* In thickets or on the ground, in nests of twigs, coarse rootlets, and leaves, lined with finer rootlets.

*Distribution.* Eastern United States. In Canada, across the southern parts of the Dominion west to Alberta.

The Brown Thrasher is probably the best common Canadian songster from Ontario westward.

Its song, very similar to that of the Song Thrush of Europe, is a succession of phrases like that of the Catbird, but without its occasional discordance and more liquid and mellow in tone. The notes are uttered close together and continue for several minutes, sometimes in great variety. Thoreau has translated some of them as "*Drop it—drop it—cover it up cover it up—pull it up, pull it up.*" The repetition of each variation is one of the peculiarities of the song of the Brown Thrasher, by which it may be distinguished from the Catbird.

This is also a bird of the thickets inhabiting open tangles, clumps of bushes in meadows, and the edges of woods and fence-rows. The thrasher is rather more retiring than the Catbird and is less easily induced to come into the home grounds.

*Economic Status.* A decidedly useful bird, over one-half of its food being injurious insects, beetles, caterpillars, grasshoppers, etc. The remainder is largely fruit, a small part of which is probably cultivated and is mostly raspberries. On the whole it does little damage and much good.

702. **Sage Thrasher.** LA GRIVE DES SAUGES. *Oreoscoptes montanus.* L, 8·00. Like a small, pale-coloured Brown Thrasher (*See* Plate LV A); back brownish ash instead of clear rufous-brown; in juvenility obscurely striped and feather-edged. Below, dull, creamy white, heavily and sharply spotted on throat, breast, and flanks with brown.

*Distinctions.* Like a Brown Thrasher but much smaller, and in general dry-earth tones, instead of clear rufous-brown, and with white tips to the outer tail feathers. The back usually shows a slight suggestion of streaking, that of the Brown Thrasher never does.

*Nesting.* In sage brush, nest of thorny sticks, slightly domed and lined with fine bark strips.

*Distribution.* Western United States, in arid sage-brush plains. In Canada known from the southern Similkameen and Okanagan Valleys. There is one record for southern Saskatchewan.

A bird of the hottest and driest sage-brush plains. Very shy and retiring and not to be seen except by the most enthusiastic and persistent student of birds.

## FAMILY—TURDIDAE. ROBINS, BLUEBIRDS, THRUSHES, ETC.

A nearly cosmopolitan family. Robins and bluebirds are familiar enough. The true thrushes are, in general, ground inhabiting birds; woody brown above, white below, usually with heavily dark-spotted breasts (Plates LVI B to LVIII A).

761. **American Robin.** LE MERLE D'AMÉRIQUE. *Turdus migratorius.* L, 10. Plate LV B. Almost too well known to require much description. Above, dark greyish brown, blackening on tail and head, and extending over face to throat where it is broken into short white dashes. All breast and abdomen pure brick-red. Young birds have breast spotted with black and flecked with dull white.

*Distinctions.* Size and full red breast distinguish the robin too well for mistake.

*Nesting.* Frequently in fruit or shade trees or about buildings. Nest of coarse grasses, leaves, rootlets, etc., with an inner cup of mud, lined with fine grasses.

*Distribution.* North America. In Canada across the Dominion, north to the limit of trees.

*SUBSPECIES.* Canadian robins are divided into eastern and western subspecies. The Eastern Robin (le Merle d'Amérique de l'Est) *Turdus migratorius migratorius* extends west to the mountains. The Western Robin (le Merle d'Amérique de l'Ouest) *Turdus migratorius propinquus* occurs in British Columbia. It is stated to have the white thumb-marks on the outer tail feathers reduced, and the black of the head extending down in a less decided cape over the back. These points are too inconstant, however, for certain individual identification and, as the Eastern Robin occurs throughout British Columbia, on migration at least, the distinctions are rather fine for popular recognition. A Northwestern Robin (le Merle d'Amérique du Nord-Ouest) *Turdus migratorius caurinus* has been proposed.

Of all the birds of North America there is none that comes into such close and intimate relationship with man as the robin. Its cheery voice

A. Bobolink; scale, $\frac{1}{3}$

Male Female

B. Meadowlark; scale, $\frac{1}{4}$

Eastern and Western Meadowlark, scarcely distinguishable in illustration

Plate LXXII

A. Yellow-headed Blackbird; scale, $\frac{1}{3}$

Male Female

B. Red-winged Blackbird; scale, $\frac{1}{3}$

Female Male

is looked for as the harbinger of spring; it often raises its brood under the same roof that shelters us; and is a constant frequenter of our lawns. Its song is the first sound heard in the grey morning and the last at darkening night. In the late autumn when it has stripped the berries from the rowan-trees and has disappeared, we know that winter is upon us. Though named after that famous Old World bird, it resembles the Robin Red-breast only superficially. It has a red breast and confiding habits, but in every other respect it is quite different. Visitors to this country sometimes rather resent our calling such a bird by the name of their childhood's favourite, until they, too, make new associations with it and take it to their hearts as do the native born. At any rate it must be remembered that it was originally named "Robin" by Englishmen in remembrance of old home scenes, and not by colonials in a spirit of substitution or imitation. In fact the American Robin has no need to imitate anything or anybody, and has on its own merits carved a place for itself in the affection of the North American people that needs neither excuse nor defence.

The spotted breast of the young robin is indicative of its thrush-like spotted ancestor. In fact all the members of the family show, in the younger stages at least, this same spotty character that is token of their common descent.

Probably the worst enemy of the robin is the domestic cat, the pet of the household. Building in readily accessible places the young Robins are subject to many disturbances, are often caused to leave the nest prematurely, and annually great numbers of them fall prey to the cat. The harm done this way is to our sensibilities rather than to the Robin as a species, for it is a strong and virile race and holds its own under many and varied conditions. Undoubtedly, sleek, well-fed cats are pleasant pets to have about, but so are Robins, and it sometimes takes the nicest adjustment of our sympathies to balance the scale between them. In general, we cannot have both cats and birds close about us, for only very rarely is it possible to teach a cat not to catch birds. The cat is an instinctive hunter, and catching birds is deeply ingrained in its nature. Of course a well-fed cat will not effect the same destruction as one that has to earn its living, but not even the best and fattest and laziest can resist the stealthy stalk, and rapid pounce, when the occasion offers, even though it afterwards refrains from eating its prey. The cat is essentially still a wild animal; it is with man but not of him, and has never yielded control to the human race as has the dog or the horse. It accepts what is offered in the way of physical comforts and takes as much more as it can get. It is, with all its purring grace, daintiness, and pretty ways, thoroughly selfish and seldom returns more than a tithe of the affection that may be lavished upon it. It is "The Cat that Walks Alone" and follows its wild instinct today as it did centuries ago before it discovered that man's hearth was warm and his protection and food agreeable. In return it gives unconsciously all it has to offer, its beauty, grace, and playfulness. As a destroyer of vermin on an important scale it is a failure. In campaigns against rodent carriers of disease it was found wanting. At the best it only reduces the superabundance of mice or rats and never clears the place of them. A few traps intelligently set are much more effective than many cats.

Of course cat-lovers are as much entitled to their pets as are bird-lovers, but they should be required to take proper care of them. Humanitarians should not be offended by the sight of half-starved hunters, with their gaunt sides and evident misery, rustling for a living, nor should these cats in their necessity be allowed to devastate bird coverts. The elimination of these neglected cats would merit a vote of thanks from the Robin population and should win the approval of real cat-lovers.

*Economic Status.* Though the Robin is an efficient aid to the agriculturist, its fondness for fruit occasionally gets it into trouble with the raiser of small fruit. Forty-two per cent of its food is animal, mostly insects, the remainder is composed largely of berries and other soft, small fruits, of which little more than 4 per cent is cultivated fruit.

763. **Varied Thrush.** OREGON ROBIN, WOOD ROBIN. PAINTED ROBIN. LE MERLE VARIÉ. *Ixoreus naevius.* L, 10. Plate LVI A. About the size of a robin and very robin-like in general appearance, but strikingly unlike in details of colour. Like a robin with sharp, black breast-bar, reddish eyebrow-line, wing-bars, and spots on flight feathers.

*Distinctions.* A breast slightly pale, tawny-red, black breast bar (quite dull in female), distinct light eyebrow streak, and bars and spots on wing. Not to be mistaken for any other species.

*Field Marks.* A robin variegated as above.

*Nesting.* In bushes and small trees, nest of moss, sticks, twigs, and rotten wood.

*Distribution.* Western North America. In Canada, British Columbia, and the Yukon, east to the Mackenzie, and adjacent parts of Alberta. Occasional east to Manitoba.

*SUBSPECIES.* The Varied Thrush of British Columbia and northward toward Alaska is the Pacific Varied Thrush (le Merle varié du Pacifique) *Ixoreus naevius naevius.* That of Mackenzie Valley has been described as the Northern Varied Thrush (le Merle varié du Nord) *Ixoreus naevius meruloides,* distinguished by some slight colour differences.

755. **Wood Thrush.** LA GRIVE DES BOIS. SONG THRUSH. *Hylocichla mustelina.* L, 8·29. Plate LVI B.

*Distinctions.* Easily recognized as a thrush, though having somewhat the general colour of the Brown Thrasher; smaller size, short tail, straight bill, and dark instead of light eye make good separation marks. From the other members of the genus it can be told by its larger size, the absolute whiteness of the breast, the sharper definition of the round spots, and the yellowish rather than reddish or olive tinge of the back, brightest on head.

*Field Marks.* The sharp spots on the pure white breast and the tawniness of the back make the best field marks.

*Nesting.* In saplings about 8 feet above the ground, in nest of leaves, rootlets, fine twigs, and weed stalks firmly interwoven and lined with mud and fine rootlets.

*Distribution.* Eastern North America; north regularly to southern Ontario; occasional or local in adjoining regions.

The Wood Thrush is a woodland bird of rather southern distribution: common in Canada only in the more southern portions.

759. **Hermit Thrush.** LA GRIVE SOLITAIRE. *Hylocichla guttata.* L, 7·17. Plate LVII A. Even tawny brown all above, except tail that is distinctly dull red or rusty; below, white, breast heavily spotted with brown.

*Distinctions and Field Marks.* Has the heavily spotted breast of the Grey-cheeked and Olive-backed, and may easily be told from any other thrush by its tail being decidedly redder than the back.

*Field Marks.* A thrush with heavily spotted breast and its tail redder than the back.

*Nesting.* On the ground in nest of moss, coarse grass, and leaves, lined with rootlets and pine needles.

*Distribution.* Northern North America and mountains of western United States. In Canada, across the Dominion, north to tree limits.

*SUBSPECIES.* A number of subspecies of Hermit Thrushes are recognized, three of these occurring regularly in Canada. The Eastern Hermit Thrush (la Grive solitaire de l'Est) *Hylocichla guttata faxoni* occurs west to the mountains, crossing them in the north into northern British Columbia and the Yukon. The Sierra Hermit Thrush (la

Grive solitaire des sierras) *Hylocichla guttata sequoiensis* is the bird of southern interior British Columbia. It is as large as the eastern bird, but slightly more olive above and greyer below with less ochraceous suggestion on flanks. West of the Coast Range occurs the Dwarf Hermit Thrush (la Grive solitaire naine) *Hylocichla guttata nanus*, which is decidedly smaller and redder. The Alaska Hermit Thrush (la Grive solitaire de l'Alaska) *Hylocichla guttata guttata*, the type form—for this is one of the few species known first to science from the west—is a subspecies of the Alaskan coast occurring in western British Columbia on migration. It is slightly more olivaceous than the Sierra Thrush and as small as the Dwarf. Audubon's Hermit Thrush has been accredited to southern interior British Columbia, but its occurrence there has not been verified and is almost certainly an error.

The Hermit Thrush is most notable for its song. Some authorities of world-wide experience have even said it has the purest and most perfect song of any bird. However true that may be, and however many favourite songsters other parts of the world may produce, this species has a purity and richness of tone, and a perfection of execution that are equalled by few other species.

758. **Olive-backed Thrush.** SWAINSON'S THRUSH. LA GRIVE À DOS OLIVE. *Hylocichla ustulata.* L, 7·17. Plate LVII B. Even tawny olive over all back; below, white, with breast heavily spotted with brown.

*Distinctions.* Separated from Wilson's Thrush by the heavy, instead of very light, breast spotting, and more olive cast to back; from the Hermit Thrush, by the tail being evenly coloured like the back instead of distinctly redder. Most like the Grey-cheeked Thrush, from which it is best separated by the distinctly tawny or ochraceous cast to the cheeks, even to showing a distinct eye-ring, and the similar tone to the breast spotting and flanks.

*Field Marks.* A thrush with tail same colour as the back, breast heavily spotted, and cheeks tawny or ochraceous instead of greyish.

*Nesting.* In bushes or small trees, in nest of mosses, coarse grasses, leaves, and bark, lined with rootlets and grass.

*Distribution.* North and South America. In Canada, across the Dominion, north through the northern spruce belt, but not as far north as the next species.

*SUBSPECIES.* Unusually enough this species was first described from the west coast, and the type race is the Russet-backed Thrush (la Grive à dos roux) *Hylocichla ustulata ustulata*, of the region west of the Cascades and the Coast Range. As its name implies, it is ruddier, less olive, the throat is more strongly suffused with ochre, and the spotting is not so strong as in the Eastern Olive-backed Thrush (la Grive à dos olive de l'Est) *Hylocichla ustulata swainsoni* that occupies the range eastward.

The next most common thrush to Wilson's; on the coast the prevailing one at low altitudes, but elsewhere summering more northerly or at higher altitudes. It has a rich, full song only slightly inferior to that of the Hermit Thrush.

757. **Grey-cheeked Thrush.** LA GRIVE À JOUES GRISES. *Hylocichla minima.* L, 7·58. Plate LVII B. Even, greyish olive over all back; below, white, with breast heavily spotted with brown.

*Distinctions.* Separated from Wilson's Thrush by the heavy instead of very light breast spotting and more olive cast to back; from the Hermit Thrush by the tail being evenly coloured with the back instead of distinctly redder. Most like the Olive-backed Thrush, from which it is best separated by the greyer cast to the cheeks in which there is little, if any, tawny, or suggestion of eye-ring, and a greyer tone to the breast spotting and flanks.

*Field Marks.* A thrush with tail same colour as back, breast heavily spotted and cheeks greyish.

*Nesting.* In low bushes or on the ground; nest bulky, compact, composed largely of mosses.

*Distribution.* Northern North America. In Canada, west to the mountains, north to the tree limits, rare on the prairies, a more northern species than the previous one.

*SUBSPECIES.* There are two varieties of this species; Bicknell's Thrush (la Grive de Bicknell) *Hylocichla minima minima* in the extreme east, breeding at higher elevations in New England and in the Maritime Provinces; Common Grey-cheeked Thrush (la Grive commune à joues grises) *Hylocichla minima aliciae,* breeding at the northern tree limit across the continent.

This thrush is likely to be confused with the Olive-backed. It is rather northern in its breeding and usually quite rare through most of its migrating range in southern Canada.

**756. Wilson's Thrush.** VEERY. CATHEDRAL-BIRD. LA GRIVE DE WILSON. *Hylocichla fuscescens.* L, 7·52. Plate LVIII A. Even, brown-tawny above; white below, with fine, blended arrowhead-spots running down from corners of mouth and spreading across chest.

*Distinctions.* The lightest tawny of our thrushes, with only the slightest suggestion of olive in the back. The faintness of the breast spotting will separate it from any comparable species.

*Field Marks.* The even, light coloration of the back and the light, suffused breast spots. The only thrush whose song begins on a high note and ends on low ones.

*Nesting.* On or near the ground, in nest of strips of bark, rootlets, and leaves, wrapped with leaves and lined with rootlets.

*Distribution.* Southern Canada and northern United States. In Canada, across the Dominion, including the southern halves of the Prairie Provinces, and southern British Columbia exclusive of the coast.

*SUBSPECIES.* Two subspecies are recognized in Canada. The eastern form, the Veery (la Grive de Wilson) *Hylocichla fuscescens fuscescens,* extends west probably to near the Manitoba border and perhaps across it. From there westward the Willow Thrush (la Grive des saules) *Hylocichla fuscescens salicicola* is the prevailing bird. It is slightly more olive on the back and the breast streaks average darker. The distinctions, however, are very slight and of little interest to the general observer.

Wilson's Thrush is the only thrush generally distributed in breeding season throughout well-settled parts of the country. In southern Canada wherever there is enough bush land to attract thrushes this species is present. Its song is a descending series of short, connected trills, "*Ree-a-ree-a-ree*"; some eight or ten syllables falling about an octave and with a tone like the jingling of a golden chain. Heard at sunset, with the mysterious darkening woods seen against the glorious skies, it has a particularly beautiful and peaceful appeal. It may not have the absolute perfection of the song of the Hermit Thrush or even of the Olive-backed and Grey-cheeked, but it is wonderfully delightful.

**766. Red-breasted Bluebird.** EASTERN BLUEBIRD. L'OISEAU-BLEU À POITRINE ROUGE. *Sialia sialis.* L, 7·01. Plate LVIII B. Above, from crown to tail including face, deep sky-blue, throat, breast, and flanks chestnut-red. Females: similar but duller; juveniles with back largely dark brown with many white flecks, throat spotted with rich brown and white, and the blue only showing strongly on wings and tail.

*Distinctions.* A solidly blue-backed bird with red throat, breast, and flanks. The Western Bluebird is similar but is a more purplish blue, and the throat is blue as well as the crown. The Mountain Bluebird is a much paler blue, but is also blue on the breast. Adult Bluebirds of this species are, therefore, easily recognized. Females with more or less red on breast are to be confused only with the Western female, the latter, however, has a distinctly grey throat. The breast of the female Mountain Bluebird is dull, light grey-ochre without any hint of red. Juveniles lately from the nest are easily known from those of the Mountain Bluebird by the darker tone of the blue on wings and tail, it being dark sky-blue instead of pale blue. Probably sometimes with difficulty separated from the young Western Bluebird, as the colouring of the blue at this age is practically the same in both species. The latter, however, has a suggestion of grey on throat. In practice, however, it is not likely that the Eastern species will ever be confused with the Western as their ranges are not known to overlap.

*Field Marks.* A blue-backed bird with solid reddish throat, breast, and flanks. In young birds distinguished from the Mountain Bluebird by the deeper tone of the blue, most strongly suggested on wings and tail.

*Nesting.* In hollow trees, posts, or stubs or in artificial nest boxes; nest of grasses.

*Distribution.* Temperate eastern North America. In Canada, across the southern part of the Dominion commonly to Manitoba, more rarely in Saskatchewan.

*SUBSPECIES.* The bluebird of eastern North America is the type form the Eastern Bluebird (l'Oiseau-bleu de l'Est) *Sialia sialis sialis.*

With the Robin and the Meadowlark in the spring comes the Bluebird, its brilliant coat shining like a jewel against the dead grass landscape, and its low, flowing warble giving promise of pleasant days. In the summer it nests freely in the bird-boxes in the garden, the fence-post out in the fields, or the old deserted flicker-hole in the telegraph pole by the wayside. In autumn its musical little warble is forgotten and it confines itself to a low voiced *"Purity-purity,"* usually heard coming mournfully down from birds passing high overhead and telling of the passing of summer.

*Economic Status.* The Bluebird feeds mainly upon insects and is, therefore, highly beneficial. Weed seeds form an important part of its food and it eats some soft fruit, but practically no cultivated kind is taken. Hence the bluebird may be regarded as a consistently useful bird.

767. **Chestnut-backed Bluebird.** L'OISEAU-BLEU À DOS MARRON. *Sialia mexicana.* L, 7. Plate LIX A. Spring male: above from crown to tail, including face and throat, intense, deep purplish blue; more or less complete bar of chestnut across back and shoulders. Breast and flanks rich chestnut-red. Abdomen dull blue lightening to white under tail. Female: similar but duller and blue of throat replaced with slate-grey. Juveniles have back largely dark brown with many white flecks. Underparts spotted with rich brown and white. Throat slightly greying in general tone. Blue showing strongly only on wings and tail.

*Distinctions.* A solidly blue-backed bird with more or less chestnut bar across shoulders and back, a blue throat, and red breast. Most like the Eastern Bluebird, but with blue throat instead of red, and the blue deeper and more purplish. The Mountain Bluebird is much paler blue and is solidly and completely blue. Adult Western Bluebirds are, therefore, easily recognized. Females with more or less red on breast are to be confused only with the Eastern Bluebird, but have a slate-grey throat. Juveniles lately from the nest are easily known from those of the Mountain Bluebird by the deeper blue on wings and tail, but probably with difficulty separated from the young Eastern Bluebird as the colouring at this age is practically the same; the Western bird, however, has usually a suggestion of grey tone on the throat. In practice, it is not likely that the Western will ever be confused with the Eastern as their ranges are not known to overlap.

*Field Marks.* A bluebird with a red breast and blue throat. Young birds recognized from the Mountain Bluebird by the deeper tone of the blue suggested on wings and tail.

*Nesting.* In woodpecker-holes or natural hollows in stubs. It takes kindly to nesting boxes.

*Distribution.* Western North America. In Canada, southern British Columbia. The common bluebird of the southwest coast.

*SUBSPECIES.* The Western Bluebird (l'Oiseau-bleu de l'Ouest), *Sialia mexicana occidentalis,* is the Canadian form of the species.

In general habit and appearance so like the Eastern Bluebird as to require no special discussion.

768. **Mountain Bluebird.** ARCTIC BLUEBIRD. L'OISEAU-BLEU DES MONTAGNES. *Sialia currucoides.* L, 7. Plate LIX B. Spring male: all solid, metallic, light sky-blue, paling on head and breast. Lower abdomen white. Female: with blue very much reduced; head and back with blue veiled with ashy grey; underparts pale brownish ash, strongest on face and throat; blue showing clearly only on wings and tail. Juveniles lately from nest almost identical with parallel plumage of Eastern and Western Bluebirds.

*Distinctions.* The all-blueness of the adult male is unlike any other Canadian bird except the Indigo Bunting. It is considerably larger and has a thrush-like instead of a sparrow bill. Females are distinctive from either of the other bluebirds by the absence of reddish on breast. Juveniles may be recognized by the paleness of the blue suggested on wings and tail.

*Field Marks.* An all-blue bird, markedly larger than the Indigo Bunting. Females: soft, light ashy birds with blue on tail, rump, and wings. Juveniles: brownish ashy, with ashy and light brown spotted or striped breast, and strong blue suffusions on wings and tail.

*Nesting.* In old woodpecker-holes and cavities in stubs and cliffs or artificial nesting boxes.

*Distribution.* Western North America. In Canada from the west coast east to Manitoba, north to the Yukon and Mackenzie Valley.

The Mountain Bluebird, a beautiful bird, has been extending east of late and is now well established more or less commonly as far as central Manitoba. It has all the pretty ways and habits of the Eastern Bluebird, but is more cerulean in its coloration. A famous writer has described the Eastern Bluebird as "The sky above, the earth beneath" referring to the blue back and red breast. Following this figure of speech, the Mountain Bluebird is purely celestial with no earthy contamination. It is at home in all kinds of places. In the tree plantations about the prairie homes it will build in the hollow cornices of the buildings or in any kind of a rough box put up for it, in dead stubs at the edge of the prairie bluffs or in old flicker-holes in telegraph poles by the roadside. Even in the austere and repellent, raw-banked coulées of the wildest bad lands it can be found adapting crannies in the rocks and cliffs to its use. Its only requirement seems to be nesting holes and it makes little difference where they are so long as they will shelter a nest.

765. **Wheatear.** LE TRAQUET MOTTEUX. *Oenanthe oenanthe.* L, 7·01. A titlark-like bird, light grey above. Male: white below, warmed with buff colour on throat; a black band through the eye and a white rump (Figure 417). The female and juvenile are similar, but duller and more buff or rust coloured and without the sharp black face patch.

Figure 417
Wheatear (male); about natural size.

*Distinctions.* The conspicuous and extensive white rump with the general colorations given above are distinctive.

*Field Marks.* With its showy white rump the bird looks like a partly albino Titlark.

*SUBSPECIES.* The subspecies of Wheatear that occurs in eastern Canada is the Greenland Wheatear (le Traquet motteux Groenlandais) *O.o. leucorhoa.*

This is a European bird of regular occurrence in Greenland, the eastern Arctic islands, and in the adjacent parts of Ungava Peninsula, but of only casual or accidental occurrence elsewhere in Canada.

754. **Townsend's Solitaire.** LE SOLITAIRE DE TOWNSEND. *Myadestes townsendi.* L, 8. Plate LX A. A little smaller than a robin. Nearly solidly grey or brownish grey, with outer tail feathers largely white; semi-concealed tawny spots on flight feathers. The body-feathers of young birds shortly from nest have large white centre spots and dark borders, producing an effect of a suit of silver scales.

*Distinctions.* More like a catbird than anything else it is likely to be confused with, but without black cap or chestnut undertail-coverts; grey brownish instead of slaty, and large amount of white in outer tail feathers. A fine white circle about the eye and the tawny spots on the flight feathers make the species very distinctive. The Dipper is a solidly grey bird of about similar size, but has a short, stubby tail and none of the above distinctive details.

*Field Marks.* A quiet acting, comparatively large, dull-grey bird with considerable white on the outer edges of the tail. Looks more like a female or juvenile bluebird than anything else, but larger, without any vague breast striping, no glint of blue anywhere, a long, ample tail, and actions somewhat like a flycatcher. In flight the tawny wing patches are quite conspicuous.

*Nesting.* In hollow under bank, crannies in rock, or upturned root. Nest of sticks, weeds, and waste vegetation lined with rootlets.

*Distribution.* Western North America. In Canada, British Columbia north through the Yukon, east to the Alberta foothills and very occasionally to Saskatchewan and Manitoba.

A bird typical of the high mountain solitudes, well named Solitaire. Its unobtrusive dull grey colour, glorious song, and romantic habitat and name, surround it with an air of mystery that piques the imagination.

## FAMILY—SYLVIIDAE. OLD-WORLD WARBLERS, KINGLETS, AND GNATCATCHERS

An Old World family represented in America by only a few species. Of these, the Old World Warblers, not to be confused with our Wood Warblers, do not occur in Canada; the kinglets are represented by two species, the gnatcatchers by one.

### Subfamily—Polioptilinae. Gnatcatchers

A small family composed of only one genus and peculiar to America. The colour is in soft bluish ash and white. The bill is superficially warbler-like but the first primary feather of the wing is small and almost aborted, being considerably less than half as long as the next, as is the case with the Warbling Vireo. Only one species occurs in Canada.

751. **Blue-grey Gnatcatcher.** LE GOBE-MOUCHES GRIS-BLEU. *Polioptila cœrulea.* L, 4·05. All even bluish grey above, wings dark, and tail black, the outer tail feathers white; below and face all white. Male has black line across forehead and over eye (Figure 418).

*Distinctions.* The small size, even blue and white coloration, and the short first wing quill are diagnostic.

*Field Marks.* Inhabiting tree tops so high up that the colours are usually difficult to make out, the outline, with long narrow tail switched about much in the manner of the Redstart, and the characteristic rather hoarse call-notes make the best recognition marks.

Figure 418
Blue-grey Gnatcatcher; about natural size.

*Nesting.* Nest of tendrils, fine strips of bark, and fine grasses firmly interwoven and covered outside with spiderweb and lichens. It is chimney-like in shape, high with straight sides, and is one of the most beautiful American bird nests.

*Distribution.* Southeastern United States north to the Canadian border along Lake Erie and Detroit River.

*SUBSPECIES.* The eastern subspecies, the Eastern Gnatcatcher (le Gobe-mouches de l'Est) *Polioptila cœrulea cœrulea*, is the typical form. A western subspecies occurs in the southwestern states.

This is a bird of the large tree forests where it usually lives and builds high up among the tree tops. As it is only regularly found in southern Ontario along western Lake Erie and has been taken elsewhere in Canada only occasionally, it must be regarded as a rare bird in the Dominion.

*Economic Status.* Too rare in Canada to be economically considered.

### Subfamily—Regulinae. Kinglets

*General Description.* The Kinglets are, next to the rare Bush Tit and the hummingbirds, the smallest of Canadian birds. They are wren-like in their short, round bodies, but more like chickadees in their habits and actions. Their colours are dull olive-green, lighter below, and they have small, brilliantly coloured crown-spots of red, orange, or yellow. The bill is small and straight, similar to but not as stout as that of the chickadees (Plate LX B, compare with Plate LI).

*Distinctions.* The kinglets might be mistaken for some of the dull, evenly coloured warblers, but as all plumages except the female and juvenile Ruby-crowned have brilliant crown patches, this will usually prevent confusion, and size should do so in any event.

*Field Marks.* Dull greenish coloration, chickadee-like restlessness, and custom of hanging head downward from pendant sprays are characteristic. Their fine, sharp conversational *"Tsee-tsee-tsee's"* soon become familiar and are easily recognized.

748. **Golden-crowned Kinglet.** GOLDEN-CRESTED WREN. GOLDCREST. LE ROITELET À COURONNE DORÉE. *Regulus satrapa.* L, 4·07. Plate LX B. Diminutive birds, yellowish green above, dull white below. Crown black with large central spot of lemon-yellow or lemon-yellow and orange. Face showing prominent white eyebrow-line against black edge of crown. Juveniles have the characteristic face mark, but are without coloured spot on crown.

*Distinctions.* The two kinglets, so nearly alike in size and general coloration, can generally be easily separated by the colours of the crowns. When crown-spots are absent the presence of the white eyebrow and black crown streaks on the face are distinctive.

*Field Marks.* Very small, chickadee-like birds, often in flocks flitting in and out of the foliage, sometimes up high in the largest trees. Dull, even greenish coloration. The yellow or yellow and orange crown-spots and the black and white eyebrow-lines are the best field marks for the species.

*Nesting.* Generally in coniferous trees. Nest pensile, of green mosses, lined with fine strips of soft inner bark, fine rootlets, and feathers.

*Distribution.* Northern North America. In Canada, across the Dominion, north to Lake Athabaska and northern British Columbia; rare in the mid-prairie parts.

*SUBSPECIES.* The Eastern Golden-crowned Kinglet (le Roitelet à couronne dorée de l'Est) *Regulus satrapa satrapa* extends west probably to the mountains. In British Columbia and the adjacent mountain slopes in Alberta occurs the Western Golden-crowned (le Roitelet à couronne dorée de l'Ouest) *Regulus satrapa olivaceus*, showing a slightly intenser green above.

After long, birdless hunting, one may often be surrounded by a large flock of these feathered mites, flitting in and out of the dense foliage and darting hither and thither so restlessly as to make it difficult to see distinctive points. They seem indifferent to the observer's presence and yet more or less attracted to it. Some hang head downward from a swaying bunch of twigs, without regard to horizontal or perpendicular, as they gravely investigate the under surfaces for succulent morsels, and others work in and out on the trunks and branches surveying every crevice with microscopic eye and keeping up a continual interchange of fine, sharp *"Tse-tse-tse's."* For a minute the observer is kept looking this way and that, hardly getting his eye on a bird before his attention is distracted to the next in a most disconcerting manner. Suddenly the confusion grows less, the foliage is empty—the happy crowd has worked away.

PLATE LXXIII

A. Baltimore Oriole; scale, $\frac{1}{3}$

Male Female

B. Bullock's Oriole; scale, $\frac{1}{3}$

Male Female

A. Brewer's Blackbird; scale $\frac{1}{3}$

Male Female

B. Bronzed Grackle; scale, $\frac{1}{4}$

749. **Ruby-crowned Kinglet.** RUBY-CROWNED WREN. LE ROITELET À COURONNE RUBIS. *Corthylio calendula.* L, 4·07. Plate LX B. Diminutive birds like the Golden-crowned Kinglet; yellowish green above; dull white below. Crown of male with spot of bright red. No face marks except a vague lightening about the eye.

*Distinctions.* The two kinglets, so nearly alike in general colour and size, may be easily separated by the crown and face coloration. The crown-spot of this species is bright red instead of yellow or yellow and orange, and the face never shows a distinct eyebrow stripe or marking other than a dull lightening about the eye.

*Field Marks.* Very small, chickadee-like birds, often in flocks in dense foliage. Dull, even greenish coloration, with evenly coloured face vaguely lightening about eye to a faint, interrupted eye-ring; without eyebrow stripe; with or without bright red crown patch. It will be noted that the Ruby-crowned has the habit of fluttering its wings occasionally during momentary pauses in its movement, which is not shared by the Golden-crowned. This, though not an absolute proof of identity, will often suggest the species.

*Nesting.* In coniferous trees; nest of moss and fine strips of bark neatly interwoven and lined with feathers—usually semi-pensile.

*Distribution.* Northern North America. In Canada, across the Dominion, north to the limit of trees.

*SUBSPECIES.* The Eastern Ruby-crowned Kinglet (le Roitelet à couronne rubis de l'Est) *Regulus calendula calendula* extends west to the east slope of the Coast Range in British Columbia. West of this, on the coast, is the Sitka Kinglet (le Roitelet de Sitka) *Regulus calendula grinnelli*, of a slightly warmer buff below; and the green above lighter and more extensive.

This species is so nearly like the Golden-crowned Kinglet that little further discussion of either habits or economic status is necessary. Its song, however, is one of nature's surprises and warrants special mention. It is so loud and clear and full throated that one can but wonder at so much volume proceeding from such a tiny being. It vies in strength and carrying power with that of the Purple Finch, and when first heard is likely to be ascribed to some of the larger sparrows. A very characteristic song may be rendered—"*Peedle-edle-edle-edle - - - Wheedle-wheedle*"—preceded by a low, preliminary warble. The last words are accented and loud and ringing, the first are lower and without pronounced carrying power. Like that of other species the song of this Kinglet seems subject to numerous local variations.

*Economic Status.* The kinglets are so largely insect-eaters that they may be looked upon as most beneficial. They are small, but their numbers, when they occur, more than make up for their small size, and what is said of the chickadee in this respect applies equally well to them.

### FAMILY—MOTACILLIDAE. MEADOW WAGTAILS AND PIPITS

A family of chiefly Old World distribution that may be defined for recognition in Canada as gregarious ground birds with warbler-like bills and long hind claw (Figure 419). They are most like the Horned Lark in general outline and habit, but are slenderer and lighter in build and of a more earthy colour. There are but two species to consider in Canada.

697. **American Pipit.** TITLARK. LE PIPIT D'AMÉRIQUE. *Anthus spinoletta.* L, 6·38. A ground-coloured and ground-haunting bird; bill very warbler-like but longer, hind claw elongated like that of the longspur and the Horned Lark (Figure 419, compare with Figure 399, page 297). Adult (in highest spring plumage): greyish above, purest on head and growing slightly olive on rump; back faintly mottled with dark feather centres; pinkish buff below, with sparse, fine breast stripes of brownish grey, tending to form a necklace across breast and extending along flanks; wings brown with faded feather edges. This is rather an exceptional plumage, the one most often seen even in spring is evenly dull olive slightly mottled above; buffy white below with diffuse and more or less aggregated spots descending sides of throat and extending across breast and along flanks.

*Distinctions.* The fine warbler-like bill, together with the long hind claw, are distinctive. The only other birds with such a claw are the Horned Larks and the Lapland Longspur, but the horns of the one (Figure 399, page 297) and the sparrow-like bill of the other make differentiation as a pipit simple. Separated from Sprague's Pipit by its practically uniform grey or dull olive back, and by its ruddy, or dull-buffy, instead of creamy, colour below.

Figure 419
Bill and foot of American Pipit; long hind claw.

Figure 420
American Pipit; natural size.

*Field Marks.* A ground-coloured bird, seen in the open in settled parts of Canada in the spring and autumn, often in large scattered flocks like the Snow Bunting and Horned Lark. Its even coloration, constant habit of tail dipping, and the conspicuous white outer tail feathers are good field marks from all species except Sprague's Pipit. Its gregariousness and its habitat of bare ground, sand dunes, or mud flats are good guides to identity.

*Nesting.* On the ground in nest of grasses.

*Distribution.* Northern North America, west Greenland, and eastern Siberia, breeding from the Arctics south to the limit of trees.

A spring and late autumn migrant, occurring sometimes in large flocks and feeding in open meadows, ploughed fields, or on dry, sandy uplands and shores. On its breeding grounds it has the skylark-like habit of mounting and singing high in the air and descending in a perpendicular dive, like a falling stone.

*Economic Status.* Coming as it does when the fields are bare, and returning after the harvest, its food is necessarily confined to weed seeds and early or belated insects. Its effect must be beneficial.

700. **Sprague's Pipit.** AMERICAN SKYLARK. MISSOURI SKYLARK. LE PIPIT DE SPRAGUE. *Anthus spraguei.* L, 6·50. A generally dry-earth coloured Pipit, streaked and variegated above with brown and creamy ochres; below even, creamy ochre, slightly warmer on breast where it is somewhat sharply streaked with brown.

*Distinctions.* Dull, soft coloration in simple design; warbler-like bill and long hind toe as a Pipit. Streaked or variegated above as Sprague's.

*Field Marks.* In life, not likely to be confused with its closest relative the American Pipit as it is a grass-haunter seldom seen when on the ground, and does not gather in flocks. As it rises from the grass it is more like a female longspur or, because of its simple white outer tail feathers, a Vesper Sparrow. However, it has an entirely different habit of flight and instead of alighting shortly it is more likely to climb into the upper air and vanish overhead.

*Nesting.* On the ground in domed nest of grass.

*Distribution.* Interior plains of North America. In Canada breeding in the prairie regions from Manitoba to Alberta north to the edge of the northern woodlands.

The Song of Sprague's Pipit is unmistakable. Flitting around in wide circles, so high in the air as to be an all but invisible speck, it repeats over and over again in a thin sweet voice its simple little song. A "*Ching,-ring,-ring,-ring,-ring,-ring,-ring,-ring*" on a steadily descending scale, dropping about an octave in all, and lasting about five seconds. This may be repeated a hundred times or more with only a few seconds' interval between. Sometimes it keeps steadily at it for twenty minutes, then it comes to earth in a straight dive like a falling stone and vanishes from sight in the short grassy covering of the prairie. It has much the sound of a very distant Wilson's Thrush song, but is longer, less rich, and silver rather than golden in tone. Some say this flight song is the equal of, or even superior to, that of the famous skylark of Europe. Needless to say these are not Europeans but North Americans who have earnestly tried to be impartial. Born Englishmen are just as emphatic the other way, which all goes to illustrate how much early associations and traditions mingle with our enjoyments, and that the native-born hears in familiar bird songs that which the expatriate can rarely appreciate in full. To those born to them the bagpipes make satisfying and inspiring music, and in those who were raised to them, the soft warble of the bluebird, the monotonous recitative of the robin, and even the thin wiry song of Sprague's Pipit coming down from the clouds on the sere, broad prairies, touch a chord that may not be stirred by the most glorious foreign songsters of the avian chorus.

## FAMILY—BOMBYCILLIDAE. WAXWINGS

The waxwings are striking birds, distributed over the northern parts of both the New and Old Worlds. They are represented in America by two species, so nearly alike and so well characterized in form and colour that family description here is unnecessary. There is remarkably little seasonal or sex variation and Figure 421 designates them plainly. The shafts of the secondaries and sometimes those of the tail are enlarged at the tips into brilliantly coloured appendages having a close resemblance to bits of red sealing-wax.

Figure 421
Family details of Waxwings.

618. **Bohemian Waxwing.** WANDERING CHATTERER. LE JASEUR DE BOHÊME. *Bombycilla garrula.* L, 8. Plate LXI A. Almost exactly similar in form and colour to the Cedar Waxwing, but larger, the secondaries are tipped with white and most of the primaries with white or yellow or both; there is likewise a small white wing-bar. The undertail-coverts are chestnut and the abdomen greyish without the yellow suffusion.

*Distinctions.* No further distinctions are necessary; the Cedar Waxwing is the only species with which it can be confused.

*Field Marks.* Their trim figures and conspicuous crests easily identify the waxwings The white or yellow on the wings and the chestnut undertail-coverts are the best specific field marks.

*Nesting.* In trees, in nest of twigs, roots, moss, etc.

*Distribution.* The northern parts of the northern hemisphere in both the New and Old Worlds. In Canada, breeding in northern Manitoba, Mackenzie District, northern British Columbia, and down the eastern slopes of the Rockies, irregularly to southern Alberta. Migrating in winter irregularly south and east over most of the Dominion.

Their irregular wandering habits in winter have given these birds the name "Bohemian" which in this sense is synonymous with "wandering." They are northwestern birds, but come into cultivated sections irregularly in winter, as does the Evening Grosbeak. They are too rare to have any great economic influence. Their favourite food is the dried waste fruit that hangs throughout the winter.

619. **Cedar Waxwing.** CEDAR-BIRD. CAROLINA WAXWING. CHERRY-BIRD. LE JASEUR DU CÈDRE (Récollet). *Bombycilla cedrorum.* L, 7·19. Plate LXI A. A very neat, nattily plumaged bird, about the size of a House Sparrow. Soft brown-fawn over head, breast, and back, changing to slate-grey on rump and pale yellow on abdomen. A prominent, sharp-tipped, erectile crest; a black bar through eyes; chin-spot of same colour. Tail tipped with lemon, as if dipped in paint. Small, reddish appendages like bits of sealing-wax on tips of secondaries and sometimes on tail feathers (Figure 421).

*Distinctions.* To be mistaken only for the Bohemian Waxwing, but is decidedly smaller; yellowish instead of faintly greyish beneath, without yellow or white on wings, and undertail-coverts creamy white instead of rich chestnut.

*Field Marks.* The natty shape and bearing, with conspicuous, usually upstanding, crest are easily recognizable field marks for this bird as a waxwing. Small size, yellowish underparts, total lack of red under the tail, and absence of yellow or white markings on closed wing will separate it from the Bohemian Waxwing. This is the waxwing most likely to be seen in southern Canada during the summer. Any such bird seen, except in winter, should be assumed to be this species until positive Bohemian details are recognized. The note, a fine, sharp wheeze, is distinctive and soon learned.

*Nesting.* In fruit or shade trees or in bushes. Nest of strips of bark, leaves, grasses, twigs, rootlets, or moss, lined with finer materials of same nature.

*Distribution.* North America. In Canada, north to well into the northern boreal forest.

The Cedar Waxwing is one of the familiar birds of the orchard. It builds in the fruit trees and is rather too well known in the vicinity of early ripening cherries. In the winter it seeks the various kinds of old dried fruit left hanging on the branches. The coloration is soft and harmonious with just enough accent of contrast to give character. The peculiar smooth silky texture of the plumage causes the feathers to cling together so that they always lie smoothly and are never awry. The red sealing-wax-like processes in which the shafts of the secondaries and sometimes the tail feathers end, common to this and the Bohemian Waxwing, are unique amongst American birds and give an added touch of individuality.

*Economic Status.* About 13 per cent of the waxwing's food is noxious insects, the remainder largely fruit. The greater part of the fruit is wild and of no economic importance, in fact, as with most birds, wild fruits are evidently much preferred to cultivated ones. However, when early cherries ripen before the wild, the damage waxwings can do is considerable. The same amount of fruit distributed over many later trees might pass unnoticed, but when the damage is concentrated upon the earliest and most valuable part of the crop the loss may be keenly felt. The protection of early fruit from the depredations of this and a few other species of like habit is a subject that has received considerable attention. To shoot all birds visiting the orchard is one solution, but a very poor one. It gives only partial protection and has to be repeated each season; for as long as any remain in the vicinity the annual increase will undo the results of previous efforts. Besides, the entire community is deprived of the valuable assistance of a number of species in order that a certain amount of early fruit may be protected for a few individuals. As the birds prefer wild to cultivated fruit, early ripening wild fruit trees in waste corners and along fences provide inexpensive protection. The Russian mulberry, serviceberry, and bush honeysuckle and, later, the black currant, mountain-ash, raspberries and blackberries, sumach, alder, wild grape, bittersweet, nightshade, snowberry, and elders, according to the fruit possibilities of the locality, will serve the purpose.

### FAMILY—LANIIDAE. SHRIKES. BUTCHER-BIRDS

*General Description.* The shrikes are medium-sized passerine birds of raptorial nature. They are easily recognized by their bills which are plainly hooked and furnished with a notch and tooth at the tip of the upper mandible (Figure 422). The two species which occur in Canada are very similar in coloration and differ in minor characters only (Plate LXI B).

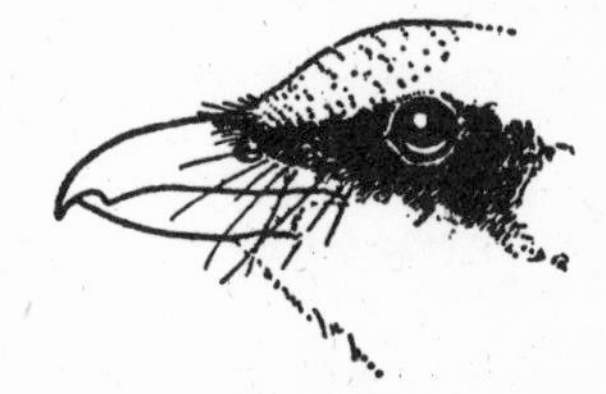

Figure 422
Shrike (Loggerhead); natural size.

The Shrikes are interesting examples of passerine or seed and insect-eating birds adapted for a predatory life. The true *Raptores*, the hawks, etc., which also prey upon the higher living forms, have powerful feet with which to secure their food and hold it while they tear it with their bills. The shrikes are without these efficient grasping and holding members, having in fact feet scarcely stronger than those of a sparrow or blackbird of equal size. They, therefore, seize prey with their bill and, to hold it while feeding, have evolved the habit of impaling it upon strong thorns, etc.; this habit gives them the popular title of Butcher-birds. Shrikes are bold and spirited and quite as daring and capable in proportion to their size as any of the true birds of prey. The family is large and widely distributed. Only one genus is represented in America and two species in North America.

621. **Northern Shrike.** BUTCHER-BIRD. LA PIE-GRIÈCHE BORÉALE. *Lanius borealis.* L, 10·32. Nearly as large as a robin. Almost identical in coloration with the Common Shrike (*See* Plate LXI B), but considerably larger and with a series of well-defined, fine, wavy lines or vermiculations across most of the underparts. Juveniles over-washed with rusty.

*Distinctions.* General coloration and notched bill (Figure 422) will distinguish it as a shrike. Size, distinct vermiculation below, and late autumn or winter season of occurrence in the regularly settled parts of Canada will characterize it as the Northern.

*Field Marks.* The sharply contrasted black and white wings, grey back, and black bar through eye will give easy recognition of either of our shrikes. Size, vermiculated breast, and late autumn or winter occurrence as above will designate this species.

*Nesting.* In low trees or bushes, nest of twigs, grasses, etc.

*Distribution.* Northern North America, breeding in the high northern forest across the continent. There is great confusion in the older breeding records between the two species of shrikes. None of the more southern nesting reports of this bird has ever been satisfactorily substantiated. Great caution should be used in identifying before reporting it in southern latitudes in summer.

*SUBSPECIES.* The Northern Shrike of most of North America is the Northeastern Shrike (la Pie-grièche du Nord-Est) *Lanius borealis borealis.* In Alaska and indefinitely eastward to Mackenzie occurs the Northwestern Shrike (la Pie-grièche du Nord-Ouest) *Lanius borealis invictus.*

The Northern Shrike is the bolder and more energetic of our two species. It is a northern breeder and is seen only in cultivated sections in the winter where it follows the flocks of Snow Buntings, redpolls, etc. It has shown some tendency to come into cities and villages in pursuit of the English Sparrow, in which work it is to be encouraged in every way. Dry, mummied mice and birds occasionally found pinned to thorns and barbs of wire fences or hanging from the close forks of twigs are usually the remains of victims of this species. Rather surprisingly, it exhibits considerable musical ability even in winter.

*Economic Status.* Though thoroughly raptorial in habit the Northern Shrike cannot be said to do a great amount of damage. It is not common enough within settlement to be a serious factor in the small bird life of the fields. It catches numbers of mice and probably its attacks on them and on the English Sparrow compensate for the seed-eating birds it takes.

622. **Common Shrike.** BUTCHER-BIRD. LOGGERHEAD SHRIKE. LA PIE-GRIÈCHE COMMUNE. *Lanius ludovicianus.* L, 9. Plate LXI B. Somewhat larger than a sparrow, smaller than a Robin. Crown and back soft, even, light slate-grey, lightening on rump sometimes to white. Wings and tail black; the former with white bar across base of primaries and tips of secondaries; the latter with outer feathers largely white from the tip. All below white. A conspicuous broad, black bar through eye and along cheek. Sexes alike.

*Distinctions.* The coloration of grey back, black and white wings and tail, black face bar, and white below, is distinctive for the shrikes. Separable from the Northern Shrike by smaller size (wing under 4·25) and the lack of distinct dark vermiculations across underparts. Juveniles and extreme western birds may have a faint vermiculation on breast and flanks, but it is soft and undecided, and not strong and distinct.

*Field Marks.* Grey back, white below, black and white wings and tail, and black bar across face are distinctive of Shrikes. Small size and summer occurrences in southern Canada are the best recognition marks for the species.

*Nesting.* Nest of strips of bark, small twigs, vegetable fibres, lined with felted wool and feathers, in bushes or small trees, usually in those of thorny nature.

*Distribution.* North America. In Canada, throughout the southern parts; rare in southern British Columbia.

*SUBSPECIES.* A number of subspecies of this bird are recognized. The eastern Canadian form is the Migrant Shrike (la Pie-grièche migratrice) *Lanius ludovicianus migrans.* It extends west probably to the eastern bluffy parts of Manitoba, though it is separated from the next form by such slight and variable characters that the geographical boundary between them is rather uncertain. Over the prairies westward is the White-rumped Shrike (la Pie-grièche à croupion blanc) *Lanius ludovicianus excubitorides* that extends to the mountains. It is very slightly paler grey, with whiter rump and more white on tips of scapulars. In southern British Columbia, the California Shrike (la Pie-grièche de la Californie) *Lanius ludovicianus gambeli* occurs as a straggler. It has a back like the Migrant, a rump like the White-rumped, but is slightly browner than either and has suggestions of vermiculations on chest and sides of breast in the adult as well as the juvenile.

The Common Shrike is a bird of open, brushy pastures and hillsides. Thornapple or similar thorny trees, cropped and trimmed by cattle until dense and repellent, are its favourite nesting sites, and in such neighbourhoods it may be seen, usually on a commanding perch, such as the tip of a dead sapling, or a telegraph wire, keenly regarding the surrounding country. The impaling of prey is not quite so strongly developed a habit in this species as in the previous one, probably because it eats more insects and can handle much of its smaller prey without so doing. At any rate evidence in the form of remains stuck on thorns is somewhat rare in haunts of the species and where they would be expected to be plentiful. The song of the Common Shrike is quite musical and pleasing, but the call-notes are harsh and discordant.

*Economic Status.* The food habits of the Common Shrike are similar to those of the Northern Shrike, differing only as would be expected in a smaller and weaker bird and a summer rather than a winter resident. Thus we find that fewer birds and mammals and more insects are taken, indeed during the height of the insect season insects seem to constitute the greater part of its food. Early in the summer great numbers of beetles are eaten, useful and harmful forms being about equally divided in numbers. Later, grasshoppers and crickets form a large proportion of the food, but numbers of caterpillars—many of them hairy—cutworms, some wasps, spiders, and other insect forms are also taken. The food of the species throughout the year is regarded by the United States Biological Survey as being beneficial in the ratio of 4 to 1.

### FAMILY—STURNIDAE. TRUE STARLINGS

An Old World family separated from the American Starlings by having, among other distinctions, ten instead of nine primaries; the first may be rudimentary as in the species below. The family is not native to America but two species have been introduced and are increasing alarmingly.

*Introduced:*

493. **Common Starling.** L'ÉTOURNEAU ORDINAIRE. *Sturnus vulgaris.* L, 8·5. A little smaller than a Red-winged Blackbird and with a shorter tail. Adult in autumn all metallic black, sharply dotted all over with cream-buff round and V-shaped spots (Figure 424). In spring with most of the light spotting worn off, the metallic iridescence very prominent, a yellow bill (Figure 423), and reddish legs. Autumn juvenile greyish brown with whitish throat.

Figure 423
European Starling (summer); scale, ½.

Figure 424
European Starling
(juvenile, winter); scale, ½.

*Distinctions.* In spring a blackbird with a yellow bill and reddish legs. In autumn a blackbird with fine, light specklings. Juvenile a brownish blackbird with a whitish throat. In all seasons a blackbird with a short tail.

*Field Marks.* Like a blackbird with a short, stubby tail. The yellow bill when obvious is very distinctive.

*Nesting.* Large untidy masses of grass, twigs, and rubbish in crevices of buildings and in hollow trees. Will occupy nest boxes.

*Distribution.* Originally west and central Europe. Introduced in New York City in 1890 and has spread over an ever-widening area. In Canada it has now occupied much of the southern parts of the Maritime Provinces and all of southern Ontario and Quebec, north and west to Port Arthur. It seems to stand our winters well and its ultimate range in the Dominion cannot be forecast.

*Economic Status.* An investigation of the economic results from this disturbing element introduced into American conditions has been made by the United States Biological Survey with the following results. As an effective destroyer of terrestrial insects the Starling has few equals among the birds of northeastern North America. The most serious objection to it in this section is its partiality to cherries. Other fruit it attacks, but not to a serious extent. Its unsightly nesting habits, competition with other birds, and its proneness to form immense roosts counterbalance much good that might otherwise be expected from it.

As though acclimatization societies and others with similar aims had not done harm enough already in introducing the English Sparrow to America, they have added another factor of unknown possibilities in the form of this bird to compete with native species, develop unforeseen qualities in a new environment, and in the absence of its natural control to increase enormously. Already the Starling exists in flocks of thousands in southern Ontario and is covering the country in ever widening circles. Any hope of its eradication is probably vain.

In its habits the Starling promises to be complementary to the English Sparrow, occupying the orchards, parks, and suburbs as the sparrow does the towns. Owing to its larger size, its nesting habits are perhaps even more objectional than those of the English Sparrow. The fact that it occupies holes brings it into serious competition with such native forms as bluebirds who are already hard pressed for nesting sites under modern orchard methods. It was hoped that the Starling would find our Canadian winters too severe, but it stands the coldest weather well and finds sustenance on the garbage piles of our cities and towns. As an indication of the potentiality for harm there is inherent in the species and the evils of its dense flocking *See* Jack Miner's experience with it at Kingsville, Ontario. There the Starlings found winter roost in his planted pine grove, resorting to it in such numbers as, by their dropping, to smother the foliage, overfertilize the ground, and finally to kill all the trees in the plantation. This in spite of an active campaign against them in which truck loads of the birds were trapped and shipped to the cities to assist in feeding the needy.

*Introduced:*

493. 1. **Asiatic Starling.** CRESTED MYNAH CHINESE STARLING. JAPANESE STARLING. L'ÉTOURNEAU DE L'ASIE. *Aethiopsar cristatellus.* L, 10·50. A very dark, nearly black bird, about the size of a Robin, with large white patch at base of primaries and secondaries; a standing crest at base of bill and over eyes; bill and legs yellowish (Figure 425).

*Distinctions.* A rather large black bird, with much white on wings, yellow bill rose coloured at base, and orange-red feet; an upstanding crest of lanceolate feathers at base of bill, covering nostrils. Not likely to be mistaken for any other species of probable occurrence in Canada.

*Field Marks.* A black bird about the size of a Robin with conspicuous white patches on wings, yellow eyes, pale yellow bill, and red-orange legs. It has a far-reaching, melodious, whistled call that can be heard above the roar of traffic in the crowded city streets.

Figure 425
Chinese Starling; scale, ½.

*Distribution.* Central and southern China. Introduced in British Columbia at Vancouver and now well established there.

A. Cowbird; scale, $\frac{1}{3}$

Male Female

B. Western Tanager; scale, $\frac{1}{3}$

Female Male

PLATE LXXVI

A. Scarlet Tanager

Male changing to autumn plumage

Male — Female

B. Rose-breasted Grosbeak; scale, $\frac{1}{4}$

Spring male — Autumn male

Spring female

The origin of the introduction, and the exact date, are unknown. It is supposed that they were originally escaped cage birds. At any rate, they are now well established about Vancouver, and are spreading without the environs. What their effect will be cannot be predicted. The introduction of a nearly allied Mynah, *Acridotheres tristis*, in the Hawaiian Islands, has not produced desirable results. At the best, it can only increase at the expense of some native species with which it comes into competition, and even if no worse effects follow, that will be enough to condemn it in the eyes of most of us. Outside of game-birds, there do not seem to be many cases where the introduction of foreign species of birds has had a happy ending. Usually introduced species fail to obtain a footing, or succeed too well, and either develop bad habits or replace native species of sentimental or economic value. Both the Canadian and the United States governments have prohibited the introduction and acclimatization of foreign species, and issued regulations controlling the practice; and it is hoped that no more species will be introduced. No introductions may now be legally made without special permits from the respective governments. This may not prevent such an accident as seems to have established this species with us, but will at least impede our knowingly importing such pests as the English Sparrow, or the European Starling (*See* preceding species).

### FAMILY—VIREONIDAE. VIREOS OR GREENLETS

*General Description.* Small, warbler-like birds, generally coloured in green and white with more or less yellow in softly suffused masses and without much definite marking. The bill is perceptibly notched and hooked at the tip (Figure 426) much like that of the shrike, but on a much smaller and lighter scale.

*Distinctions.* The Vireos are most likely to be mistaken for warblers which in habit, size, and general coloration they resemble. The bills, however, are stouter, more strongly arched on the culmen, higher for the width, and more evidently hooked and notched at the tip. The Yellow-breasted Chat (Figure 455, page 364) has a bill that might answer this description in outline, but it is neither hooked nor notched.

Figure 426
Notched bill of Vireo (Red-eyed); natural size.

*Field Marks.* In addition to specific markings, which form the best guide to species, the vireos can be recognized by their warbler-like habits but slower and more sluggish movements, peering under leaves and gleaning from the branches and twigs with less activity.

The vireos constitute a small family of tree-top birds peculiar to America. Three genera occur in Canada, represented by six species.

*Economic Status.* Economically the vireos may be treated together as they are similar in their food habits. Their food consists of 91 per cent of insects and the remainder of fruits that are almost without exception wild varieties. The insects taken are among the most harmful, including scales and other close-lying species that no birds but the careful, close-peering vireos ordinarily seek. They are among our most useful birds.

631. **White-eyed Vireo.** LE VIREO AUX YEUX BLANCS. *Vireo griseus.* L, 5·27. A small vireo like the Warbling but of much richer green colour on back and with yellow loral mark and eye-ring; iris white. Throat and underparts almost pure white; strongly yellow on flanks; wings have two yellowish bars (Figure 427).

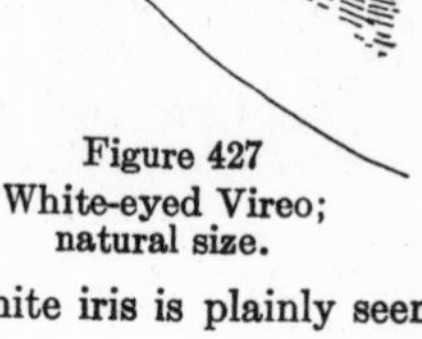

*Distinctions.* White iris, yellow eye-ring and loral mark, strong yellow on flanks, and white breast and abdomen.

*Field Marks.* The Solitary Vireo with pronounced white eye-ring has been occasionally identified as this species, but note that in that species the iris is dark brown, practically black. This species is too rare in Canada and too similar to other species to be recorded on eyesight observation unless the white iris is plainly seen.

Figure 427
White-eyed Vireo; natural size.

*Nesting.* Nest usually similar to that of the Red-eyed.

*Distribution.* All forms of the species are southern. The White-eyed Vireo occurs in the eastern United States north to New York and Massachusetts and is only accidental in Canada.

*SUBSPECIES.* The White-eyed Vireo is represented by several subspecies, the type form, the Northern White-eye (le Vireo aux yeux blancs du Nord) *V. g. griseus* being the only one that occurs in Canada.

A bird of the south noted for its remarkable voice. This species is included here on the basis of a few records scattered along the southern borders of Ontario.

632. **Hutton's Vireo.** LE VIREO DE HUTTON. *Vireo huttoni.* L, 4·75. The smallest of the Canadian vireos. Like a Warbling but generally darker, more dull olive above and below, with a pale, indistinct ring about eye and white wing-bars.

*Distinctions.* As above.

*Field Marks.* Like a small, dark Warbling Vireo, with pale eye-ring and white wing-bars. Likely to look more like a female Ruby-crowned Kinglet, except for size, than anything else. Its songs and notes are very distinctive and unlike those of any other bird it is likely to be confused with.

*Nesting.* Nest semi-pensile, from forks of branch; of mosses lined with fine grass.

*Distribution.* Western United States and Mexico. Occurring regularly in Canada only on southern Vancouver Island, rare on adjoining mainland. It is probably resident wherever found.

*SUBSPECIES.* The type form the Northern Hutton's Vireo (le Vireo de Hutton du Nord) *Vireo huttoni huttoni* is the form accredited to the Canadian section of its range.

One of the most inconspicuous of our woodland birds. Its limited range and small numbers in Canada, combined with its retiring habits, keep it from being very well known by Canadian ornithologists. Alone among our vireos it is practically resident wherever found, and does not migrate in winter to a noticeable extent.

628. **Yellow-throated Vireo.** LE VIREO À GORGE JAUNE. *Vireo flavifrons.* L, 5·95. Slightly smaller than the Red-eyed and larger than the Warbling Vireos. Head, cheeks, and back greenish; rump and tail slaty; breast and throat bright yellow; white below. Wings with two distinct bars.

Figure 428
Yellow-throated Vireo; natural size.

*Distinctions.* The bright yellow of the breast of this species is distinctive amongst the vireos. It has white wing-bars; the Solitary is the only other vireo within its range that has this character. In general coloration, the Yellow-throated Vireo is most like the Pine Warbler, but has considerably more white on the underparts and the yellow ends almost sharply at the lower breast-line. The finely hooked bill (Figure 426), of course, will distinguish it as a vireo.

*Field Marks.* The bright yellow on throat will prevent confusion with any other vireo, and the larger amount of white and the decided termination of the yellow breast against it will separate it from the Pine Warbler. Its voice is much like that of the Red-eyed, but the notes follow each other more slowly.

*Nesting.* Nest pensile, from fork of branch, of strips of bark, plant fibres, etc., lined with fine grasses and covered externally with lichens and spider webs.

*Distribution.* Eastern North America. In Canada, only in the most southern parts of Ontario and Quebec west to and including southern Manitoba.

A woodland and orchard bird. Besides its characteristic song it is a maker of many queer noises and has an extensive vocabulary.

629. **Solitary Vireo.** LE VIREO SOLITAIRE. *Vireo solitarius.* L, 5·61. Plate LXII A. A little smaller than the Red-eyed, larger than the other vireos except the Yellow-throated. Back, greenish, shading into grey on head and face; white loral spot and ring about eye; all underparts white with suffusion of yellow and olive on flanks; two white wing-bars.

*Distinctions.* The ashy blue crown and face and the conspicuous white lores and eye-ring.

*Field Marks.* The Solitary Vireo has a rather thick-headed appearance in life. It is the only Canadian vireo with conspicuous or decided markings. The bluish crown and cheeks contrasted with pure white lores, eye-ring, and throat are very distinctive and the bird should not be mistaken for any other species.

*Nesting.* Nest pensile, between the forks of a branch, of wood fibres, bark strips, pine needles, and plant-down.

*Distribution.* North America. In Canada, across the Dominion. In the central provinces north to Mackenzie Valley, but in British Columbia confined to the southern parts.

*SUBSPECIES.* Canadian birds divided into two subspecies. The Blue-headed Vireo (le Vireo à tête bleue) *Vireo solitarius solitarius* extends west to the mountains. In British Columbia we find Cassin's Vireo (le Vireo de Cassin) *Vireo solitarius cassini,* somewhat duller, darker in coloration; the grey head not so sharply defined from the green back.

The Solitary is the brightest coloured and the prettiest of our vireos, and a common resident or migrant of woodland or orchard. Its notes are reminiscent of those of the Red-eyed, but more varied and contain some harsh, scolding notes.

625. **Yellow-green Vireo.** LE VIREO JAUNE-VERDÂTRE. *Vireo flavoviridis.* L, 6·5. Like the Red-eyed but a little larger and more yellowish below. Underwing and tail coverts decidedly yellow and flanks decidedly greenish yellow.

*Distribution.* Mexico. There is one extraordinary record for Godbout on the north side of the Gulf of St. Lawrence. It is improbable that it will ever be detected in Canada again.

624. **Red-eyed Vireo.** PREACHER-BIRD. TEACHER. LE VIREO AUX YEUX ROUGES. *Vireo olivacea.* L, 6·23. Plate LXII B. Of the size of a small Sparrow. White below, dull greenish olive above, with a grey crown and decided white eyebrow stripe. Sexes alike.

*Distinctions.* The Red-eyed may be distinguished from other vireos by its superior size, lack of yellow, the grey confined to the crown, and the white eyebrow-line bordered with dark both above and below. The iris is red, but this can be seen only on very close examination.

*Field Marks.* The markings of the face of the Red-eyed make the best field mark. The white eyebrow bordered with darker colour and the lower line through the eye can usually be seen as the bird peers through the leaves at the intruder.

*Nesting.* Suspended from between the forks of a small branch 5 to 15 feet above the ground; pensile nest or hanging-cup, woven of strips of bark, dead-wood fibres, paper, plant-down, or birch bark, lined with fine materials.

*Distribution.* North and South America. In Canada, north to Mackenzie Valley, west to Vancouver Island.

The Red-eyed Vireo is one of the commonest frequenters of our groves and woods. Its song, a leisurely repetition of slight variants of the same phrase with pauses between, and continued *ad libitum,* can be heard in the tree tops almost anywhere in Canada and has given the species the name of Preacher-bird.

626. **Philadelphia Vireo.** LE VIREO PARESSEUX. *Vireo philadelphicus.* L, 4·75. Almost exactly similar in size, form, and coloration to the Warbling Vireo (Plate LXIII A), but more generally suffused with yellow on the breast, flanks, and underparts.

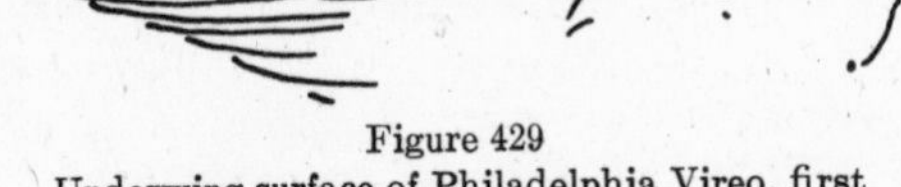

Figure 429
Underwing surface of Philadelphia Vireo, first primary long; natural size.

*Distinctions.* The Philadelphia is likely to be mistaken only for the Warbling Vireo, but is yellower below and can almost always be separated by the first visible primary being nearly as long as the next (Figure 429) instead of being reduced to rudimentary conditions (Compare with Figure 430).

*Field Marks.* In life it looks like a Warbling Vireo with unusually yellow underparts. The light eye-brow stripe is usually a little stronger than in that species, and may at times suggest the head of a small Red-eyed Vireo.

*Nesting.* Nest pensile, suspended from a branch, of fibres and birch bark.

*Distribution.* Eastern North America. In Canada, west to Alberta and north to Lake Athabaska.

A rather rare little vireo, too inconspicuous to be seen or recognized by the casual observer.

627. **Warbling Vireo.** LE VIREO MÉLODIEUX. *Vireo gilvus.* L, 5·80. Plate LXIII A. A small vireo, looking like a dull, grey-green warbler. Above: dull grey, slightly olive, especially on rump. White below from throat to tail-coverts. A faint, light eye-brow-line.

*Distinctions.* One of the dullest, most inconspicuously coloured birds we have, without any special detail in marking except the soft eye-brow line. In general most like the Tennessee Warbler, but duller coloured; less green on back and less grey on crown, and with vireo hooked bill (*See* Figure 426). The even, unmarked coloration will separate it from any other vireo except the Philadelphia. The lack of yellow overwash on throat and below will usually be diagnostic from that species. The almost finally determinative character of this vireo, however, is the rudimentary condition of the first primary, barely three-quarters of an inch long (Figure 430, compare with 429).

*Field Marks.* Like a small, dull-greenish or greyish warbler, but more evenly and less conspicuously coloured than any of them, the only pattern detailed being a soft faint eyebrow stripe. Rather slower in action and less agile than a warbler. Separated from the other vireos by smaller size and duller coloration, especially the lack of yellow below and the faintness of the eyebrow stripe.

Figure 430
Underwing surface of Warbling Vireo, first primary very short; natural size.

*Nesting.* Nest pensile, suspended from forks of small branch, composed of fine bark strips and plant fibres, smoothly and firmly interwoven and lined with pine needles and hairs.

*Distribution.* Temperate North America. In Canada, across the Dominion, north to Mackenzie Valley.

*SUBSPECIES.* Divided into Eastern and Western forms. The Eastern Warbling Vireo (le Vireo mélodieux de l'Est) *Vireo gilvus gilvus* ranges west to the mountains. The Western Warbling Vireo (le Vireo mélodieux de l'Ouest) *Vireo gilvus swainsoni*, declared to be slightly smaller and darker, occupies British Columbia and some of the more eastern territory to the north in Alberta and Mackenzie. The two races are so difficult to differentiate that the distinction of the two ranges has not been well defined.

The Warbling Vireo, hidden in the leafy tree tops, is more often heard than seen. Its song is unlike that of the Red-eyed or even its closer relative the Philadelphia, being a rather long, continuous warble, which in summer is one of the most characteristic sounds in its habitat.

## FAMILY—COMPSOTHLYPIDAE. WOOD WARBLERS

*General Description.* Small birds, only one Canadian species being over 6·28 inches long and very few over 5·75. They are usually bright-coloured woodland and tree-top birds, though a few inhabit the ground and the grass. They are, as a family, difficult to diagnose. The genera may be most easily recognized by the bills (Figures 431, 432, 433), though considerable familiarity with the species is necessary to recognize the generic characteristics.

Figure 431
Bill of Tennessee Warbler; natural size

Figure 432
Bill of Myrtle Warbler; natural size.

Figure 433
Bill of Water-Thrush; natural size.

*Field Marks.* No reliable field marks covering the whole family can be given. However, after a little experience with them their small size, bright colours, and sprightly actions are easily recognized. They are most likely to be confused with the vireos, but *See* bill, Figure 426 (compare with 431-33).

*Nesting.* The nesting habits of the family are various; some build in trees, near the ground or well up towards the taller tops, others on the ground or in grass, and some in holes in dead stubs.

*Distribution.* Most of the Wood Warblers breed in the northern spruce woods beyond the limits of general settlement. Some nest in the more cultivated sections and a few in our most southern parts. All are migratory and, according to species, spend the winter from northern United States south to the Amazon.

The American Wood Warblers constitute a large family peculiar to the Americas. In fact they divide the honours in point of numbers with the sparrows. The warblers are the delight of amateur bird-observers. So small that few but the enthusiast ever see them, but so numerous and brilliantly coloured that their discovery opens up a new world of interest to the novice. The sexes are usually dissimilar and there is considerable seasonal change in plumage. This, multiplied by the large numbers of species, makes the task of identifying all of them seem almost hopeless to the beginner. It is not, however, as difficult as it seems at first. The spring males are usually distinctly marked and as many of them are furnished with descriptive names their differentiation is comparatively simple. As the females and autumn birds usually retain suggestions of the characteristic spring markings of the males the difficulty is really less than is generally anticipated. Of course, puzzling specimens occur which give even the experts some difficulty, but it is usually an alternative between two species which can be settled by giving attention to one or more small details. In studying the warblers the observer is advised to become familiar with the spring males first. When the males of the common species are known, quite an easy matter with such strongly characterized forms, most of the females are recognized without much difficulty, as they usually carry a subdued reflection of their mate's brighter colour pattern. In the autumn, most juveniles resemble the females closely enough to make recognition easy. There are thus few plumages besides those of the spring males that have to be learned individually. The Canadian warblers represent twelve genera, seven of which are represented by single species only. *Dendroica* has sixteen species, *Vermivora* five, and three others are represented by three species each. The generic details of the most important will be discussed under their proper headings.

Though called "warblers" their song should, as a rule, hardly be dignified by such a term. With few exceptions the songs are only insignificant little notes without much prolonged continuity, but as they are often specifically distinctive the student is advised to pay close attention to them, for when the great warbler migrations are on, the presence of a new or rare species is often first made known by a single unfamiliar sound directing attention from the many to the one that would otherwise escape notice.

*Economic Status.* The warblers are highly insectivorous. A few take seed, and a little fruit that is almost invariably wild, and no complaints have been made against any of the family. Their effect, therefore, is wholly beneficial. Being active, they reach all kinds of insect habitats from axils of highest flung leaves to between blades of grass on the ground, and as they are small, they are satisfied with insects and insect eggs that are too insignificant or too well hidden to receive the attention of larger birds.

### Creeping Warblers

There is but one genus and one species of this group within our domains and it is so well characterized by habit and coloration as to be recognized at sight.

636. **Black and White Warbler.** BLACK AND WHITE CREEPER. LA FAUVETTE NOIRE ET BLANCHE. *Mniotilta varia.* L, 5·30. Plate LXIII B. A sharply striped black and white warbler of pronounced creeping habits.

*Distinctions.* With its strong black and white striping, most likely to be confused with the spring Black-polled Warbler. Besides smaller size, more intense contrasts of black and white, and creeping woodpecker habits, its crown with a white median stripe instead of being solid black will separate it easily from that species in the spring. In the autumn the two birds are quite different. Autumn and spring adult Black and White Warblers are practically alike, but juveniles are slightly overwashed with buff and have less black on the throat. On the southern coast of British Columbia where the Black and White is not known to occur, is another black and white coloured warbler, the Black-throated Grey Warbler, that bears a general resemblance to it (*See* page 354).

*Field Marks.* Strong black and white striped coloration and median crown stripe. Creeping habits like a woodpecker. It is the only black and white warbler to be seen in autumn elsewhere than on the southern British Columbia coast.

*Nesting.* On the ground, at the base of stump, log, or rock, in nest of strips of bark, grasses, etc., lined with rootlets and long hair.

*Distribution.* Eastern North America and northern South America. In Canada, across the Dominion to the foothills, north into Mackenzie Valley, breeding in the northern wooded sections.

This is one of the first warblers to arrive in the spring and one of the easiest to identify at any time, as it is always well marked and there is little difference in seasonal or sexual coloration.

637. **Prothonotary Warbler.** LA FAUVETTE PROTONOTAIRE. *Prothonotaria citrea.* L, 5·50. A golden yellow warbler, bright rich chrome or golden on head and most of underparts and with greyish wings, tail, and rump. There is little plumage variation.

*Distinctions.* The only warbler with an intense even golden head, neck, and breast, without wing-bars. The Pine and Wilson's Warblers have green or black crowns; the Yellow Warbler is without the grey wings and tail and is lemon-yellow rather than orange or golden.

*Field Marks.* The Prothonotary is too rare a species in Canada to record from living specimens.

*Nesting.* In a hole in a stub or stump in nest of rootlets, fine twigs and moss, plant-down, or feathers.

*Distribution.* Mississipi Valley north barely to Canadian boundary which it only crosses accidentally in the lower Great Lakes region.

This is only included in the Canadian list on the basis of a few accidental occurrences in the lower Great Lakes region. It is a bird of drowned lands, and of bushes standing in dead water.

## GENUS—VERMIVORA. WORM-EATING WARBLERS

The genus *Vermivora* is a group of small, slightly built warblers in which the following characters are most easily recognized. The bill is small, sharply pointed, almost spine-like, and the culmen line is straight or almost concave rather than convex or slightly arched (Figure 431). The tails are solidly coloured and without white spots.

639. **Worm-eating Warbler.** LA FAUVETTE VERMIVORE. *Helmitheros vermivorus.* L, 5·51. Dull olive above; head buffy with conspicuously contrasting dark brown lines through the eye and bordering crown. There is little plumage variation.

Figure 434
Worm-eating Warbler; about natural size.

*Distinctions.* The only warbler with this distinctive dark and buffy head marking. The bill is rather heavy for a warbler of this genus.

*Field Marks.* Too rare in Canada to trust to sight record for identification.

*Nesting.* On ground; nest of rootlets, leaves, and bark.

*Distribution.* Eastern United States; only one record in Canada, in southern Ontario.

A bird of wooded banks or swampy thickets, feeding near the ground.

642. **Golden-winged Warbler.** LA FAUVETTE À AILES DORÉES. *Vermivora chrysoptera.* L, 5·10. A blue-grey warbler; male, white or very light grey below darkening on the flanks, with yellow cap and wing-patch and black cheeks and throat (Figure 435). Female similar to male but somewhat reduced in brightness and the blacks represented by dark grey. There is little age or seasonal plumage variation.

*Distinctions.* The blue-grey body, yellow wing-patch, and black throat and eye patches are distinctive.

*Field Marks.* The above marks are easily recognizable in life. The black throat somewhat suggests the chickadee, but the other marks make it easy to separate them.

Figure 435
Golden-winged Warbler (male): natural size.

*Nesting.* On ground or in bushy fields or second growth.

*Distribution.* Eastern United States; regularly crossing our borders only in southern Ontario along Lake Erie and the lower corner of Lake Huron. Occasional records for southern Manitoba.

Usually found in shrubby wastes or the bushy edges of woodland. To be expected only in southern Ontario.

641. **Blue-winged Warbler.** LA FAUVETTE À AILES BLEUES. *Vermivora pinus.* L, 4·80. A green warbler with yellow forehead, throat, breast, and underparts; a fine black line through eye and blue-grey wings and tail. Two white wing-bars. Female similar but duller. Little plumage variation.

*Distinctions.* The bright yellow face and underparts with black eye stripe and blue-grey wings with white bars are distinctive.

*Field Marks.* Too rare in Canada to rely on field marks for identification.

*Nesting.* On ground generally in or at the border of second growth in nest of bark and leaves lined with fine strips of bark and tendrils, firmly wrapped with leaves.

*Distribution.* Eastern North America; regularly stopping south of the Canadian border and only accidentally crossing it in southern Ontario.

Though taken only twice in Canada this is a most interesting species as it hybridizes with the next species, the Golden-Winged, forming puzzling hybrids that were long regarded as separate species under the names of Lawrence's and Brewster's Warblers.

647. **Tennessee Warbler.** LA FAUVETTE OBSCURE. *Vermivora peregrina.* L, 5. Back of male green, underparts nearly pure white. Head and hindneck ash-grey, suffusing on cheeks. White eyebrow-line and suggestion of dark line through eye (Figure 436). Females and juveniles have the grey head and hindneck replaced by the green of the back which suffuses more or less as dull yellow or greenish yellow over breast and underparts. The eyebrow-line is always visible as a lighter coloration of the green.

Figure 436
Tennessee Warbler (male); natural size.

*Distinctions.* The general green and white coloration and light eyebrow-line are the best distinctions in any plumage.

*Field Marks.* General coloration as above, with light eyebrow-line and without wing-bars, tail patches, or the whitish spot at base of primaries of the Black-throated Blue Warbler.

*Nesting.* In moss on the ground in small, dense, coniferous growth, in nest of fine grass, rootlets, and long hairs.

*Distribution.* Mostly eastern North America. In Canada, across the Dominion to the eastern slope of the mountains, north to the limit of trees. Occurs and breeds in northern British Columbia, and has been taken in migration in the southern parts of that province.

646. **Orange-crowned Warbler.** LA FAUVETTE À COURONNE ORANGÉE. *Vermivora celata.* L, 5. Plate LXIV A. A dull yellowish, grey-green warbler, mostly yellow below, with a concealed orange-rufous crown patch. Very little sexual difference. Immatures are without the crown-spot, and the brightness of the yellow below is reduced to almost the colour of the back.

*Distinctions.* Similar to the Nashville but without the grey or greyish on the head. The crown-spot when present is still more concealed than that of the Nashville and often entirely hidden until the feathers are separated to show their coloured bases. The yellow throat is duller than in the Nashville. The juvenile is an almost evenly greyish green bird with faint suggestions of ashy and rather similar to the immature Tennessee but without the faint, light eyebrow-line; it is more evenly coloured, and without any suggestion of white below (Compare with Figure 437).

*Field Marks.* Like a very dull-coloured Nashville Warbler or a juvenile Tennessee without the faint eyebrow-line.

*Nesting.* On or near the ground in nest of leaves and fine grasses.

*Distribution.* North America. In Canada, rare east of the Great Lakes, but common throughout the west as far north as the limit of trees.

*SUBSPECIES.* Two subspecies in Canada are recognized by the Check-list. The Common Orange-crowned (la Fauvette à couronne orangée commune) *Vermivora celata celata* extends west to the east slope of the mountains. In British Columbia occurs the Lutescent Warbler (la Fauvette dorée) *Vermivora celata lutescens*, a bird that shows considerably more yellow, especially the juvenile. A third form, *Vermivora celata orestera*, rather intermediate between these two, has been postulated for the mountain interior and has received some recognition.

A. Black-headed Grosbeak; scale, $\frac{1}{3}$
Male Female

B. Lazuli Bunting; scale, $\frac{1}{3}$
Male
Female

A. Evening Grosbeak; scale, $\frac{1}{3}$

Female

Male

B. Purple Finch; scale, $\frac{1}{3}$

Male

Female

645. **Nashville Warbler.** RED-CAPPED WARBLER. LA FAUVETTE À JOUES GRISES. *Vermivora ruficapilla.* L, 4·77. A yellow and green warbler with a greyish face and a more or less concealed chestnut crown-patch (Figure 437). Sex, season, and age plumages varying only in intensity of yellow and the amount of chestnut in cap. In females, the cap may be entirely concealed by the grey edgings of the feathers and occasionally it may be altogether absent.

Figure 437
Nashville Warbler (male); natural size.

*Distinctions.* The unmarked green above and yellow all below to tail, but brightest on throat and breast; and the grey or greyish head and cheeks are distinctive. This greyish head and hindneck may not be marked, but is always present as a slight differentiation from the green back. When present the chestnut crown (not orange-rufous as in the Orange-crowned Warbler) is an unmistakable specific character.

*Field Marks.* Bright yellow, unstreaked underparts and grey crown and cheeks.

*Nesting.* On the ground in partial clearings or tree-grown pastures, in nest of grasses and moss lined with finer grasses and fine rootlets.

*Distribution.* North America. In Canada, practically across the Dominion, occurs in Manitoba, common in southern British Columbia, but rare in the intervening region. Has been taken as far north as Great Slave Lake.

*SUBSPECIES.* The eastern and western representatives of this species are subspecifically distinct. The eastern Nashville Warbler (la Fauvette à joues grises de l'Est) *Vermivora ruficapilla ruficapilla* occurs west to Alberta. The Calaveras Warbler (la Fauvette à joues grises de l'Ouest) *Vermivora ruficapilla ridgwayi* is the form occurring in southern British Columbia. It shows perceptibly brighter yellow below and on rump.

This warbler is most likely to be found in open shrubbery and small growth along streams.

648. **Parula Warbler.** BLUE YELLOW-BACKED WARBLER. LA FAUVETTE PARULA. *Compsothlypis americana.* L, 4·73. Above and sides of face and neck blue, almost bright blue, with yellow suffusion over middle of back. Below white, throat and breast clear yellow, with a vaguely defined black (or bluish black) and rufous band across breast (Figure 438). Females and juveniles are duller, without the breast-band, and with the yellow more or less suffused over all upperparts, but strongest in middle of back. White wing-bars in all plumages.

Figure 438
Parula Warbler (male); natural size.

*Distinctions.* The blue back, either pure or overwashed with yellow, wing-bars, and yellow breast and throat are always distinctive.

*Field Marks.* *See* just above.

*Nesting.* In bunches of *Usnea* (old-man's-beard) or other hanging lichens.

*Distribution.* Eastern North America. In Canada, west regularly to the Great Lakes. Has been taken in southeastern Manitoba.

*SUBSPECIES.* The form recognized in Canada is the Northern Parula Warbler (la Fauvette parula du Nord) *Compsothlypis americana pusilla.*

## WOODLAND WARBLERS

The Genus *Dendroica* is composed of warblers of slightly sturdier build than the Worm-eating Warblers. The bill is somewhat longer and the culmen more decidedly arched (Figure 439). The tail except in the Yellow Warbler always contains a considerable amount of white.

652. **Yellow Warbler.** SUMMER YELLOW-BIRD. LA FAUVETTE JAUNE. *Dendroica aestiva.* L, 5·10. Plate LXIV B. Male: bright yellow, greening slightly on back, with fine rufous stripes across breast and along flanks. Females and juveniles are similar but duller and without breast stripes, and in some specimens almost more generally green than yellow.

*Distinctions.* Practically the only all-yellow warbler. Some specimens of Orange-crowned, Nashville, Wilson's, or other warblers may approach occasional Yellow Warblers in colour, but none of them has the inner webs of the tail feathers distinctly yellow as has this species.

*Field Marks.* The even and uniform bright yellow of spring birds is unmistakable. Some females are more green than yellow, but the green-edged wings and yellow tail, lack of colour contrasts, size, and actions of the bird are easily recognized.

*Nesting.* In an upright crotch in bushes and small trees in nest of fine fibres and a large amount of plant-down, lined with plant-down and sometimes long hairs.

The Yellow Warbler is one of the few species that sometimes refuses to incubate Cowbirds' eggs. Instead of throwing out the intruding egg, however, it often builds a new nest over the old one, burying it and its entire contents, including often some of its own eggs, in the foundation of the new structure, in which another set of eggs is deposited.

*Distribution.* North and South America. In Canada, across the Dominion north to the limit of trees.

*SUBSPECIES.* Two races are recognized in Canada. The Eastern Yellow Warbler (la Fauvette jaune de l'Est) *Dendroica aestiva aestiva* west to the Pacific slope. On the west coast the Alaska Yellow Warbler (la Fauvette jaune de l'Alaska) *Dendroica aestiva rubiginosa* is the accredited form. It is slightly more olive on the back and the breast stripes may be slightly fewer and less decided, but the distinctions are so fine that it is difficult to delimit the ranges of the two.

This is the commonest breeding warbler in southern Canada. It shares with the Goldfinch the popular name of "Wild Canary," but the lack of black anywhere will determine it at a glance. It is found in shrubby localities in open country along stream or marsh edges. It is a common visitor to the garden and its cheery little song is very pleasing. In the autumn the Yellow Warbler is one of the first species to leave.

657. **Magnolia Warbler.** BLACK AND YELLOW WARBLER. LA FAUVETTE À TÊTE CENDRÉE. *Dendroica magnolia.* L, 5·12. Plate LXV A. Male: above, mostly blue-grey, clear on crown but with a black saddle and yellow rump; below, to near tail-coverts, bright yellow, with a broken breast-band of black, continuing down the flanks in stripes. Face and cheeks black, bordered by thin white line above. Female: similar, but with details subdued and softened. Autumn birds are dull grey on crown, shaded with green on back, changing to yellow on rump, all below clear yellow with flank stripes but faintly suggested or absent.

*Distinctions.* The bright yellow breast and underparts distinctly striped with black; black cheeks; greyish upperparts and yellow rump are quite distinctive in spring. The Magnolia Warbler has a general resemblance to the Canadian and to Townsend's Warblers. Distinguished from the Canadian by the yellow rump and from Townsend's by absence of yellow eyebrow. In autumn it still retains veiled suggestions of spring plumage, but the breast and flank markings are reduced or absent; the head and face evenly greyish and the back greyish shaded with green.

*Field Marks.* The yellow below and on rump will separate the Magnolia from all warblers but the Cape May. The latter's yellow breast is sharply and more evenly striped with black and it has the chestnut ear patch. It may also be suggested by Townsend's Warbler (Plate LXVI B), but it never has a black throat or yellow eyebrow and the rump is always yellow. Close examination of the Magnolia in autumn plumage always shows a vague, light ashy bar across the upper breast. The tail is also a good identification mark. The characteristic white marking of the tail is well back from the tip and rather extensive, giving, when seen from below, the appearance of a white tail broadly banded with black.

*Nesting.* In coniferous trees 3 to 6 feet from the ground in nest of fine twigs and leaf stems lined with hair-like rootlets.

*Distribution.* Eastern North America. In Canada, across the Dominion to the eastern slope of the mountains, occasionally in interior and northern districts of British Columbia, but never to the coast; north to Mackenzie Valley.

650. **Cape May Warbler.** LA FAUVETTE TIGRÉE. *Dendroica tigrina.* L, 5. Male: throat, breast, and most of underparts bright yellow, finely and sharply striped with black on lower throat, breast, and flanks. A chestnut patch in the middle of the cheek cuts sharply against the yellow (Figure 439). Top of head black continuing as elongated spots on the yellow-green of back. The rump is yellow and the wing has a large white patch. Female: olive-grey above, dirty white below warmed with yellow suffusion across breast which is faintly striped with dark. Rump yellowish, and white wing-patch replaced with vague bars. Juvenile: similar to spring birds but less bright; male, without chestnut cheeks. Females: even, dull olive-grey, slightly yellow on rump; dull white slightly olive below, faintly streaked with soft, dark lines, and with faint washes of yellowish olive on breast and flanks.

Figure 439
Cape May Warbler (male); natural size.

*Distinctions.* Males are distinctive with their tiger-like colours of yellow with black stripings. Adult females show enough of the male's pattern to be recognizable. Juvenile females are more difficult to recognize. However, all show at least an appreciable yellowness on the basal parts of the feathers on the sides of the neck just behind the ears. This slight tinge sometimes shows in life when the bird turns its head, but with the bird in the hand the feathers must be separated to show it.

*Field Marks.* Adults and juvenile males are distinctive. Juvenile females may be recognized by the peculiar, fine, dim striping of breast against a slightly buffy, light olive-grey ground or by the concealed yellow spot on sides of the neck as described above.

*Nesting.* On low branches in small trees in pastures or woodlands in partly pensile nest of twigs and grasses fastened together with spider-web and lined with horsehair.

*Distribution.* Eastern North America. In Canada, west regularly to Manitoba, occasionally to central Alberta. Has been taken as far north as Mackenzie Valley.

654. **Black-throated Blue Warbler.** LA FAUVETTE BLEUE À GORGE NOIRE. *Dendroica caerulescens.* L, 5·28. Male: deep blue above from crown to tail-coverts; below, white; cheeks, throat, foreneck, and flanks black (Figure 440). Female: dull, dark olive all above, lightening on throat, breast, and abdomen to dull olivaceous-cream. White spot at base of primaries in all plumages.

*Distinctions.* The male, so descriptively named and strongly marked, is very distinctive. The female, however, especially in autumn, is more difficult to distinguish; it may resemble either the juvenile of the Tennessee, the autumn Black-poll, or the Bay-breast. The streaked back and wing-bars, however, of the two last are absent. It is darker and more greyish green than the Tennessee above and more buffy below. An indistinct and partly concealed white or light spot at the base of the primaries is always diagnostic of females of this species.

Figure 440
Black-throated Blue Warbler (male); natural size.

*Field Marks.* The male is distinctive. The female in any plumage can usually be recognized from all other evenly coloured dull green warblers by the sometimes very faint light spot at the base of the primaries, which shows more conspicuously in life than might be expected.

*Distribution.* Eastern North America. In Canada, common east of the Great Lakes. Reported on two occasions from eastern and southern Manitoba.

*SUBSPECIES.* The subspecies accredited to Canada is the Northern Black-throated Blue (la Fauvette bleue à gorge noire du Nord) *Dendroica caerulescens caerulescens.*

655. **Myrtle Warbler.** YELLOW-RUMPED WARBLER. LA FAUVETTE À CROUPION JAUNE. *Dendroica coronata.* L, 5·65. Plate LXV B. Male: slaty blue above; white on throat and below. A broad black breast-band extending brokenly along flanks; spot on crown; rump and patches between flank and breast lemon-yellow. Female: the same but duller, the black less pure and the blue clouded with buffy rust. Juveniles: similar in general, but back very rusty, breast dirty white with fine dark streaks, but with yellow marks as above always more or less evident.

*Distinctions.* Except within the range of Audubon's Warbler unmistakably recognized by the characters above. The species differs from Audubon's Warbler only in having a white instead of a yellow throat (Compare with Plate LXVI A). Young birds of the latter species may be very difficult to separate from the Myrtle, but there is almost always some trace of yellow on the throat. When this trace is absent, as occasionally happens, it is perhaps impossible to distinguish them as no specific character is absolutely constant.

*Field Marks.* The yellow rump is always distinct and bright and makes a most conspicuous field mark. The throat being white instead of yellow will, when observed, separate the Myrtle from Audubon's Warbler.

*Nesting.* In coniferous trees; in nest of vegetable fibre lined with grasses.

*Distribution.* North America except the western states. In Canada, across the Dominion and into Alaska, north to the tree limit. Less common in British Columbia than farther east.

*SUBSPECIES.* The form occupying eastern Canada to Alberta is the Eastern Myrtle Warbler (la Fauvette à croupion jaune de l'Est) *Dendroica coronata coronata.* The northwestern bird from Alaska to the Mackenzie and central British Columbia is Hoover's Warbler (la Fauvette de Hoover) *Dendroica coronata hooveri*, stated to be slightly larger and to have slight colour differences. An early Warbler to arrive in spring and late to depart in autumn.

One of the most conspicuous and most characteristic warblers in migration time. Sometimes, especially in the autumn when the majority of other small birds have gone, the bushy wastes and weedy roadsides will be swarming with Myrtle Warblers, each showing its bright rump spot and giving voice to a metallic little cheep in proof of identity as it darts away.

656. **Audubon's Warbler.** LA FAUVETTE D'AUDUBON. *Dendroica auduboni.* L, 5·65. Plate LXVI A. Like the Myrtle Warbler, but with a yellow instead of white throat. Young birds may not show a completely yellow throat, but it is unusual when some yellow is not indicated.

*Distinctions.* With its distinctive coloration, especially the contrastive yellow rump, mistakable for no other species than the Myrtle Warbler (Compare with Plate LXV B). Occasional young birds without the yellow throat are practically indistinguishable from that species, but in the majority of specimens enough yellow is suggested for the recognition of the species.

*Field Marks.* The yellow rump is always distinct and bright and makes a conspicuous field mark to separate the species from all others but the Myrtle. Separated from that species by yellow instead of white throat.

*Nesting.* Usually in coniferous trees. Nest of strips of bark, pine needles, lined with fine roots and grasses.

*Distribution.* Western North America. In Canada, east to the Alberta foothills, occasionally to Saskatchewan, north to central British Columbia.

*SUBSPECIES.* The only subspecies formally recognized in Canada is the northern one, *Dendroica auduboni auduboni.*

A species so like the Myrtle in habits and action as to require no separate discussion.

665. **Black-throated Grey Warbler.** LA FAUVETTE GRISE À GORGE NOIRE. *Dendroica nigrescens.* L, 5. A striped black and white warbler; male, with solid black throat, cheeks, and crown, and a small lemon-yellow spot in front of the eye (Figure 441). Females and juveniles similar, but duller and lacking black throat partly or completely.

Figure 441
Black-throated Grey Warbler (male); natural size.

*Distinctions.* With black and white striping to be confused only with the spring Black-poll or the Black and White Warbler, but not occurring within the regular range of either of them. Any black and white warbler on the southern coast of British Columbia is probably this species.

*Field Marks.* A black and white streaked warbler with solid black throat, cheeks, and crown.

*Nesting.* In low thicket or high pines. Nest of bleached plant fibres lined with feathers.

*Distribution.* Western North America. In Canada only in southwestern British Columbia, lower Fraser Valley, and adjoining areas.

668. **Townsend's Warbler.** LA FAUVETTE DE TOWNSEND. *Dendroica townsendi.* L, 5. Plate LXVI B. Male: a contrastive yellow and black warbler. Breast and face marks bright yellow. Crown, cheeks, throat, breast, and flanks, black. Females or juveniles similar but duller and the black of throat veiled or absent.

*Distinctions.* Not likely to be confused with any other species except when it straggles east of the mountains. It may have a general resemblance to the Magnolia, Blackburnian, or Black-throated Green Warblers. The black throat when present separates it from the first two; the yellow eyebrow-line and black crown further differentiate it from the Magnolia; the conspicuous bright, instead of subdued, yellow face marks, and breast, from the Blackburnian; and the dark cheeks and crown, from the Black-throated Green.

*Field Marks.* A dark warbler with bright yellow breast and face marks; black crown, cheeks, and flank stripes, and, in adult male, black throat.

*Nesting.* In willows, nest of rotten plant fibres and roots lined with rootlets, hair, and plant-down.

*Distribution.* Western North America. In Canada, British Columbia north to the Yukon, east to the Alberta foothills, and casually beyond.

667. **Black-throated Green Warbler.** LA FAUVETTE VERTE À GORGE NOIRE. *Dendroica virens.* L, 5·10. Plate LXVII A. A green-backed, golden-faced warbler, white below, with full black throat and breast. Females have the black throat broken and juveniles may lack it entirely.

*Distinctions.* Adults with golden face and black front are unmistakable. Juveniles without the black throat are distinguished by their whiteness below and almost solid golden face.

*Field Marks.* Adults, black throat and breast contrasting with yellow face. Juveniles, green back, yellow cheeks, and white below.

*Nesting.* In coniferous trees in nest of small twigs and moss lined with rootlets, fine grasses, and tendrils.

*Distribution.* North America. In Canada, west to the east slope of the mountains and north to Lake Athabaska and southern James Bay.

658. **Cerulean Warbler.** LA FAUVETTE AZURÉ. *Dendroica cerulea.* L, 4·50. Male: all sky-blue and white. Above, all blue with fine black markings on back and sides of crown (Figure 442). Below, pure white with blue breast-band and flank-stripes; wing-bars white. Female: even, dull greenish blue above; white below, more or less stained with suggestions of greenish and yellow. Juvenile similar to female but yellower all over.

*Distinctions.* The male is unmistakable. Other plumages have a peculiar bluish green, instead of olive or yellowish green like other species, that is quite characteristic. The juvenile with its yellow-greenish underparts and eye-stripe somewhat similar to the young Tennessee Warbler (Figure 436), but its white wing-bars and tail patches will at once separate it from that species.

Figure 442
Cerulean Warbler (male); natural size.

*Field Marks.* All blue and white of the male and the decided bluish sheen of other plumages. Otherwise like a Tennessee Warbler, but with white wing-bars and white in tail.

*Nesting.* In tree 20 to 60 feet above ground in nest of fine fibres bound with spider's web, lined with strips of bark with a few lichens on outer surface.

*Distribution.* Eastern United States except coast area; north to southern Ontario. Occasional in southern Manitoba.

662. **Blackburnian Warbler.** LA FAUVETTE À GORGE ORANGE. *Dendroica fusca.* L, 5·25. Plate LXVII B. Spring male mostly black above and white below; clear black on head and cheeks; with bright orange breast, throat, eye-brow line, and median streak in crown. Female like male but much duller. Juveniles mostly dull greenish, lightening below much like autumn Black-poll and Bay-breasted Warblers.

*Distinctions.* Most specimens are unmistakable. Autumn females may be confused with autumn Black-polls and Bay-breasts, but the clearer yellow on throat, absence of greenish tinge below, and dark ear-coverts with conspicuous buff eyebrow-line are diagnostic.

*Field Marks.* The bright orange or warm yellow confined to throat and breast and orange-yellow or buff eyebrow stripe in contrast with the dark cheeks and crown, make the best field marks.

*Nesting.* In coniferous trees in nest of fine twigs and grasses, lined with grasses and tendrils.

*Distribution.* Eastern North America. In Canada, west to Manitoba. Occasional in Saskatchewan. A single record for Alberta.

659. **Chestnut-sided Warbler.** LA FAUVETTE À FLANCS MARRON. *Dendroica pensylvanica.* L, 5·14. Male: crown yellow (Figure 443); back black and grey in stripes, overwashed with yellowish green; below white with chestnut bands along flanks; two white or yellowish wing-bars. Female similar but duller. Juvenile an almost even yellowish green above, white below, cheeks grey; usually with suggestions of the chestnut sides of the adult.

*Distinctions.* Superficial attention to the above description might confuse this species with the Bay-breasted, but the white throat and cheeks are distinctive (Compare with Figure 444). Spring birds with their yellow cap, chestnut sides, and white underparts; and autumn ones white below, yellowish green above, and yellowish wing-bars are easily recognized.

*Field Marks.* The white underparts and peculiar lemon-yellowness of the green above are good recognition marks even in plumages where the characteristic markings do not show.

*Nesting.* In bushes some 3 feet from the ground in nest of strips of bark, leaf stems, etc., lined with tendrils and rootlets.

*Distribution.* Eastern North America. In Canada, west to Manitoba and parts of northern Saskatchewan.

Figure 443
Chestnut-sided Warbler (male); natural size.

660. **Bay-breasted Warbler.** LA FAUVETTE À POITRINE BAIE. *Dendroica castanea.* L, 5·63. Male: finely striped with dull olive-ochre and black above; underparts white; top of head, throat, foreneck, and flanks bay colour (reddish chestnut); forehead and cheeks black; a light ochre spot on side of neck (Figure 444). Female has all these characteristic marks, veiled and dimly indicated, but obvious enough for recognition. The autumn birds, however, are entirely different; above, yellowish green faintly striped with dark; below, white, more or less tinged with yellowish or buffy greenish; the bay of the sides is often indicated by a slight ruddy warmth or by individual, fully coloured feathers.

Figure 444
Bay-breasted Warbler (male); natural size.

*Distinctions.* Spring birds are distinctive enough. Autumn specimens resemble the juvenile Black-poll so closely that often they can be separated only with difficulty even when in the hand. The Bay-breasted almost invariably has a certain amount of warm ochre on the flanks which is lacking in the Black-poll and the undertail-coverts are cream instead of pure white. The presence of wing-bars will distinguish these two species from other plain greenish warblers.

*Field Marks.* The adult male is distinctive in colour. The spring female always shows enough of the bay breast for recognition. Adult autumn birds usually have a trace of the bay on the flanks and the warm ochreish of these parts can generally be seen in juveniles. When these characters fail to distinguish the species, however, close attention will show that the breast colour is perfectly even and sharp eyes or good glasses will usually reveal very faint dark stripings showing on the sides of the breast of the Black-poll. None of these marks, however, can be seen except in the most favourable circumstances, but in mixed flocks one can usually tell the proportion of each species with fair accuracy.

*Nesting.* In coniferous trees, 5 to 20 feet above the ground, in nest of grasses and plant fibres lined with plant-down and long hairs.

*Distribution.* Eastern North America. In Canada, west commonly to Manitoba, less frequently to Saskatchewan, and occasionally to southeastern Alberta, northwest to Lake Athabaska.

The Bay-breasted Warbler in spring migration prefers brushy growth in sandy wastes, roadsides, etc., but often comes close about the house plantation. The similarity of the autumn Bay-breasted and the autumn Black-poll, a bird in full plumage totally different, is one of the interesting phenomena of bird coloration. The autumn plumages of these two birds were at one time confused with each other under the name of Autumnal Warbler.

661. **Black-polled Warbler.** LA FAUVETTE RAYÉE. *Dendroica striata.* L, 5·56. Spring birds, black and white striped. Male with solidly black crown, and back striped with black and grey; below and cheeks white with series of stripes from base of bill, down sides of neck and along flanks (Figure 445). Female: dull greenish above, faintly striped; dull greenish white below, with suggestion of striping like male. Autumn birds altogether different and almost indistinguishable from autumn Bay-breasts (*See* preceding species).

Figure 445
Black-poll Warbler (male); natural size.

*Distinctions.* Spring male Black-polls with their clear black and white striping may be mistaken for no other bird within their regular range except the Black and White Warbler. Their non-creeping habits and crown solidly black instead of with a white median line, easily identify them. Spring females with their general greenish colour and suggestion of striping are also easily recognized. The Black-throated Grey Warbler of the extreme southwestern coast of British Columbia is a similar appearing, striped black and white bird, but the male has a black throat and all plumages have black, or almost black, cheeks (*See* Figure 441).

*Field Marks.* Spring males are largely striped black and white, with solid black crown, and white cheeks and throat. The female is greenish, whiter below and more or less streaked with black on sides of throat and flanks. Autumn birds are olive-green above, with wing-bars of white; greenish cream below, almost exactly like autumn Bay-breasts, but as a rule with very faint stripes, visible only to sharp eyes and good glasses, showing through the yellowish of breast and flanks.

*Nesting.* Generally in spruce trees, in nest of twigs, mosses, rootlets, etc., lined with fine grasses and tendrils.

*Distribution.* North and South America. In Canada, across the Dominion, north to the limit of trees. Absent or scarce in British Columbia.

671. **Pine Warbler.** LA FAUVETTE DES PINS. *Dendroica pinus.* L, 5·52. A dull green warbler, the green changing to dull yellow on throat and breast (Figure 446), with greyish or brownish wings and tail, and faintly white wing-bars; in high plumage rarely becoming fairly bright yellow on throat and breast. There is little sexual or seasonal change.

Figure 446
Pine Warbler (male); natural size.

*Distinctions.* Very similar to the Yellow-throated Vireo, but greener in colour and with the yellow below stronger and more extensive. The white abdomen is inconspicuous. The bill is lighter and warbler-like, instead of being stout, hooked, and of vireo type (Compare with Figure 426). From the Yellow Warbler it may be separated by its duller colour and the contrast between its wings and tail, and body. Its preference for pine trees is at least suggestive of its identity.

*Field Marks.* A dull green warbler, yellow on breast with greyish brown wings, white wing-bars. Canadian specimens are usually somewhat soiled and bedraggled in appearance. Almost invariably found in pine trees.

*Nesting.* In pine trees, 10 to 80 feet above the ground, in nest of strips of bark, leaves, plant fibres, etc.

*Distribution.* Eastern North America. In Canada, rare or casual west to Alberta.

670. **Kirtland's Warbler.** LA FAUVETTE DE KIRTLAND. *Dendroica kirtlandi.* L, 5·75. Blue-grey above heavily striped with black on back, and finely striped on crown (Figure 447). All below, except undertail, pale yellow with black stripes on sides of breast and flanks. Females and juveniles similar but duller, and breast stripes broken and forming spots.

Figure 447
Kirtland's Warbler (male); natura size.

*Distinctions.* Kirtland's Warbler resembles the Canadian Warbler, but is larger; the yellow is paler, the black stripes are on the flanks and do not tend to make necklace suspended from the ears as in that species; and the back is marked with black instead of being clear grey. The only other warbler that might be mistaken for it is the Magnolia but the black does not cross the breast as it does in adult Magnolias, and there is no yellow or greenish on the back or rump.

*Field Marks.* The species is too rare to be accepted on eye identification alone.

*Nesting.* On ground at foot of pine or oak trees in nest of soft bark, strips of vegetable fibre, and grass lined with fine grass, pine needles, and hair.

*Distribution.* Winters in the Bahama Islands. The only known breeding station is a limited section of the jack-pine plains in the northern part of the lower peninsula of Michigan. The species has only been taken twice in Canada, both specimens being taken in the lower Great Lakes region. Its nest should be looked for in Bruce Peninsula, Ontario, and around the Great Lakes west to the Lake Superior country.

In the winter this species is confined within a limited oceanic island habitat and is an instance of the difficulties in the way of abnormally increasing the numbers of native species. It is evident that we can never have in the north a greater number of Kirtland's Warblers than can live through the winter on the Bahama Islands.

673. **Prairie Warbler.** LA FAUVETTE DES PRAIRIES. *Dendroica discolor.* L, 4·75. A green and yellow warbler. Throat, cheeks, and all underparts of male bright yellow; a black line through the eye, a black wedge below the ear coverts, and a succession of black lines along the sides of the breast and flanks (Figure 448). Middle of back has a saddle of reddish spots. Female similar but occasionally almost or quite without the reddish on back. Juveniles similar but colours reduced and veiled, the underparts yellow, brightest on breast, and the black lines on the face, side of breast, and flanks only indicated.

Figure 448
Prairie Warbler (male); natural size.

*Distinctions.* The fine black facial marks against bright yellow, their sharp continuation along flanks, and the reddish back spots are the best distinguishing features of adults. In juveniles the underparts brightest on breast rather than throat or elsewhere and the indications of stripes on the sides instead of in the middle of breast make the easiest recognition characters.

*Field Marks.* Too rare in Canada to be recorded by sight unless the observer has had considerable experience.

*Nesting.* In briery bushes, in nest of plant fibres and plant-down lined with rootlets and long hairs.

*Distribution.* Eastern United States, north rarely, though perhaps locally regular across the Canadian border in the lower Great Lakes region. It has lately been found nesting near the south end of Georgian Bay.

The Prairie Warbler prefers dry, sandy, or open second growth wastes.

A. Pine Grosbeak; scale, $\frac{1}{3}$

Male
Female

B. Common Redpoll; scale, $\frac{1}{3}$

Female or juvenile — Male

Plate LXXX

A. American Goldfinch; scale, $\frac{1}{3}$

Female Male

B. Spotted Towhee; scale, $\frac{1}{3}$

672. **Palm Warbler.** YELLOW RED-POLLED WARBLER. LA FAUVETTE À COURONNE ROUSSE. *Dendroica palmarum.* L, 5·25. A dull yellowish warbler. Male: all underparts suffused yellow; cap reddish chestnut (Figure 449). The breast and flanks are streaked more or less with rufous, and a yellow eyebrow-line contrasts with dark cheeks and red cap. Females similar but colour subdued. Juveniles and autumn birds are greyish brown above; buff below with faint streaks, almost white on throat, and suffused with distinct yellow increasing to pure yellow on undertail-coverts. There is a blended yellowish rump-patch in all plumages.

*Distinctions.* The yellow underparts and red cap are unmistakable in all spring birds. In autumn the vaguely striped underparts, brown back, and yellow undertail-coverts are distinctive.

The Nashville Warbler is the only other warbler with a reddish cap, but it is pure yellow instead of only yellowish below and has no streaking anywhere.

*Field Marks.* The habitual, sandpiper-like upward jerk of the tail will distinguish this from other warblers with yellow underparts. The bright yellow confined to the undertail-coverts, light throat, and vaguely striped buff breast of the juveniles will assist in separation of the species from comparable forms.

*Nesting.* On or near the ground in boggy ground or sphagnum barrens in nest of coarse grass lined with feathers.

*Distribution.* Eastern North America. In Canada, west to Manitoba, casually (?) to Alberta, and north to Mackenzie Valley.

Figure 449
Palm Warbler (male); natural size.

*SUBSPECIES.* Two subspecies occur in Canada, in the extreme east, Nova Scotia to Quebec, the Yellow Palm Warbler (la Fauvette à couronne rousse de l'Est) *Dendroica palmarum hypochrysea* occurs. Westward the prevailing form is the Western Palm Warbler (la Fauvette à couronne rousse de l'Ouest) *Dendroica palmarum palmarum.*

## Water-Thrushes or Wagtail Warblers

Birds of the genus *Seiurus* look more like thrushes than warblers, as is indicated by the popular names of Golden-crowned and Water-Thrushes that are sometimes given them. They are, however, true warblers of woodland habits; ground birds, walking instead of hopping; of large size for warblers; brown or dark olive coloration above, white below with the breast heavily streaked. Bills similar to those of the warblers, the greater size of the bird being considered (Figure 433, page 347). They may be mistaken for thrushes either in life or in the hand, but by attention to specific characters they can be easily distinguished.

674. **Oven-bird.** GOLDEN-CROWNED THRUSH. LA FAUVETTE À FOURNEAU. *Seiurus aurocapillus.* L, 6·17. Plate LXVIII A. A large, thrush-like, ground-frequenting warbler. Above, uniform olive-brown, white below sharply and regularly streaked with dark brown across breast. A partly concealed median stripe or spot of dull yellow or old-gold between two brown lines on crown. All plumages alike.

*Distinctions.* The partly concealed dull golden crown patch bordered with brown will always determine this species.

*Field Marks.* Though very thrush-like, there is generally little probability of actual confusion between this species and the thrushes. Its pure white throat, foreneck, and underparts with little or no suffusion of other colour and the sharply contrasting stripes rather than spots of the breast are easily distinctive.

*Nesting.* On the ground, in a bulky structure of coarse grasses, weed stalks, leaves, and rootlets; covered over with leaves, and with the entrance at the side like an oven, giving the bird its specific name.

*Distribution.* North America. In Canada, west to the foot of the mountains; north to Great Slave Lake.

It is a woodland bird, usually common wherever open timber is interspersed in the heavier woods. Its common song "*Teacher--teacher--teacher--teacher,*" beginning low and ending very loud, is a familiar woodland sound and once heard will be remembered.

675. **Northern Water-Thrush.** WATER-THRUSH. LA FAUVETTE DES RUISSEAUX DU NORD. *Seiurus noveboracensis.* L, 6·04. Dark olive-brown above, yellowish white finely and sharply streaked with dark below; disconnected lines on throat, breast, and flanks. A buffy, blended line over the eye and a fine, sharp, dark one through it.

*Distinctions.* Easily distinguished from the Oven-bird by its finer, more generally distributed striping and general yellowish colour below; its darker colour above (sooty brown rather than olive-brown); its decided face marks, especially strong superciliary line and the solid dark (nearly black) crown (Figure 450). From any of the true thrushes it may be separated by its smaller size, darker, almost black, coloration above and yellowish below, and its distinct face marks. No true thrush has a distinct superciliary line or eye-bar.

Figure 450
Northern Water-Thrush (male); natural size.

*Field Marks.* The Water-Thrushes may be known by their thrush-like look, small size, and dark coloration and the habitual upward jerking of the tail (like some sandpipers) as they walk or stand.

*Nesting.* On mossy bank or in turned-up roots of a tree, usually near or over water, in nest of moss lined with tendrils and fine rootlets.

*Distribution.* North America. Across Canada, except southwestern British Columbia; north to tree limit.

*SUBSPECIES.* Two subspecies are recognized. The Northeastern Water-Thrush (la Fauvette des ruisseaux du Nord-Est) *Seiurus noveboracensis noveboracensis* should not occur west of Ontario. Grinnell's Water-Thrush (la Fauvette des ruisseaux de Grinnell) *Seiurus noveboracensis notabilis* is more sooty and less olive above; less yellow below; and should occupy the remainder of the specific range in Canada. The distinctions, however, are so fine that there is considerable difficulty in defining the ranges of the two forms and the ordinary observer can well disregard them.

The favourite haunt of the Water-Thrush is in wet cedar swamps or the thick undergrowth bordering woodland streams. Its voice is loud and clear and it has a weird, fascinating sound in admirable keeping with the mystery of its surroundings.

676. **Louisiana Water-Thrush.** LARGE-BILLED WATER-THRUSH. LA FAUVETTE DES RUISSEAUX DE LA LOUISIANE. *Seiurus motacilla.* L, 6·28. Dark olive-brown above, buffy white below finely streaked with sharp, dark, disconnected lines from upperneck to breast and flanks. A sharp, white line over the eye and a fine, blended dark line through it.

*Distinctions.* Easily separated from the Oven-bird by lack of dull orange crown streak; very similar to the Northern Water-Thrush but separated by slightly larger size, comparatively larger bill, pale buffy rather than yellowish underparts, and by the whiteness of the face markings.

*Field Marks.* The Louisiana Water-Thrush has the jerking tail habit of the Northern Water-Thrush and can be distinguished from it in life only by attention to the differences given above.

*Nesting.* Similar to that of the Northern Water-Thrush.

*Distribution.* Eastern United States, appearing in Canada only occasionally in southwestern Ontario.

Very similar to the Northern Water-Thrush in habits as well as in color and form. It is, however, a bird of more southern distribution and is of only rare occurrence in Canada.

## Ground Warblers

The Ground Warblers are rather larger than the Woodland Warblers, but considerably smaller than the Wagtail Warblers, and have comparatively stout legs and short wings. Their colours are largely green and bright yellow. They inhabit low shrubbery and are seldom seen far above the ground.

677. **Kentucky Warbler.** LA FAUVETTE DU KENTUCKY. *Oporornis formosus.* L, 5·40. Greenish above; all underparts clear yellow; forehead black, shading off on mid crown; bright yellow eyebrow-line extending around eye. A sharp black patch extends from base of bill, including lores and most of ear coverts, to side of neck (Figure 451). Female and autumn birds similar but duller, the black face mark being more or less veiled though still visible.

Figure 451
Kentucky Warbler (male); natural size.

*Distinctions.* Coloured much like the Prairie Warbler but with the black leaving only a narrow eyebrow-line in front of the eye instead of a largely yellow cheek, and without flank stripes. Somewhat similar to the Canadian Warbler but with back greenish instead of grey and without breast markings of any kind.

*Field Marks.* Too rare in Canada to be identified in life by sight.

*Nesting.* On or near ground in bulky nest of twigs and rootlets firmly wrapped with several thicknesses of leaves and lined with fine rootlets.

*Distribution.* Eastern United States, not reaching the Canadian border in southern Ontario except as an accidental straggler.

This species has been taken in Canada on only a few occasions. It can be reasonably looked for only in the most southern sections in the region of the lower Great Lakes.

678. **Connecticut Warbler.** LA FAUVETTE VERTE À GORGE GRISE. *Oporornis agilis.* L, 5·40. A greenish warbler. Male: clear lemon-yellow below; face and throat to upper breast even bluish grey with a fine white eye-ring (Figure 452). The female is similar, but grey paler. Juveniles have the grey replaced by a lighter buffy shade of the back coloration.

Figure 452
Connecticut Warbler (male); natural size.

*Distinctions.* This species is so like the Mourning and Macgillivray's Warblers that at times it can be separated only with difficulty. Adult males, having a conspicuous eye-ring and perfectly even grey throat and breast, are distinctive enough. Females may be told by the eye-ring and by having the top of the head strongly suffused with the olive of the back and not showing clear grey. Juveniles when they show the eye-ring are usually quite distinctive, though Mourning and Macgillivray's Warblers of similar age have an indication of it. When the eye-ring is not conclusive evidence, the difference in the colour of the throat and breast, a buffy olive instead of an even lightening and greying of the pure yellow below, is a good guide.

The most conclusive distinction is, however, size; a bird with wing over 2·60 inches is undoubtedly this species.

*Field Marks.* The evenly grey throat and white eye-ring of adults and the buffy olive throat and buff eye-ring of the juveniles. Both this bird and the Mourning Warbler walk instead of hop.

*Nesting.* On the ground in nest of dry grass.

*Distribution.* Eastern North America. In Canada, southern Ontario and Manitoba west to northern Alberta.

One of the rarest of our warblers. Its nest has seldom been found. It is very retiring and very local. It should be looked for on the ground in waste brush.

679. **Mourning Warbler.** LA FAUVETTE PETIT-DEUIL. *Oporornis philadelphia.* L, 5·63. Much like Plate LXVIII B. A greenish warbler. Male: clear lemon-yellow below; whole head, neck, and breast bluish grey with semi-concealed black spots on breast and throat giving a fancied resemblance to crape, which suggests the common name. The female is similar, but the grey lighter and without the crape markings on breast, thus resembling the male of the Connecticut. Juveniles have the grey of the crown, etc., replaced with the body green, and the yellow of the underparts extends up neck to throat, slightly modified by lighter and greyish tinges.

Figure 453
Mourning Warbler (male); natural size.

*Distinctions.* The Mourning Warbler is almost identical with Macgillivray's of the western prairie and mountain regions. Adult males are separable from it by the general even greyness of face without definite black in front of eye or white spots on the eyelids (Figure 453, compare with 454). Juveniles or females are often inseparable from that species. Somewhat similar to the Connecticut Warbler, adult males are separable from it by the crape-like black on the breast and the lack of white eye-ring (Compare with Figure 452). Juveniles and females may have suggestions of eye-rings, but see that species for details. Any such bird with wing under 2·60 inches long is undoubtedly either Mourning or Macgillivray's, or perhaps Maryland Yellow-throat.

*Field Marks.* A green ground warbler, bright yellow below with even grey head (no black on face or white on eyelids) and crape-like black across breast. For juveniles the large amount of bright yellow underparts right to undertail-coverts, and greyish head. This species, like Macgillivray's and the Connecticut Warblers, walks instead of hops. Some juveniles and females cannot be reliably separated from the above species in life.

*Nesting.* On or near the ground in nest of strips of bark and other fibrous material, lined with hair.

*Distribution.* Eastern North America. In Canada across the Dominion west to the Alberta foothills; north to the dense spruce forest.

680. **Macgillivray's Warbler.** TOLMIE'S WARBLER. LA FAUVETTE DES BUISSONS. *Oporornis tolmiei.* L, 5·63. Plate LXVIII B. A greenish backed warbler; bright lemon-yellow below back to undertail-coverts. Head, neck, and breast bluish grey with black in front of eye; a conspicuous white spot on either eyelid, and breast covered with semi-concealed and coalescing black spots, producing a fancied resemblance to crape as in the Mourning Warbler. The female is simliar but duller and without the crape markings on breast or the black in front of eye. Juveniles have the grey of the crown, etc., replaced by the green of the body; and the yellow of the underparts extended up the neck to throat, slightly modified by lighter and greyish tinges.

*Distinctions.* Because of geographical range likely to be confused only with the Mourning Warbler. Adult male separated from it by black face and white eyelid markings (Figure 454, compare with 453). Females and juveniles may be indistinguishable from that species. Except in northern Alberta, not likely to occur where the Connecticut Warbler does, but for distinctions see that species.

Figure 454
Macgillivray's Warbler (male); natural size.

*Field Marks.* A green ground warbler, bright yellow all below; grey head, black face, white spots on eyelid, and black crape markings on breast. For juveniles, the large amount of bright yellow all below and greyish head. This species, like the Mourning Warbler, walks instead of hops. Some females and juveniles cannot be reliably separated from that species in life.

*Nesting.* Near the ground in nest of dried grasses lined with finer grasses and sometimes horsehair.

*Distribution.* Western North America. In Canada, British Columbia east sometimes to Saskatchewan. Rather supplementary in range to the Mourning Warbler.

681. **Maryland Yellow-throat.** LA FAUVETTE MASQUÉE. *Geothlypis trichas.* L, 5·33. Plate LXIX A. Male: a green-backed ground warbler with bright lemon-yellow throat and a black mask over eyes and cheeks. Female: similar but duller and without black mask. Juvenile: still duller, the yellow on breast ochre instead of lemon-yellow and all more or less overwashed with rusty.

*Distinctions.* The adult male with its black mask is easily recognized and needs no special characterization. Juvenile males have sufficient indications of the mask to be easily recognizable. Adult and juvenile females are very much alike. They may be recognized by their even coloration above, warm yellow throat, buffy white underparts washed with darker on flanks, and undertail-coverts yellowish. They are most likely to be mistaken for the Mourning, Macgillivray's, or Connecticut juveniles, but the sharp division between throat and cheek colours, the brightness of the throat, and the general warmer yellow tint will separate them. They have been confused with the Nashville and the Tennessee, but the grey rather than buffy or ruddy olive head and crown of the former and the nearly white breast instead of distinct yellow of the latter should make separation easy.

*Field Marks.* In addition to coloration, the marshy habitat, hiding habits, and characteristic actions of the Maryland Yellow-throat soon become familiar to the observer. Its scolding, wren-like note is easily recognized.

*Nesting.* On or near the ground in bulky nest of strips of bark, coarse grasses, and dead leaves, lined with fine grasses, tendrils, and rootlets.

*Distribution.* North America. In Canada, across the Dominion, north to the edge of the northern spruce forest and in southern British Columbia.

*SUBSPECIES.* Three subspecies are recognized in Canada. The Northern Yellow-throat (la Fauvette masquée du Nord) *Geothlypis trichas brachidactyla* extends west to, and perhaps across, the Manitoba line. The Western Yellow-throat (la Fauvette masquée de l'Ouest) *Geothlypis trichas occidentalis* occupies the prairies and westward. It is characterized mainly by having a broader white forehead line above the black mask.

The particular haunts of the Maryland Yellow-throat are damp marshes where the wire-grass grows long and clumpy. It regards its immediate neighbourhood as its own particular property and vigorously resents intrusion. The usual song of the Yellow-throat is one of the characteristic sounds of the damp meadows. It has been poetically translated as "*Witchery—witchery—witchery,*" which gives a close approximation to it.

However, like many species of wide distribution, it seems subject to having local dialects just as the human language does. These are sometimes so different from what he has been accustomed to as to occasionally puzzle the observer who is perfectly familiar with the notes in other localities.

## CHAT OR BRUSH WARBLER

The genus *Icteria*, composed of a single species, is the most un-warbler-like of the warblers. The specific description following is sufficient diagnosis for the genus.

683. **American Chat.** LA FAUVETTE POLYGLOTTE. *Icteria virens.* L, 7·44. The largest and one of the least warbler-like of its family. All upperparts and cheeks green; lores black bordered above and below with white (Figure 455); throat to breast bright clear yellow; underparts white; bill comparatively shorter and stouter than that of any other warbler.

Figure 455
Chat; natural size.

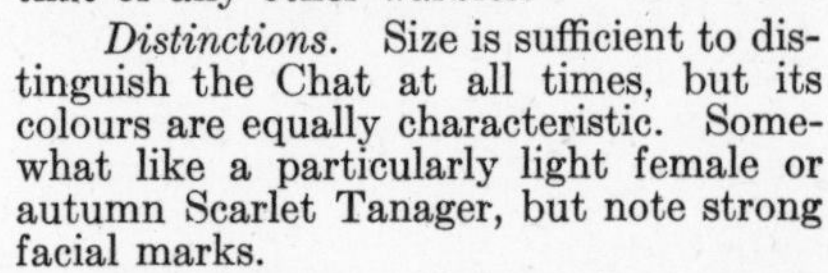

*Distinctions.* Size is sufficient to distinguish the Chat at all times, but its colours are equally characteristic. Somewhat like a particularly light female or autumn Scarlet Tanager, but note strong facial marks.

*Field Marks.* Large size, bright yellow foreparts, and black lores bordered above and below with white make striking field marks.

*Nesting.* In a crotch near the ground in rather bulky nest of coarse grasses, leaves, and strips of bark lined with finer grasses.

*Distribution.* United States. In Canada, the most southern parts of Ontario, close along the International Boundary in southwestern Saskatchewan, and the warm interior valleys of southern British Columbia. (*See* discussion under Carolina Wren, page 320.)

*SUBSPECIES.* Two subspecies of the Chat are recognized in Canada. The eastern or Yellow-breasted Chat (la Fauvette polyglotte de l'Est) *Icteria virens virens* is the Ontario form. The Long-tailed Chat (la Fauvette polyglotte de l'Ouest) *Icteria virens longicauda* has the tail averaging slightly longer, and shows some slight colour differences, especially in the white stripe from base of the lower mandible being larger and more pronounced. The distinctions, however, are too fine and too inconsistent for general popular recognition. This latter, however, is the race to which our western birds should be referred.

The chat, though rare in Canada, is a most interesting bird. It is the spirit of the tangled thickets and brushy wastes and like a spirit it comes and goes unseen, but not unheard. It laughs and cackles, whistles, and mocks. Full of insatiable curiosity, part clown and largely a gossip and a meddler, it hides in the tangled undergrowth to tell the intruder just what it thinks of him. Its language at times will not stand translating—not for nothing is the interior of its mouth black!

## Flycatching Warblers

The genera *Wilsonia* and *Setophaga* are rather small, lightly built warblers with bills slightly flattened and furnished with fine, projecting bristles about the gape (Figure 456).

684. **Hooded Warbler.** LA FAUVETTE À CAPUCHON. *Wilsonia citrina.* L, 5·67. Male: green above and bright yellow below; entire head and neck black with a bright yellow mask similar in shape to the black one of the Maryland Yellow-throat (Figure

Figure 456
Bill of Flycatching Warblers.

Figure 457
Hooded Warbler (male);
natural size.

457). The female is without the black except for an indistinct patch on rear head and the yellow mask blends softly into the yellow of throat and underparts.

*Distinctions.* The adult male of this species is too distinctive for confusion. The yellow face with dark hind crown of the female is also easily recognized.

The Hooded Warbler is included here on the basis of a few Canadian records in the Lake Erie region of southern Ontario.

685. **Black-capped Warbler.** WILSON'S WARBLER. WILSON'S BLACK-CAPPED WARBLER. LA FAUVETTE À BONNET NOIR. *Wilsonia pusilla.* L, 5. Plate LXIX B. A small green warbler. Male is all bright yellow below with a sharply defined black cap on crown (Figure 458). The sexes are similar, but some juvenile females are entirely without the cap, and in others it is present but less perfect than in adults.

*Distinctions.* The black cap and all-green and yellow coloration are distinctive of the adults and young males. When without the cap the vague yellow eyebrow stripe is characteristic. Birds without the black cap may resemble a small Yellow Warbler, but the inner webs of the tail feathers are never yellow.

*Field Marks.* The small size, all bright yellow and green, with black cap or traces of it, or having yellow eyebrow-line when the cap is absent.

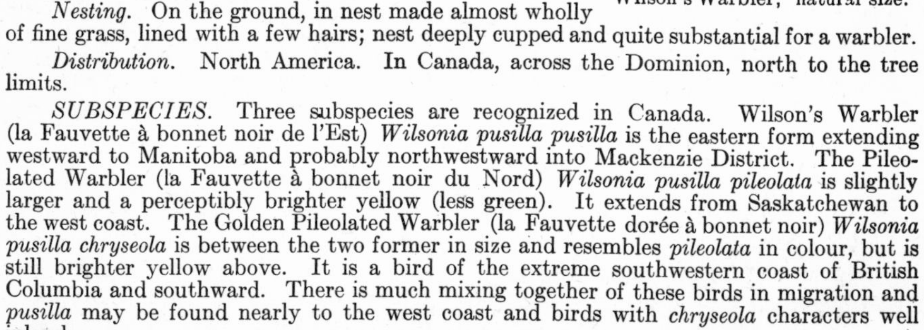

Figure 458
Wilson's Warbler; natural size.

*Nesting.* On the ground, in nest made almost wholly of fine grass, lined with a few hairs; nest deeply cupped and quite substantial for a warbler.

*Distribution.* North America. In Canada, across the Dominion, north to the tree limits.

*SUBSPECIES.* Three subspecies are recognized in Canada. Wilson's Warbler (la Fauvette à bonnet noir de l'Est) *Wilsonia pusilla pusilla* is the eastern form extending westward to Manitoba and probably northwestward into Mackenzie District. The Pileolated Warbler (la Fauvette à bonnet noir du Nord) *Wilsonia pusilla pileolata* is slightly larger and a perceptibly brighter yellow (less green). It extends from Saskatchewan to the west coast. The Golden Pileolated Warbler (la Fauvette dorée à bonnet noir) *Wilsonia pusilla chryseola* is between the two former in size and resembles *pileolata* in colour, but is still brighter yellow above. It is a bird of the extreme southwestern coast of British Columbia and southward. There is much mixing together of these birds in migration and *pusilla* may be found nearly to the west coast and birds with *chryseola* characters well inland.

A very pretty little golden warbler, usually found in willow or similar thickets near water.

686. **Canada Warbler.** CANADIAN FLYCATCHER. LA FAUVETTE DU CANADA. *Wilsonia canadensis.* L, 5·61. Male: even grey above slightly marked with black on crown; all below bright yellow except undertail-coverts which are white, yellow preloral line and eye-ring; black lores extending down sides of neck and forming a necklace of short stripes across upper breast, leaving throat clear yellow (Figure 459). Female is similar, but necklace and black reduced, though usually remaining strong enough to retain the easily recognized specific character. Juveniles are like the female, but the necklace almost obliterated, showing only in vague, suffused, and interrupted cloudings.

Figure 459
Canada Warbler (male); natural size.

*Distinctions.* The even grey above without markings and yellow below with the black necklace marks either sharp, dim, or suggested.

*Field Marks.* *See* distinctions.

*Nesting.* In mossy banks or under roots in nest of strips of bark and bits of dead wood wrapped in leaves and lined with fine rootlets.

*Distribution.* Eastern North America. In Canada, west to Manitoba and northwest to Lake Athabaska. Occasionally in southern Saskatchewan and Alberta.

687. **American Redstart.** LA FAUVETTE FLAMBOYANTE. *Setophaga ruticilla.* L, 5·41. Plate LXX A. Adult male: shining black with white abdomen and undertail-coverts, orange spots at sides of breast, on wings, and sides of tail. Female and juveniles with black replaced by dull olive, changing to greyish on head and brown on wings and tail. Throat dusky white, changing to white below. Spots at sides of breast and on wings and tail similar to those of the male but reduced to dull yellow.

*Distinctions.* A perfectly characteristic bird in all plumages. No other warbler has anything like this combination of orange-red and black, the former replaced in female by similar yellow or white patches on tail and wings. Juveniles have a slight yellow suffusion over breast and are without the wing blotch, but that of the tail is always present. Some young males in the spring look like females, but with irregular patches of the perfect male plumage showing on throat.

*Field Marks.* Colour is the most easily noted distinction, but even in black silhouette, the manner in which the long tail is thrashed about soon becomes familiar and distinctive.

*Nesting.* In the crotch of a sapling in nest of fine strips of bark, fibres, and plant down lined with tendrils and fine rootlets and nearly always covered outside with silvery bark strips.

*Distribution.* North America and northern South America. In Canada north to the Mackenzie and northern British Columbia.

The brilliancy of a high-plumage Redstart against the dark green of the trees is a constant source of pleasure to even the most blasé observer and is a sight that never loses its charm. Its sprightly movements, constant fluttering, and spreading of wings and tail give it a vivacity that few other species exhibit. Like many other American birds it was named by early settlers who regarded it as a familiar Old World form, though the resemblance is far from close.

## FAMILY—PLOCEIDAE. WEAVER FINCHES

An Old World family having no native American representatives. One species has been successfully introduced, the English Sparrow. It was long classified under the sparrows but has lately been referred to this family.

*Introduced:*

**English or House Sparrow.** LE MOINEAU DOMESTIQUE. *Passer domesticus.* L, 6·50. Plate LXX B. Male: striped with chestnut and black on back; crown slaty and broad bar from eye to shoulders chestnut; cheeks and below, white or whitish, with extensive black throat and breast patch. Female: general dull olive or dirty white below; back streaked with olive and brown; a white wing-bar.

*Distinctions.* Black bib of the male is distinctive. Females have an olive suggestion and might be confused with the female Purple Finch were it not that they are unstreaked below. The female or autumn plumages of the bobolink are somewhat suggestive of this plumage, but the pronounced streakiness above and the general yellowness are quite distinctive of the bobolink. With a little observation of the species in our streets or barnyards, no one need confuse this species with anything else.

*Field Marks.* The characteristic notes and chirrups of the English Sparrow make the best recognition mark in the field. The male carries a conspicuous black bib and throat and prominent white wing-bars.

*Distribution.* Originally distributed over all Europe and most of Asia. Now found throughout North America to the limits of settlement and in places beyond.

This bird is not native to America, but is one of our most undesirable importations from Europe. In spite of its obvious seed-eating habits and structure, it was originally introduced as a caterpillar destroyer. It does, of course, like nearly all birds, sometimes eat caterpillars, but does not approximate in this direction the capacity of the birds it has displaced. Being a bird of cities and barnyards most of its activities are in localities where there is plenty of food of non-insectivorous character, garbage, waste

A. Lark Bunting; scale, $\frac{1}{3}$

Female Male

B. Savannah Sparrow; scale, $\frac{1}{3}$

PLATE LXXXII

A. Vesper Sparrow; scale, $\frac{1}{3}$

B. Juncos; scale, $\frac{1}{3}$

Slate-coloured Junco　　　　Oregon Junco

grain, etc. In the autumn, it makes excursions into the country and visits fields in large flocks, mostly after harvest when waste grain is abundant, but occasionally before, and then causes considerable loss. Its food habits thus are harmful or not according to circumstances, and perhaps the balance lies well in its favour. The principal other objections to the English Sparrow are two in number. It drives more useful species away and it is very dirty about buildings.

The English Sparrow drives other birds away by three methods: monopolizing the food supply; occupying their nesting places; and by pugnacious and bulldozing habits. During the nesting season while the young are being fed they come into direct competition with other species depending for the support of their young on the same insect forms (the young of all passerine birds require insects, though those of this species are not long dependent upon them). Thus far perhaps they may be nearly as useful as the forms they displace, but most of the displaced birds are continuous insect hunters and the English Sparrow only a seasonal one. After nesting duties are over they again turn their attention to waste material and become of smaller importance, whereas the superseded birds continue to be useful through the season. The English Sparrows are with us through the winter, showing no tendency to migrate, hence they are on the ground in the early spring, and when our native summer residents, which are with only one or two exceptions more or less migratory either as species or individuals, arrive they find the most attractive nesting sites already occupied. The difficulty of keeping sparrows out of nesting boxes is proof enough of this situation. They are quarrelsome, also, and though, when once established, most native species are quite able to hold their own against aggression, they do not like the constant turmoil in which they must engage when in the vicinity of the English Sparrow. Hence few other birds care to live in their immediate neighbourhood.

The nests are great, bulky, untidy masses of straw and grasses and the tendency of these birds to fill down-spouts and load with litter every projecting architectural feature of buildings makes them objectionable. Added to the nesting habits of the English Sparrows, their congregation in numbers throughout the whole year in sheltered corners under cornices and porches causes accumulations of filth that are exasperating to the householder. Today one of the important problems in architectural offices is to design satisfactory detail that will not harbour sparrows, whose dirt disfigures the most careful design and disintegrates the material of which the building is composed.

Without doubt the introduction of the English Sparrow into America was a mistake. It was known in its original home as a rather undesirable species and unfitted for the work it was brought over to perform. In this country, removed from the natural checks that kept it under control, it has multiplied beyond all reason and though its objectionable features have increased, its commendable ones have not. However, the English Sparrow is here to stay. It has been legislated against, and large sums have been spent in the attempt to control it, but without avail. Local endeavour reduces the number from time to time, but only to have new hordes pour in from surrounding country when the effort has spent itself. Constant endeavour will keep the numbers reduced, but only continent-wide persistent effort will destroy the species altogether. Traps, poisons, and systematic destruction of the nests are the most satisfactory means of control. Poison is effective, but care must be taken that it is used only in the seasons and places where no other species have access to it. Wire fabric traps that are always set and will catch numbers at a time are the most satisfactory. A good type of such trap has been described by the United States Biological Survey in *Farmers' Bulletin 493*.

The common use of the automobile and the reduction of the number of horses on our streets and roads have given the first real check that the species has received in this country since it was introduced. In consequence of the reduced food supply, especially in winter, the number of the species is considerably less than it was a few years ago, and it seems as though this unexpected factor has done more to keep the English Sparrow within bounds than all the fulminations that have been directed against it.

### FAMILY—ICTERIDAE. AMERICAN STARLINGS

This family includes the blackbirds, orioles, and meadowlarks. They are closely related to the sparrows and clear differentiation cannot be made between them in a popular description. Most of them have rather long, pointed, tapering bills (Figures 461-463) and some have the middle of the culmen running up in a short keel on the forehead. The bobolink and the cowbird have quite sparrow-like bills (Figures 460 and 464), but they are shortened icterine rather than passerine bills. These species can also be separated easily by their marked colour patterns.

494. **Bobolink.** SKUNK BLACKBIRD. LE GOGLU. *Dolichonyx oryzivorus.* L, 7·25. Plate LXXI A. A little larger than a House Sparrow with a sparrow-like bill (Figure 460). Spring male: striking black and white with a cream-coloured nape and hindneck. Female and autumn birds of both sexes: buffy yellow, striped with dark brown on back.

*Distinctions.* The spring male has a slight resemblance to the male Lark Bunting of the western prairies, but is white on the shoulders and rump instead of on the wings, and there is a large cream-coloured area on the hindneck. Females, juveniles, and autumn birds of both sexes are entirely different and might be taken for another species at this season. They resemble the sparrows in general coloration, especially the longspurs, and particularly the autumn Smith's Longspur. However, the tail of the Bobolink is composed of stiff, pointed feathers and shows no white, and the general colour is yellowish and olivaceous rather than brownish.

Figure 460
Bobolink; about natural size.

*Field Marks.* The striking black and white male and his ecstatic flight song are perfectly distinctive. The Lark Bunting has a remarkable flight song also, but white is restricted to the wings. Female and autumn bobolinks are best recognized by the yellowish tone of their general coloration, dark bar from eye, and light superciliary line, absence of white in the tail, and by their note, a short, sharp, metallic "*Klink.*"

*Nesting.* Nest of grass, on the ground in the grass.

*Distribution.* North and South America. In Canada, along the southern borders, in open places across the continent to the prairies. Scarce in southern British Columbia.

The Bobolink in spring and summer is a bird frequenting hay and clover fields. It may be seen any summer's day perched on the surrounding fences or launching into the air on quivering wings, pouring forth its song of ecstasy. Later in the season the rollicking male doffs his parti-coloured gayness for the duller ochre and brown stripes of the female. His song is replaced by metallic klinks, and with hundreds of others of this species joined together in flocks he seeks the marshes until autumn. On leaving Canada for his winter home in South America he stops for a time in the rice fields of the Carolinas and here he is hailed not as Bobolink, the merry songster, beloved for both practical and sentimental reasons, but as the obnoxious "Ricebird" that settles upon the crops in thousands and causes decided damage. In the south before the Migratory Birds Convention Act was in force he was shot in great numbers and sold for food.

*Economic Status.* The bobolink in Canada is an irreproachable bird who charms us with his song and whose bad habits have yet to be discovered. In May and June, 90 per cent of its food consists of injurious insects, and 10 per cent of weed seeds with a few useful insects. In July and August a very little grain is added. Yet this bird, owing to its devastation of the rice fields, is regarded as a pest in the southern states.

Flocks of from 25,000 to 30,000 have been reported on 60 acres of rice and the damage done a year is estimated at about one-quarter of the entire crop. This is a striking example of the economic status of a species changing with season, locality, and circumstance.

501. **Eastern Meadowlark.** L'ÉTOURNEAU DES PRÉS DE L'EST. *Sturnella magna.* L, 10·75. Plate LXXI B.

*Distinctions.* Unmistakable for any other species in eastern Canada (Bill, Figure 461), but so like the Western Meadowlark in form and coloration as not to be easily distinguished from it in species. Fortunately their ranges in Canada are not known to overlap and their voices are decidedly distinct. (For other distinctions *See* next species.)

*Field Marks.* The striking, yellow breast with sharp, black necklace; while flying, the white outer tail feathers, and peculiar manner of flight are good recognition marks for a meadowlark. Eastern occurrence and the familiar clear, long whistle, quite different from that of the Western Meadowlark, are characteristic.

*Nesting.* On ground, nest of grasses, usually arched over like an oven.

*Distribution.* Eastern North America north to the limits of cultivation.

The clear call of the meadowlark is often the first indication of the coming of spring. Coming with or sometimes even before the robin and the bluebird, it haunts upland pastures and from the top of an isolated tree or fence-post, pours out its rich, clear, far-carrying calls.

*Economic Status.* The meadowlark is one of the farmer's most valuable assistants. Living close to the ground it attacks most of the worst crop foes. Its food is made up of 75 per cent insects, 12 per cent weed seeds, and 13 per cent grain nearly all taken in the late autumn and early spring months and obviously owing to the scarcity of insects. This bird should receive absolute protection.

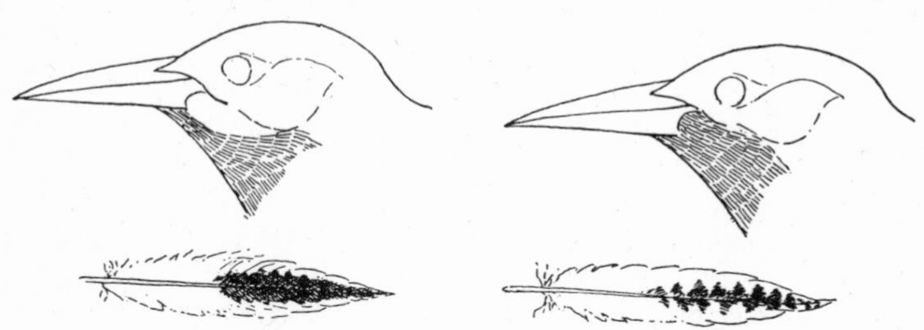

Figure 461
Eastern Meadowlark. Western Meadowlark.
Distinction details of the two meadowlarks. Heads and uppertail-coverts.
The shaded areas on the throats show the extent of the yellow colour.

501. 1. **Western Meadowlark.** L'ÉTOURNEAU DES PRÉS DE L'OUEST. *Sturnella neglecta.* L, 10·75. Plate LXXI B. In colour practically identical with the Eastern Meadowlark. About the size of a large robin, striped brown above, lemon-yellow throat, breast, and underparts with contrastive black necklace or gorget. Bill, long and pointed (*See* Figure 461).

*Distinctions.* Not to be mistaken for any other species except the Eastern Meadowlark, of which, however, there is no evidence of occurrence in Canada west of the Great Lakes. It differs from that species in having the yellow of the throat and breast extending farther up the face, including the base of the lower mandible, and the feathers of the upper-tail-coverts being more narrowly centre streaked with a sharper saw-toothed pattern (*See* Figure 461).

*Field Marks.* Large size, brown back, yellow throat, breast, and underparts with jet black necklace and breast crescent, white outer tail feathers showing in flight, make the species easy to recognize as a meadowlark. Geography—occurrence west of the Great Lakes in Canada—is probably determinative. Its voice is entirely different from that of the Eastern Meadowlark. One of its most characteristic calls has been well syllabized by a western ornithologist as "*King-chigle-a-bunk*" in contrast with the eastern bird that may say "*Toodle-de-you.*" There are many variants, of course, of either of these calls, but they are both common with their respective species.

*Nesting.* Nest of grasses on the ground in the grass, usually arched over like an oven.

*Distribution.* Western North America. In Canada, the southern prairies and southern British Columbia.

Though beautiful as a bit of colour, the Western Meadowlark derives most of its well-earned fame from its voice, which rings rich, full, and true over the open fields and prairies. To the easterner hearing the Western Meadowlark for the first time, no matter how well prepared for it he may be, there comes a distinctly pleasant surprise. The bird itself is an exact replica of his old familiar friend of the eastern provinces in appearance and habit, but the voice bears no resemblance, except in occasional commonplace notes. It is not a glorified Eastern Meadowlark song, but one entirely different, and at first sound he can scarcely connect it with the familiar-looking bird on the nearby fence-post. To attempt to describe the song and give a fair idea of its peculiar richness and quality to one who does not know it is an interesting but perhaps futile experiment. The above typical examples are perhaps as close as can be arrived at. The only quality that can be well expressed is its ventriloquistic effect. It sounds in the ear loud and close and one glances up at the near fence-line for it, only to finally discover it across the intervening field some hundred yards away.

After the long winter, when the chinook winds have melted away the dreary white expanse of snow surrounding the prairie ranch house, the clear notes of the meadowlark proclaim the first advent of spring. No bird is so well known or as much beloved by the western plainsman as is the meadowlark.

*Economic Status.* Similar to preceding species.

**497. Yellow-headed Blackbird.** L'ÉTOURNEAU À TÊTE JAUNE. *Xanthocephalus xanthocephalus.* L, 10·0. Plate LXXII A. Slightly larger than the Red-winged Blackbird, with a bright yellow hood over head, neck, and breast, and conspicuous white area at base of primaries on forepart of wings. Female: uniform dark brown with throat and upper breast dull white or dull yellow. Younger juvenile birds are like females, but with rusty-ochre hood.

*Distinctions.* The adult male is unmistakable. In females and young birds, the white wing marks are missing, but the whitish or dull yellow throat and the well-defined, rusty-ochre hood are distinctive. This latter description may suggest the autumn Rusty Blackbird, but the rusty colour of that species blends away on the body and never resembles a hood.

*Field Marks.* The male, with its black body, yellow hood, and white wing-patches, is very conspicuous. The light, or dull yellow, throat and foreneck of the female and the dull ochre hood of the juvenile are almost as easily recognized.

*Distribution.* Western North America. In Canada, the Prairie Provinces, north to southern Mackenzie, and southern British Columbia. Scarce or absent west of the Coast Range.

*Nesting.* Nest of grasses, etc., tied to reeds or tules over water.

The Yellow-headed and Red-winged Blackbirds have much in common; they inhabit reedy or tule marshes and sloughs, and both are clownish. The nesting marsh of a colony of blackbirds is a noisy and busy place. There is continual going and coming, visiting, forays, and alarums; much fluttering of black wings, with incidental display of brilliant colour as yellow heads or red epaulettes flash in the sun; and a constant conversational croaking and gurgling of harsh, rough voices, with intermittent outbreak of strenuous, raucous objection and expostulation. In these, both species take equal part.

The song of the Yellow-headed—if song it can be called, as it lacks every musical quality—is like that of no other Canadian bird. Climbing stiff-leggedly up a reed or tule stalk the male, with wings partly raised, lowers his head as if about to be violently ill, and disgorges a series of rough, angular consonants, jerkily and irregularly, with many contortions and writhings, as if their sharp corners caught in the throat and they were born with pain and travail. They finally culminate and bring satisfied relief in a long-drawn, descending buzz, like the slipping of an escapement in a clock spring and the consequent rapid unwinding and futile running down of the machinery. The general effect of the performance may be somewhat suggested by the syllables "*Klick-kluck-klee---klo-klu-klel---kriz-kri-zzzzzzz-zeeeeee.*"

The Yellow-headed seem to require rather larger marsh areas than do the Red-winged, and, except locally, are not as numerous as that species. In the late summer and autumn, they join together in large flocks, sometimes mixed with other species of blackbirds, and lead lives of roving irresponsibility and good feeding. The days are spent on the bountiful stubble fields, and the nights in the marshes. A blackbird roost just before sunset is an interesting place indeed. The birds come in from every direction, talking and croaking loudly, in vast black clouds, looking, on the horizon, like wisps of smoke blowing before the wind. They pitch into a bed of reeds already occupied by earlier arrivals, until each stalk seems strung with big, black beads. At the onslaught of the incoming contingent, birds are dislodged right and left, there is a babel of protesting voices and a fluttering of many wings that whirr loudly in the still air as the surface of the green marsh boils with black forms seeking new resting places. The confusion gradually subsides until the next arriving flock starts the hubbub over again. Thus it goes as the sun sinks, until all are in, and then the evening wind chases waves over the soft green surface of the reed beds, without revealing a hint of the hordes of black bodies beneath that are resting through the stillness of the night.

*Economic Status.* Though a bird of the marshes, the Yellow-headed Blackbird does not confine its attention to the immediate neighbourhood, but forages about corrals, barnyards, freshly ploughed ground, and similar places. It is a ground feeder, and insects harmful to vegetation constitute 30 per cent of its food. Grain, mostly oats, constitutes a fairly large proportion of its food, but as much of this grain is waste, little complaint can be lodged against this species.

498. **Red-winged Blackbird.** SOLDIER BLACKBIRD. L'ÉTOURNEAU À ÉPAULETTES. *Agelaius phoeniceus.* L, 9·51. Plate LXXII B. Male: black with brilliant red shoulders. Female: dark brown above, softly tinged and striped with rusty and dull ochre; below, striped with dull white and dark brown.

*Distinctions.* The spring male, with his jet black body and the brilliant crimson and yellow shoulder bars formed of the upperwing-coverts, is unmistakable. The brown female, sharply striped below, is also easily recognizable. Young males have the black more or less feather edged with rusty and the red of the wings reduced to scattered spots of red or orange.

*Field Marks.* The black body and red shoulders of the male. The female's general blackbird appearance and the sharp striping below. The Red-wing has many notes common to nearly all the blackbirds, but the most distinctive one may be rendered a clear drawn-out *"O-ke-leeee"* or *"O-ke-reeee"* with a rising inflexion at the end. It is a characteristic and not unmusical sound of the marshes and sloughs.

*Nesting.* In well-made structure of grasses tied to rushes or tules, above the water.

*Distribution.* North America, from central Mackenzie south. In western Canada, across the continent, in all suitable reedy or tule marshes of the Prairie Provinces and southern British Columbia.

*SUBSPECIES.* The Check-list recognizes a number of geographical races of this species. The Eastern Red-winged (l'Etourneau à épaulettes de l'Est) *Agelaius phoeniceus phoeniceus* occurs east of the Great Lakes, the Greater Red-wing (le Grand Etourneau à épaulettes) *Agelaius phoeniceus arctolegus* inhabits the Prairie Provinces and northward. The bird of the interior valleys of southern British Columbia is referred to the Nevada Red-wing (l'Etourneau à épaulettes du Nevada) *Agelaius phoeniceus nevadensis*, and that of the southwestern coast is the Northwestern Red-wing (l'Etourneau à épaulettes du Nord-Ouest) *Agelaius phoeniceus caurinus.* The differences between these forms are so slight and variable as to be of little popular interest and only possible of recognition by the enthusiastic expert.

No reedy marsh in Canada is complete without one or more pairs of Red-wings chasing each other or clinging to the cat-tails or tules, the males spreading their wings and tail and twisting themselves into constrained attitudes as they squeeze out their clear *"O-ke-ree"* with a roll on the last syllable, in sight and hearing of the females. In the spring the Blackbirds usually arrive in large flocks of mixed species which keep together for a few days and then separate. The Red-wings repair to the marshes and before the reeds begin to grow they settle down to their domestic arrangements. When the family cares are over for the season all blackbird species unite again in flocks that darken the sky, roosting together in the marshes when possible, and scattering during the day in groups of various sizes which frequent the harvest fields.

*Economic Status.* The character of its food makes the Red-wing decidedly beneficial. Weed seeds and injurious insects form 80 per cent of its food, and grain about 15 per cent. In July and August more grain is eaten, and in the early days of settlement when the acreage under cultivation was small and blackbirds numerous, they were a serious menace to the crops.

506. **Orchard Oriole.** L'ORIOLE DES VERGERS. *Icterus spurius.* L, 7·32. A small oriole, like the Baltimore (*See* Plate LXXIII A) with the orange of that bird replaced by seal-brown and with a black tail. The female is an even, dull green. The young male is like the female, but has a black throat.

*Distinctions.* The seal-brown and black coloration of the male is unmistakable. The female has a certain resemblance to the female tanager, but is smaller and of more delicate shape and has a fine-pointed, unnotched bill (Compare Figures 462 and 465, page 377).

*Field Marks.* Colour, size, and voice somewhat like that of the Baltimore Oriole, but richer and with characteristics of its own.

*Nesting.* Nest woven of green grass hanging from a crotch. A beautiful structure, not as elaborate nor as deeply bagged as that of the Baltimore.

*Distribution.* Eastern North America, more southern than the Baltimore. In Canada, local in southern Ontario and has been taken in southern Manitoba.

507. **Baltimore Oriole.** HANG-NEST. GOLDEN ROBIN. L'ORIOLE DE BALTIMORE. *Icterus galbula.* L, 8·00. Plate LXXIII A. Between a robin and sparrow in size. Male: a rich golden orange with black head, back, wings, and most of tail. Female: dull orange below and smooth shades of brown and dull olive above.

*Distinctions.* Likely to be confused only with its nearby relative, Bullock's Oriole, with which it may be associated in southern Alberta and adjacent parts of Saskatchewan. The adult male is easily distinguished from that species in having an all-black head and little or no white on the wings. The female is too like the female of Bullock's to be readily separated from it, but, in general, is richer in coloration, usually more orange below, and with many dark centres to feathers of back, especially on crown. Juvenile males are much like females and various intermediate stages up to the adult spring plumage occur.

*Field Marks.* Throughout the east and the Prairie Provinces, except in southern Alberta and adjacent Saskatchewan, this is the only oriole to be regularly expected. The bright flashing orange and black livery of the male is easily recognized. In above localities the all-black face is distinctive from Bullock's Oriole. The female, larger than any other bird of similar coloration except Bullock's Oriole and the tanagers, in its dull orange and green, is easily recognizable. It may not always be separable in life from the former except by geographical probability, but is easily distinguished from the latter by its general orange tone instead of plain dull green. The voices of the orioles are always distinctive; a rich contralto whistle with numerous musical themes.

Figure 462
Baltimore Oriole; scale, about $\frac{2}{3}$.

*Nesting.* The nest of the Baltimore Oriole is one of the avian curiosities. It is in the form of a bag woven of fibres, plant-down, hairs, and string, and hangs from the end of long, drooping branches. With her sharp, awl-like bill the female thrusts a fibre into the side of the nest, then reaching over to the inside pulls it through, tugging to make all tight and solid, another fibre is thrust in and the process repeated until when complete the nest is so knitted, woven, and felted together that though tossed at the end of long, flexible, whip-like branch tips through summer and winter storms, it remains intact for several years.

*Distribution.* Eastern North America. In Canada, west to the mountains and north to the central parts of the Prairie Provinces. A single specimen has been reported from Chilliwack, British Columbia.

Open country with scattered groves and occasional large isolated elms is the ideal habitat of the Baltimore Oriole. It obtains its name from its brilliant orange and black livery, the colours of Lord Baltimore, under whose patronage the state of Maryland was first settled and in whose honour the bird was named by the early settlers.

*Economic Status.* The food of the oriole consists mostly of insects, including, in order of numbers, caterpillars, click-beetles, of which the pestilent wire worms are the larvæ, May beetles, and grasshoppers. Very few predaceous beetles are taken. The amount of vegetable matter is small. This species, therefore, ranks very high as an insect destroyer. Complaints are sometimes made that the oriole spoils fruit, and it has been accused of puncturing grapes for the juice. Though the Baltimore Oriole cannot be altogether exonerated from these charges, they are very easily exaggerated, and are of little import over most of Canada. The good the bird can do is great, and the harm occasional and slight, except under local and particular conditions.

508. **Bullock's Oriole.** L'ORIOLE À AILES BLANCHES. *Icterus bullocki.* L, 8·25. Plate LXXIII B. Between a robin and a sparrow in size, averaging a little larger than the Baltimore Oriole. Male: a rich golden orange with elongated black bib, crown, line through eye, back, wings, and most of tail. Female: dull orange, or warm yellowish to white below, and smooth dull olive above.

*Distinctions.* Most likely to be confused with its near relative, the Baltimore Oriole, with which it may be associated in southern Alberta and adjoining parts of Saskatchewan. The adult male is easily distinguished from that species by its golden face and superciliary line; and conspicuous amount of white on the wing, the greater and adjoining coverts being mostly white, instead of white only on the tips of the greater. The female is too like the female of the Baltimore to be readily separated from it, but, in general, is paler, with few, if any, dark feather centres on the back, and the crown usually uniform yellow or golden olive. Juvenile males are like the female, and various intermediate stages up to the adult spring plumage occur.

*Field Marks.* Throughout southern British Columbia this is the only oriole to be expected. In southern Alberta and adjacent Saskatchewan, either this or the Baltimore may occur. The black and orange plumage of the orioles is easily recognized. From the Baltimore, Bullock's Oriole is distinguished by its golden face and superciliary stripe separated by a black line. The female in its dull yellow or orange and olive is larger than any other bird of similar coloration, except the Baltimore Oriole and the Western Tanager. It may not always be separable in life from the former except by geographical probability, but is best distinguished from the latter by its general warm orange or yellow tone instead of cold, dull green. The voices of the orioles are always distinctive, a rich contralto whistle with numerous musical themes, but the voice of Bullock's Oriole is not so fine nor so full as that of the Baltimore.

*Nesting.* A deep bag of woven fibres, plant-down, hairs, and string hanging from the tips of long branches. Similar to that of the Baltimore Oriole.

*Distribution.* Western North America. In Canada, southern British Columbia, chiefly east of the Coast Range, and extreme southern Alberta and adjoining Saskatchewan.

Very similar in habits and general status to the Baltimore Oriole, but rather less musically pleasing and less conspicuous than that species.

*Economic Status.* Food analysis of stomach contents in fruit districts shows that about 79 per cent of the food of Bullock's Oriole is animal matter and 21 vegetable. Lepidoptera, in the form of moths, pupæ, and caterpillars, are the largest item, but scales are a standard item of diet. Beetles, almost all harmful species, bulk largely in the food supply. Nine per cent of the vegetable food is fruit, largely cultivated varieties where they can be obtained. With its good record as a fruit-pest destroyer, only the prejudiced or particularly unfortunate sufferer will fail to admit that it is mostly beneficial.

509. **Rusty Blackbird.** RUSTY GRACKLE. LE MAINATE ROUILLÉ: *Euphagus carolinus.* L, 9·55. Very like Brewer's Blackbird (*See* Plate LXXIV A). About the size of the Red-winged and Brewer's Blackbirds. All black or all black washed with rusty. Much larger than the Cowbird, but considerably smaller than the Bronzed Grackle. Eyes, straw coloured in both sexes.

*Distinctions.* With size and plain black coloration, easily confused with Brewer's Blackbird, but the spring male has green instead of purple reflections on the head. In autumn, the Rusty Blackbird is strongly overwashed with ruddy rusty above, solid and complete on crown; and rusty ochre below, strongest on superciliary line and throat. Females are solid smoky black, slightly darker than the female Brewer's, and usually with faint traces of rusty on breast or back. The throat does not lighten to ashy. On the average the bill is slightly longer and more slender. Some specimens are very difficult to separate.

*Field Marks.* Medium size, and solid black coloration, or black with much rusty overwash and decided ochreish superciliary line. Eyes in both sexes pale straw-yellow. Male recognized from Brewer's by green instead of purple reflections about head; the female by having pale, straw-coloured eyes.

*Nesting.* A bulky structure in coniferous trees or on the ground.

*Distribution.* Eastern and northern North America. In Canada, across the continent, west to the mountains, breeding from northern tree limit to the edges of the prairies. Occasional in southern British Columbia in migration, where it seems to be increasing of late years. This is only a migrant throughout most of the breeding range of Brewer's Blackbird.

A. Tree Sparrow; scale, $\frac{1}{3}$

B. Chipping Sparrow; scale, $\frac{1}{3}$

Adult Nestling

PLATE LXXXIV

A. Clay-coloured Sparrow; scale, $\frac{1}{3}$

B. White-crowned Sparrow; scale, $\frac{1}{3}$

(Gambel's Sparrow)

Juvenile Adult

The Rusty Blackbird comes in great numbers in spring and autumn, joining and forming a considerable part of the large flocks of mixed blackbirds that are seen about the fields and marshes. The name Grackle which is commonly applied to the two yellow (nearly white) -eyed blackbirds is doubtlessly derived from the sound of their harsh, crackling notes.

*Economic Status.* Though the Rusty Blackbird is fairly omnivorous, it shows a decided preference for animal, over vegetable, food. The animal matter amounts to 53 per cent, very little of which is of sources beneficial to man. Grain constitutes a remarkably small percentage of the whole. As the bird is mostly a migrant through cultivated sections, coming in numbers only after the harvest, and haunting stubble principally, most of the grain taken is necessarily waste.

510. **Brewer's Blackbird.** LE MAINATE À TÊTE POURPRÉE. *Euphagus cyanocephalus.* L, 10. Plate LXXIV A. About the size of the Red-winged and Rusty Blackbirds. All black. Much larger than the cowbird, considerably smaller than the Bronzed Grackle. Eyes, straw coloured in male, brown in female.

*Distinctions.* With size and plain black coloration, easily confused with the Rusty Blackbird. The male has purple instead of green reflections on the head. In autumn there are very slight feather edgings of ashy on head, breast, and back, but never any distinct rusty. Females and juveniles are solidly smoky black, a little lighter than the female Rusty Blackbird, with slightly more of a brown, instead of a grey, tone, to underlying body colour, and usually lightening to ashy on throat and face. In the average, the bill is slightly shorter and heavier. Some specimens are difficult to separate from that species, and on the whole the ashy tone of the breast, throat, and face is the best guide to separation.

*Field Marks.* Medium size and solid black coloration, never with rusty overwash or strong ochreish superciliary line. Eyes of male pale straw-yellow. Male separated from the Rusty Blackbird by purple instead of greenish reflections on head, and female by having brown instead of light straw-coloured eyes.

*Nesting.* A bulky structure of grasses, etc., in trees, stumps, low bushes, or on the ground.

*Distribution.* Western North America. In Canada, from Manitoba west to the coast, north to central British Columbia and the heavy forests of the Prairie Provinces.

Brewer's Blackbird is one of the commonest birds of the west. It is not so restricted to the marshes as the Red-winged or Yellow-headed Blackbirds, but scatters all over the country wherever a little brushy scrub occurs, preferably, but not necessarily, near water. It frequents the barnyard and often nests in the immediate vicinity of habitations. It is slightly gregarious in nesting and small colonies are common. It associates with cowbirds about sheep and cattle and may often be seen perched on their backs seeking the parasites.

*Economic Status.* Although blackbirds flying in flocks that darken the air have always been looked upon with suspicion, few complaints have been laid against this particular species. An analysis of its food shows that 32 per cent is animal and 68 vegetable. Of the animal portion, a large amount consists of grasshoppers, caterpillars, and insect pupæ, mostly of ground-inhabiting forms. Of the vegetable food, grain is largely represented, but is greatest in the winter months when obviously waste. Though it takes some fruit, it has been known to desert cherries for newly ploughed fields nearby, and is evidently not a pronounced fruit destroyer. On the whole, it seems to be a most valuable bird.

511. **Crow Blackbird.** BRONZED GRACKLE. LE GRAND MAINATE. *Quiscalus quiscula.* L, 12. Plate LXXIV B. The largest of the blackbirds

Figure 463
Bronzed Grackle; scale, about ⅔.
Bill left white to show shape.

*Distinctions.* Large size, complete iridescent blackness, and straw-coloured eyes.

*Field Marks.* The all-black body, straw-yellow eyes, and size are good field marks. When flying the long tail of the male is "boated," that is, spread and turned up at the sides so that a cross-section through it would be U-shaped. This is a most characteristic feature and easily seen in outline against the sky in spring, but is less evident or absent in autumn.

*Nesting.* Usually in communities in coniferous trees; nest, a large, bulky mass of grass and mud. Some in hollow trees.

*Distribution.* Temperate North America, east of the Rockies. In Canada common west to southern Manitoba, growing scarcer and local towards the mountains in the southern parts of the Prairie Provinces.

*SUBSPECIES.* The Canadian representative of this species is the Bronzed Grackle (le Grand Mainate bronzé) *Quiscalus quiscula aeneus.* Many old lists record the Purple Grackle (le Grand Mainate pourpré) *Quiscalus quiscula quiscula* in the eastern provinces, but evidently under misapprehension as it is a more southern race and there is no evidence of occurrence in Canada.

The Crow Blackbird is a gregarious bird and likes to nest in company with its own kind. Evergreens are its favourite nesting trees and it often takes possession of ornamental rows, edging gardens. Its metallic colours and yellow eyes make it a brilliant and striking bird. It walks with comical pomposity over the lawn, or uncouthly gesticulates while it voices unusually discordant noises. As an early morning songster in the garden it is often a decided nuisance.

*Economic Status.* Through the months the bird is in Canada, insects constitute 29·7 per cent of its food and vegetable matter 70·3 per cent. The insects include useful predaceous species, but not in large numbers. The vegetable matter contains about 48 per cent of grain and domestic fruit, the remainder being wild fruit, mast, and weed seeds. Much of the grain is waste, and the total cultivated fruit is only 2·9 per cent. On the whole the work of the Bronzed Grackle is beneficial, but its numbers should not be allowed to increase greatly. It is an inveterate nest robber, and a poor bird to have about the garden if other more attractive species are desired.

495. **Cowbird.** COW BLACKBIRD. BUFFALO-BIRD. LE VACHER. *Molothrus ater.* L, 7·92. Plate LXXV A. The smallest of our blackbirds. Male: solid black with seal-brown head and neck.

*Distinctions.* A small blackbird, with short, sparrow-like bill (Figure 464). Male: jet black with metallic reflections and a seal-brown head. Female: uniform, ashy brown, lighter on throat. Juveniles are similar to the female, but more light-buffy with many soft, broken, dark stripes below, and all feathers edged with buffy ochre.

*Field Marks.* A small blackbird, with dark eyes and short bill; no decided markings anywhere. Notes, a harsh rattle and a grating squeak.

*Nesting.* Eggs laid in nests of other, usually smaller, birds. Entirely parasitic.

*Distribuion.* North America, south to Mexico. In Canada, across the continent; in the west, southern British Columbia and from the Mackenzie southward.

*SUBSPECIES.* The subspecies recognized by the Check-list as inhabiting eastern Canada is the type form the Eastern Cowbird (le Vacher de l'Est) *Molothrus ater ater.* A western subspecies, the Nevada Cowbird (le Vacher du Nevada) *Molothrus ater artemisiae,* has a slightly more slender bill, but this feature is not very marked or very constant. Western females show a faint striping below that is less apparent in eastern specimens. This is the form to be expected from Manitoba westward.

The Cowbird is our only habitually parasitic bird. It never builds a nest nor incubates nor cares for its young. In the absence of the rightful owners it takes the opportunity of depositing one of its own eggs in the unguarded nest of other birds. Usually the birds so imposed upon accept the foreign egg without protest, at other times there are strong objections and final resignation. In a few cases, the nest is deserted or a new nest is built over the offending egg, as is sometimes done by the Yellow Warbler. On incubation an interesting case of adaptation is shown. The Cowbird's egg usually hatches a few hours before those of the original occupant of the nest and consequently the interloper is strong and well grown when the proper occupants of the nest break their shell. It can monopolize the food, thus increasing the difference in strength, and is able finally to hoist its competitors from the nest to perish on the ground while it receives the attention that should have been given to the rightful brood. Thus practically every Cowbird is raised to maturity at the expense of a brood of another species and the Cowbird must be considered one of the greatest enemies of the species imposed upon. Once the foster parents accept the intruding egg they do not make any distinction between it and their own. The Cowbird receives its name from its habit of following cattle, evidently attracted by the flies and insects which gather about those animals.

Figure 464
Bill of Cowbird natural size.

In the early days, it probably followed the buffalo, which suggested its old, nearly forgotten name of Buffalo-bird.

*Economic Status.* From a study of their food, Cowbirds would seem to be purely useful birds. They consume large amounts of weed seeds and harmful insects and only small quantities of grain or fruit, the grain largely waste and the fruit wild. Their effect upon other equally useful birds, however, puts a different complexion on their activities. Practically every Cowbird raised to the fledgling stage means the elimination of a nest full of other species. Perhaps the economic effects of the changelings equal those of the individuals they displace, but the substitution cannot be looked upon with equanimity.

### FAMILY—THRAUPIDAE. TANAGERS.

*General Description.* Brilliantly coloured birds; in Canada, about the size of, or slightly larger than, the English Sparrow. Bills rather sparrow-like in outline, but slightly longer, and with an evenly curved culmen. Cutting edge of upper mandible toothed and notched as in Figure 465.

*Distinctions.* The spring males are very distinctively brilliant in colour. Autumn birds and juveniles are generally recognized by their soft, uniform yellow-green coloration, resembling some of the dull green vireos or warblers, but much larger. In the field, most likely to be confused with the orioles, but less active, more sluggish, and entirely different in action and bearing.

Figure 465
Scarlet Tanager, showing notched bill.

The tanagers are a typically American family that reaches its highest development in the tropics and is regularly represented in Canada by only two species. As a family the tanagers are so closely related to the sparrows that the status of some extralimital species is still undetermined.

607. **Western Tanager.** LOUISIANA TANAGER. CRIMSON-HEADED TANAGER. LE TANGARA DE L'OUEST. *Piranga ludoviciana.* L, 7. Plate LXXV B. Male in spring: bright lemon-yellow with crimson head and black saddle, wings, and tail; in autumn, with only traces of the crimson on head. Female and juveniles: dull yellow-green, yellowing on breast and below, with brownish wings and tail.

*Distinctions.* Male most like a bright male oriole, but with crimson or nearly solid yellow head, without black crown or bib. Females and juveniles with characteristic tanager bill (Compare Figures 465 and 462) and greener and less orange than female orioles. Females are more difficult to separate from female Scarlet Tanagers. Geographical range is a good guide, as the latter is not regularly found west of Manitoba nor the former east of western Saskatchewan. The Western female is not as clear a green above, the back is noticeably darker than the crown and nape, instead of being evenly coloured with it, and it has distinct white wing-bars that are absent in the Scarlet Tanager.

*Field Marks.* The spring male, a black and yellow bird with a crimson head, is unmistakable. Female and juvenile: evenly dull greenish birds, a little larger than an English Sparrow. Much more sluggish and less agile than the orioles. The characteristic note of the Western Tanager is an oft-repeated, quickly uttered "*Pricklydick.*"

*Nesting.* Nest, in trees or bushes, of twigs, rootlets, and moss, lined with soft material.

*Distribution.* Western North America. In Canada, east to western Saskatchewan, north to Mackenzie Valley.

One of the showiest of our western birds. Though not as spectacular as the Scarlet Tanager, it is much like it in general habit. It has a pleasant little song, suggesting the rolling syllables of the robin, but more continuous.

*Economic Status.* The food of the Western Tanager is composed mostly of insects, many of them of harmful species. It may, at rare intervals, take an appreciable amount of small fruit, but the good it does far outweighs the occasional damage.

608. **Scarlet Tanager.** RED BIRD. FIRE BIRD. WAR BIRD. LE TANGARA ÉCARLATE. *Piranga erythromelas.* L, 7·25. Plate LXXVI A. Spring male: a brilliant scarlet all over except wings and tail which are intense black. Female: dull greenish yellow, lightening to yellow on breast and underparts. Male, both adult and juvenile, in autumn similar to female, but with wings and tail black.

*Distinctions.* The intensely brilliant scarlet spring male, with sharply black wings and tail, is unmistakable. Female and autumn birds resemble female orioles, but are greener and with characteristic tanager notched bill (Compare Figures 465 and 462). They are more difficult to separate from the female and juvenile Western Tanager. Geographical range is a good guide. Specimens from Manitoba are most likely to be this species. They are clearer green than birds of the Western species, and the back is the same colour as the head and nape.

*Nesting.* Usually near the extremity of a branch on small tree in nest of leaves, strips of bark, etc.

*Distribution.* Eastern North America. In Canada, west rarely to southern Manitoba, and has been known to occur in Saskatchewan. One record for Vancouver Island.

The Scarlet Tanager shows remarkable seasonal and sexual plumage changes. In the spring the sexes are so entirely different that one wonders at their specific identity, and in the summer the brilliant scarlet male gradually assumes the dull green of his mate. In midsummer some moulting males, remarkably pied in scarlet and green, may be seen.

The Scarlet Tanager is a bird of light woodlands, where large timber grows with a sprinkling of small underbrush below, but in spring it occasionally visits the orchard. On arrival in spring the Scarlet Tanager is a most conspicuous object, but as the trees put on their leaves it becomes cautious in exposing itself and if it were not for its distinctive note "*Chip-chur*" that attracts attention it would be most difficult to find. The song is cheerful, rhythmical, and fairly sustained, something like a Robin's but more connected and not quite so clear.

*Economic Status.* The food of the Scarlet Tanager consists mostly of insects and fruit. The insects are mostly woodland species and their destruction is of importance to the forester and fruit grower. The fruit eaten is mostly wild, in fact most birds prefer wild to domestic fruit and given an abundance of the former seldom eat the latter. The Scarlet Tanager does no serious damage.

610. **Summer Tanager.** LE TANGARA ROSÉ. *Piranga rubra.* L, 7·50. Much like the Scarlet Tanager, but with red instead of black tail and dull brownish wings edged and tinged with red; the females bear the same relation to the male as do those of the Scarlet Tanager.

*Distinctions.* The wings and tail are different from those of the Scarlet Tanager and the red is more rose-coloured, less brilliant and lighter below than on the back. The female is a warm orange-green of quite a different shade to the cold greenish of the allied female. She bears a fairly close resemblance to the female Baltimore Oriole, but the evenly coloured, unmarked back and wings and the Tanager bill make separation easy.

*Distribution.* Southeastern United States and north to the latitude of southern Ohio. Has been recorded in Canada near the southern boundary along the lower Great Lakes and in New Brunswick and Nova Scotia.

The Summer Tanager is an accidental straggler in Canada, from the south, along the lower Great Lakes and in Nova Scotia and New Brunswick.

FAMILY—FRINGILLIDAE. SPARROWS, LINNETS, FINCHES, OR BUNTINGS

*General Description.* As represented in Canada this is generally an easily recognized family. It is composed of small birds—no Canadian species being over $8\frac{1}{2}$ inches in length—with unnotched conical bill adapted for cracking seeds, and the gape of the mouth usually decidedly turned down (Figures 466-468). This latter feature is not equally well developed in all species and some of the American Starlings (page 368), and the so-called English "Sparrow" (*See* page 366) as previously described, exhibit it strongly; but, having other marked characters, they can be easily distinguished from the sparrows.

Figure 466
Bill of Rose-breasted Grosbeak; about natural size.

Figure 467
Bill of Song Sparrow; about natural size.

Figure 468
Bill of Crossbill; about natural size.

*Distinctions.* The conical bill is the best point of recognition; that of the ordinary domesticated canary is of the characteristic sparrow type. The birds most likely to be mistaken for members of this family are the English Sparrow (page 366), the Bobolink (Figure 460, page 368) and Cowbird (Figure 464) of the previous family, and the tanagers of the next one. These, except the English Sparrow, are all easily separated by their striking colours (*See* under specific headings). The tanagers show notches in the cutting edges and tip of the mandibles which make them easy to recognize (Figure 465, page 377). In one group of sparrows, the crossbills, the tips of the bill cross each other (Figure 468); in another, the grosbeaks, the bill is very large and heavy (Figure 466).

The sparrows form the largest and most important family of the Perchers, and are probably the most important family of birds in the world. They are found everywhere except in Australia, and are represented in all habitats from wet swamps, grassy uplands, and brushy thickets to dry plains and sand dunes. The terms sparrow, linnet, finch, and bunting are almost synonymous and are applied to various species irrespective of their relationship. The name sparrow is, therefore, a very broad one and may be applied to many species. It is a pity that one objectionable introduced form (and that not a true member of the group) should, in America, have cast discredit upon a large family which includes many beautiful as well as useful birds and some of great sweetness of song. The most typical feature of the sparrows in popular estimation is a plain earthy coloration, but some of the brightest plumages are found amongst them and in place of the commonly expected sparrow chirp are some remarkable vocal achievements. The sparrows may be divided roughly into ground species, tree species, winter wanderers, and grosbeaks. Superficially observed, the first are dull in appearance, but on close examination often show beautiful colour harmonies. The tree species are often very brightly coloured. The winter wanderers usually exhibit large amounts of dull reds. The grosbeaks, recognized by their great, heavy bills (Figure 466), are highly coloured. This is not a scientific subdivision, but as the recognition of sparrows is difficult to the amateur any classification that will help is of use.

593. **Cardinal.** RED-BIRD. CARDINAL GROSBEAK. LE CARDINAL. *Richmondena cardinalis.* L, 8·25. A large sparrow and a typical grosbeak. The male is bright cardinal red with a black splash about the base of the bill and throat (Figure 469). Both sexes have a decided crest as prominent as that of the Blue Jay. The female is warm buff in colour, almost white below and olive-buff on the back, the wings, tail, and crest approaching the rosy colour of the male. The black face and throat of the male are faintly indicated.

Figure 469
Cardinal (male); natural size.

*Distinctions.* Absolutely unmistakable for anything else. The Pine Grosbeak may suggest the cardinal, but the red is never as solid and brilliant and it is without the crest or the striking black face mark. The Scarlet Tanager is as brilliantly red, but is without crest or face mark and the wings and tail are black.

*Field Marks.* The brilliant all red coloration of the male, the flash of warm reddish on the wings and tail of the female, and the prominent crest and large red bill in both sexes.

*Nesting.* In bushes, in nest of twigs, rootlets, and strips of bark, lined with grasses and rootlets.

*Distribution.* The cardinal in its various subspecies has a wide distribution in the United States and the type form crosses the Canadian border commonly along the western end of Lake Erie, occurring as scattered individuals and in isolated communities there and in adjoining localities. There is one record for Manitoba. The Eastern Cardinal (le Cardinal de l'Est), the one here considered, is the type form of the species.

The Cardinal is not generally distributed in Canada, but is a permanent resident wherever it is found, and its gorgeous colouring and brilliant whistling give an added interest to nature. It may surprise many that this southern bird ever occurs in Canada, but in some sections along the Lake Erie shore it is not only regular but common. It should be rigorously protected for its beauty as well as for more material reasons.

*Economic Status.* The cardinal feeds largely upon locusts, cicadas, potato bugs, rose chafers, plum and cherry scales, cutworms, weevils, and other destructive pests. In addition, it takes weed seeds in considerable amount and some wild fruit. There is no evidence that it damages cultivated fruit.

595. **Rose-breasted Grosbeak.** LE GROS-BEC À POITRINE ROSE. *Hedymeles ludovicianus.* L, 8·12. Plate LXXVI B. Spring male: tail, wings, back, head, and neck black, with conspicuous white patches on wings, rump, and tail; breast rose-red; below pure white. The female is an altogether different looking bird, with its typical sparrow-like striping above in dull olive-brown and pale ochres; below, white, sharply striped on breast and flanks. Autumn males are similar to the female, but warmer in general colour and with an undercolouring of rose on breast. In any plumage with large, light-coloured bill (Figure 466).

*Distinctions.* The spring male, with black back and head, flashing white-spotted wings and tail, and brilliant red bib, is unmistakable. The female resembles a Purple Finch in the olive plumage, but is obviously larger, much more contrastive in colour, and the underparts are purer white. Still more likely to be confused with the female of the Black-headed Grosbeak in the few regions where both species may occur. They resemble each other in nearly every detail of colour distribution and size, but the female Rose-breasted is decidedly duller in general tone and the breast is whiter and more obviously streaked (Compare with Plate LXXVII A). Juvenile and autumn males can always be recognized by having rose underwing-coverts.

*Field Marks.* The flashing black and white of the male with its conspicuous rose-coloured bib is always easily recognized. The female may be mistaken for the female Purple Finch, except for its larger size, whiter or more buffy underparts, with sparser stripings, white wing-bars, and, especially, its much more distinct light line over the eye. It is doubtful if it can always be satisfactorily known from the female Black-headed Grosbeak in life.

*Nesting.* In bushes or trees, 5 to 20 feet from ground, in poorly built nests of fine twigs, weed stalks, and rootlets.

*Distribution.* Eastern North America. In Canada, west to the base of the mountains and north to Athabaska Lake.

The Rose-breasted Grosbeak is one of our most beautiful birds, and with a very pleasing song much like that of a Robin. In the autumn its most frequent note is a curt, metallic "*klip*" that will often attract attention when it is hiding in dense foliage. It prefers tangled thickets and large trees, interspersed with open spaces. It frequents thickets along rivers, edges of woodland clearings, and sometimes orchards.

*Economic Status.* If the number of Rose-breasted Grosbeaks could be greatly increased on the farms the potato-bug scourge would soon disappear. This bird is one of the few that eats potato-beetles, and it takes them in both adult and larval stages. One-tenth of the contents of the stomachs examined consisted of potato-bugs, and against other insect pests this species is even more effective. To increase the numbers of Rose-breasted Grosbeaks may be difficult, but the next best thing is to conserve what we have, protect them from preventable destruction, and see that suitable nesting corners are left in waste corners of the farm and wood-lot. In carrying out plans for clean cultivation and the elimination of waste places, care should be taken that bits of shrubbery are left to afford shelter for birds which without these sanctuaries must disappear. The preservation of the birds will more than compensate for the small losses entailed.

596. **Black-headed Grosbeak.** LE GROS-BEC À TÊTE NOIRE. *Hedymeles melanocephalus.* L, 8·10. Plate LXXVII A. Male: head, face, wings, and tail, with a broken saddle across shoulders, black. Conspicuous white patches on wing and in tail. Throat,

breast, flanks, a ring about base of neck, streaks in black saddle, and rump are tawny buff, brightening in centre of abdomen to lemon-yellow. Female: striped above with brownish black, ochre, and white; white below; pale ochre suffusion across breast and sharply striped along flanks. Like the female Rose-breasted Grosbeak, but stronger in colour and more decided in pattern (Compare with Plate LXXVI B).

*Distinctions.* The black head and large areas of solid tawny buff of breast and around base of neck are perfectly distinctive for the male. The female is very much like the female Rose-breasted Grosbeak, but the colours are much stronger and contrastive, the breast is more ochraceous, and the stripings below are sparser, sharper, and confined more closely to the flanks. The dark of the head deepens to nearly black instead of only to a dark olive-brown. The markings and colours are much too decided to be confused with those of the Purple Finch, even if size of the bird were not a sufficient distinction.

*Field Marks.* Black head, wings, and tail, both the latter with contrastive patches of white, and the uniform buffy ochre of breast and flanks for the male. For the female, large size, general striped appearance, and the conspicuous white line over the eye. Almost black cheek and crown. Probably it cannot be separated readily from the female Rose-breasted Grosbeak in life.

*Nesting.* In bushes or trees, in nest of fine twigs, weed stalks, and rootlets.

*Distribution.* Western North America. In Canada, the southern parts of the western provinces, east to western Saskatchewan.

The Black-headed Grosbeak is a frequenter of deciduous growth and thickets, especially near water. It is a charming songster like the Rose-breasted Grosbeak, and resembles it in most of its habits.

*Economic Status.* The Black-headed Grosbeak has been accused of damaging fruit, and in California a very complete investigation was made of its food habits. The findings substantiate some of the charges, but also prove that from April to September its insect food amounts to practically three times the bulk of the vegetable supplies that it takes. These insects include many of the worst pests, codling moths, cankerworms, and several kinds of scales. As much of the vegetable food consists of weed seeds and wild fruits, except in very exceptional cases, it seems that any fruit it may take is small pay for the good it does.

597. **Blue Grosbeak.** LE GROS-BEC BLEU. *Guiraca caerulea.* L, 7·00. Heavy grosbeak bill and largely deep purplish blue with space in front of eye and chin black. Back blackish and some rusty on wings. Juvenile and female mottled brown and blue.

*Distinctions.* Size, general blueness, and heavy bill.

*Field Marks.* In life the blue is not as evident as might be expected and the bird is likely to appear of an ill-defined dusky colour like a female Cowbird. Juvenile Bluebirds may sometimes be mistaken for this species.

*Distribution.* Eastern North America, normally north to Maryland and southern Illinois. We have old and rather uncertain records for southern Nova Scotia.

598. **Indigo Bunting.** INDIGO BIRD. LE BRUANT INDIGO. *Passerina cyanea.* L, 5·59. Rather small, about the size of a Chipping or a Clay-coloured Sparrow. Male: brilliant blue all over, darkening on head. Female: dingy brown, rather whitish with indistinct stripes below and somewhat rusty above. Faint suggestions of blue on outer webs of wing and tail feathers. Autumn adults are between these two. Juveniles are softly striped below and decidedly washed with rusty above.

*Distinctions.* The male Indigo Bunting and the Mountain Bluebird are the only all-blue birds to be met with in Canada. The two are too far separated geographically, however, often to require special distinction. The bunting is much smaller, has a typical sparrow bill, and darkens instead of lightens towards the head. The female and juvenile are too dissimilar to be confused with the Bluebird, but are like the similarly sized Lazuli Bunting.

*Field Marks.* Small size and all-blue coloration of male, and the even, unstreaked dull or rusty coloration of the female and juvenile.

*Nesting.* Generally in the crotch of a bush; nest of grasses, dead leaves, and strips of bark, lined with fine grasses, rootlets, and long hairs.

A. White-throated Sparrow; scale, $\frac{1}{3}$

B. Song Sparrow; scale, $\frac{1}{3}$

Dakota Song Sparrow Rusty Song Sparrow

Plate LXXXVI

A. Lapland Longspur; scale, $\frac{1}{3}$

Female Male

B. Chestnut-collared Longspur; scale, $\frac{1}{3}$

Female Male

*Distribution.* Eastern North America. In Canada, west to southern Manitoba. One record for southwestern Saskatchewan, and one for Alberta.

The Indigo Bunting commonly frequents brushy, overgrown wastes, burnt land, or slashes. It has a pleasing song.

*Economic Status.* Our knowledge of the food of the Indigo Bunting is not complete. There is little doubt that it has the usual food habits of its family; in the east it is credited with doing good work against the brown-tailed moth.

599. **Lazuli Bunting.** LE BRUANT LAZULI. *Passerina amoena.* L, 5·50. Plate LXXVII B. A small sparrow, about the size of the Chipping or Clay-coloured Sparrow. Male: of striking bright blue, ruddy buff, and white. Female and juvenile: even, dull rusty-olive above, slightly bluing on rump; white below, with soft, warm, tawny suffusion across breast.

*Distinctions.* The male, with its strongly contrasted brilliant coloration, is unmistakable. The female and juvenile are recognizable by their evident sparrow-like bill, dull, even coloration, and usually the soft suggestion of blue on rump and the outer webs of tail and wing feathers. The only practically unstreaked, small, dull, earth-coloured sparrow in the west. Likely to be confused only with the Indigo Bunting, but so far separated in range from it as seldom to require comparison.

*Field Marks.* The adult male is unmistakable. The juvenile and female are recognized by small size and soft, even, earthy or slightly ruddy coloration.

*Nesting.* Generally in bushes. Nest of grasses, dead leaves, and strips of bark, lined with fine grasses, rootlets, and long hair.

*Distribution.* Western North America. In Canada, southern British Columbia and adjoining parts of Alberta, north to Jasper Park. Occasional records for southern Saskatchewan and Great Slave Lake..

The male is a veritable living jewel, that flashes in the sun. The female, as is the case with many bright species, is duller coloured. It is a bird of brushy wastes, and sings a sustained little warble that is very pleasing. In general habits and song quite similar to the Indigo Bunting of the east.

604. **Dickcissel.** LITTLE MEADOWLARK. LE DICKCISSEL. *Spiza americana.* L, 6. About the size of an English Sparrow. Male: back striped with dark brown and dull red, changing to solid dull red on wing-coverts; hindneck slate-grey to crown, where it is strongly tinged with yellow; cheeks grey, with pure yellow eyebrow-line. Below, white; breast pure yellow with a sharply defined black throat patch or bib (Figure 470). The female has a very close general resemblance to a female English Sparrow, but is paler, has sharper back streaks, and usually a suggestion of yellow in centre of breast and over eye.

Figure 470
Dickcissel (male); natural size.

*Distinctions.* The Dickcissel with its yellow breast and black bib, slightly suggestive of the much larger meadowlark, is very distinctive. The female might be mistaken for the female Bobolink, but is much less sharply marked and without any general ochre coloration. Differs from the female English Sparrow in its paler coloration, and suggestion of lemon-yellow on centre of breast and over eye.

*Field Marks.* A medium-sized sparrow, with yellow breast and black bib. Female is much too grey to be often confused, even in life, with the Bobolink, but, unless its associate male is present, the voice recognized, or the yellow on the breast visible, it may be difficult to separate it from the House Sparrow. The song of the male is very distinctive. the notes being a loud, clear "*Chup-chup-klip-klip-klip.*"

*Nesting.* On the ground, or in low bushes. Bulky nest of coarse grass and leaves, lined with finer grasses and hairs.

*Distribution.* Eastern North America. In western Canada, noted only occasionally from southern Manitoba and in single occurrences for southern Saskatchewan and Okanagan Valley, British Columbia. A frequenter of open fields or shrubby wastes, and is very rare in Canada. (*See* remarks under Carolina Wren, page 320.)

514. **Evening Grosbeak.** LE GROS-BEC ERRANT. *Hesperiphona vespertina.* L, 8. Plate LXXVIII A. One of the largest of the sparrows, with a very large, powerful, typical grosbeak bill (like Figures 466 and 469). It is coloured in broad masses of strong lemon-yellow, with black wings, tail, and crown; secondaries and tertiaries largely white; a bright yellow bar on forehead. The female is similar, but much duller and with an ashy wash over all.

*Distinctions.* Size; large yellowish or pale greenish bill; large amount of yellow and contrastive black and white wings. The male is unmistakable. The female, with her light-coloured bill, lemon-yellow on body, and large patch of white on black wings, is quite different from any other grosbeak (*See* Plates LXXIX A, LXXVI B, and LXXVII A).

*Field Marks.* Males are unmistakable. Large size, short tail, yellow coloration, pale-coloured bill, and large white patch in black wings. As it is usually a winter visitor within settled sections, females are most often to be compared with female Pine Grosbeaks (Plate LXXIX A), another winter migrant, but they are not so dull or evenly coloured and have pale beaks and contrastive black and white wings. The females of the Rose-breasted and Black-headed Grosbeaks are both sharply streaked (Plates LXXVI B and LXXVII A).

*Nesting.* In trees; nest of small twigs, lined with bark, hair, and rootlets. Nestings have been located in the western mountain districts and in the heavy spruce forest in the region north of Lake Superior, nests have usually been in the tops of tall trees and difficult to locate.

*Distribution.* Central and western North America. Breeding in the northern coniferous forest from western Ontario westward, and along the mountains to New Mexico. Migrates south and east in winter.

*SUBSPECIES.* The species is divided into two races in the Check-list; the Eastern Evening Grosbeak (le Gros-bec errant de l'Est) *Hesperiphona vespertina vespertina* occupies the mid-section of the continent. The Western Evening Grosbeak (le Gros-bec errant de l'Ouest) *Hesperiphona vespertina brooksi* inhabits the mountains of the west. It is distinguished from the eastern one by the bill averaging slightly slenderer and with more and darker olive in the yellow of the male. The female has a darker crown in slight contrast with the back. This last detail seems the most constant distinction. This is only a winter visitor to most of the prairie country, and an irregular wanderer in the east. It is very irregular in its summer and breeding range, being present one year and absent the next. In summer it is very retiring and unobtrusive, frequenting the tallest trees where it is very difficult to observe. It is only recently that we have succeeded in getting any authentic data north of Lake Superior on the breeding range of the eastern race, though that of the western one has long been known.

*Economic Status.* The Evening Grosbeak, coming only in winter, can do very little harm. Its favourite food is the seed of the Manitoba maple left hanging on the trees. The fact that the Manitoba maple has in recent years been planted extensively in many parts of Canada may affect the migration habits of this bird. Almost any dried winter fruit is taken and it delights to remove the seeds from old rotten apples left hanging through the winter. The charge that it damages trees by picking off the buds may contain an element of truth, but the habit cannot be seriously considered as a source of appreciable damage.

517. **Common Purple Finch.** LE PINSON POURPRÉ COMMUN. *Carpodacus purpureus.* L, 6·22. Plate LXXVIII B. About the size of the English Sparrow. Adult male: head, breast back, and rump washed with dull purplish rose, more or less variegated or striped with brown on back. Wings and tail brown, slightly edged with rose. Below, white. Females and juveniles: dull brownish olive, more or less broken into stripes above, and heavily striped with olive on white below.

*Distinctions.* To be seriously confused only with Cassin's Finch of the interior of British Columbia. The adult male is red like the Pine Grosbeak, but very much smaller; the female and juveniles, with their considerable olive streaking, are quite distinctive from that species. This Purple Finch may bear a superficial resemblance to the crossbills, but is larger and the mandibles are not crossed (Compare with Figure 468). From Cassin's Finch, it can be distinguished only by attention to small details. The crown of the adult male is solid rosy, but not as bright as in Cassin's and it blends into the nape without forming a definite cap. In other plumages the olive is of a slightly darker shade and the streakings below are softer. The undertail-coverts are generally unstreaked, or at least never so sharply, and the bird is appreciably smaller. A bird, though within the normal range of Cassin's Finch, with a wing of 3·3 inches or under, is probably this species.

*Field Marks.* Size, general colour of adult male, like a small Pine Grosbeak. General olive and white striping below of female and juvenile. Probably not separable with certainty from Cassin's Finch in life. That species, however, may be expected in Canada only in southern British Columbia east of the Coast Range, where the common Purple Finch does not regularly occur.

*Nesting.* In coniferous trees; nest of twigs, grass, and rootlets.

*Distribution.* Most of North America. In Canada, most of the wooded area, except British Columbia east of the Coast Range. Migrates south through the prairies.

*SUBSPECIES.* The form occurring throughout most of Canada is the Eastern Purple Finch (le Pinson pourpré de l'Est) *Carpodacus purpureus purpureus.* On the west coast of southern British Columbia occurs the California Purple Finch (le Pinson pourpré de la Californie) *Carpodacus purpureus californicus.* Its chief distinctions from the eastern race are: slightly smaller average size, more even coloration, and less striping in the red male, and a greener olive in the female.

Purple Finches, so called, are not "purple" in the ordinary use of the term. "Magenta" would better describe it in modern terminology, but it has lately been said that the colour is really "purple" in the original application of the word. It is one of our finest songsters and is occasionally caged for that purpose. Like its allies, the Pine Grosbeak and the crossbills, when kept in captivity it loses the bright redness of its plumage and assumes a ruddy yellow, so peculiar and characteristic that escaped caged birds can be recognized at sight. The song is a continued and clear warble like that of a Warbling Vireo, but more rapidly delivered. The young male in the autumn sings almost as well as the adult.

*Economic Status.* The Common Purple Finch eats largely of buds and fruit. The fruit eaten is generally trifling, as the bird retires from the borders to less cultivated sections in the breeding season and is not numerous in summer in fruit-growing sections. The fruits it takes are, therefore, mostly waste winter left-overs or wild forms, and it is specially fond of mountain-ash or rowan-berries. The charge that it eats buds is more serious, but so far has been based upon general assertions not substantiated by results of stomach examinations.

518. **Cassin's Purple Finch.** LE PINSON DE CASSIN. *Carpodacus cassini.* L, 6·75. Almost exactly similar to the Purple Finch (Plate LXXVIII B).

*Distinctions.* To be seriously confused only with the Common Purple Finch, and then only in the southern interior of British Columbia. Distinguished from that species by small details: the crown of the red male is a brighter, more crimson, red and forms a definite cap, and the body is pinker. In other plumages, the olive is of a slightly greyer shade, more of an earth brown, and the streakings below are sharper and better defined. The undertail-coverts are always sharply centre-streaked, and the bird is appreciably larger than the Common Purple Finch. A Purple Finch with wing over 3·3 is probably this species. Otherwise, the male has a general resemblance to the Pine Grosbeak, but is considerably smaller, and various plumages may suggest those of the crossbills, although the mandibles are not crossed (Compare Figure 468) and the bird is slightly larger.

*Field Marks.* Size, general colour of adult, like a small Pine Grosbeak. General olive and white streakiness of the female and juvenile. Probably not separable from the Purple Finch in life, except on geographical considerations.

*Nesting.* In coniferous trees; nest of twigs, grass, and rootlets.

*Distribution.* Western North America. In Canada, regularly found only in the southern interior of British Columbia, east of the Coast Range. It thus fills the gap between the Eastern Purple Finch of the prairies and the California Purple Finch of the coast; a distinct but closely allied species interposed between the ranges of two allied subspecies.

General habits and economic status not differing greatly from those of the Common Purple Finch.

515. **Pine Grosbeak.** LE GROS-BEC DES PINS. *Pinicola enucleator.* L, 9·08. Plate LXXIX A. One of the largest of the sparrows, with typical, heavy grosbeak bill (like Figure 466). Dull, uniform grey, but the adult male suffused with strong rosy or scarlet hues over head, back, wings, and breast. Females and juveniles with rusty yellow suffusion over head and rump.

*Distinctions.* The red male is rather similar to the Purple Finches, but is a rosier red and much larger. By reason of winter occurrence in most localities, likely to be confused only with the Evening Grosbeak. The Pine Grosbeak, however, has a dark instead of a light-coloured bill, and the wings are dull brownish grey with white wing-bars, but not conspicuously black and white. Unlike the female Rose-breasted or Black-headed Grosbeaks it has no stripes anywhere in any plumage.

*Field Marks.* Size; dark, grosbeak bill, and the general red of adult male. The majority of birds that come south during migration are in the dull juvenile or female plumage, and a flock gives the effect of a number of large, dull, slate-coloured birds, in favourable lights warming to yellow on crown and rump. They are usually accompanied by a few rosy red individuals. The ordinary notes are ridiculously small and thin for so large a bird, though it has a clear, loud whistle.

*Nesting.* In coniferous trees; nest of twigs and rootlets.

*Distribution.* Northern parts of Europe, Asia, and North America. In America, the northern parts of the continent and down the mountains to New Mexico. In Canada, breeding in the northern coniferous forest and south along the western mountains. Migrates southward in winter.

*SUBSPECIES.* Divided, by slight characters, into a number of geographical races. Those accepted in the Check-list for Canada are as follows: the Canadian Pine Grosbeak (le Gros-bec des pins du Canada) *Pinicola enucleator leucura* is the eastern bird, breeding throughout the northern forest, west to the Mackenzie. The Rocky Mountain Pine Grosbeak (le Gros-bec des pins des Rocheuses) *Pinicola enucleator montana* of the boreal summits of the mountains from central Alberta southward. The Alaska Pine Grosbeak (le Gros-bec des pins de l'Alaska) *Pinicola enucleator alascensis* breeds from the Mackenzie into Alaska and down the mountains to the state of Washington. The Kodiak Pine Grosbeak (le Gros-bec des pins de Kodiak) *Pinicola enucleator flammula* breeds on the southern Alaskan coast. A rich rosy form from the Queen Charlotte Islands (le Gros-bec des pins de Reine-Charlotte) *Pinicola enucleator carlottae*, the best-marked form of all, has recently been described. All these forms may occur south of their breeding range in winter migration. As the characters are difficult of recognition, the wanderings of the races have not been accurately mapped.

These, throughout most of southern Canada, are winter visitors from the north. Their presence can rarely be anticipated, for their movements are very irregular. They are frequenters of coniferous trees, but are very fond of the mountain-ash or rowan-tree berries and the fruit of the sumach.

*Economic Status.* As the Pine Grosbeak spends the summer in the northern woods and visits settled sections only in winter, the damage it can do is reduced to a minimum. It eats wild and waste fruit left hanging on the trees, so that its economic effect is too slight to be appreciable.

524. **Common Rosy Finch.** GREY-CROWNED LEUCOSTICTE. PINK SNOW-BIRD. LE PINSON ROSE COMMUN. *Leucosticte tephrocotis.* L, 6·15. A medium-sized sparrow. Seal-brown over most of body; black cap; conspicuous patch of light grey on face and across nape (Figure 471); rump, flanks, and abdomen and the greater part of the wings washed with light rose.

Figure 471
Hepburn's Rosy Finch; natural size.

*Distinctions.* A seal-brown sparrow with considerable rose suffusion. Cannot be mistaken for any other species known to occur in Canada.

*Nesting.* Nest of bark and grass; on the ground, between or under rocks at high altitudes.

*Distribution.* Western North America. In Canada, breeding only in the mountains above timber-line in British Columbia and the Yukon. Comes in winter to lower levels, and spreads over the prairies, sometimes as far as Manitoba.

*SUBSPECIES.* Two subspecies of this bird are recognized. The type form, the Grey-crowned Rosy Finch (le Pinson rose à joues brunes) *Leucosticte tephrocotis tephrocotis* is characterized by having the cheeks and ear-coverts brown, like the rest of the body. This is the bird of the main Rockies to central Yukon and Alaska. Hepburn's Rosy Finch (le Pinson rose à joues grises) *Leucosticte tephrocotis littoralis* has the grey of the face extended over the cheeks and ear-coverts, and sometimes across the chin. It is the representative of the species along the Coast Range from Alaska Peninsula southward. It is not confined to the immediate vicinity of the coast and the division between the two forms has not been well mapped. In the intermountain lowlands of British Columbia, both subspecies may occur in winter, even associated together in the same flock. On the plains, *tephrocotis* is the bird to be expected though occasional *littoralis* may occur as far east as Saskatchewan.

A most charming little bird, spending the summer on the snow edges of the highest mountains. In winter it comes in large flocks to the lowlands and even invades the streets of the foothill cities.

## Redpolls (*See* Plate LXXIX B)

*General Description.* Small sparrows with short, sharp bills; crown with a dull crimson cap; a suffused black chin-spot; back and flanks streaked with browns, ashy, and white. Adult males have rosy breasts and the rump more or less tinged with pink; suggestions of this tint show in other plumages.

*Distinctions.* The small crimson cap is always distinctive.

*Nesting.* In low shrubs; nest of grasses lined with hair, often white rabbit or fox fur, feathers, or plant-down.

*Distribution.* Circumpolar and Arctic in breeding range, migrating south irregularly in winter.

There are two species of redpolls in Canada, divided into five subspecies, all so nearly alike that it requires special experience to differentiate them accurately. The dividing line between species is very fine, the subspecies intergrade, numerous hybrids have been reported, and, as considerable individual and age variation exists, it is only by attention to small details that the different forms can be separated.

The distinctive characters are given more as suggestions than as final differentiations.

*Economic Status.* *See* Common Redpoll.

527. **Arctic Redpoll.** LE SIZERIN ARCTIQUE. *Acanthis hornemanni.* L, 5. Light-coloured redpolls with unspotted white or rosy rump. Characteristic adults with feather edgings light so that a typical bird looks like a Common Redpoll (Plate LXXIX B) seen through a white veil, but many birds, even in breeding maturity, show little of this frosting and are inseparable from the Common Redpoll except by other characters.

*Distinctions.* The rump, unspotted or unstriped, is the best means of separating this species from other redpolls, although this point is sometimes not easy to determine.

*Distribution.* The Arctic and sub-Arctic parts of the northern hemisphere. In America, breeding across the Arctic, migrating throughout most Canadian provinces in the winter.

*SUBSPECIES.* The Hoary Redpoll (le Sizerin blanchâtre) *Acanthis hornemanni exilipes* is the American form of this species, and the only one so far reported from southern Canada. The Greenland Redpoll (le Sizerin Groenlandais) *Acanthis hornemanni hornemanni* is similar to the Hoary in colour, but much larger. It has never been detected in Canada south of the sub-arctic regions even in winter.

In general habits so nearly like the next species, which is much more common, that separate discussion is unnecessary. This species is generally so rare in settled districts that its identification must be made with caution. During occasional winters this species occurs in greater or less numbers with large flocks of the Common Redpoll, but there is no regularity in its visits.

528. **Redpolled Linnet.** LE SIZERIN À TÊTE ROUGE. *Acanthis linaria.* L, 5-5·5. Plate LXXIX B. A rather dark redpoll with rump more or less heavily streaked, and body not noticeably frosted with white.

*Distinctions.* The streaked rump is the most distinctive character.

*Distribution.* Northern parts of northern hemisphere. In America, breeding across the Arctic regions. Migrates in winter practically everywhere in Canada.

*SUBSPECIES.* The species is divided into three subspecies: the Common Redpoll (le Sizerin commun à tête rouge) *Acanthis linaria linaria* which is commonest in fact as well as name; Holboell's Redpoll (le Sizerin de Holboell) *Acanthis linaria holboelli*, a slightly larger form whose occurrence in America is a matter of some doubt; and the Greater Redpoll (le grand Sizerin à tête rouge) *Acanthis linaria rostrata*, the largest of the species. There are small differences visible to the eye of the expert in the bills and details of coloration, but size is, on the whole, the best criterion though it should not be entirely relied upon as intergrades occur. The wing of the Common Redpoll should be 2·9 inches, Holboell's 3·0 with slightly longer bill, and the Greater 3·5 with bill shorter and stouter. However, in identifying redpolls it should be remembered that the Common is the one likely to be met with anywhere in Canada, and, though redpolls are likely to wander widely in winter, we have no definite evidence of any other form of *linaria* than the Common Redpoll west of the Great Lakes.

With more or less regularity our winter fields and waste lands are taken possession of by immense flocks of tiny sparrows, feeding on the weed-tops which project from the snow, or perching in the low trees and bushes nearby. From many little throats comes a subdued but constant twitter, no one of the birds producing a song in the usual sense of the word, but collectively making an undercurrent of low music that is distinctly agreeable. The round, fluffy, heavily plumaged bodies; the little, rich crimson cap; and the occasional flash of rosy breast and pink rump declare them redpolls. They are tame and unsuspecting little fellows and if the observer conducts himself discreetly they may at times alight all about him, or even upon his person, with as much indifference as if he were a stump or some other inanimate feature of the landscape. They remain until the spring breakup when they vanish until another winter. Their winter wanderings are irregular and erratic.

*Economic Status.* Coming in flocks of large numbers and searching weed-tops diligently the redpolls should be hailed by the farmer with pleasure, not only for their pretty ways but also for the evident good they do in destroying weed seed. One cannot go over the ground where they have fed and examine it closely without being impressed with the amount of good work they have done. Their tracks are seen everywhere in the snow and every little weed-top seems to have been scrutinized with microscopic eye. Considering their numbers and that they come in the coldest weather, when they require much food, it is evident that their presence must have a marked deterrent effect upon the following season's weed crop.

533. **Pine Siskin.** LE CHARDONNERET DES PINS. *Spinus pinus.* L, 5. Small, goldfinch-like birds striped with olive-brown on a dull white ground, some slightly tinged with yellowish; lighter below and a lemon-yellow spot and suffusion on the wings (Figure 472).

*Distinctions.* General streakiness and suffused yellow wing-spot.

*Field Marks.* Goldfinch-like habits and voice, and general streakiness.

*Nesting.* In coniferous trees; nest of twigs and rootlets lined with plant-down.

*Distribution.* North America. Breeding in the northern coniferous woods across the continent, and down the mountains in the west to Lower California. An irregular migrant throughout all southern Canada; breeding locally in suitable localities.

Figure 472
Pine Siskin; natural size.

This is another of the irregular, sporadic winter wanderers. It is irregular in its nesting, both in time and place, and individuals in evident breeding condition may be found in midsummer in large flocks of supposedly non-breeding birds.

*Economic Status.* As it is usually only a winter visitor to most cultivated sections, and shows strong partiality for the fruit of coniferous trees, it is a neutral species, perhaps doing no great good but certainly no harm.

529. **American Goldfinch.** THISTLEBIRD. WILD CANARY. LE CHARDONNERET JAUNE. *Spinus tristis.* L, 5·10. Plate LXXX A. A small, canary-like bird. Spring male: bright lemon-yellow with black cap, wings, and tail. Females: generally similar, but without black cap; the wings and tail more brown than black, and yellow overwashed, especially on upper parts, with olive-green. Winter birds of both sexes similar to the summer female, but colours still further flattened and greyed, and almost pure white below. The male, however, still retains his black wings and tail, but broadly feather-edged with white.

*Distinctions.* The summer male, with strongly contrasted black and yellow, can be mistaken for no other species. The female, except for its typical sparrow bill, might be confused with some of the small, green warblers or vireos. In winter, the colours are less distinctive, but there is always a suggestion of yellow about the head and back if not elsewhere, and the wings of the male, at least, remain decidedly black with only edgings of white or buffy. Separated from the Pine Siskin by an entire lack of streakiness in any plumage.

*Field Marks.* Bright yellow, or general yellow and green colour with black wings and tail. By actions and form obviously sparrows and not warblers or vireos. In habit, notes, and disposition, Goldfinches resemble Pine Siskins or crossbills, but are distinguished from the first by their lack of streakiness and from the latter by absence of any shade of red, lighter coloration when in green plumage, and white uppertail-coverts.

*Nesting.* Nest of grasses and plant-down, lined with the latter.

*Distribution.* North America, from southern Canada, south. In Canada, across the southern parts.

*SUBSPECIES.* Three subspecies of Goldfinch are recognized in western Canada. The Eastern Goldfinch (le Chardonneret jaune de l'Est) *Spinus tristis tristis* extends west to eastern Manitoba. In the interior of British Columbia is the Pale Goldfinch (le Chardonneret jaune pâle) *Spinus tristis pallidus*, a bird practically indistinguishable in summer from *tristis*, but much paler in the winter plumage. The form of the prairies, from western

Manitoba to the mountains, is postulated to be *pallidus*. However, corroborative specimens have not been seen by the writer. Late autumn and winter specimens are greatly to be desired from this area. The bird of the southern British Columbia coast is the Willow Goldfinch (le Chardonneret jaune des saules) *Spinus tristis salicamans*, which has a slightly darker coloration even than *tristis*, and the saddle of the summer male averages a more olive-green. The distinctions shown by Canadian specimens, except in the case of the winter plumage of *pallidus*, are very fine indeed.

One of the merriest of summer birds. It is a great lover of fluffy white thistle and dandelion seed-heads and may often be seen plucking the down, cutting off the fruiting end, and letting the airy tops float away on the wind. Its song is as pleasant as its bright appearance as it sits on some lone elevation and sings "*Sweet-sweet-chewit-chewit-chewit*" or as it goes speeding off through the air in a merry flock repeating a cheerful "*Per-chic-o-pee.*" The American Goldfinch, though a relative of the Old World bird of the similar name, is an entirely different species, named, as the original settlers named many birds, from various fancied or real resemblances to the familiar forms known at home.

*Economic Status.* A bird of no bad habits and many good ones. Weed seeds are its staple food, and grain is rarely touched. If the English Sparrows do not exhaust the supply prematurely, sunflower seed-heads are a never-failing attraction to goldfinches and a supply of these along the back fence will ensure their constant attendance through the autumn and winter. Insects are taken more or less and some fruit, usually wild species, as no complaint is made of any damage done to cultivated varieties.

521. **Red Crossbill.** AMERICAN CROSSBILL. CROSSBILL. LE BEC-CROISÉ ROUGE. *Loxia curvirostra.* L, 6·19. A small or medium-sized sparrow with the bill-tips prolonged and crossing each other when closed (Figure 473). The male is dull red, brighter on rump; females and juveniles similar, but the red replaced by greenish or yellow. No wing-bars. Many mixed and intergrading plumages between the green and red are to be met with; the red may vary from yellowish orange to pure brick-red, and a series of specimens may show a bewildering array of different shades and tints.

Figure 473
Bill of Crossbill; natural size.

*Distinctions.* The crossed bill is distinctive of the crossbills; the lack of white wing-bar designates this species.

*Field Marks.* Small birds, usually in winter, often in large flocks, some individuals showing red coloration. Notes somewhat similar to those of goldfinches. Climbing, almost parrot-like, habits.

*Nesting.* Usually in coniferous trees; nest of twigs and grasses lined with moss and rootlets. May nest almost any month of the year from January to September.

*Distribution.* Europe, northern Asia, and northern North America. In America, the coniferous forests across the continent, south in the western mountains to Mexico. Migrates irregularly south in winter.

*SUBSPECIES.* The Red Crossbill of most of Canada is the American Crossbill (le Bec-croisé rouge d'Amérique) *Loxia curvirostra pusilla*, breeding from Quebec to central Alaska. The Newfoundland Crossbill (le Bec-croisé rouge de Terre-Neuve) *Loxia curvirostra percna* is the bird of Newfoundland and Nova Scotia as Bendire's Crossbill (le Bec-croisé rouge de Bendire) *Loxia curvirostra bendirei* is of interior British Columbia southward. The crossbill of the west coast is the Sitka Crossbill (le Bec-croisé rouge de Sitka) *Loxia curvirostra sitkensis*.

The crossbills are winter birds throughout most of settled Canada, and come irregularly out of the north for successive seasons, and then are not seen again, perhaps for years. In the mountains, where altitude brings northern conditions in close proximity to cultivation, they are more

Plate LXXXVII

Snow Bunting; scale, $\frac{1}{3}$

often seen. Like several other birds of similar irregular habits, especially their close relative the White-winged Crossbill, they are most uncertain in their breeding, both as to time and place, and their presence at any given season or locality can not be depended upon.

*Economic Status.* The species feeds very largely upon the seeds of coniferous trees, and the speed with which they husk off the scales of various cones for the seed beneath causes one to think that the crossed bill is particularly adapted for the purpose. Almost any dried fruit hanging on the winter trees is acceptable to them. They seem specially fond of the little woolly aphis. It was very interesting to watch a captive specimen open galls on poplar leaves. Seizing the fleshy tissue with the bill tips so that the points crossed within the mass, it gave a little twist of the head that split the gall wide open and the aphides within were removed with the tongue.

522. **White-winged Crossbill.** LE BEC-CROISÉ À AILES BLANCHES. *Loxia leucoptera.* L, 6·05. Similar to preceding species, but with white bars on wings (*See* Figure 474).

*Distinctions.* Perhaps brighter in coloration and a rosier red than the Red Crossbill, but showing considerable variation in tint and shade. The white wing-bars and crossed bill are always diagnostic.

*Field Marks.* Similar to those of the Red Crossbill, but with a white bar on the wing.

*Nesting.* Usually in coniferous trees; in nest of twigs and grasses, lined with moss and rootlets. May nest almost any month of the year from January to September.

*Distribution.* Northern North America. In Canada, across the continent, through the northern coniferous forest and south in the mountains to southern British Columbia. Migrates irregularly south in winter.

So similar to the preceding in habits and occurrence, that no special discussion is necessary. As a rule it is a bird of the spruces as the Red Crossbill is of the pines.

592. 1. **Green-tailed Towhee.** LE TOWHEE À QUEUE VERTE. *Oberholseria chlorura.* Entirely different from the other more common towhees of Canada. Olive-green above, white below and on throat. A grey breast-band and a bright brick-red cap (Figure 474). Females duller than males.

*Distinctions.* A rather large, greenish backed sparrow with striking red cap and white throat.

*Distribution.* Central Oregon and Montana southward. There is a single record for southern Saskatchewan.

Figure 474
Green-tailed Towhee; natural size.

587. **Eastern Towhee.** RED-EYED TOWHEE. GROUND ROBIN. CHEWINK. LE TOWHEE DE L'EST. *Pipilo erythrophthalmus.* L, 8·35. Male: almost exactly like the male Spotted Towhee (Plate LXXX B), but without the white spotting on the wing-coverts and scapulars; the outer vanes of the primaries, near the base, are white, making a white spot on the closed wing. The female is like the male, but has the black replaced with rusty wood-brown.

*Distinctions.* Requiring separation only from the Spotted Towhee as above.

*Field Marks.* A mere glimpse of the black or brown head and back, red flanks, and white underparts cutting in a sharp band across the breast, is sufficient whereby to recognize this Towhee. As it dashes away into the underbrush, the flash of black and white in the male, or the brown and white in the female, is unmistakable. The rich brown of the female and the lack of small spotting on the shoulders and wings will separate from the Spotted Towhee in the few areas where the two species may occasionally overlap in range.

*Nesting.* On or near the ground, in nest of dead leaves and strips of bark, lined with fine grasses.

*Distribution.* Eastern North America. In Canada, the more southern parts west to include southern Manitoba.

*SUBSPECIES.* The only subspecies represented in Canada is the Red-eyed Towhee (le Towhee aux yeux rouges) or Chewink *Pipilo erythrophthalmus erythrophthalmus.*

The Towhee is a bird of brushy wastes or wood-edges, where its distinctive note "*Chewee*" or "*To-wee*" is a familiar sound. It delights to perch on the top of a sapling standing alone in the underbrush and sing its clear "*Dick-yoo, chiddle-chiddle-chiddle.*" On being disturbed it drops straight down into the underbrush, its black and white uniform flashing an instant, then vanishes in the tangle, whence it peers about uttering its usual "*Che-wee*" in inquisitive accents. In feeding it scratches over the surface like a hen, making the dead leaves fly in all directions.

588. **Spotted Towhee.** LE TOWHEE TACHETÉ. *Pipilo maculatus.* L, 8·35. Plate LXXX B. Male: jet black above, including head, neck, and upper breast, cutting sharply across chest against pure white underparts. A broad bar of reddish brown or bay along flanks. Wing-coverts and outer scapulars conspicuously spotted with white. Female similar, but the black greyish.

*Distinctions.* Only to be confused with the preceding Eastern Towhee, but easily distinguished by the liberal white spotting of the wing-coverts and scapulars. The back, head, and upper breast of the female are greyish black instead of light wood-brown, as in that species.

*Field Marks.* The large amount of contrasting black and white, and the reddish flanks are enough to identify this species at a glance. The amount of spotting on the wings and the grey-black, instead of wood-brown, of the female will separate it from the Eastern Towhee in the few localities where their ranges may occasionally overlap.

*Nesting.* On or near the ground in brush; nest of dead leaves and strips of bark, lined with fine grasses.

*Distribution.* Western North America. In Canada, from southeastern Manitoba and south Saskatchewan westward through southern British Columbia to the coast. Migrant elsewhere, it is resident on the coast.

*SUBSPECIES.* The towhee of the prairie regions is the Northern Spotted Towhee (le Towhee tacheté du Nord) *Pipilo maculatus arcticus.* That of the interior of British Columbia, the Nevada Towhee (le Towhee du Nevada) *Pipilo maculatus curtatus* (shown in Plate LXXX B) is very slightly different from it. On the coast, however, the Oregon Towhee (le Towhee de l'Orégon) *Pipilo maculatus oregonus* shows quite distinct characters, the white spotting of the wings and back is very much less, and the red of the flanks is deeper and richer in colour.

Like the Eastern Towhee, the Spotted is a bird of the brush and almost identical with it in general habits. To those familiar with the former, the latter presents nothing strikingly new. The notes are similar enough to be recognized as a towhee's, but with a sufficiently different tone and accent to attract attention. On the whole, the Spotted Towhee's voice is hoarser, and its song less clearly musical than that of its eastern relative.

*Economic Status.* Probably not different from that of the Eastern Towhee.

605. **Lark Bunting.** LE BRUANT NOIR ET BLANC. *Calamospiza melanocorys.* L, 7·2. Plate LXXXI A. About the size of an English Sparrow. The spring male is a very conspicuous bird, solid black with a large white patch on the wings. The female and male in autumn, and the juvenile are dull-coloured birds, striped above in light, dull, earthy browns; below, white, sharply striped on breast and flanks.

*Distinctions* The spring male, black and with conspicuous white wing patches, is unmistakable. Other plumages resemble that of the female English Sparrow, except for the stripes on breast, or those of dull-coloured Purple Finches, but are earthy in tone rather than olive. From all comparable species they may be known by the white, in young birds cream, upperwing-coverts.

*Field Marks.* Spring male like a small blackbird with white patches on wings. Females are likely to look like female English Sparrows with a striped breast and white spots on the end of the tail feathers. Being an open-field bird, it is not often to be confused with the Purple Finch, which is essentially a tree-inhabiting species.

*Nesting.* On the ground; nest of grasses and fine roots.

*Distribution.* The plains of central North America. In Canada, southern Saskatchewan and probably adjoining parts of Alberta. There are occasional records for southern British Columbia and southwestern Manitoba.

A bird of our most southern and open prairies. It is shy and difficult to approach, but the male is recognizable at long range by its striking colour. It has a delightful flight song that has suggested the name of "Lark" Bunting.

541. **Ipswich Sparrow.** LE PINSON D'IPSWICH. *Passercules princeps.* L, 6·25. Like a large and very pale Savannah Sparrow (*See* next species).

*Distinctions.* Distinguished from the Savannah Sparrow by larger size and light coloration; in autumn, also, by an almost complete lack of yellow on the bend of the wing and in front of the eye. Distinguished from the Vesper Sparrow by light coloration, lack of red on shoulders, and, in spring, by yellow on the bend of the wing and in front of the eye. Distinguished from the Song Sparrow by its lighter colour and, in spring, by the yellow as above.

*Field Marks.* A very pale sparrow about the size of a Vesper Sparrow.

This bird has a limited and isolated distribution. Its only known breeding place is Sable Island, off the Nova Scotia coast, about 60 miles south of Cape Breton. In winter it migrates down the Atlantic coast never wandering far inland. It is of small economic importance.

542. **Savannah Sparrow.** LE PINSON DES SAVANES. *Passerculus sandwichensis.* L, 5·68. Plate LXXXI B. A rather small sparrow striped above with brown, ashy, and intermediate shades. Below, white with sharp brown streaks on the breast, flanks, and in some cases on the throat. Yellow on the bend of the wing and a spot in front of the eye. Autumn birds are generally overwashed with buffy and the markings are softer and more diffused.

*Distinctions.* The Savannah Sparrow may be distinguished from the Song Sparrow by the yellow spots in front of the eye and on the bend of the wing and by the lack of the aggregated streaks which form a spot in the middle of the breast of the Song Sparrow.

*Field Marks.* The Savannah Sparrow may be recognized in the field by striped breast, yellow line over the eye, and by its notes. Its song is a fine, insect-like "*Tsip-tsip-you-re-e-e-e-e-you,*" the first notes often too faint to be heard and the whole with a peculiar far-carrying intensity and high pitch that leave one in doubt whether it is close at hand or very far away.

*Nesting.* On the ground, in nest of grasses lined with finer material.

*Distribution.* North America, north to the Arctic coast. Breeds practically everywhere in Canada except on the Arctic Islands.

*SUBSPECIES.* Divided into a number of subspecies, of which the following are recognized as occurring in Canada. The Eastern Savannah Sparrow (le Pinson des savanes de l'Est) *Passerculus sandwichensis savanna* is the bird of the east and may extend west to eastern Manitoba and northwestward probably to interior Alaska. There is a dark, northeastern form, the Labrador Savannah Sparrow (le Pinson des savanes du Labrador) *Passerculus sandwichensis labradorius*, the extent of whose range is as yet uncertain. The Savannah Sparrow of the prairies, long lumped with the next form, *alaudinus*, has lately been separated as the Prairie Savannah Sparrow (le Pinson des savanes des Prairies) *Passerculus sandwichensis campestris* which by some is regarded as a synonym of the Nevada Savannah Sparrow (le Pinson des savanes du Nevada) *Passerculus sandwichensis nevadensis.* The southern interior of British Columbia is occupied by the Western Savannah Sparrow (le Pinson des savanes de l'Ouest) *Passerculus sandwichensis alaudinus* and the southwest coastal region by the small, dull Dwarf Savannah Sparrow (Le petit Pinson des savanes) *Passerculus sandwichensis brooksi*, not recognized in the current Check-list but undoubtedly a distinct race.

The Aleutian Savannah Sparrow (le Pinson des savanes des Aléoutiennes) *Passerculus sandwichensis sandwichensis* breeds on the western Alaskan Islands and migrates along the British Columbia coast. This is a large bird, somewhat rufous in colour and with bright yellow lores and eyebrow stripes.

A bird of damp meadows and waste land, where the grass grows in rank and coarse bunches and water lies close to the surface; or of sandy barrens where the grass and weeds grow in scattered clumps. It runs in the grass like a mouse and rises with a low quick flight, often before a good view of it can be obtained. It is an interesting little bird, but is so inconspicuous as easily to pass unnoticed by the casual observer.

*Economic Status.* Besides great quantities of weed seed, the Savannah Sparrow consumes more insects than do most sparrows, and more beetles than any other. These beetles include a great number of weevils and other harmful forms. Although inhabiting waste places it frequents cultivated land often enough to make it an efficient helper to the agriculturist.

546. **Grasshopper Sparrow.** YELLOW-WING SPARROW. LE PINSON SAUTERELLE. *Ammodramus savannarum.* L, 5·38. A small grass-haunting sparrow. Back marked with fine, short streaks of brown, ashy, and light buff in indefinite pattern; dull white below, with a light buffy wash across the breast fading away on the sides of the throat. A yellow spot in front of the eye; upperwing-coverts and the bend of the wing yellow or yellowish. In fresh, unworn plumage, a condition of specimen that is but rarely secured, the back shows many light semicircles that give a scaly appearance. There is a decided vinaceous general cast owing to considerable red or bay that later wears or fades away. Tail of sharply pointed feathers like Figure 476.

*Distinctions.* The yellowish upperwing-coverts are distinctive of the species. The unstriped and unspotted breast will separate it from most of the other small grass sparrows.

*Field Marks.* This species can be distinguished from most of the other small sparrows by its unstreaked, faintly buff-coloured breast. Its song is like the last part of the song of the Savannah Sparrow, without the opening phrase and final syllable, and dies gradually away like *"Bz-bz-bz-z-z-z-z."*

*Nesting.* On the ground, in nest of grasses, arched over.

*Distribution.* United States, to South America. Occurring in Canada only in limited localities in southern parts of Ontario, Manitoba, and British Columbia. *See* discussion under Carolina Wren, page 320.

A most inconspicuous little ground sparrow, inhabiting dry, grassy meadows and to be sought for by ear rather than eye. It gets its common name from its insect-like little song. It may be expected in southeastern Saskatchewan.

545. **Baird's Sparrow.** LE PINSON DE BAIRD. *Ammodramus bairdi.* L, 5·25. Like a pale Savannah Sparrow (*See* Plate LXXXI B), but all markings sharper, shorter, and sparser. The face and hindneck suffused with light ochre, warming to burnt orange in the broken, median crown-stripe. No lemon-yellow on lores or bend of wing (Figure 475).

Figure 475
Baird's Sparrow; natural size.

*Distinctions.* The ochre and dull orange background of face and crown separates it from all other species.

*Field Marks.* A Savannah Sparrow-like bird with warm ochre suffusion over face and head. Markings clearer and sharper, white more general, are the best recognition marks for the eye. The best identification, however, is by the voice. Instead of the insipid, insect-like little trill of the Savannah Sparrow, it utters quite a little warble, *"Zip-zip-zip-zre-e-eeeeeee,"* the opening *"zips"* being very plain and characteristic.

*Nesting.* On the ground in the grass.

*Distribution.* The Great Plains of North America. In Canada, the southern prairies.

Though widely distributed over the prairies, this species is rather local. It inhabits damp ground around sloughs, but is specially partial to dry alkaline flats a little back from shrinking pools. Amidst the great number of Savannah Sparrows and other small species in such places, it is very inconspicuous, as is indicated by the fact that, though the country it inhabits had been often visited by ornithologists, it was thirty years after the first specimen had been brought to the attention of science before the species was rediscovered as common in Colorado and Dakota.

548. **Leconte's Sparrow.** LE PINSON DE LECONTE. *Passerherbulus caudacatus.* L, 5. A very small sparrow, streaked above and on flanks. Tail feathers sharp and tapering (Figure 476). Adult: crown, dark brown with greyish buff median stripe. Nape, vinaceous, with greyish edgings. Back, dark brown with light buff stripes. Suffused with ochre on breast, throat, and superciliary line. Grey cheeks, and a brown line back from eye. Abdomen white. Juveniles are streaky ochre and brown. More heavily streaked above; paling to nearly white on abdomen. Finely striped across breast and on flanks, but clear elsewhere below.

*Distinctions.* Among the smallest of the sparrows. Most likely to be confused with Nelson's Sparrow. Adult separated from it by the vinaceous nape-band and lack of any tendency towards olive or green on back. The Grasshopper Sparrow has also a vinaceous nape, but the lesser wing-coverts and bend of wing are yellow. The juvenile of Leconte's is very like that of Nelson's, but is generally a paler ochre, lightening to almost white on abdomen, and finely but distinctly streaked across breast.

*Field Marks.* A diminutive sparrow that gets up from the long grass, flies a short way, and drops into it again, is probably this or the next species. Only close observation of the colour characters above, or familiarity with their notes, will separate them in life. This species is not quite as closely confined to damp or wet ground as Nelson's.

*Nesting.* On the ground; nest of fine grass.

*Distribution.* Central North America. In Canada, the Prairie Provinces, north occasionally to Great Slave Lake. Accidental in southern Ontario.

A very inconspicuous bird that only a careful observer will note or identify.

547. **Henslow's Sparrow.** LE PINSON DE HENSLOW. *Passerherbulus henslowi.* L, 5. A very small grass sparrow. Back of head and lower neck yellowish olive, and back vinaceous; both colours streaked with short strokes of brown. Below, white, finely streaked across breast and on flanks with dark brown. Bill large for the size of the bird and tail feathers pointed.

*Distinctions.* Olive and vinaceous ground colour of upper parts and fine streaking of breast.

*Field Marks.* A small bird that runs in the grass and is very difficult to flush. Rises with a quick, low, zigzag flight and drops back into the grass with unexpected suddenness. The best identification character in life is its note, a fine penetrating *se-slick* of such light volume as to be almost inaudible close at hand, yet decided enough to have considerable carrying power.

*Nesting.* On ground, in nest of grass exceptionally well hidden.

*Distribution.* Eastern United States, occurring in eastern Canada only in southern Ontario. The species has been taken in northern Minnesota just across the International Boundary at Pembina and may be expected to occur occasionally or irregularly in southern Manitoba as it is another species that fluctuates in number beyond the margins of its normal habitat as described under Carolina Wren, page 320.

*SUBSPECIES.* Eastern Henslow's Sparrow (le Pinson de Henslow de l'Est) *Passerherbulus henslowi susurrans* is the form of Ontario. The race to be expected in Manitoba is probably the Western Henslow's Sparrow (le Pinson de Henslow de l'Ouest) *Passerherbulus henslowi henslowi.*

One may be in the midst of quite a colony of Henslow's Sparrows without knowing it, as they are rarely seen unless attention is directed to them by their notes. Waste grass-grown meadows are their favourite habitats.

549. **Sharp-tailed Sparrow.** LE PINSON À QUEUE AIGUË. *Ammospiza caudacuta.* A very small sparrow with sharp, tapering tail feathers like Leconte's (*See* Figure 476); streaked above and on flanks. Adult: crown dark brown with slate-grey median stripe. Nape-band, slaty-olive. Back, dark brown with white stripes. Below, white with rich ochre breast-band extending up sides of neck over face, producing strong superciliary line. Cheeks, grey with dark stripe back from eye (Figure 477). Juveniles are rich ochre over all, striped above with brown, and with no suggestion of white any place.

*Distinctions.* Among the smallest of the sparrows. Very likely to be confused with Leconte's Sparrow. Adult certainly separated from it by the olive or slaty olive nape-band and sharp white feather-edge stripes on back. The juvenile is even more like Leconte's, but has no stripes on breast or undersurface, and the ochre is deep and rich, lighter on abdomen, but never approaching white.

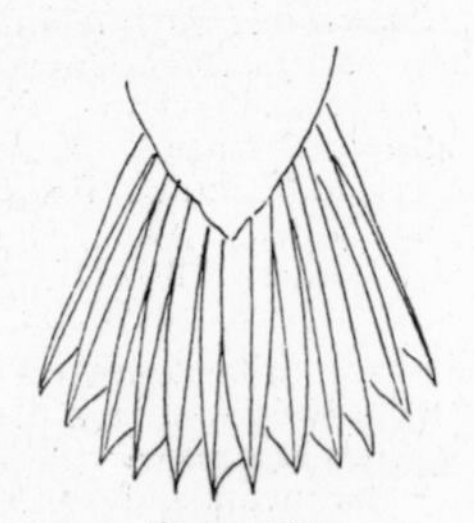

Figure 476
Tail of Sharp-tailed Sparrow; scale, ½.

Figure 477
Nelson's Sparrow; natural size.

*Field Marks.* A diminutive sparrow that gets up from the long grass in damp or wet places, flies a short way, and drops into it again, and then steals mouse-like through the cover, is probably either this species or Leconte's. Only close observation of the colour characters above, or familiarity with their notes, will separate them in life.

*Nesting.* On the ground; nest of fine grass.

*Distribution.* Eastern North America. In Canada, the Maritime Provinces north to St. Lawrence River, throughout the prairie regions (except the southwestern), and occasionally to Great Slave Lake. Occasional in southern Ontario.

*SUBSPECIES.* The Sharp-tailed Sparrow of the Maritimes and the lower St. Lawrence is the Acadian Sharp-tailed (le Pinson à queue aiguë d'Acadie) *Ammospiza caudacuta subvirgata.* That of the west is Nelson's Sparrow (le Pinson à queue aiguë de l'Ouest) *Ammospiza caudacuta nelsoni*, a more richly coloured bird.

Another of the inconspicuous little grass sparrows, that none but the keenest observer will see or recognize.

540. **Vesper Sparrow.** GRASS FINCH. BAY-WINGED SPARROW. LE PINSON À AILES BAIES. *Pooecetes gramineus.* L, 5·75. Plate LXXXII A. A dull, earth-coloured ground-bird; softly streaked with shades of brown above; below, white, with suffused brown streaks across breast, on sides of throat, and flanks. Lesser wing-coverts, brownish red. Tail dark with white outer feather on each side (Figure 478).

Figure 478
Tail of Vesper Sparrow; scale, ½.

*Distinctions.* Like a number of ground sparrows, especially the Song Sparrow, but characterized by the red-brown (bay) shoulders and white outer tail feathers. Spotting on breast softer and less profuse than on the Song Sparrow, and not aggregated into a central breast-spot.

*Field Marks.* An earth-coloured sparrow, with white breast streaked with dark. Separated from the Song Sparrow by lack of central breast-spot and the presence of white outer tail feathers. The junco has similar white tail feathers, but is a darker and more slaty (or rufous) bird. Somewhat suggestive of the juvenile longspurs, but the breast streaked, and much less white in tail (Figure 478, compare with 485 and 488, pages 407 and 409).

*Nesting.* In the grass; nest of grasses, rootlets, and hairs.

*Distribution.* Temperate North America. In Canada, across the continent, north into the edges of the northern forest.

*SUBSPECIES.* Three subspecies are recognized in Canada. The Eastern Vesper Sparrow (le Pinson à ailes baies de l'Est) *Pooecetes gramineus gramineus* extends from the east coast to Ontario. All birds west of the Great Lakes are generally referred to the Western Vesper Sparrow (le Pinson à ailes baies de l'Ouest) *Pooecetes gramineus confinis.* It is lighter and greyer than the eastern type race, and averages a little longer in the tail.

The Vesper Sparrow is comparable with the Song Sparrow in its habits, song, and general appearance. It is less a bird of the brush, however, and usually frequents the edges of fields, or where there is slight cover or long weeds, as in the vicinity of ditches or roads. Its song is similar to that of the Song Sparrow, but may be readily distinguished from it by the experienced ear, particularly by its not beginning with the two, or more, single notes.

*Economic Status.* This is one of the most beneficial of the sparrows. It feeds farther afield than most of the common summer sparrows and takes a greater percentage of insects than they, and large quantities of weed seeds. Some grain is found in its stomach, but in circumstances that point to its being waste from the stubble or roadways. The Vesper Sparrow, therefore, should receive every possible protection.

552. **Lark Sparrow.** LE PINSON À JOUES MARRON. *Chondestes grammacus.* L, 6·25. A very striking and conspicuously marked sparrow. Above, striped with brown and buffy brown; below, white with buffy flanks. Crown, chestnut-brown with conspicuous white median line; ear-coverts chestnut-brown in strong contrast with the white face; and three sharp, black lines, one through eye, one from lower mandible to ear-coverts, and one along sides of throat (Figure 479). Outer tail feathers, and ends of all except the middle ones, white.

Figure 479
Lark Sparrow;
scale, ½.

*Distinctions.* The bright reddish brown ear-coverts contrasting with black and white face are certain distinguishing characters of the species.

*Field Marks.* The strongly marked head and face and the large amount of white in the tail make easily recognized field marks.

*Nesting.* In low trees or bushes, in nest of grasses lined with fine grass, rootlets, and hairs.

*Distribution.* Mississippi Valley to the Pacific coast. Scarce in southern Ontario, accidental farther east. In western Canada, along the southern border of the Prairie Provinces and the interior warm valleys of southern British Columbia.

*SUBSPECIES.* The Eastern Lark Sparrow (le Pinson à joues marron de l'Est) is *Chondestes grammacus grammacus.* The subspecies of western Canada is the Western Lark Sparrow (le Pinson à joues marron de l'Ouest) *Chondestes grammacus strigatus,* a slightly lighter bird than the eastern race.

In the open brushy wastes of the bad lands, where the creek beds, between raw, eroded banks, are lined with occasional poplars, backed by dry sagebrush benches, the Lark Sparrow is most common. It is not entirely confined to such places, for an open, park-like area with scattered tree growth is another favourite haunt. It has a pleasing little song, and its bright, happy ways gladden many an otherwise monotonous landscape.

575. **Summer Sparrow.** LE PINSON D'ÉTÉ. *Aimophila aestivalis.* L, 5·8. A rather indeterminately coloured sparrow. Above, reddish brown, much feather margined with grey. Below, white with breast and flanks washed with light brownish ash. Bend of wing yellow.

*Distinctions.* More like a large, dull-coloured Grasshopper Sparrow than any other Canadian species, but back more ruddy and more softly striped.

*Distribution.* Southeastern United States. There is a single record for southern Ontario.

*SUBSPECIES.* There are several subspecies of this species. The type form is called the Pine-woods Sparrow. The only Canadian specimen has been referred to Bachman's Sparrow (le Pinson d'été de Bachman) *Aimophila aestivalis bachmani*, the more northern race occurring regularly to southern Indiana and southern Ohio.

574. **Sage Sparrow.** LE PINSON DES SAUGES. *Amphispiza nevadensis.* L, 6. A rather small sparrow. Crown and face soft, light grey, clay coloured and lightly streaked on back and sides, throat and below white. White spots in front of, and behind, eye and black streaks from base of bill down sides of throat. Black centre-breast spot more or less evident.

*Distinctions.* Probably soft greyness of crown and nape and white face marks.

*Field Marks.* Too obscurely coloured and too rare in Canada to be identified unless in hand.

*Distribution.* Sage-brush plains of western United States north to Washington and Montana. There is a single record for Canada, Lulu Island, British Columbia coast, October, 1930. Its presence has been suspected in the Okanagan Valley, but never demonstrated.

*SUBSPECIES.* The single Canadian specimen seems referable to the Northern Sage Sparrow (le Pinson des sauges du Nord) *Amphispiza nevadensis nevadensis.*

567. **Slate-coloured Junco.** BLACK SNOWBIRD. LE JUNCO ARDOISÉ. *Junco hyemalis.* L, 6·27. Plate LXXXII B. About the size of a Song Sparrow. Mostly dark or slate-grey; white below, cutting in a straight line sharply across the breast; outer tail feathers white. Bill, flesh coloured. Juveniles and females are less decided in colour and often show noticeable amounts of rusty on back and flanks suggesting the next species.

*Distinctions.* Easily recognized as a junco by its grey or black head and breast, ending sharply against the white underparts; flesh-coloured bill, and dark tail, with contrasting white outer feathers.

*Field Marks.* Dark or grey head, and breast sharply defined against white underparts, flesh-coloured bill, and contrasting white outer tail feathers, conspicuous in flight. The Vesper Sparrow has somewhat similarly coloured outer tail feathers, but is a buffy appearing bird, instead of a dark grey or reddish one.

*Nesting.* On or near the ground. Nest of grasses, moss, and rootlets, lined with finer grasses and long hairs.

*Distribution.* North America, from tree limits, southward. Breeding throughout Canada, except in the more southern parts and most of British Columbia.

*SUBSPECIES.* The Slate-coloured Junco for a long time was classed as subspecifically allied to a number of forms that are now given full specific status. A late decision, with which the present author is inclined to agree, has given this eastern dark grey race full specific distinction from the red-backed *oreganus* of the western mountains and the pale grey *mearnsi* of the southern Canadian prairies and southward. Puzzling intergrades between these races occur, but they seem more of the nature of hybrids than of blending subspecies, and a clearer view of the complicated relationship of these forms is presented by this concept. At present but one race of *hyemalis* is recognized in Canada, the Northern Slate-coloured Junco (le Junco à dos roux) *Junco hyemalis hyemalis.*

The Junco, with its black breast, light-coloured bill, and white-bordered tail, is conspicuous amongst the large flocks of sparrows passing through or tarrying in the spring and autumn.

*Economic Status.* The effect of the junco on agriculture is almost wholly beneficial. During its stay in the more settled sections it consumes large quantities of weed seeds. The insects it takes are mostly harmful. Little or no exception can be taken to it, as it does no perceptible damage to crops or fruit.

567a. **Red-backed Junco.** LE JUNCO DE L'OUEST. *Junco oreganus.* L, 6·27. Plate LXXXII B. Like the above, but the head and breast blacker and the back rusty red.

*Distinctions.* Easily recognized as a Junco by its black head and breast cutting sharply against white underparts, flesh-coloured bill, and dark tail with contrasting white outer feathers. As this species by its strongly rusty back.

*Field Marks.* Black or grey head and breast sharply defined against white underparts, flesh-coloured bill, and contrasting white outer tail feathers conspicuous in flight will mark it as a Junco; perceptible or marked rusty on the back, and far western occurrence will assist in recognizing this species.

*Nesting.* The same as the Slate-coloured Junco.

*Distribution.* Western north America. In Canada the west coast, and most of central and southern British Columbia.

*SUBSPECIES.* This species and its races hitherto have generally been regarded as subspecies of the Slate-coloured Junco above. It is now given full specific status. It probably hybridizes rather freely with that species and puzzling specimens occur, especially on the borders where the two are in contact. There is a good deal of uncertainty as to the recognizable geographical races of the species. The following seem to be the most evident. The Oregon Junco (le Junco de l'Orégon) *Junco oreganus oreganus*, with the strongest reds on back and flanks and the blackest heads and breasts, west of the coast range. Shufeldt's Junco (le Junco de Shufeldt) *Junco oreganus shufeldti*, with these colours reduced but still evident, occupies most of the interior of British Columbia. The Montana Junco (le Junco du Montana) *Junco oreganus montanus*, with the *oreganus* colours still further reduced towards *hyemalis*, has been accredited to the mountain regions of western Alberta, but to the present author does not seem worthy of systematic recognition.

*Economic Status.* Same as in the previous species, though the species appears in unusual numbers during migration when, as sometimes occurs, its partiality for small seeds makes gardening a little difficult.

567g. **Pink-sided Junco.** LE JUNCO À FLANCS ROSES. *Junco mearnsi.* L, 6·27. Like the Slate-sided Junco (*See* Plate LXXXIII B), but much paler, the head and breast colouring being no darker than light slate, the back slightly rusty, and the flanks washed with vinaceous pink.

*Distinctions.* Like a pale-coloured Slate-coloured Junco.

*Field Marks.* As above. Only likely to be met with in Canada in southwestern Saskatchewan.

*Nesting.* Like the two previous Juncos.

*Distribution.* In Canada it has so far been found only on the north slopes of Cypress Hills in southwestern Saskatchewan. It occurs south to Mexico.

*Economic Status.* Probably similar to the other juncos.

559. **Tree Sparrow.** LE PINSON HUDSONIEN. *Spizella arborea.* L, 6·36. Plate LXXXIII A. About the size of a Song Sparrow, but redder above, a brownish red cap, the breast greyish with a single suffused brown spot in the centre. Bill, upper mandible, dark, lower one mostly yellow.

*Distinctions.* Size of Song Sparrow; red-brown cap; prominent white wing-bars; ashy grey throat with semi-concealed dark blot in centre of unspotted breast.

*Field Marks.* Red-brown cap, prominent white wing-bars, ashy grey throat, and dark spot in middle of the evenly coloured, unspotted breast.

*Nesting.* On or near ground, in nest of grasses, rootlets, and hair.

*Distribution.* Northern North America, breeding in the spruce woods to the barren grounds of the far north. Migrating throughout southern Canada.

*SUBSPECIES.* The Western Tree Sparrow (le Pinson hudsonien de l'Ouest) *Spizella arborea ochracea* differs from the Eastern (le Pinson hudsonien de l'Est) *Spizella arborea arborea*, in having slightly longer tail and wing, and a somewhat paler coloration. Breeds from Alaska east to Mackenzie Valley. Migrants through British Columbia and the western Prairie Provinces are this form, but its distinctions are too slight to be easily recognized and the geographic limits of the two races have not been well defined.

76916—26½

Among the hosts of sparrows that congregate in the shrubbery in the autumn or return early in spring, is the Tree Sparrow. In the southern parts of the Dominion it sometimes remains all winter, but is a migrant elsewhere. It is a natty little bird and its modest song in the early spring is most welcome after the long, silent winter.

*Economic Status.* The Tree Sparrow is valuable for its destruction of weed seeds and seems to have no bad habits.

560. **Chipping Sparrow.** CHIPPIE. HAIR-BIRD. LE PINSON FAMILIER. *Spizella passerina.* L, 5·37. Plate LXXXIII B. A small sparrow with unspotted breast; a red-brown cap; grey face; white superciliary line, and narrow dark bar through eye. Juveniles have a finely streaked white breast and are without the solid red cap or characteristic facial marks; are much streaked above and below in clay-like colours, and are sometimes difficult to separate from Clay-coloured Sparrows.

*Distinctions.* A familiar little sparrow with red cap, a grey face, narrow black bar through eye, and white eyebrow streak. Separated from the Swamp and Tree Sparrows, which also have red caps, by its much smaller size. Juveniles closely resemble Clay-coloured Sparrows, but the streakings of the breast are more pronounced and numerous, and the breast is not suffused with light buffy. Very juvenile specimens are difficult to separate from that species, and from Brewer's Sparrow, although adults are quite distinct.

*Field Marks.* Small size. For adults: red cap, grey face with narrow, black eye-bar and white eyebrow-line, and spotless light greyish breast. Its song, a long drawn out series of unaccented cheeps, forming a sustained trill, is very characteristic. On the prairies, where the Clay-coloured Sparrow occurs, juveniles may be difficult to separate from that species.

*Nesting.* In trees or bushes, in nest of grasses, rootlets, and fibres, plentifully intermixed with long hairs. The amount of horsehair used in the nest is the origin of one of this bird's popular names.

*Distribution.* North America, north throughout the northern spruce woods to Great Bear Lake and central Yukon. In Canada, breeding wherever found. Scarce on the open prairies.

*SUBSPECIES.* The Chipping Sparrow of the east is the Eastern Chipping Sparrow (le Pinson familier de l'Est) *Spizella passerina passerina.* West of the Great Lakes the birds are generally referred to the Western Chipping Sparrow (le Pinson familier de l'Ouest) *Spizella passerina arizonae* distinguished from the eastern form by slightly larger average size and paler coloration. The distinction, however, is too fine for general recognition and requires a series of specimens for its demonstration.

The Chipping Sparrow, except in the open prairie regions, is rarely absent from the vicinity of surburban or village homes, coming close to houses and frequenting the orchard and shade-trees, the front yard, and even the doorstep. It does not fear man, but, though not avoiding him, often it escapes notice through its quiet and unobtrusive habits.

*Economic Status.* The Chipping Sparrow is a greater insect eater than most of the family. In fact, through June, 93 per cent of its food is composed of insects, only 1 per cent of which are beneficial species, such as predacious beetles and parasitic wasps. The average for the year is 38 per cent of insects, and for the months spent by the bird in Canada the average must be considerably higher. The vegetable matter consumed consists of small weed seeds in which those of crab-grass, lamb's quarters, and ragweed predominate. A bird having these desirable qualities and coming into the immediate vicinity of the garden is most useful and one to be encouraged in every manner possible.

561. **Clay-coloured Sparrow.** LE PINSON PÂLE. *Spizella pallida.* L, 5·20. Plate LXXXIV A. A small sparrow with upperparts streaked in light buff and dark brown to crown, where a whitish median stripe is indicated or suggested. A faint collar of slaty suffusion about back of neck. White below, slightly buffy on flanks.

*Distinctions.* Like a Chipping Sparrow in size, but crown sharply streaked like back. No black bar through eye, but a brown one back from it, and conspicuously brownish, dusky ear-coverts. Juvenile birds, lately from nest, are very similar to young Chipping Sparrows of the same age, but the breast is usually suffused with the buffy of flanks and the dark breast streaks are less sharp, fewer, or even absent. The only other species the Clay-coloured is likely to be mistaken for in Canada is Brewer's Sparrow, which see.

*Field Marks.* An inconspicuous, pale, earthy coloured little sparrow like a Chipping Sparrow, but without the strongly characterized face and crown-marks of that species. Instead, the ear-coverts are brownish and are more conspicuous for being lightly lined with darker above and below. It may be best recognized by its song, a low, flat "*buz-buz-buz*" that can be confused with no other bird song on our prairies.

*Nesting.* On the ground or in low bushes, in nest of grasses lined with hairs.

*Distribution.* The interior of North America. In Canada, the Prairie Provinces eastward to north of Lake Superior, and northward to Great Slave Lake, breeding wherever found. It has been taken once in Okanagan Valley, British Columbia, and is occasional in southern Ontario.

A very typical prairie bird, found wherever a little tangle of rose canes, sage brush, or wolf willow furnishes a suggestion of shelter. It is characterless in colour. Its song, though very distinctive, is flat and insect-like, and were it not a very common and relatively confiding little bird, it would be easily overlooked.

*Economic Status.* As a weed and insect eater it must rank close to the Chipping Sparrow, which it closely resembles in habit, but no detailed study of its food is at present available.

562. **Brewer's Sparrow.** LE PINSON DE BREWER. *Spizella breweri.* L, 5·4. A small sparrow, of the same general size and appearance as the Clay-coloured (*See* Plate LXXXIV A), but even more inconspicuously coloured. Evenly streaked in dull ashy and brown all above, and dull white below. Like a faded Clay-coloured Sparrow, without decided cheek patch or suggestion of median crown stripe.

*Distinctions.* Most likely to be mistaken for the Clay-coloured Sparrow, except as above. The crown is evenly streaked and there is no decided cheek patch. The adult is very like the juvenile Chipping Sparrow but for its general grey coloration, and it lacks the striping of the breast. When in similar striped juvenile condition, the two species probably can only be separated by the expert.

*Field Marks.* Like a Clay-coloured Sparrow, but paler and duller, with softly blended ashy brown face, without evident cheek patch. Best recognized by its song, a "*buz-buz-buz,*" not as flat as that of the Clay-coloured, but approaching the Chipping Sparrow in quality. This is often immediately followed by a long succession of twittering notes, suggesting the conclusion of the song of the Vesper Sparrow.

*Nesting.* In low brush; nest of grasses and fine plant fibres.

*Distribution.* Western North America. In Canada, occurring locally in heavy sage brush land in southern and northern British Columbia, and southern Alberta and Saskatchewan. Occasionally as far north as Jasper Park. This is a very obscure little sparrow of the sage brush. It is very local and by eyesight alone would often be passed over amongst the many Clay-coloured Sparrows that it associates with in similar situations. It can hardly be overlooked, however, by one familiar with the bird songs of the sage brush.

*SUBSPECIES.* The generally distributed form of the species is the common Brewer's Sparrow (le Pinson de Brewer) *Spizella breweri breweri.* A race of Brewer's Sparrow has lately been described from Atlin region, northwestern British Columbia, as the Timberline Sparrow (le Pinson alpin de Brewer) *Spizella taverneri.* It has since been taken in migration in Okanagan Valley and at Chilliwack, British Columbia. In spite of the apparent discontinuous distribution it has probably correctly been reduced to a subspecies, *Spizella breweri taverneri.*

563. **Field Sparrow.** LE PINSON DES CHAMPS. *Spizella pusilla.* L, 6·68. A small sparrow of the same general colour as the Chipping, but with the colours subdued, suffused, and blended. The red crown is darker and inconspicuous and there is no line of black through the eye. The bill is cinnamon coloured instead of black.

*Distinctions.* The above distinctions are sufficient to distinguish this bird.

*Field Marks.* Dull reddish crown, lack of facial marks other than a touch of red on ends of ear coverts, and cinnamon-coloured bill. The song is its most easily recognized characteristic and when learned is the best means of identification.

*Nesting.* On ground or in low bushes, in nest of rather coarse grasses, weed stalks, and rootlets, lined with fine grasses and hair.

*Distribution.* Eastern America; in Canada including most of the better settled sections of southern Ontario, but rather local in distribution and unaccountably absent from some localities well within its range.

*SUBSPECIES.* The Field Sparrow is divided into an eastern and western subspecies; the former, the type form, is the only one that has so far been detected in Canada.

The Field Sparrow is an inconspicuous bird and though often very common is so like a Chipping Sparrow with worn plumage that it may be mistaken for it. It is a bird of the open fields and fence rows and though not shy or unusually retiring, must be looked for and listened for to be found.

*Economic Status.* Very much like the Chipping Sparrow in food habits, taking a few more useful insects though not enough to perceptibly affect its usefulness.

553. **Harris's Sparrow.** LE PINSON À FACE NOIRE. *Zonotrichia querula.* L, 7·50. A large sparrow. Above, striped in shades of brown and brownish ash with a black crown, throat, and upper breast; cheeks ashy grey, and underparts pure white. Adults of both sexes, spring and autumn, practically alike. Juveniles similar, but the black crown broken, the face ochraceous to base of bill; throat white, the black being confined to a conspicuous breast-spot.

*Distinctions.* A large sparrow; white below, with black cap, face, and throat, or with a large black spot across breast.

*Field Marks.* A large, black and white sparrow, with black face and throat or large black spot across centre of breast.

*Nesting.* On the ground under bushes; nest of grass. Nest rarely discovered.

Figure 480
Harris's Sparrow; scale, ½.

*Distribution.* Central North America; north to edges of barren grounds. Nesting area in the sub-arctic regions. In Canada, migrating throughout all the prairie sections. Occurring rarely, but with increasing frequency, in winter, in southern British Columbia.

A very handsome Sparrow, frequenting brushy places during migration.

554. **White-crowned Sparrow.** LE PINSON À COURONNE BLANCHE. *Zonotrichia leucophrys.* L, 6·88. Plate LXXXIV B. Adult: back striped in rich seal-brown and light grey; below, white. Face, neck, and breast light ash-grey. Crown, black with conspicuous white median stripe. The immature plumage has back striped with brown and brownish cream and the clear grey of face, neck, and breast replaced with dull ashy; the crown is rusty brown with a lighter median centre.

Figure 481
Subspecies of White-crowned Sparrow.
*a*, Eastern White-crowned;
*b*, Gambel's Sparrow.

*Distinctions.* Only to be mistaken for the Golden-crowned and White-throated Sparrows. Brighter coloured than the first, with white instead of golden yellow median stripe, and without the white throat and yellow loral spot of the second. Juveniles are difficult to separate from the Golden-crowned, but the latter almost always have some suggestion of yellow on the crown and are duller and darker in general tone.

*Field Marks.* Brilliant black and white crown and without white throat or yellow loral mark, separates adults from mature White-throats. In juvenility, when the loral spot cannot be seen, the latter has a distinctly red, rather than grey, cast on the back. Distinguished from the Golden-crowned by the white instead of yellow median line. Juveniles are probably difficult to distinguish in life from that species, but the crown shows distinctly reddish instead of yellowish or flat olive.

*Nesting.* On the ground or in low bushes. Nest of grasses and fine vegetable fibres.

*Distribution.* North America from tree limits southward. Throughout Canada as a breeder or migrant.

*SUBSPECIES.* Three subspecies are recognized in Canada. The Eastern White-crown (le Pinson à couronne blanche de l'Est) *Zonotrichia leucophrys leucophrys* extends westward over the prairies to the Rocky Mountains. It is notable that, although this form in the east breeds only in high latitudes, it is the nesting form of the hills of southwestern Saskatchewan. Gambel's or the Intermediate Sparrow (le Pinson à couronne blanche de Gambel) *Zonotrichia leucophrys gambeli* (by some regarded as a full distinct species) occupies the northern prairies, and the interior of British Columbia, northward into Alaska. It is distinguished from *leucophrys* mainly by the lores being white instead of black[1] (Figure 481, compare a with b). On the coast of British Columbia is Nuttall's Sparrow (le Pinson à couronne blanche de Nuttall) *Zonotrichia leucophrys nuttalli.* This is like Gambel's, but the grey of the back is slightly olivaceous, the stripes are less reddish and a darker and richer brown, and there is a trace of pale yellow on the edge of the first wing-joint. The Eastern White-crowned is the common migrant in the east and Gambel's in British Columbia. Throughout the prairies and much of British Columbia both forms occur.

One of the most beautiful of the sparrows. Though it lacks gaudy colours, its sharply contrasting black and white crown and grey throat and neck give it distinction. Its song, too, is sweet, but it is usually heard at its best only on its breeding grounds.

Ordinarily it is a great weed-seed destroyer, but when it occurs in immense flocks, as in some parts of British Columbia, some complaints have been made that it eats off the shoots of sprouting garden seeds or even scratches up the seeds themselves. This objection, however, is more or less local.

557. **Golden-crowned Sparrow.** LE PINSON À COURONNE DORÉE. *Zonotrichia coronata.* L, 7. Slightly larger than the White-crowned Sparrow; like it in coloration, but the white median crown-patch is replaced by bright lemon-yellow, and the general coloration is duller, more ochraceous; the clear grey of neck and breast is more brownish ash and it has not the black line back from the eye (Figure 482). The juvenile is similar to the juvenile White-crowned, but the crown-spot is not as clear reddish and is usually tinged with yellow in the centre.

*Distinctions.* The yellow crown in adult and traces of it in juvenility, otherwise a slightly larger and duller-coloured bird than the White-crowned.

*Field Marks.* Like a White-crowned Sparrow, with no distinct white superciliary line and with golden instead of white crown streak. It may sometimes be impossible to separate juveniles from that species.

Figure 482
Golden-crowned Sparrow; scale, ½.

*Nesting.* On the ground; nest of fine grasses and rootlets.

*Distribution.* Pacific Coast region of North America. In Canada, British Columbia and western mountain regions, northward into Alaska and the adjoining foothills in Alberta. Nesting in the mountains south to Jasper Park region and Cariboo District of British Columbia. A regally crowned Sparrow typical of the alpine meadows of the mountains.

558. **White-throated Sparrow.** CANADA BIRD. CANADA WHITE-THROAT. PEABODY-BIRD. LE PINSON À GORGE BLANCHE. *Zonotrichia albicollis.* L, 6·75. Plate LXXXV A. Adult: back striped in reddish and dark browns; white below. Face and foreneck light ash-grey with well-defined white throat. Crown, black with conspicuous white median stripe. Superciliary stripe bright yellow in front of eye, changing to white behind. Juvenile has back striped with rufous and brown; dull ashy white below, duskier on breast but whiter on throat. Yellow spot in front of, and over, eye always perceptible.

*Distinctions.* The yellow spot in front of, and over, eye, and distinctly lighter throat are the best distinctive characters.

[1] Some species of White-crowns occur with the white eyebrow streak and loral spot separated by a narrow black bar. These birds seem referable to *leucophrys* and are not necessarily to be regarded as intermediates or hybrids with *gambeli.*

*Field Marks.* Distinctions as above. It is the reddest-backed of all the autumn Sparrows.

*Nesting.* On the ground or in low bushes; nest of coarse grasses, rootlets, and moss, lined with finer grass.

*Distribution.* Eastern North America. In Canada, west to the mountains and north to the limit of trees. Occasionally in southern British Columbia, breeding in the northern half of that province.

This is the most famous songster of the Canadian north woods. At its best the song is a clear, flute-like, slowly measured whistle which has been very well put into words. "*Hard-times-can-a-da-can-ada*" or "*Poor-Bill-Pea-bo-dy-Pea-bo-dy-Pea-bo-dy.*" The White-throat is a brushwood bird; tangled thickets or brush piles in the vicinity of open ground are its favourite haunts. Throughout most of the cultivated sections of Canada the bird is a migrant only, and its best song is rarely heard. In the autumn when the young birds fly south the notes are heard in a softened, shortened version.

*Economic Status.* The White-throat is a valuable bird. It is important as a destroyer of weed seeds, especially of ragweed, and consumes a considerable number of insects and a little wild fruit. As the species comes down in great numbers to the thickly cultivated sections in early autumn, its effect on the succeeding season's weed crop must be pronounced.

585. **Fox Sparrow.** LE PINSON FAUVE. *Passerella iliaca.* L, 7·26. A rather large, reddish sparrow, exhibiting, according to geographical range, three distinct types of coloration. West to the Rocky Mountains (the *iliaca* type): above, bright reddish brown, solid on tail and rump, but broadly striped on dull slaty back, hindneck, and crown; below, white, heavily spotted and streaked with red like the back on sides of throat, across breast, and on flanks. The centre of throat is almost free from markings and the spots tend to aggregate on the breast in a centre spot. West of the mountains, except the coast, we have a rich brown and grey bird (the *schistacea* type), like the last except that the reds are darkened to chocolate brown and there is little striping on the grey, which also suffuses largely over face. On the coast (the *unalaschcensis* type), the brown still deeper and richer, nearly or quite supplanting the grey, and the stripes below much more extensive, broader, and more coalescent.

*Distinctions.* Large size for a sparrow. East of the mountains, large amount of foxy red, solid on the tail and rump, heavily streaking the breast and flanks. In the interior of British Columbia, face, head, shoulders, and back, mostly grey; chocolate-brown wings, tail, and stripes on breast and flanks. The west coast type, a solidly dark, maroon-brown bird, the colour only broken by more or less coalescent white flecks on foreneck and abdomen.

*Field Marks.* A large sparrow with much foxy red; dull grey head and back, brown tail and breast-streaks; or solid dark brown with white flecks on throat and below.

*Nesting.* On the ground, or in low trees or bushes. Nest of coarse grasses lined with finer grass, hair, moss, and feathers.

*Distribution.* Northern and western North America, breeding far to the north of ordinary cultivation.

*SUBSPECIES.* A remarkably variable species, breaking up into a number of extraordinarily distinct subspecies. Indeed, some doubt may well be expressed as to whether some of the differences are not fully specific. The Eastern Fox Sparrow (le Pinson fauve de l'Est) *Passerella iliaca iliaca* extends west to the mountains and northwest throughout the interior of Alaska. It is a distinctly foxy red bird, as suggested by the vernacular name of the species. This form stands apart from all the rest in coloration, and shows, at least within our borders, no tendency to intergrade with the next following subspecies that occupies the interior of central and southern British Columbia and the foothills of Alberta. The Slate-coloured Fox Sparrow (le Pinson fauve ardoisé) *Passerella iliaca schistacea* has grey predominating on face and back, and the reds darkened to brown. This bird extends south to Nevada, though some Canadian representatives are sometimes differentiated from it under the name of Alberta Fox Sparrow (le Pinson fauve de l'Alberta) *Passerella iliaca altivagans.* On the British Columbia and Alaskan coast, we get a series of subspecies of the *unalaschcensis* type, solidly maroon and brown birds with little white below. These are heavily feathered birds, that appear larger than their measurements seem to warrant. Four subspecies are recognized in the Check-list, more by other authorities. Beginning with the Shumagin Fox Sparrow (le Pinson fauve des îles Shumagin) *Passerella iliaca unalaschcensis*, of the Alaska Peninsula; the Kodiak Fox Sparrow (Le Pinson fauve de Kodiak) *Passerella iliaca insularis* is next along the coast, extending eastward to the base of the Alaska Panhandle. Townsend's Fox Sparrow (le Pinson fauve de Townsend) *Passerella iliaca townsendi* occupies the Panhandle itself, and the northern British Columbia coast; and the Sooty Fox Sparrow (le Pinson fauve fuligineux) *Passerella iliaca fuliginosa*, Vancouver Island and the closely adjoining Washington coast. They vary from each other slightly in colour and size details, but are too much alike to be satisfactorily separated without a large series of specimens for comparison. Any of those dark forms may be expected on the British Columbia coast in migration. The Vancouver Island bird, the Sooty Fox Sparrow, is the only one permanently resident in its breeding locality and is the darkest and most saturated in colour of the series. Other forms that have been, or may be, recognized in migration on the coast are the Valdez Fox Sparrow (le Pinson fauve de Valdez) *Passerella iliaca sinuosa*, and the Yukutat Fox Sparrow (le Pinson fauve de Yukutat) *Passerella iliaca annectens*.

This sparrow remains within the limits of civilization only for a few days in spring and autumn. Occasionally in spring it greets us with a song of full clear tone that is equalled by few other birds and rarely surpassed by any.

583. **Lincoln's Sparrow.** LE PINSON DE LINCOLN. *Melospiza lincolni.* L, 5·75. Like the Song Sparrow but with a belt of buffy across the breast which is marked also with small, fine spots not aggregated into a central blotch.

*Distinctions.* The above distinctions will separate Lincoln's from all other sparrows it may be confused with.

*Field Marks.* A good view will show the faint buff breast and fine spotting. Otherwise it is with difficulty separated in life from the Song Sparrow. The back is rather greyer than the Song Sparrow and this often arouses a suspicion of the presence of Lincoln's Sparrow that may be confirmed by other characters.

*Nesting.* Similar to that of the Song Sparrow, on the ground.

*Distribution.* The species is distributed all over America, breeding in the northern coniferous woods.

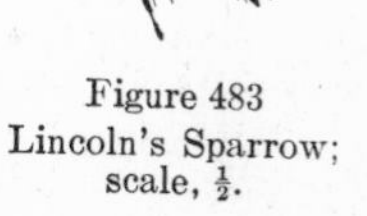

Figure 483
Lincoln's Sparrow; scale, ½.

*SUBSPECIES.* The Eastern Lincoln's Sparrow (le Pinson de Lincoln de l'Est) *Melospiza lincolni lincolni* extends west to the Coast Range. Forbush's Sparrow (le Pinson de l'Ouest de Lincoln) *Melospiza lincolni gracilis* is accredited to the coast, breeding south to Sitka region, Alaska, and migrating along the British Columbia coast. It is a faintly defined race, slightly more olivaceous on back, and with the dark streaks heavier and more numerous. It is not unanimously accepted and the difficulty of identifying individual specimens makes the separation of range of the two forms very uncertain.

584. **Swamp Sparrow.** LE PINSON DES MARAIS. *Melospiza georgiana.* L, 5·89. Much like the Song Sparrow, but of stronger and less blended coloration and without any distinct breast-streaks or markings.

Figure 484
Swamp Sparrow; natural size.

*Distinctions.* The Swamp Sparrow is difficult to separate from several other forms comparable in both colour and size. It may be distinguished from the Song Sparrow, with which it is most likely to be confused, by the unstreaked breast, and, in adult birds, by the red crown. Young autumn birds strongly resemble juvenile White-throats, but lack the faint yellow loral spot, are not as evenly ruddy on the back, and usually have a suggestion of an ashy bar across the shoulders at the base of the neck, an ashy cast to the crown, and eyebrow-lines that are absent in that species. It may be known from the Tree Sparrow by the lack of the dark middle-breast-spot or white wing-bars.

*Field Marks.* It resembles a Song Sparrow without breast-streaks, a White-throat without white throat or yellow loral spot, or a Tree Sparrow without wing-bars or breast-spot. In summer when the Tree Sparrow is not present, the red cap is distinctive.

*Nesting.* Nest similar to that of the Song Sparrow, on the ground, sometimes in the grass.

*Distribution.* North America, mostly north and east of the Great Plains. Rare or absent in migration in the prairie regions. One record for central British Columbia.

As its name implies, this is a bird of the swamps and marshes. The long grass and shrubby edges of marshes are its typical haunts. Late in the autumn it joins the large, mixed flocks of sparrows in the brush heaps and tangled fence-rows and then comes into closer contact with man.

*Economic Status.* The food habits of the Swamp Sparrow are not very different from those of other comparable sparrows. Owing to its living in waste places the species is not important.

581. **Song Sparrow.** LE PINSON CHANTEUR (Improprement Rossignol). *Melospiza melodia.* L, 6·30 (on northwest coast to 7·50). Plate LXXXV B. A medium-sized brown and white streaked sparrow. Underparts white; breast and flanks heavily and sharply striped with brown; the stripes aggregated to form a dark spot in the centre of the breast.

*Distinctions.* Rather like the Vesper Sparrow in size and general coloration, but darker and more decided in tone; lacks the white outer tail feathers. The breast-streaks are also sharper and darker brown and aggregated in the middle into a well-defined spot. The lack of the yellow stripe over the eye separates the Song from the Savannah Sparrow and the sharply streaked breast from any of the other sparrows of comparable size and habit. The Song Sparrows of British Columbia are so much darker in general coloration than those of farther east that it is unlikely that they will be often confused with these species.

*Field Marks.* Sharply striped breast and central spot. The absence of the white outertail feathers will guard against confusion with the Vesper Sparrow, and longer tail, lack of yellow lores, voice, and general attitude distinguish the Song Sparrow from the Savannah. The song is very distinctive, especially in its opening, which always consists of a single distinct note repeated at least once, and has been humorously interpreted as "*Pres-pres-presbyteri-eri-erian.*" The first part of this rendition is very good. The latter part of the song is too variable to be rendered by any single set of syllables.

*Nesting.* On the ground, more rarely in bushes, in nest of coarse grasses, rootlets, dead leaves, strips of bark, etc., lined with finer grasses and sometimes long hairs.

*Distribution.* The Song Sparrow inhabits all America to near the tree limits.

*SUBSPECIES.* The Song Sparrow shows a wonderful adaptability to various conditions. Scarcely any large area in North America but has Song Sparrows that have become specially modified to agree with regional conditions. Some of these specialized forms are well marked and easily recognizable, but others differ so slightly as to tax discrimination to the utmost. The arid deserts of the southwest have their small, pale forms and the humid coast has produced a number of very large, dark ones, culminating in the comparatively gigantic race of the damp Aleutian Islands. Especially have a great number of geographical races been produced in the broken country adjoining the west coast of America. In the east, physical and climatic conditions are more uniform and there has been less tendency to subspecific division in the species. West of the Great Lakes to the coast, the American Ornithologists' Union Check-list ascribes four breeding subspecies and a number of more migrant ones. The Eastern Song Sparrow (le Pinson chanteur de l'Est) *Melospiza melodia melodia* extends west to eastern Manitoba and probably northward through the wooded regions to northern Alberta and Great Slave Lake. The Dakota Song Sparrow (le Pinson chanteur du Dakota) *Melospiza melodia juddi* is the form of southern Manitoba, Saskatchewan, and Alberta. It is barely distinguishable from the Eastern Song Sparrow, though averaging slightly lighter, with clearer and sharper markings. According to the latest study of the species most of British Columbia is occupied by the Rusty Song Sparrow (le Pinson chanteur rouillé) *Melospiza melodia morphna.* This is the first of a series of Song Sparrows strikingly different from the two light eastern races. They are very dark and saturated in colour, enough so that if they did not intergrade through various southern races they might well be regarded as a well-defined species. Of these dark races, *morphna* averages ruddy in the brown tones, especially on the back. The Sooty Song Sparrow (le Pinson chanteur fuligineux) *Melospiza melodia rufina* occupies the islands of the Alaska Panhandle, including the Queen Charlotte Islands within Canadian territory. It is a large-appearing bird, with the browns sooty instead of ruddy.

Along the coast of Alaska, eastward to the point of the Aleutian Islands chain, a number of forms are distributed. These, reading westward, are: the Yukutat Song Sparrow (le Pinson chanteur de Yukutat) *Melospiza melodia caurina;* The Kenai Song Sparrow (le Pinson chanteur de Kenai) *Melospiza melodia kenaiensis;* Bischoff's Song Sparrow (le Pinson chanteur de Bischoff) *Melospiza melodia insignis,* and the Aleutian Song Sparrow (le Pinson chanteur aléoutienne) *Melospiza melodia sanaka.* These have the browns of the back generally greyer than the preceding races, and are separated from each other by small distinctions. They progressively increase in size until, in the Aleutian Song Sparrow, we find a bird comparatively huge for a Song Sparrow, that approaches the Fox Sparrow in measurement. Some of these may be expected along the British Columbia coast in migration, but though extremes are marked, the distinctions between adjoining races are too slight to be briefly defined here or to be recognized without an ample series for comparison.

It is difficult to form a just and unprejudiced estimate of the standing of the Song Sparrow in the avian chorus. Its little medley of chirps and trills makes a sustained song of some duration and to those who listen to it sympathetically it has a gladness, brightness, and sweetness of tone that are difficult to surpass. The bird is almost omnipresent. It lives in the shrubbery close about the house and is one of the familiar birds of the garden. It haunts the thickets on the edge of the wood-lot or bordering rivulets. The deep woods and the clean, open fields are the only places where it is generally absent, and even there it sometimes surprises us with a burst of liquid song.

*Economic Status.* The great numbers of the Song Sparrow render it most important to the agriculturist. An analysis of its food shows that only 2 per cent is composed of useful insects and 18 per cent of harmful ones. Waste grain constitutes 4 per cent and weed seeds 50 per cent. The remainder is composed of wild fruit and other unimportant material. It is seen from this that the Song Sparrow is of considerable economic importance. Investigation has shown that one-quarter of an ounce of weed seed a day is a fair estimate of the amount consumed by a seed-eating sparrow. During the nine months the Song Sparrow is with us in the average Canadian locality the consumption amounts to four and a quarter pounds an individual a year. Allowing seventy-five Song Sparrows a square mile as a very conservative estimate of population, we get a total for the southern cultivated parts of Ontario of over eleven thousand tons of weed seeds destroyed annually by this one species; other sections are probably in proportion.

539. **McCown's Longspur.** LE BRUANT À COLLIER GRIS. *Rhynchophanes mccowni.* L, 6·0. Spring male: streaked in ashy ochre and brown above, and a black cap; underparts, throat, and face, white with a black streak from corner of bill, and a black crescentic gorget across breast. White of throat extending around back of neck in a grey collar, and ear-coverts ashy grey (Figure 486). Lesser wing-coverts chestnut. Female generally

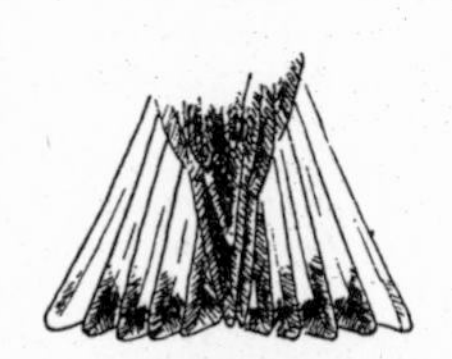

Figure 485
Tail of McCown's Longspur; scale, ½.

Figure 486
McCown's Longspur; scale, ½.

ashy grey, softly streaked with brown above, and nearly even white below; slightly ashy across breast. Juvenile very much like that of Chestnut-collared Longspur, but larger and more white in tail. All the feathers of the tail, except middle ones, white, tipped with dark (Figure 485, compare with 488).

*Distinctions.* The spring male, with its black cap and white face, and throat bordered by black crescentic gorget, is unmistakable. The female and juveniles are very much like those of the Chestnut-collared Longspur, but more ashy in general coloration and with much more white in the tail. Size is a good distinction from that species (wing over 3·25). The back is not as strongly streaked as in the Lapland Longspur, and there is no dark spot about the ear-covert tips as in the Lapland and Smith's.

*Field Marks.* As a summer resident in southern Canada, usually requiring separation only from the Chestnut-collared Longspur. Adult male: black-crowned, white-throated, with light face and crescent-shaped black gorget across breast. Females are best distinguished in life by association with male, but separated from the Vesper Sparrow, which may have similar general colour effect, and the Chestnut-collared Longspur, by the large amount of white in tail (Figure 485, compare with 488 and 478), all the tail, except the middle feathers and a terminal bar, being white.

In common with the Chestnut-collared Longspur, the male has a charming flight song that is given while slowly dropping from a height, with wings extended high over the back.

*Distribution.* The Great Plains region of North America. In Canada, regularly only in the drier parts of the prairies of Saskatchewan and Alberta. It is irregular and local in distribution, but has been taken at Chilliwack, British Columbia.

Very much the same habits and disposition as the Chestnut-collared Longspur.

536. **Lapland Longspur.** LE BRUANT LAPON. *Calcarius lapponicus.* L, 6·25. Plate LXXXVI A. Adult male: streaked with dark brown, buff, and traces of ruddy ochre above; bright chestnut nape and hindneck band. Crown, black, broken by more or less defined median stripe of light ochre. Below, white with black throat, foreneck, and face; a white superciliary line. Black stripes and spots along flank. Females and younger males similar in general colour plan, but dingier and without solid colour anywhere. The chestnut nape always present or suggested, and the black of the face and foreparts represented by veiled, broken masses about the edges of the areas. Some autumn juveniles are mostly streaky ochreous, lightening to white on abdomen. The nail of the hind toe is elongated as in the Horned Lark (*See* Figure 399).

*Distinctions.* In the hand, only likely to be mistaken for one of the other longspurs. The adult male has the throat black like the face, instead of white as in McCown's, or buffy as in Smith's and the Chestnut-collared Longspurs. Harris's Sparrow has a similar black face and bib, but is otherwise an entirely different-appearing bird, with light grey ear-coverts, and no chestnut collar. Females and juveniles with the distinct or semi-obscured chestnut collar are easily separated from McCown's and Smith's, but may be very similar to the Chestnut-collared. They are distinctly larger birds, however, wing 3·50 and over, instead of 3·25 or under, and the collar is well developed instead of vaguely defined or absent. The whole bird is more sharply streaked. The black suffuses around ear-coverts and across the lower neck, and the underparts are solid white. Female and juvenile Chestnut-collared Longspurs may have a veiled black spot below a light throat, but the abdomen is a dusty buffy and usually shows more or less irregular intrusion of black. Autumn juveniles are still more confusing. They have a general appearance of a streaked buffy bird, with white, rarely cream, abdomen, with but traces of veiled black down sides of throat from corners of bill, and across upper breast. The tips of the ear-coverts are bordered by a conspicuous brown or black patch that is absent in the Chestnut-collared and McCown's Longspurs and much smaller or absent in Smith's. The best test for the species, in this plumage, is the white or faintly cream abdomen.

*Field Marks.* By habit and association much like the Snow Bunting, the Horned Lark, or the other longspurs. Lack of the great amount of white, especially in wings, and the coarser, harsher note will separate from the Snow Bunting; sparrow bill and lack of yellow throat or ear tufts, and undulating flight, from the Horned Lark. The adult male, with his black face and bib, is distinct from the other longspurs. In addition to details previously mentioned, other plumages are more streaky than other longspurs, and never as evenly buffy as Smith's. It is only a spring and autumn migrant, and not to be met with in southern Canada in summer when the Chestnut-collared and McCown's Longspurs are most common.

*Distribution.* The greater part of the northern hemisphere, breeding in the Arctics and migrating or wintering throughout southern Canada.

*SUBSPECIES.* Two subspecies are recognized in Canada. The form common to Europe and eastern America is the type one, the Common Longspur (le Bruant lapon commun) *Calcarius lapponicus lapponicus*. The Alaska Longspur (le Bruant de l'Alaska) *Calcarius lapponicus alascensis* breeds in Alaska and east towards the Mackenzie. The subspecific distinction is slight and the boundaries of the ranges are not well defined. On the western prairies and in British Columbia, both forms may occur during migration.

In the autumn, when most of the other longspurs, the Chestnut-collared and McCown's, have departed for the south, the sere-frosted prairies are visited by flocks of innumerable ground sparrows. They rise from the ground ahead of the observer in small groups and large flocks with happy undulating flight, lilting a merry chorus of little "*chirs*." Most of these are Lapland Longspurs, though occasional flocks of Smith's occur.

*Economic Status.* Coming as they do in early spring and autumn, weed seed is about all that they can attack. Their myriad numbers and the closeness with which they search the ground must be responsible for an enormous consumption of weed seed.

537. **Smith's Longspur.** PAINTED LONGSPUR. LE BRUANT ÉLÉGANT. *Calcarius pictus.* L, 6·50. A brownish buffy bird, striped with brown above. Adult male with black crown; a white superciliary line; cheek black with white spot in centre and with narrow white line below, separating the black from the pale warm buff throat, which latter colour extends evenly over all lower parts, but is ruddiest on breast (Figure 487). Lesser wing-coverts black with a large white spot. Females are similar, but have the black and white head marks replaced by buffy stripes on crown and a dark spot at tip of ear-coverts, like the autumn juvenile Lapland Longspur. Autumn juveniles are like the female, but with less white on wing-coverts.

Figure 487
Smith's Longspur; scale, ½.

*Distinctions.* A generally buffy bird. The spring male, with its striking black and white head-marking, is unmistakable. Females and juveniles very like juvenile Lapland Longspurs, but buffier and with the abdomen almost concolour with breast instead of being nearly or quite white. At a glance, somewhat like the female or autumn Bobolink, but more even and of a ruddier buff, and the crown without a well-marked median line. One of the largest of the longspurs.

*Field Marks.* Spring male a buffy bird, with strikingly patterned black and white head, buff throat, and breast. The most buffy of the longspurs.

*Nesting.* On the ground, on the northern barren grounds.

*Distribution.* The interior of North America. Breeds from Mackenzie River to Hudson Bay, migrates through the Prairie Provinces, and has occurred in British Columbia.

Only a migrant in cultivated Canada, passing through quickly in spring and autumn. Not nearly so common nor so generally distributed as the Lapland Longspur, but appearing in flocks of considerable size when it does occur.

538. **Chestnut-collared Longspur.** LE BRUANT À COLLIER CHÂTAIN. *Calcarius ornatus.* L, 5·85. Plate LXXXVI B. A smaller longspur than the preceding two. Spring male: breast and most of underparts, black, often more or less tipped with grey feather-edges and sometimes with chestnut. Throat and face cream; crown and tips of ear-coverts, black. A strong, white, superciliary line. A distinct chestnut collar about nape and base of neck. Back streaked in shades of brown and ashy ochre. Female: dull ashy brown, striped above, but often the streaks are nearly worn away. Throat generally light to white, and usually more or less black feather bases showing vaguely through the light of the breast and underparts. Autumn juveniles show very little distinctive character, mostly ashy ochre, softly streaked with brown above.

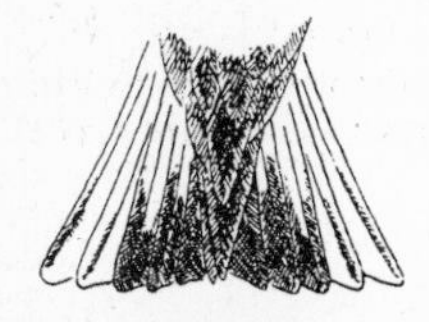
Figure 488
Tail of Chestnut-collared Longspur; scale, ½.

*Distinctions.* The smallest of the longspurs (wing 3·25 or under). The spring male is unmistakable, with cream throat and face, black breast and underparts. The Lapland Longspur has a similar chestnut collar, but has black throat and is white beneath. The latter is, however, only a migrant through southern Canada, instead of a summer resident. In summer, needs to be separated only from McCown's Longspur, which is larger and has a white throat, face, and underparts, and a crescentic black gorget across the breast. Females are light ashy grey, softly striped above and nearly uniform below, like those of the Chestnut-collared, but are decidedly whiter, being ashy rather than ochreish. Females and juveniles are best distinguished from other longspurs by smaller size.

*Field Marks.* Adult male: a small sparrow with creamy throat, black breast and underparts. Females: best distinguished in life by association with male, but separated from Vesper Sparrow, which may be similar in general colour effect, by much more white on sides of tail, two and a half or more feathers white, instead of little more than one, the area of white increasing towards the base of tail (Figure 488), instead of an even border; from McCown's Longspur by having less white in tail, all the tail of the latter, except a terminal band and centre feathers, being white (Compare with Figure 485). The Chestnut-collared, in common with McCown's, has a very pretty flight song that is given when the wings are extended high over the back, as it slowly drops from a height.

*Nesting.* On the ground on the open prairie; nest of grasses and rootlets.

*Distribution.* Great Plains region of North America. In Canada, all of the prairie section. A casual straggler in British Columbia.

In many parts of the prairies, especially the more arid sections, one of the commonest and most characteristic birds. In the bright spring and early summer days, its beautiful twittering flight song, repeated on every hand by many rival birds, gives a delightful air of gladness to the awakening prairies.

534. **Snow Bunting.** SNOWFLAKE. LE BRUANT DES NEIGES (L'Oiseau blanc). *Plectrophenax nivalis.* L, 6·88. Plate LXXXVII. A medium-sized sparrow, showing much white. In breeding plumage, assumed only on the nesting grounds in the Arctic regions, almost immaculate white with black saddle across shoulders. Flight and tail feathers black, with almost equal areas white. As they visit lower latitudes, however, they are heavily veiled over head and throat with rusty, and the black feathers are all edged with rusty ochre and white.

*Distinctions.* Sharply contrasting black and white colouring with most of the feathers heavily bordered with rusty, especially on the head, back, and breast-band. Through the winter the rusty borders gradually wear off and the breeding plumage of black and white results without moult. The general scheme of colouring of the Snow Bunting is found in no other Canadian bird.

*Field Marks.* Very white, gregarious ground sparrows showing large amounts of white on black wings when flying.

*Nesting.* On the ground in moss, nest of grass, rootlets, and moss lined with feathers and fur.

*Distribution.* Circumpolar Arctics. In Canada, breeding from the edge of barren grounds northward across the continent. In migration, throughout Canada.

*SUBSPECIES.* Only one of the two recognized subspecies, the Common Snow Bunting (le Bruant des neiges commun) *Plectrophenax nivalis nivalis*, is known to occur in Canada.

Winter visitors in southern Canada, feeding on the weed-tops that project from the snow in open fields and rarely perching in trees. A flock alights in the weed-spotted snow and gradually works across it, the rear of the flock rising up from time to time like a flurry of snow and pitching ahead, the process being repeated until the whole field has been gone over.

## GLOSSARY

**Albinism.** The occasional and erratic occurrence of white specimens, either pure or partial, complete or in irregular spots, in species that normally are not white. It is nothing more than a freak caused by a deficiency of colouring matter in the plumage (*See* page 6).

**Axillars or Axillaries.** A fan-shaped group of feathers under the wing closing the space between the innermost flight feathers and the body when in flight.

**Bars.** In descriptions of bird coloration, bars designate lines across the body and not parallel with the shafts of the feathers (*See* stripes).

**Bluff.** In western parlance is any isolated clump of trees or patch of woods on the prairies. As so used and as applied in this work, it carries no sense of steep hill-side or rise of ground.

**Cere.** A wax-like swelling about the base of the upper mandible, present in some species, especially the Hawks (*See* Figure 34 a and b, page 30).

**Coulée.** Steep, ravine-like valleys cut below the prairie level by streams. They may be quite narrow or a mile or more across.

**Coverts.** The feathers covering the bases of the larger flight and tail feathers. There are upper and underwing-coverts and upper and undertail-coverts. The upperwing-coverts are divided into greater and lesser coverts, the former being the largest line immediately next to the flight shafts and resembling them to some degree in texture (Figure 1, page 24).

**Crepuscular.** Pertaining to twilight.

**Crown.** The top of the head from the forehead to near the base of the skull.

**Culmen.** This may be called the ridge line of bill. Viewed sideways, the line forming the top outline of the bill from the spring of the first forehead feathers to the tip is the culmen line. It is measured in a straight line, as with dividers, not following the curves as with a tape line (Figure 1, page 24).

**Dichromatism.** The normal occurrence of two different colorations in the same species due to neither sex, season, nor age and only partly hereditary. Both colorations may occur in the same brood, though the tendency is for like to produce like and one form may predominate in any given locality (*See* page 6).

**Emarginate.** When applied to the shape of feathers indicates that more or less of one web is cut away as if a shaving had been removed with a jack-knife (Figure 184, page 124).

**Extralimital.** In describing distribution refers to the subject occurring beyond the geographical bounds of the area under discussion.

**Family.** In zoological classification is one of the larger groups of animals having enough mutual resemblance to be classed together and apart from all other forms. It is the next larger group to a genus and next smaller to an order or suborder. For example, all the Ducks, Geese, and Swans belong to the same family, Anatidae (*See* page 4).

**Flanks.** The sides of the body, below or under the closed wing. They are often covered by a loose group of feathers that may be laid at will either over or under the shafts of the closed wing (Figure 1, page 24).

**Genus** (plural, genera). In zoological classification is one of the smaller groups of animals having enough resemblance to be classed together and apart from all other groups of like rank. It is a subdivision of a family or subfamily and next above a species. A genus is, therefore, a group of species, and a group of genera is a family (*See* page 4).

**Gular Pouch.** A pouch of bare skin depending from the under side of the lower bill between its Y-shaped arms and joining it to the neck below. Some species have only the merest trace of it, and others have it remarkably developed, though in most species it is entirely absent (Figures 90, 94, pages 52 and 56).

**Hybrid.** The offspring between parents of two different species—a "cross."

**Iris.** The coloured part of the eye. The pupil, except in albinism, is always black and the surrounding circle of colour is the iris.

**Lanceolate.** Lance shaped, i.e., long and narrow with parallel edges or tapering gradually to a point.

**Length.** Abbreviated in descriptions by its initial L and given in inches and tenths of an inch. Length is taken in a straight line, as with dividers, from the tip of the bill to the end of the longest tail feather, the bird being laid out flat on its back and stretched just sufficiently to straighten the curves of the neck.

**Lores.** A small spot between the eye and the base of the bill (Figure 1, page 24).

**Mandibles.** The two members forming the bill; thus there is an upper and a lower mandible.

**Mantle.** A term covering the back, shoulders, upperwing-coverts, and secondaries. Applied more especially to the gulls where the even colouring of these parts suggests a mantle covering the whole upper part of the body and closed wings.

**Mast.** Soft-shelled nuts, like acorns, beechnuts, etc.

**Melanism.** The opposite of albinism. It is the more or less erratic occurrence of very dark or black individuals in a normally lighter-coloured species. It usually occurs less frequently than albinism, though some species are more liable to it and it glides imperceptibly into dichromatism in some cases. Albinism usually denotes a lack of virility. Melanism does not seem to be an evidence of weakness and hence melanistic strains have better chances of surviving. A melanistic animal is said to be a Melano (*See* page 6).

**Nape.** A small space at the back of the neck just below the base of the skull (Figure 1, page 24).

**Neck.** The space between the throat and the breast in front, and between the hind head and shoulders behind. It is divided into foreneck and hindneck whose meanings are obvious (Figure 1, page 24).

**Order.** In zoological classification a group of families having strong enough mutual resemblance to separate them from all other groups. It is next larger than the family and is the largest subdivision of birds that we have to deal with in Canada (*See* page 4).

**Pectinate.** Furnished with comb-like teeth. In ornithology usually applied to the claws of some species that are so furnished (Figure 99, page 59).

**Pelagic.** Living largely or almost entirely at sea.

**Pensile.** Applied to nests that hang suspended like a bag between the forks of a branch or other such support, with nothing supporting from below.

**Primaries.** The large flight feathers secured to the first joint of the wing from the wrist to the tip (*See* Secondaries). (Figure 1, page 24.)

**Race.** As used here, practically synonymous with subspecies. In general, any group within a species exhibiting recognizable common characters differentiating it from others of the same species.

**Rufous.** Of a red or reddish colour.

**Rump.** The lower end of the back just before the root of the tail (Figure 1, page 24).

**Secondaries.** The large flight feathers secured to the second joint of the wing between the wrist and the elbow (*See* Primaries). (Figure 1, page 24.)

**Slough** (pronounced "Slew"). In western parlance any small pond or wet spot on the prairie. They are usually more or less seasonal and may be either clear, grassy, or reed grown. They are not necessarily quagmires.

**Species.** In zoological classification the smallest constant group. It is the scientific term to denote what is understood in common language as a "kind of animal." Thus a house cat is a species, whether Maltese, tortoise shell, or tabby; the dog, whether greyhound or spaniel is another; and a horse, whether Shetland pony or draught, is a third (*See* page 5).

**Speculum.** A somewhat rectangular patch of contrasting colour on the centre of the upper surface of the wing. It often shows metallic iridescence and is a common feature of coloration in some families, as in the Ducks (Figure 127, page 88).

**Stripes.** In ornithological descriptions, stripes always run lengthways of the bird; lines across the body are spoken of as bars (*See* bars).

**Sternum.** The breast bone. In a bird a deeply keeled structure to which the wing muscles are attached.

**Subspecies.** In ornithological classification, synonymous with geographical race or variety, denoting a division of the species usually correlated with geographic limitations. It differs essentially from a full species by showing intergradations with allied races of equal rank. Taking the horse as a representative species, the various breeds or strains, such as Arab, Clydesdale, or Shetland pony are subspecies (*See* page 5, for discussion).

**Superciliary Stripe.** A stripe over the eye like an eyebrow-line (Figure 1, page 24).

**Tarsus.** The metatarsal bones of the foot fused together into a single bone. This is what we popularly regard as the bird's leg but is properly the foot, extending between the juncture of the toes and the end of the "drum stick." A comparison with the joints of the human leg will make it obvious that the knee is between the "drum stick" and the "second joint" of the fowl and that the first external joint on the bird corresponds with our heel, the "feet" being true toes (Figure 1, page 24).

**Tule** (pronounced "Tu-lee"). *Scirpus* or bulrush, a round-stemmed, reed-like plant growing in the water.

**Type.** In zoological nomenclature the "type form" is that form first properly described and named and the specimen from which the description was written is the type specimen. It does not of necessity mean that the form is typical in the ordinary sense of the word, though for convenience it is assumed to be so (*See* page 7).

**Vermiculation.** In descriptions of plumage, vermiculation refers to fine, irregularly wavy lines suggesting the pathways of innumerable small worms, from which the word is derived.

**Vinaceous.** Wine coloured. A peculiar purplish pink shown or suggested in the coloration of some birds.

76916—27

# INDEX

## General





76916—27½

## French

## Index to Check-List Numbers

s. Birds - Canada

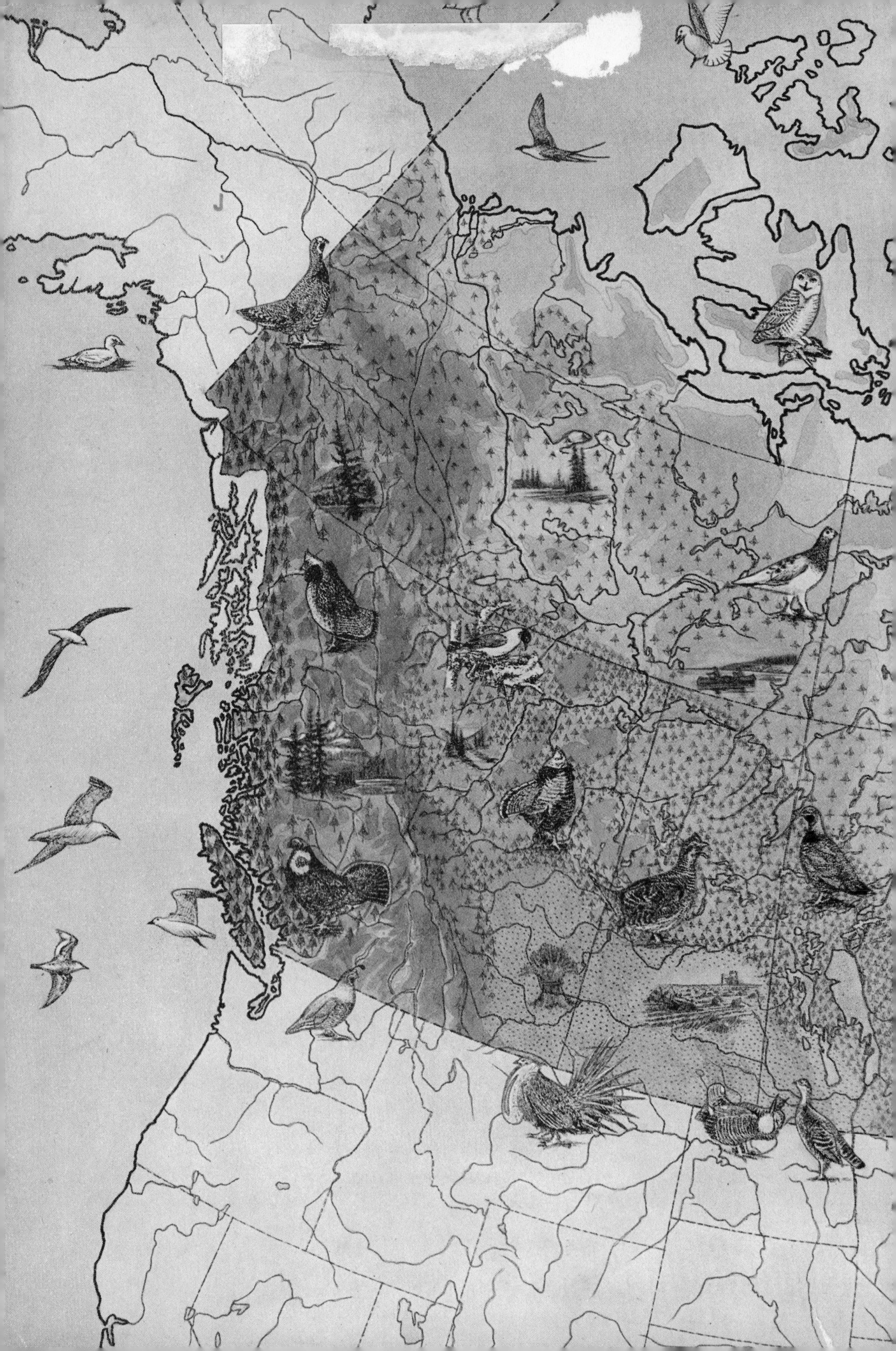